# SYNTHESIS AND APPLICATIONS OF ISOTOPICALLY LABELED COMPOUNDS 1985

# SYNTHESIS AND APPLICATIONS OF ISOTOPICALLY LABELED COMPOUNDS 1985

Proceedings of the Second International Symposium,
Kansas City, Missouri, U.S.A., 3–6 September 1985

Edited by

## RICHARD R. MUCCINO

*Chemical Research Department, Hoffman-La Roche Inc., Nutley, NJ 07110, U.S.A.*

## ELSEVIER
Amsterdam — Oxford — New York — Tokyo   1986

ELSEVIER SCIENCE PUBLISHERS B.V.
Sara Burgerhartstraat 25
P.O. Box 211, 1000 AE Amsterdam, The Netherlands

*Distributors for the United States and Canada:*

ELSEVIER SCIENCE PUBLISHING COMPANY INC.
52, Vanderbilt Avenue
New York, N.Y. 10017, U.S.A.

Library of Congress Cataloging-in-Publication Data
Main entry under title:

Synthesis and applications of isotopically labeled
   compounds, 1985.

   Proceedings of the Second International Symposium on
the Synthesis and Applications of Isotopically Labeled
Compounds.
   Includes index.
   1. Radioactive tracers--Congresses.  I. Muccino,
Richard R. (Richard Roberts)  II. International
Symposium on the Synthesis and Applications of
Isotopically Labeled Compounds (2nd : 1985 : Kansas
City, Mo.)
QD607.S96  1986     543'.0884      86-2015
ISBN 0-444-42612-4 (U.S.)

ISBN 0-444-42612-4

Printed in The Netherlands

v

# TABLE OF CONTENTS

## PLENARY LECTURES

Chairmen: R.R. Muccino, A.B. Susan, E.A. Evans

## MECHANISTIC STUDIES USING ISOTOPES IN DRUG METABOLISM

Chairman: T.A. Baillie

ISOTOPES IN ORGANIC AND BIOORGANIC REACTION MECHANISMS

Co-chairmen: E. Buncel, J.R. Jones

CLINICAL APPLICATIONS OF NUCLEAR MAGNETIC RESONANCE IMAGING

Chairman: R. Robinson

THE SYNTHESIS AND USE OF RADIOLIGANDS IN BINDING STUDIES

Chairman: L. Pichat

THE SYNTHESIS AND APPLICATIONS OF ORGANIC COMPOUNDS LABELED WITH
ISOTOPIC HYDROGEN

ISOTOPES IN CLINICAL PHARMACOLOGY: THE USE OF DEUTERATED
ANALOGS OF DRUGS AS MEDICINAL AGENTS

SYNTHESIS AND APPLICATIONS OF LABELED PEPTIDES

SYNTHESIS AND APPLICATION OF ORGANIC COMPOUNDS LABELED WITH ISOTOPES
OTHER THAN THOSE OF HYDROGEN 1

APPLICATIONS OF ISOTOPES IN CLINICAL RESEARCH

Chairman: S.P. Markey

APPLICATIONS OF TRITIUM NUCLEAR MAGNETIC RESONANCE SPECTROSCOPY

Chairman: J.R. Jones

ISOTOPICALLY LABELED COMPOUNDS IN MEDICAL CHEMICAL DEFENSE AND RELATED
RESEARCH

STATE OF THE ART IN THE INSTRUMENTATION FOR ANALYSIS OF ISOTOPICALLY LABELED
COMPOUNDS

TRENDS IN THE SYNTHESIS AND APPLICATIONS OF ISOTOPICALLY LABELED COMPOUNDS

COMPOUNDS LABELED WITH ISOTOPES OTHER THAN THOSE OF HYDROGEN II

## INTERNATIONAL SCIENTIFIC COMMITTEE

RICHARD R. MUCCINO, Chairman
Hoffman-La Roche, Inc.
Nutley, New Jersey

E. ANTHONY EVANS
Amersham International, plc.
Buckinghamshire, England

SHIGEO BABA
Tokyo College of Pharmacy
Tokyo, Japan

MERVYN A. LONG
University of New South Wales
Sydney, Australia

THOMAS BAILLIE
University of Washington
Seattle, Washington

SANFORD P. MARKEY
National Institute of Mental Health
Bethesda, Maryland

ALEXANDER T. BALABAN
Polytechnic Institute of Bucharest
Bucharest, Roumania

LOUIS PICHAT
C.E.N. Saclay
Gif-sur-Yvette, France

ACHILE BENAKIS
University of Geneva
Geneva, Switzerland

ALEXANDER SUSAN, Co-chairman
Sandoz Research Institute
East Hanover, New Jersey

DALE W. BLACKBURN
SmithKline Beckman Corporation
Philadelphia, Pennsylvania

THOMAS W. WHALEY
Los Alamos Scientific Laboratory
Los Alamos, New Mexico

ERWIN BUNCEL
Queen's University
Kingston, Canada

## ORGANIZING COMMITTEE

WILLIAM P. DUNCAN, Co-chairman
Eagle-Picher Industries, Inc.
Lenexa, Kansas

ALEXANDER SUSAN
Sandoz Research Institute
East Hanover, New Jersey

ROBERT A. SANDMANN, Co-chairman
School of Pharmacy
University of Missouri-Kansas City
Kansas City, Missouri

DONALD WILK, Symposium Coordinator
School of Pharmacy
University of Missouri-Kansas City
Kansas City, Missouri

RICHARD R. MUCCINO, Chairman,
  International Scientific Committee
Hoffmann-La Roche, Inc.
Nutley, New Jersey

JANET N. STRATTON, Publications
  Coordinator
Extended Programs
University of Missouri-Kansas City
Kansas City, Missouri

H.A. MUSALLAM
Walter Reed Army Institute of Research
Washington, D.C.

PARTICIPANTS OF THE
SECOND INTERNATIONAL SYMPOSIUM ON THE SYNTHESIS AND
APPLICATIONS OF ISOTOPICALLY LABELED COMPOUNDS

Dr. Donald J. Aberhart
Worcester Foundation for
  Experimental Biology
222 Maple Avenue
Shrewsbury, MA    01545

Dr. David G. Ahern
DuPont NEN Products
549 Albany Street
Boston, MA    02118

Ms. Jennie G. Ahern
DuPont NEN Products
549 Albany Street
Boston, MA    02118

Dr. Per N.I. Ahlberg
University of Goteborg
Organic Chemistry/Kemigarden 3
Goteburg, Sweden    41296

Dr. Alfred M. Ajami
Tracer Technologies, Inc.
225 Needham Street
Newton, MA    02164

Dr. John Allen
Lab. d'Etudes et de Recherches
  Synthelabo (L.E.R.S.)
31, av. P.V. Couturier
92220 Bagneux, Paris, France

Mr. Arthur Alter
Abbott Laboratories
Abbott Park, AP-9
North Chicago, IL    60064

Dr. David J. Anderson
Abbott Laboratories
Abbott Park, AP-9  L.L.
North Chicago, IL    60064

Dr. Maurice J. Arnaud
Nestle Research Dept.
Av, Nestle
Vevey, Switzerland    1800

Dr. John Arnold
Quincy Research Center
5100 East  24th Street
Kansas City, MO    64127

Mr. Michael Arnold
Ontario Hydro
2700 Lakeshore Road, West
Mississauga, Ont., Canada L5J 1K3

Dr. Vincent L. Avona
Isotec, Inc.
7542 McEwen Road
Centerville, OH    45459-3995

Dr. Shigeo Baba
Tokyo College of Pharmacy
1432-1 Horinouchi
Hachioji, Tokyo 192-03 Japan

Mr. Calvin J. Bacon
IN/US Service Corporation
1275 Bloomfield Avenue
Fairfield, NJ    07006

Dr. Tom Baillie
Dept. of Medicinal Chemistry
University of Washington
School of Pharmacy-BG 20
Seattle, WA    98195

Dr. Dezso Banfi
Central Research Institute
  for Chemistry
Hungarian Academy of Sciences
Pusztaszeri ut 59/67
P. O. Box 17
H-1525 Budapest, Hungary

Dr. R. J. Baranczuk
Biomedical Research Lab.
7899 Mastin
Overland Park, KS  66204

Dr. Jean-Pierre Beaucourt
Service des Molecules
  Marquees-CEA
Gif-sur-Yvette-France
Cedex, France    91191

Dr. Achile Benakis
Lab. Drug Metabolism
Department of Pharmacology
University of Geneva
Geneva, Switzerland

Dr. Diana D. Bender
Rohm and Haas Company
727 Norristown Road
Spring House, PA   19477

Dr. Dennis M. Bier
Washington University
660 Euclid Avenue
St. Louis, MO   63110

Dr. Dale W. Blackburn
Smith Kline & French Labs
1500 Spring Garden Street
Philadelphia, PA   19101

Dr. Thomas E. Boothe
Mount Sinai Medical Center
Cyclotron Facility
4300 Alton Road
Miami Beach, FL   33140

Mr. Bernt Borretzen
Norsk Hydro Research Center
The Netherlands
N-3901 Porsgrunn, Norway

Dr. Joel C. Bradley
Cambridge Isotope Labs, Inc.
20 Commerce Way
Woburn, MA   01801

Dr. Alan J. Brattesani
Wizard Laboratories, Inc.
1362 Monarch Lane
Davis, CA   95616

Ms. Susan I. Brown
Chemsyn Science Laboratories
13605 West  96th Terrace
Lenexa, KS  66215-1297

Dr. Thomas M. Brown
Department of Entomology
Clemson University
Clemson, SC   29634-0365

Dr. T. R. Browne
Department of Neurology
Boston University
School of Medicine
150 South Huntington Avenue
Boston, MA   02115

Dr. Derek E. Brundish
Ciba-Geigy AG
Zentrale Forschungs Lab.
CH-4002 Basel, Switzerland

Dr. Ouri Buchman
Nuclear Res. Centre-Negev
Radiochemistry Department
P. O. Box 9001
Beer-Sheva, Israel   84190

Dr. Milon W. Bullock
American Cyanamid Company
P. O. Box 400
Princeton, NJ   08540

Dr. Erwin Buncel
Queen University
Dept. of Chemistry
Kingston,Ontario,Canada K7L 3N6

Mr. Raymond A. Burrell
ICI Plant Protection Division
Jealott's Hill Research Station
Bracknell, Berkshire,
England     RG12 6EY

Dr. Melvin Calvin
University of California
Department of Chemistry
714 University Hall
Berkeley, CA   94720

Mr. Patrick Carlucci
Matheson
30 Seaview Drive
Secaucus, NJ   07094

Jorge Carrasquillo, M.D.
National Cancer Institute
Bldg. 10, Room 1C401
9000 Rockville Pike
Bethesda, MD   20205

Dr. Frederick D. Cazer
Norwich-Eaton Pharmaceuticals
17 Eaton Avenue
Norwich, NY   13815

Dr. Naba K. Chaudhuri
Ciba-Geigy Corporation
Saw Mill River Road
Ardsley, NY   10502

Dr. Jacques Chenu
SANOFI-RECHERCHE
195, Route d'Espagne BP-1072
31035 Toulouse, Cedex, France

Dr. Edward H. Chew
Eagle-Picher Industries, Inc.
Chemsyn Science Laboratories
13605 West  96th Terrace
Lenexa, KS  66215-1297

Dr. David H.T. Chien
Chemsyn Science Laboratories
13605 West 96th Terrace
Lenexa, KS 66215-1297

Dr. Ping-Lu Chien
Ortho Pharmaceutical Corp.
Route #202
Raritan, NJ 08869

Dr. Yong M. Choi
Carter-Wallace, Inc.
Wallace Labs
Half Acre Road
Cranbury, NJ 08512

Dr. Robert M. Coates
Department of Chemistry
University of Illinois
1209 West California Street
Urbana, IL 61801

Dr. John P. Coghlan
Institute of Experimental
   Physiology and Medicine
University of Melbourne
Melbourne, Victoria, Australia

Mr. Alex Cohen
National Bureau of Standards
Chemistry/A-361
Gaithersburg, MD 20899

Dr. Robert Cohen
Laboratory of Cerebral Metabolism
National Institute of Mental Health
10/4N317, 9000 Rockville Pike
Bethesda, MD 20205

Dr. I. Cooke
Merck & Company, Inc./Isotopes
West Germany

Mr. John O. Cozad
Celanese Research Company
86 Morris Avenue
Summit, NJ 07901

Dr. Henry L. Crespi
Argonne National Laboratory
Chemistry Division, Bldg. 200
Argonne, IL 60439

Dr. Timothy A. Cross
Department of Chemistry
Florida State University
Tallahasse, FL 32306-3006

Dr. D. Crout
Department of Chemistry
University of Warwick
Coventry, England CV4 7AL

Dr. Frederick W. Dahlquist
Institute of Molecular Biology
University of Oregon
Eugene, OR 97405

Dr. Kalyani M. Damodaran
Diagnostic Systems Labs, Inc.
100 East Nasa Road
Webster, TX 77598

Dr. Michael V. Darby
Ohio State University
Comp. Cancer Center
410 West 12th Avenue
Suite #302
Columbus, OH 43210

Mr. Gary Darland
Merck & Company
Rahway, NJ 07065

Dr. James H. Davis
Department of Physics
University of Guelph
Guelph, Ontario, Canada N1G 2W1

Mr. Steve A. de Keczer
Syntex Laboratories, Inc.
3401 Hillview Avenue
Palo Alto, CA 94394

Dr. H. Denutte
Lab of Medicinal Biochemistry
& Institute of Nuclear Sciences
University of Ghent
Harelbekestraat 72
B-9000 Gent, Belgium

Dr. Dominic M. Desiderio
University of Tennessee
School of Medicine
Department of Neurology
800 Madison Avenue
Memphis, TN 38163

Dr. Randy Dimond
Promega Biotech
2800 South Fish Hatchery Road
Madison, WI 53711

Mr. Thomas K. Dobbs
Chemsyn Science Laboratories
13605 West 96th Terrace
Lenexa, KS 66215-1297

Ms. Mary K. Dornhoffer
Chemsyn Science Laboratories
13605 West 96th Terrace
Lenexa, KS 66215-1297

Dr. William P. Duncan
Chemsyn Science Labs
P. O. Box 15027
Lenexa, KS 66215-1297

Dr. Mahmoud M. Ebeid
University of Qatar
P.O. Box 2713
Doha, Qatar, Arabian Gulf

Mr. David A. Ebert
Chemsyn Science Laboratories
13605 West 96th Terrace
Lenexa, KS 66215-1297

Mr. Peter Egli
E.R. Squibb & Sons
P. O. Box 4000
Princeton, NJ 08540

Dr. D. S. Ehler
Los Alamos National Labs
University of California
INC-4, MS C345
Los Alamos, NM 87545

Dr. F. Etzkorn
Eagle-Picher Industries, Inc.
Chemsyn Science Laboratories
13605 West 96th Terrace
Lenexa, KS 66215-1297

Dr. E. Anthony Evans
Amersham International plc
Research Products Division
White Lion Road/Amersham,
Buckinghamshire, England HP7 9LL

Dr. P. B. Farmer
MRC, Toxicology Unit
Woodmansterne Road/Carshalton,
Surrey, England SM5 4EF

Dr. Hans-Peter K. Faro
E. Merck, Darmstadt
Institut Grafing
Am Feld 32
8018 Grafing, West Germany

Mr. William J. Fields, Jr.
Univ. of Missouri-Kansas City
H2-C26 TMC, 2301 Holmes
Kansas City, MO 64108

Dr. Sanford K. Figdor
Pfizer, Inc.
Eastern Point Road
Groton, CT 06340

Dr. Crist N. Filer
DuPont, NEN Products
100-2 East Canton Street
Boston, MA 02118

Dr. H. Filthuth
Laboratorium Prof. Dr. Berthold
D-7547 Wilbad, West Germany

Mr. Daniel L. Fischer
Chemsyn Science Laboratories
13605 West 96th Terrace
Lenexa, KS 66215-1297

Mr. Cal Fisher
Packard Instrument Company
2200 Warrenville Road
Downers Grove, IL 60515

Dr. Donald R. Flint
Mobay Chem. Corp.
Ag. Chemical Division
P. O. Box 4913
Kansas City, MO 64120

Ms. Mary T. Fong
SRI International
333 Ravenswood
Menlo Park, CA 94025

Dr. David L. Foxall
Varian
611 Hansen Way, D-162
Palo Alto, CA 94303

Dr. Robert C. Freeman
Monsanto Company
700 Chesterfield Village Pkwy
St. Louis, MO 63198

Dr. Jean-Pierre Frideling
Centre Int. de
    Recherches Dermatologiques
Sophia Antipolis
06565, Valbonne, Cedex, France

Dr. T. Roy Fukuto
Department of Entomology
University of California
Riverside, CA 92521

Dr. William A. Garland
Hoffmann-La Roche, Inc.
Dept. of Pharmacokinetics,
Biopharmaceutics, & Drug Metab.
340 Kingsland Road
Nutley, NJ    07110

Mr. Keith T. Garnes
SmithKline Beckman Corp.
1500 Spring Garden Street
Philadelphia, PA  19101

Mr. Gregory J. Gatto
Merck & Company, Inc.
P. O. Box 2000
Rahway, NJ 07065

Dr. Lars I. Gawell
Astra Pharmaceuticals
S-15185 Sodertalje, Sweden

Dr. Jacques Godbillon
Ciba-Geigy - C.R.B.
2-4, Rue L. Terray/BP 308
92506  Rueil-Malmaison,
Cedex, France

David Goldenberg, M.D.
Center for Molecular Medicine
  and Immunology
University of Medicine and
  Dentistry of New Jersey
100 Bergen Street
Newark, NJ    07103

Dr. Asher Gopher
Weizmann Institute of Science
Department of Isotope Research
P. O. Box 26
Rehovot, Israel  76100

Mr. Benjamin E. Gordon
Lawrence Berkeley Lab.
University of California
1 Cyclotron Road
Berkeley, CA  94720

Dr. Myra Gordon
Merck & Company, Inc./Isotopes
P. O. Box 899
Pointe Claire-Dorval,
Quebec, Canada  H9R 4P7

Ms. Patricia Butler Grant
ICI Americas
Concord Pike & New Murphy Rd
Wilmington, DE   19897

Mr. Derek Greenslade
Wellcome Foundation
Research Labs
Langley Court
Beckenham,Kent,England BR3 3BS

Dr. Robert G. Griffin
Francis Bitter Natl Magnet Lab.
Massachusetts Institute of Tech.
77 Massachusetts Avenue
Cambridge, MA    02139

Dr. F. Peter Guengerich
Department of Biochemistry and
  Center in Molecular Toxicology
Vanderbilt University
Nashville, TN    37232

Dr. Sam Halpern
San Diego Veterans Hospital
3350 La Jolla Village Drive
San Diego, CA    92161

Dr. Gordon W. Halstead
The Upjohn Company
7000 Portage Road, 7843-259-22
Kalamazoo, MI 49001

Dr. Michel D. Hamon
Inserm U. 288
Neurobiologie Cellulaire
  et Fonctionnelle
91 Boulevard de l'Hopital
Faculte de Medecine Pitie-
  Salpetriere
75634 Paris, Cedex 13, France

Dr. Robert P. Hanzlik
Department of Medicinal Chem.
University of Kansas
School of Pharmacy
Lawrence, KS    66045

Dr. Donald E. Hardies
PPG Industries, Inc
Chemical Division
P. O. Box 31
Barberton, OH 44203

Dr. John R. Harding
Imperial Chem. Industries plc
Alderley Park/Macclesfield,
Cheshire, England  SK10 4TG

Mr. Jon D. Hartman
Warner Lambert/Parke Davis
2800 Plymouth Road
Ann Arbor, MI  48105

Dr. Masaru Hasegawa
Daiichi Pure Chemicals Co., Ltd.
13-5, Nihombashi 3-chome
Chuo-ku, Tokyo 103, Japan

Dr. Saifunnissa B. Hassam
Philip Morris, Inc.
P. O. Box 26583
Richmond, VA 23261

Ms. Ute J. Haynes
Bristol-Myers Co.
R & D Division
P. O. Box 4755
Syracuse, NY 13221-4755

Dr. Sheryl J. Hays
Warner-Lambert/Parke-Davis
2800 Plymouth Road
Ann Arbor, MI 48105

Dr. Donald L. Helman
Radio Analytic, Inc.
5102 South Westshore
Tampa, FL 33611

Dr. Leonard F. Herzog, II
Nuclide Corporation
State College, PA 16801

Dr. Alan J. Heslop
Imperial Chemical Industries plc
P. O. Box 1/Billingham,
Cleveland, England TS23 1LB

Mr. Daniel Heusse
Institut de Biopharmacie
Rhone-Poulenc
20, avenue Raymond-Aron
92160 Antony, France

Dr. J. Richard Heys
Smith Kline & French Labs
1500 Spring Garden Street, F50
Philadelphia, PA 19101

Mr. James L. Hicks
Warner Lambert/Parke Davis
    Pharmaceutical Research
2800 Plymouth Road
Ann Arbor, MI 48105

Dr. John A. Hill
Burroughs Wellcome Company
3030 Cornwallis Road
Research Triangle Park, NC 27709

Mr. Donald B. Hines
Monsanto Company
800 North Lindbergh Blvd. (T3E)
St. Louis, MO 63167

Dr. Rona Hirschberg
Univ. of Missouri-Kansas City
School of Basic Life Sciences
Spencer Chemistry Building
Division of Molecular Biology
5100 Rockhill Road
Kansas City, MO 64110-2499

Dr. Kurt J. Hoffmann
A B Hassle
S-431 83
Molndal, Sweden

Dr. Victor Hruby
Department of Chemistry
University of Arizona
Tucson, AZ 85721

Dr. Richard S. P. Hsi
The Upjohn Company
Kalamazoo, MI 49001

Ms. Ruo Ling Hua
University of California-
    San Francisco
School of Pharmacy
Dept. of Pharm. Chemistry
San Francisco, CA 94143

Dr. Che C. Huang
Warner Lambert/Parke-Davis
    Pharmaceutical Research
2800 Plymouth Road
Ann Arbor, MI 48105

Mr. Philip F. Hurst
Bioscan, Inc.
4590 MacArthur Blvd, N.W.
Washington, DC 20007

Dr. Paul M. Hyde
LSU Medical School
1901 Perdido Street
New Orleans, LA 70112

Dr. A. R. Hylton
Clark Ca College
501 Kennedy Drive
Las Vegas, NV 89110

Dr. Rodney D. Ice
Eagle Picher Industries
P. O. Box 798
Quapaw, OK 74363

Mr. George Ivanovics
Moravek Biochemicals, Inc.
577 Mercury Lane
Brea, CA 92621

Mr. Hwan-Soo Jae
Chemsyn Science Laboratories
13605 West 96th Terrace
Lenexa, KS 66215-1297

Dr. Robert A. Jamieson
Procter & Gamble
Miami Valley Labs
P. O. Box 39175
Cincinnati, OH 45247

Mr. Ingming Jeng
M.I.P.
5400 Arsenal Street
St. Louis, MO 63139

Dr. Satya P. Jindal
Nathan Kline Institute
Orangeburg Road
Orangeburg, NY 10962

Mr. Jerome A. Johemko
Finnigan MAT
355 River Oaks Parkway
San Jose, CA 95134

Dr. J. R. Jones
University of Surrey
Chemistry Department/Guildford,

Dr. Peter J. Jones
Univ. of Chicago Medical Center
P. O. Box 163
5841 South Maryland Avenue
Chicago, IL 60637

Dr. George W. Kabalka
The University of Tennessee
Dept. of Chemistry
Knoxville, TN 37996-1600
Surrey, England GU2 5XH

Dr. Zvi E. Kahana
Weizmann Institute of Science
Department of Isotope Research
P. O. Box 26
Rehovot, Israel 76100

Mr. Jules Kalbfeld
Stauffer Chemical Company
1200 South 47th Street
Richmond, CA 94804

Dr. Maurice A. Kashdan
E. I. Dupont de Nemours & Co.
NEN Research Products
549 Albany Street
Boston, MA 02118

Dr. Frans M. Kaspersen
Organon International B.V.
P. O. Box 20
Oss, Noord-Brabant 5340-BH
The Netherlands

Dr. John A. Kepler
Research Triangle Institute
P. O. Box 12194
Research Triangle Park,NC 27709

Dr. Michael J. Kessler
RADIOMATIC INSTRUMENTS
5102 South Westshore Blvd.
Tampa, FL 33611

Mr. Raja G. Khalifah
KS Univ. Biochem. Department
 & VA Medical Center
4801 Linwood Boulevard
Kansas City, MO 64128

Mr. John M. Kinzie
A.H. Robins Company, Inc.
1211 Sherwood Avenue
Richmond, VA 23220

Ms. Janet Knobbe
DuPont NEN Research Products
549 Albany Street
Boston, MA 02118

Dr. H. J. Koch
MSD Isotopes
P. O. Box 899
Pointe Claire-Dorval,
Quebec, Canada H9R 4P7

Mr. Robert Koch
Mobay Chemical Corporation
8400 Hawthorn Road
P. O. Box 4913
Kansas City, MO 64120

Dr. Alfred J. Kolb
Beckman Instruments, Inc.
Campus Drive at Jamboree Blvd.
Irvine, CA 92713

Dr. Wilhelmus C. Kokke
Smith Kline & French Labs
1500 Spring Garden F50
Philadelphia, PA 19101

Dr. Gert Kollenz
University of Graz
Institute of Organic Chem.
Heinrichstrasse 28
A-8010 Graz, Austria

Mr. Kenneth C. Kolwyck
Chemsyn Science Laboratories
13605 West 96th Terrace
Lenexa, KS 66215-1297

Dr. Ildiko M. Kovach
University of Kansas
Ctr. for Biomedical Research
2099 Constant Avenue
Lawrence, KS 66045

Dr. Werner Krause
Schering AG
Muller Strasse 170-178
Berlin 65 (FRG) 1000, Germany

Ms. Jane A. Kreuzberger
Chemsyn Science Laboratories
13605 West 96th Terrace
Lenexa, KS 66215-1297

Dr. Kikuo Kumazawa
Dept. of Agricultural Chemistry
University of Tokyo
Bunkyo-Ku, Tokyo, Japan

Mr. George Y. Kuo
Smith Kline & French Labs
620 Allendale Road
King of Prussia, PA 19406

Mr. Gilles Labelle
Cambridge Isotope Laboratories
20 Commerce Way
Woburn, MA 01801

Dr. Maurice P. LaMontagne
Chemsyn Science Laboratories
13605 West 96th Terrace
Lenexa, KS 66215-1297

Dr. Aviva Lapidot
Weizmann Institute of Science
Isotope Department
P. O. Box 26
Rehovot, Israel 76100

Dr. Eric Larsen
The Dow Chemical Company
Chemicals Research
768 Building
Midland, MI 48667

Dr. Rolf O. Larsen
Norsk Hydro Research Center
N-3901 Porsgrunn, Norway

Mr. Bruce W. Leander
Amersham Corporation
2636 South Clearbrook Drive
Arlington Heights, IL 60005

Dr. Peter S. Lee
General Motors Corporation
Biomedical Science Department
General Motors Research Labs
Warren, MI 48090-9058

Dr. W. D. Lehmann
Abteilung Medizinische Biochemie
Institut fur Physiologische Chemie
Universitats-Krankenhaus-Eppendorf
Martinistrasse 52
D-2000 Hamburg 20, West Germany

Dr. Peter Leichner
Radiation Oncology
Johns Hopkins Oncology Center
601 North Broadway
Baltimore, MD 21205

Dr. Leonard C. Leitch
University of Ottawa
Nicholas Street
Ottawa, Ontario, Canada

Dr. Irvin Lesk
MSD Isotope
Merck Frosst Canada, Inc.
P. O. Box 899
Pointe Claire-Dorval,
Quebec, Canada H9R 4P7

Dr. David J. Lester
Imperial Chem. Industries plc
P. O. Box 1/Billingham,
Cleveland, England TS23 1LB

Mr. Yan Leung
University of Washington
Dept. of Medicinal Chemistry
BG-20
Seattle, WA 98195

Dr. S. Levinson
Smith Kline & French Labs
1500 Spring Garden Street
Philadelphia, PA 19101

Dr. Arnold A. Liebman
Hoffmann-La Roche, Inc.
340 Kingsland Street
Nutley, NJ 07110

Dr. Yu-Ying Liu
Hoffmann-La Roche, Inc.
340 Kingsland Street
Nutley, NJ 07110

Dr. William J. S. Lockley
Fisons plc Pharmaceutical Div.
Bakewell Road/Loughborough,
Leicestershire, United Kingdom

Dr. Wilfried Loeffler
Siemens Medical Systems, Inc.
Iselin, NJ    08830

Dr. Mervyn A. Long
University of New South Wales
School of Chemistry
P. O. Box 1/Kensington,
New South Wales, Australia   2033

Dr. Anthony Y. H. Lu
Dept. of Animal Drug Metabolism
Merck Sharp and Dohme Res. Labs.
Rahway, NJ    07065

Mr. Richard Macko
Packard Instrument Company
2200 Warrenville Road
Downers Grove, IL    60515

Mr. John N. Maddox
U.S. Department of Energy
Washington, D.C.    20545

Mr. James I. Mann
Air Products & Chemicals, Inc.
P. O. Box 538
Allentown, PA    18105

Mr. Suraj P. Manrao
Merck & Company, Inc./Isotopes
126 East Lincoln Avenue
Rahway, NJ    07065

Dr. Sanford P. Markey
Natl. Institute of Mental Health
Dept. of Health & Human Sciences
9000 Rockville Pike
Bethesda, MD    20205

Dr. Manfred Marsmann
Bayer AG
Friedrich-Ebert-Strasse 217
Wuppertal, West Germany   5600

Mr. Wataru T. Maruyama
Shoko Company, Ltd.
Landic Shimbashi Building
3-8-3 Nishi Shimbashi
3-Chome Minatoku,Tokyo 105,Japan

Mr. David L. Masters
Packard Instrument Company
2200 Warrenville Road
Downers Grove, IL    60515

Dr. Nicholas A. Matwiyoff
University of New Mexico
Ctr for Non-Invasive Diagnosis
900 Camino de Salud, N.E.
Albuquerque, NM    87131

Dr. Michael K. May
Lederle Laboratories
Division of American Cyanamid
Building 65-B/Room 204
Pearl River,  NY   10965

Dr. Alfred J. McCabe
Berthold Instruments, Inc.
136 Bradford Avenue
Pittsburgh, PA   15205

Dr. Leslie P. McCarty
The Dow Chemical Company
U.S. Area Medical
Midland, MI    48674

Mr. John F. McCombe
Amersham International
White Lion, Amersham
Buckinghamshire,England HP7 9LL

Mr. Lionel D. McCreary
The Procter & Gamble Co.
Miami Valley Labs
P. O. Box 39175
Cincinnati, OH   45247

Dr. Lennon H. McKendry
Dow Chemical
Agricultural Department
9001 Building
Midland, MI   48640

Dr. L. Lee Melhado
University of Illinois
Roger Adams Laboratory
P. O. Box 28
1209 West California Street
Urbana, IL   61801

Ms. Veronica J. Michna
Amersham Corporation
2636 South Clearbrook Drive
Arlington Heights, IL    60005

Dr. Thomas R. Mills
Los Alamos National Lab.
Group INC-4/Mail Stop J568
Los Alamos, NM   87544

Mr. William P. Milne
LKB Instruments, Inc.
9319 Gaither Road
Gaithersburg, MD   20877

Dr. Hemant K. Misra
Faculty of Pharmacy &
    Pharmaceutical Sciences
University of Alberta
Edmonton,Alberta,Canada T6G 2N8

Dr. Sandor Mlinko
Central Research Institute for
  Chemistry of the Hungarian
  Academy of Sciences
Pusztaszeri ut 59/67
P. O. Box 17
H-1525 Budapest, Hungary

Dr. Stephen M. Moerlein
Lawrence Berkeley Laboratory
1 Cyclotron Road
Berkeley, CA    94720

Dr. Taj Mohammad
University of Saskatchewan
College of Pharmacy/Saskatoon,
Saskatchewan, Canada    S7N 0W0

Dr. Paul R. Moran
Bowman Gray School of Medicine
Department of Radiology
Winston-Salem, NC    27103

Dr. Josef Moravek
Moravek Biochemicals, Inc.
577 Mercury Lane
Brea, CA    92621

Dr. John G. Morgan
Mobay Chemical Corporation
8400 Hawthron Road
P. O. Box 4913
Kansas City, MO    64120

Dr. Phillip J. Morgan
Cambridge Research Biochem. Ltd.
Button End/Harston,
Cambridge, United Kingdom CB2
5NX

Dr. Taizo Morishita
Shoko Company, Ltd.
Landic Shimbashi Building
8-3 Nishi Shimbashi 3-Chome
Minato-ku, Tokyo 105, Japan

Ms. Ruth E. Moths
Chemsyn Science Laboratories
13605 West  96th Terrace
Lenexa, KS  66215-1297

Dr. Richard R. Muccino
Hoffmann-La Roche, Inc.
340 Kingsland Road
Nutley, NJ    07110

Dr. B. Muralidharan
Labeled Compounds Section
  Isotope Group
Bhabha Atomic Research Centre
Bombay, India    400 085

Dr. William Murphy
Mallinckrodt Institute of
  Radiology
510 S. Kingshighway Boulevard
St. Louis, MO    63110

Dr. H. A. Musallam
Contracting Office Tech. Rep.
Department of the Army
Walter Reed Army Institute
  of Research
Walter Reed Army Hospital
Washington, DC  20307

Dr. Nilolai F. Myasoedov
Institute Molecular Genetics
Academy of Science of USSR
Kurchetov Square, 46
Moscow, Russia (USSR) SU-123182

Mr. Allan K. Nadian
Ministry of Agriculture,
  Fisheries & Food
Tolworth Lab., Hook Rise South
Tolworth,Surrey,England KT6 7NF

Dr. Motupalli V. Naidu
Shell Development Company
P. O. Box 4248
Modesto, CA  95350

Dr. Iwao Nakatsuka
Sumitomo Chem. Co., Ltd.
2-1, 4-Chome, Takatsukasa
Takarazuka, Hyogo 665    Japan

Dr. N. Narasimhachari
Dept. of Psychiatry
Medical College of Virginia
P. O. Box 710
Richmond, VA  23298

Mr. Jack H. Newman
A. H. Robins Company, Inc.
1211 Sherwood Avenue
Richmond, VA 23220

Ms. Nancy A. Nungesser
Chemsyn Science Laboratories
13605 West  96th Terrace
Lenexa, KS    66215-1297

Dr. Lars-Inge O. Olsson
Pharmacia AB
Department of Chemical Research
S-751 82 Uppsala, Sweden

Dr. P. Osinski
Catholic University of Louvain
Unit of Experimental Med.
Av. Emmanuel Mounier 73-UCL
7340-1200 Brussels, Belgium

Dr. Donald G. Ott
Los Alamos National Lab.
Mail Stop MS-880
Los Alamos, NM   87545

Dr. Elena D. Oziashvili
Research Institute of
    Stable Isotopes
Stanomonetnc per 26
Moscow, Russia (USSR) SU-109180

Dr. Donald E. Pack
Chevron Chemical Company
940 Hensley Street
Richmond, CA   94804

Mr. Daniel Parker
Teknivent Corporation
10774 Trenton Avenue
St. Louis, MO   63132

Dr. Howard Parnes
Syntex Research
3401 Hillview Avenue
Palo Alto, CA   94304

Dr. T. L. Pazdernik
Department of Pharmacology,
   Toxicology & Therapeutics
Ralph L. Smith Research Center
Univ. of Kansas Medical Center
Kansas City, KS     66103

Dr. Chin-Tzu Peng
University of California at
    San Francisco
San Francisco, CA   94143

Mr. Tom Penno
Amersham Corporation
2636 South Clearbrook Drive
Arlington Heights, IL 60005-4692

Mr. Bill Perry
Pathfinder Laboratories, Inc.
11542 Fort Mims Drive
St. Louis, MO   63146

Dr. Clark Perry
Boehringer Ingelheim Pharm.
90 East Ridge Road
Ridgefield, CT   06877

Mr. Rick Perullo
DuPont NEN Research Products
549 Albany Street
Boston, MA     02118

Ms. Catherine A. Phillips
E. I. DuPont de Nemours & Co.
Glenolden Laboratory
Glenolden, PA   19036

Dr. Louis J. Pichat
Atomic Energy Commission
CEN Saclay
Director of Research Bldg. #47
91191 Gif/Yvette, Cedex, France

Ms. Susan Pinnow
Amersham Corporation
2636 South Clearbrook Drive
Arlington Heights, IL 60005-4692

Mr. Albert J. Poje
Mobay Chemical Corporation
P. O. Box 4913
Kansas City, MO   64120

Dr. E. Ponnusamy
Dept. of Physiology & Biophysics
Univ. of Illinois at Chicago
P. O. Box 6998
Chicago, IL   60680

Mr. James L. Powers
P. O. Box 14216
San Francisco, CA     94114

Dr. Shimoga R. Prakash
Merck & Company, Inc.
P. O. Box 2000
Rahway, NJ 07065

Mr. Bruce F. Raby
AECh Radiochemical Company
P. O. Box 13500
Kanata, Ontario, Canada

Dr. Raghavan Rajagopalan
Mallinckrodt, Inc.
675 McDonnell Blvd.
St. Louis, MO     63042

Dr. Gurusamy Rajendran
Department of Chemistry
Purdue University
West Lafayette, IN     47907

Dr. Siya Ram
Cyclotron/PET Facility
Division of Nuclear Medicine
University of Michigan
    Medical School
Ann Arbor, MI    48109

Dr. T. V. Ramamurthy
Labelled Compounds Section
Isotope Group, B.A.R.C.
Bombay, India    400 085

Dr. Malcolm Randall
DuPont NEN Research Products
549 Albany Street
Boston, MA    02118

Dr. Pemmaraju N. Rao
Southwest Foundation for
    Biomedical Research
West Loop 410 @ Military Drive
P. O. Box 28147
San Antonio, TX    78284

Mr. Joe E. Ratledge
Oak Ridge National Laboratory
P. O. Box X
Oak Ridge, TN    37774

Dr. Bruce David Ray
I.U.P.U.I./Physics Dept.
P. O. Box 647
Indianapolis, IN    46223

Dr. Martin Reisfeld
Los Alamos National Lab.
P. O. Box 1663/M-880
Los Alamos, NM    87545

Dr. Albert W. Rettenmeier
Department of Pharmaceutics
University of Washington
Bagley Hall, B6-20
Seattle, WA    98195

Dr. Sung W. Rhee
SRI International
333 Ravenswood Avenue
Menlo Park, CA    94025

Dr. Jay K. Rinehart
PPG Industries, Inc.
P. O. Box 31
Barberton, OH    44203

Dr. Ralph Robinson
University of Kansas
Medical Center
39th and Rainbow Boulevard
Kansas City, KS    66103

Mr. Gary A. Rotert
Chemsyn Science Laboratories
13605 West  96th Terrace
Lenexa, KS  66215-1297

Dr. Robert W. Roth
Chemsyn Science Laboratories
13605 West  96th Terrace
Lenexa, KS  66215-1297

Dr. Ivor Royston
University of California
Hematology/Oncology Sect. (111E)
Veterans Administration Hospital
San Diego, CA    92161

Dr. Paul H. Ruehle
Chemsyn Science Laboratories
13605 West  96th Terrace
Lenexa, KS  66215-1297

Dr. Alfonse W. Runquist
Aldrich Chemical Company, Inc.
940 West St. Paul Avenue
Milwaukee, WI    53233

Dr. Daniel P. Ryskiewich
Ciba-Geigy Corporation
410 Swing Road
Greensboro, NC    27409

Dr. Christer S. Sahlberg
Astra Pharmaceuticals
S-151 85 Sodertalje, Sweden

Dr. Akio Sakamoto
2nd Dept. of Surgery
Chiba University
School of Medicine
1-8-1 Inohana, Chiba 280    Japan

Dr. Bhaskar R. Samant
Chemsyn Science Laboratories
13605 West  96th Terrace
Lenexa, KS    66215-1297

Mr. Duane Sanderson
LKB Instruments, Inc.
9319 Gaither Road
Gaithersburg, MD    20877

Dr. Robert A. Sandmann
U.M.K.C. School of Pharmacy
5005 Rockhill Road
Kansas City, MO    64110-2499

Dr. Beverly J. Sandmann
U.M.K.C. School of Pharmacy
5005 Rockhill Road
Kansas City, MO    64110-2499

Ms. Lisa A. Santay
Warner Lambert/Parke Davis
2800 Plymouth Road
Ann Arbor, MI 48105

Dr. J. H. Saugier
Eagle-Picher Industries, Inc.
Chemsyn Science Laboratories
13605 West 96th Terrace
Lenexa, KS 66215-1297

Mr. David Saunders
Smith Kline & French Res., Ltd.
The Frythe/Welwyn,
Hertfordshire, England AL6 9AR

Dr. William H. Saunders, Jr.
Chemistry Department
University of Rochester
500 Joseph C Wilson Blvd.
Rochester, NY 14627

Mr. Ronald D. Savidge
ICI Americas, Inc.
Murphy Road & Concord Pike
Wilmington, DE 19897

Dr. Bernard Schmall
Brookhaven National Laboratory
Upton, NY 11973

Dr. Dale A. Schoeller
The University of Chicago
Department of Medicine
P. O. Box 163
5841 South Maryland Avenue
Chicago, IL 60637

Dr. Paul-Eberhard Schulze
Schering AG
Muller Strasse 170-178
Berlin 65 (FRG) 1000 Germany

Mr. Albert J. Schuster
Merrell Dow Res. Institute
Indianapolis Center
9550 Zionsville Rd
Indianapolis, IN 46268

Mr. Anthony Schwally
LKB Instruments, Inc.
9319 Gaither Road
Gaithersburg, MD 20877

Dr. Roger A. Schwind
Isotec, Inc.
7542 McEwen Road
Dayton, OH 45459-3995

Dr. S. G. Senderoff
SmithKline Beckman
Radiochemistry, F-50
1500 Spring Garden Street
Philadelphia, PA 19101

Mr. William T. Shebs
Shell Development Company
P. O. Box 481
Houston, TX 77001

Ms. Emma J. Shelton
Syntex Corporation
3401 Hillview Avenue
R-4/109
Palo Alto, CA 94304

Dr. P. W. Sheppard
Cambridge Res. Biochemicals, Ltd.
Button End Industrial Estate
Harston, Cambridge,
England CB2 5NX

Dr. Henry J. Shine
Texas Tech. University
Chemistry Department
Lubbock, TX 79409

Dr. Arthur Y. L. Shu
SmithKline Beckman Corporation
1500 Spring Garden Street/F-50
Philadelphia, PA 19101

Dr. Seth Shulman
Bioscan, Inc.
4590 MacArthur Blvd, N.W.
Washington, D.C. 20007

Mr. Roger L. Simonsson
AB Hassle
Karragatan 5
S-431 83 Molndal, Sweden

Dr. Miklos Simonyi
Central Research Institute
    for Chemistry
Hungarian Academy of Sciences
H-1525 Budapest Pf 17, Hungary

Dr. Lorna T. Sniegoski
National Bureau of Standards
Building 222, Room A-361
Gaithersburg, MD 20899

Dr. Paul L. Spangler
Pathfinder Laboratories, Inc.
11542 Fort Mims Drive
St. Louis, MO 63146

Mr. Jay A. Spicer
Univ. of KS Medical Center
Dept. Diagnostic Radiology
39th Street at Rainbow Blvd
Kansas City, KS    66103

Dr. Prem C. Srivastava
Nuclear Medicine Group
Oak Ridge National Labs
Oak Ridge, TN    37831

Dr. Dennis Sprott
National Research Council
100 Sussex Drive
Ottawa,Ontario,Canada K1A 0R6

Mr. Michael A. Stanga
Chemsyn Science Laboratories
13605 West  96th Terrace
Lenexa, KS    66215-1297

Dr. Howard Stead
Central Research Establishment
Home Office Forensic
    Science Service
Aldermaston, Reading
Berkshire, England  RG7 4PN

Dr. John M. Stewart
University of Colorado
School of Medicine
4200  9th Avenue, East
Denver, CO    80262

Dr. Michael Stiasni
Boehringer Ingelheim KG
Department of Biochemistry
Postfach, Ingelheim/Rhein
D6507 West Germany

Dr. David I. Stirling
Celanese Research Company
86 Morris Avenue
Summit, NJ    07901

Dr. Alexander B. Susan
Sandoz Research Institute
East Hanover, NJ    07936

Dr. John R. Sutton
Amersham International plc
Forest Farm Whitchurch/Cardiff,
Wales, Great Brittain  CF4 7YT

Dr. John E. Swigor
Bristol-Myers Company
Pharmaceutical R & D Division
P. O. Box 4755
Syracuse, NY  13221-4755

Dr. C. T. Tan
MSD Isotopes
P. O. Box 899
Pointe Claire, Dorval,
Quebec, Canada    H9R 4P7

Dr. Yui-Sing Tang
Lawrence Berkeley Labs
University of California
1 Cyclotron Road
Berkeley, CA 94720

Mr. Daniel L. Timmons
Chemsyn Science Laboratories
13605 West  96th Terrace
Lenexa, KS 66215-1297

Dr. Kou-Yi Tserng
Clinical Pharmacology Dept.
Case Western Reserve Univ.
10900 Euclid Avenue
Cleveland, OH    44106

Dr. Hwei-Ru Tsou
American Cyanamid Company
P. O. Box 400
Princeton, NJ    08540

Dr. John T. Uchic
Chemsyn Science Laboratories
13605 West  96th Terrace
Lenexa, KS 66215-1297

Mr. Takao Ueda
Tokai Laboratories/Daiichi Pure
    Chemicals Company, Ltd.
2117 Muramatsu/Tokai-mura
Naka-gun, Ibaraki-ken 319-11
Japan

Mr. Clifford J. Unkefer
Los Alamos National Laboratory
INC-4  MS  C345
Los Alamos, NM    87545

Dr. Shiro Urano
Tokyo Metropolitan Inst.
    of Gerontoloy
35-2 Sakae-cho
Itabashi-ku, Tokyo 173  Japan

Dr. S. van Cauter
United Technologies Packard
2200 Warrenville Road
Downers Grove, IL    60515

Professor Robert L. van Etten
Chemistry Department
Purdue University
West Lafayette, IN    47907

Dr. N. Venkatasubramanian
IDL-Nitro Nobel Basic
    Research Institute
Post Bag 397, Sankey Road
Bangalore, India    560 003

Dr. Arpad Veres
Institute of Isotopes
Hungarian Academy of Sciences
P. O. Box 77
H-1525 Budapest, Hungary

Dr. Thomas W. Vickroy
Abbott Laboratories
Neuroscience Research Div.
Department 47H/Building AP10
Abbott Park, IL    60064

Mr. Anthony J. Villani
Smith Kline and Beckman Corp.
1500 Spring Garden Street
Philadelphia, PA    19101

Dr. Rolf Werner Voges
Sandoz, Ltd.
Biopharmaceutical Department
Lichtsctrasse 35
CH-4002 Basle, Switzerland

Professor F. J. Volenec
UMKC-Basic Life Sciences
Biology Building/Room 109
Kansas City, MO    64110-2499

Dr. Gerd E. von Unruh
Massenspektrometrie Labor 73
Medizinishe Universitats
Klinik Venusberg
Sigmund-Freud-Strasse 25
5300 Bonn 1, West Germany

Dr. Eugene R. Wagner
Merrell Dow Research Institute
9550 Zionsville Road
Indianapolis, IN    46268

Dr. Thomas E. Walker
Los Alamos National Lab.
INC-4/Mail Stop C-345
Los Alamos, NM    87545

Dr. Shih-Chen Wang
Center of Nuclear Medicine
   of the Capitol Hospital
Beijing,   China

Ms. Lisa A. Warden
Chemsyn Science Laboratories
13605 West  96th Terrace
Lenexa, KS   66215-1297

Mr. Robert W. Waring
Air Products & Chemicals, Inc.
P. O. Box 538
Allentown, PA    18105

Dr. Larry E. Weaner
McNeil Pharmaceutical
Welsh and McKean Roads
Spring House, PA  19477-0776

Dr. A. Weisz
National Inst. of Mental Health
Laboratory of Clinical Science
Building 10-3D40
Bethesda, MD   20205-1000

Mr. Tom F. Werner
Kabivitrum AB
Lindhagensg 133
Stockholm, Sweden   S-112-87

Dr. Robert M. Wester
R. M. Wester & Associates, Inc.
3317 Highway 94 North
St. Charles, MO   63301

Dr. Thomas W. Whaley
Los Alamos National Lab.
Group LS-1, Mail Stop M-880
Los Alamos, NM   87545

Dr. William J. Wheeler
Eli Lilly & Co, Research Labs
Lilly Corp Ctr Bldg. 88/4
307 E. McCarty Street
Indianapolis, IN   46285

Mr. David F. White
Imperial Chem. Industries plc
Alderley Park/Macclesfield,
Cheshire, England    SK10 4TG

Mr. James C. Wiley, Jr.
Chemsyn Science Laboratories
13605 West  96th Terrace
Lenexa, KS   66215-1297

Dr. William R. Wilkes
Monsanto Research Corp.-Mound
P. O. Box 32
Miamisburg, OH   45342

Dr. Alfred P. Wolf
Brookhaven National Laboratory
Department of Chemistry
Upton, NY    11973

Dr. Joseph A. Wursch
F. Hoffmann-La Roche & Company
Grenzacherstrasse 124
CH-4002 Basle, Switzerland

Dr. Steven D. Wyrick
Div. Medicinal Chemistry
University of North Carolina
309 Beard Hall/200-H
Chapel Hill, NC  27514

Dr. Z. Q. Xia
Shanghai Second Medical College
280 South Chong-qing Road
Shanghai, China

Dr. Alfred Yergey
National Institute of Child
    Health & Human Development
Building 6, Room 136
Bethesda, MD    20205

Mr. Richard E. Youngstrom
Schering Corporation
60 Orange Street
Bloomfield, NJ  07003

Dr. Sun-Shine Yuan
Tracer Technologies, Inc.
225 Needham Street
Newton, MA    02164

Dr. Jeffrey G. Zaloom
Aldrich Chemical Company
940 West St. Paul Avenue
Milwaukee, WI    53233

Mr. Horst Zipp
Dr. Karl Thomae GMBH
Department of Biochemistry
Postfach 17 55
D-7950 Biberach on der Riss
West Germany

Dr. Yuri A. Zolotarev
Institute Molecular Genetics
Academy of Science of USSR
Kurchatov Square, 46
Moscow, Russia (USSR)  SU-123182

PREFACE

The Second International Symposium on the Synthesis and Applications of Isotopically Labeled Compounds was held in Kansas City, Missouri, on September 3-6, 1985. Publication of the plenary lectures, invited papers and other selected presentations has been arranged in order to provide a valuable reference to researchers in the field and an indication of the direction of future research.

A total of 337 participants from 19 countries attended the Symposium. The countries represented were: Australia, Austria, Belgium, Canada, China, France, Hungary, India, Israel, Japan, The Netherlands, Norway, Qatar, Soviet Union, Sweden, Switzerland, United Kingdom, United States and West Germany.

A Symposium of this size requires the hard work and cooperation of many people and, therefore, we would like to thank all members of the International Scientific Committee for their help in designing this year's program. We would also like to acknowledge the help of all the Session Chairmen and all those who have contributed to the conference by the presentation of their papers.

Special thanks are due to the Co-Chairmen of the Organizing Committee, Drs. William P. Duncan and Robert A. Sandmann, and to the Symposium Coordinator, Dr. Donald Wilk, the Publications Coordinator, Ms. Janet N. Stratton, and to Ms. Phyllis C. Vaughn for the preparation of the Symposium publications and to Mr. David Malarek for proofreading the Proceedings.

We acknowledge the University of Missouri-Kansas City for their sponsorship and organizational help and for providing a stable base from which to operate. Major funding was provided by a generous grant from the U.S. Army Medical Research and Development Command. Co-sponsors of the Symposium are Chemsyn Science Laboratories, a Division of Eagle-Picher Industries, Inc. and Amersham International. Additional contributors included: Berthold Instruments, Inc., Ciba-Geigy Corporation, DuPont's New England Nuclear, Hoffmann-La Roche, Inc., Merck Sharp and Dohme/Isotopes, Norwich-Eaton Pharmaceuticals, Sandoz, SmithKline Beckman Corporation, and Wizard Laboratories.

Richard R. Muccino
Nutley, New Jersey, U.S.A.
September 1985

## OPENING REMARKS

Richard R. Muccino
Hoffmann-La Roche, Inc.
Nutley, New Jersey 07110

Welcome to Kansas City, and to the Second International Symposium on the Synthesis and Applications of Isotopically Labeled Compounds. To those of you who are visitors to this country, I welcome you to the United States and invite you to get to know each other and us. In the dissemination of knowledge, scientists recognize no borders and admit no ideology. This freedom from obstacles permits us not only to exchange knowledge and ideas unfettered by political restraints, but also to learn about each other.

It was this desire for an exchange which prompted the organization of the First International Isotope Symposium in Kansas City in 1982. It was realized then that the state of the science of isotopes had reached a level of sophistication such that any future meetings would have to be multidisciplinary. Therefore, the objective of the First Symposium was to bring together in one encompassing conference the entire community of both makers and users of isotopically labeled compounds, both stable and radioactive. Prior to this 1982 Symposium, a number of separate meetings had been organized on individual topics. Many of these meetings were discontinued after the initial interest on the particular topic had peaked.

Meetings emphasizing carbon-14 and tritium were the first to be organized because of the easier means of production and detection of these nuclides. These meetings were first organized in the United States by New England Nuclear Corporation between 1957 and 1961, and then later in Europe by Euroatom between 1964 and 1966. The last meeting to be concerned with the classical radioisotopes was held in 1970 in Saclay, France.

By the 1970's, there were meetings concerned with the use and preparation of stable isotopes as a consequence of the greater availability of these nuclides as well as the increasingly sophisticated technology available for their analysis. These increased quantities of isotopically enriched compounds were made possible by the separation facilities at Los Alamos Scientific Laboratory. At about the same time, the most significant development to promote stable isotope methodology was introduced, the technique of combined gas chromatography-mass spectrometry along with such innovative methods as "twin ion" or "isotope cluster" techniques. Several international stable isotope conferences were organized in the 1970's by Drs. Peter Klein, Tom Baillie, and H. L. Schmidt. The last meeting on stable isotopes was held in 1981 at Julich, West Germany.

A third group of meetings which emerged emphasized the preparation and detection of short-lived positron emitters. These radiopharmaceutical meetings, held every two years, were organized by Drs. Alfred Wolf, Michael Welch, and Gerhard Stocklin. The last meeting in this series was held in 1984 in Tokyo, Japan.

In summary, each type of isotope attracted its own following, who then organized their own conferences. Some of these meetings such as those on radioisotopes and stable isotopes, were discontinued when the initial enthusiasm in the field waned.

The continued interest, however, in both these areas was demonstrated by the enthusiastic response to the first Kansas City Symposium. The fundamental strength of the 1982 meeting, which was organized by Drs. William P. Duncan and Alexander B. Susan, was its emphasis on the complimentary nature of radioactive and stable isotopes because it is at the borders between fields of science where cross fertilization of ideas results and significant discoveries are made. A total of 291 participants from 17 countries attended the 1982 meeting in which 104 oral papers and 56 poster papers were presented.

The response to the 1982 meeting was so overwhelming that this second conference was immediately planned. At least 178 presentations are scheduled in the 20 sessions of this meeting of which 108 will be oral and 70 will be poster. The broad general scope of the First Symposium has been retained for maximum flexibility. In addition to three sessions of oral presentations concerned with the synthesis of labeled compounds, a fourth session has been added which attempts to give an overview of contemporary approaches to labeling synthesis.

The main emphasis of this symposium, however, is on the new applications of labeled compounds. For this reason, sessions have been organized in the following areas: The Preparation and Use of Labeled Peptides; The Application of Radioligands in Binding Studies; The Utility of Labeled Monoclonal Antibodies; The Application of Labeled Compounds in Recombinant DNA Research; and The Use of Deuterated Analogs of Drugs as Medicinal Agents. In addition, sessions have been organized in: The Use of Labeled Compounds in NMR Imaging; The Applications of

Deuterium and Nitrogen-15 NMR Spectroscopy; and The State of the Art in the Instrumentation for the Analysis of Isotopically Labeled Compounds.

The group assembled here is a heterogeneous one. Each can, therefore, teach as well as learn. It is in this spirit that I look forward to a stimulating four days and hope that this brief contact may serve as a basis for a continuing dialogue.

## AWARD PRESENTATION

Our banquet speaker and award recipient is Professor Melvin Calvin, a pioneer in the synthesis and applications of isotopically labeled compounds. In 1937, Professor Calvin joined the staff of the Chemistry Department at the University of California, Berkeley. He is currently University Professor of Chemistry at Berkeley and was former Director of the Laboratory of Chemical Biodynamics and former Associate Director of the Lawrence Berkeley Laboratory.

Professor Calvin has published seven books, over six hundred technical papers and holds numerous patents. Recitation of his many awards, honorary degrees, honorary lectureships, and his service on distinguished committees and in honorary societies would easily consume the remainder of this evening. Among his many honors are the Nobel Prize in Chemistry in 1961 for his work on photosynthesis, the Davy Medal of the Royal Society in 1964, the Priestley Medal of the American Chemical Society in 1978, which is the highest award in American Chemical Science, the Gold Medal of the American Institute of Chemists in 1979, and the Sterling B. Hendricks Medal of the Agricultural Research Service U.S. Department of Agriculture in 1983.

Professor Calvin has freely given his time and ability in service to governments, scientific organizations, academic institutions and colleagues. His thirty-five year involvement includes service on the President's Science Advisory Committee for Presidents Kennedy and Johnson. He was Chairman of the Committee on Science and Public Policy of the National Academy of Sciences and he was Chairman of and has served on several Advisory Committees for NASA. He currently serves as a member of the Energy Research Advisory Board for the Department of Energy.

Professor Calvin was President of the American Society of Plant Physiologists in 1963 and 1964, and President of the American Chemical Society in 1971. He was elected to the National Academy of Science in the United States, the Royal Society of London, the Japan Academy, the Royal Netherlands Academy of Sciences, and to many other distinguished societies of other nations.

Professor Calvin's pioneering use of radioactive isotopes in the successful study of photosynthesis clearly demonstrated the utility of isotopic labeling as a research tool. His book on "Isotopic Carbon" enabled researchers throughout the world to set up laboratories in which they could prepare the labeled compounds necessary for their studies. Since that time, the world-wide use of isotopes and isotopic labeling in chemical, biochemical, and medical research has been legion.

Melvin Calvin has been called a "Scientist among Scientists" for the breadth of his interests, ranging from pure organic chemistry to chemical evolution. His interest in living things has been ascribed as a fundamental motivation for most of his scientific work. His influence upon other scientists has been called "catalytic". His laboratory in Berkeley has been described as one of the foremost interdisciplinary groups in the world.

A few quotations from Professor Calvin will describe, in his own words, what he feels about science and how it should be done:

There is no such thing as pure science. By this I mean that physics impinges on astronomy, on the one hand, and chemistry on biology, on the other. The synthesis of a really new conception requires some sort of union in one mind of the pertinent aspects of several disciplines....An essential feature of this climate is an atmosphere of curiosity about the nature of the world around us and the freedom to satisfy that curiosity....Education must be such as to enable the young scientist to explore deeply and well some particular area of natural phenomena. There is no substitute for this sort of concentrated activity and concentration of thought. However, it must be accompanied by the conviction that the student is to follow, and, in fact, has the duty to follow, the exploration of any natural phenomena into whatever area the light may lead him. In this way will the creation of new horizons overlapping existing divisions of science be encouraged.

It is in this spirit, captured by his own words, that we present our award to Melvin Calvin, a man who "Follows the Trail of Light" to wherever it may lead him with enthusiasm, energy, and scientific integrity.

R.R.M.

BANQUET ADDRESS

Melvin Calvin
University of California
Department of Chemistry
Berkeley, California

# USEFUL VARIABLE ATOMS

## Chronology Of Tracer Isotope
Discoveries In The Last Fifty Years

1923    HEVESY. First biological tracer experiment using $^{212}$pb (Thorium B).

1929    GIAUGUE. Discovery of oxygen-17, oxygen-18.

1931    BIRGE, et al. Calculates chemical atomic weight of hydrogen and indicates presence of heavier isotope.

1932    UREY. Sees D in hydrogen spectrum.

1933    G. N. LEWIS. Obtained pure $D_2O$ from electrolytic cells producing $H_2$ for liquid $H_2$ used by Giaugue. Lewis used first sample of pure $D_2O$ to show that seeds did not germinate as rapidly in $D_2O$ and that there was an isotope effect in $D_2O$ chemistry.

1934    HEVESY. Used deuterium to measure exchange of body water for fish in its surroundings as well as measuring average life of water in humans (14 days).

1935    SCHOENHEIMER and RITTENBERG. Extensive work with deuterium as tracer. Synthesis of deuterium labeled steroids to determine their metabolic rate.

1935    FERMI, SEGRE, et al. Discovery of phosphorus-32.

1936    CALVIN. Exchange of deuterium with water on polarized platinized electrode. One of early uses of deuterium in pure chemical form.

1937    UREY. Enrichment of nitrogen isotope, mass 15.

1937    SCHOENHEIMER. Use of enriched nitrogen isotope as tracer in biological experiments, particularly protein turnover and amino acid synthesis.

1938    UREY. Enrichment of oxygen-17 and oxygen-18.

1939    RUBEN, HASSID, and KAMEN. Discovery of carbon-11 (half-life 20 minutes) and its use as a tracer in photosynthetic studies. (First observation of carbon-11 had been in 1934.)

1940     RUBEN and KAMEN. Discovery of carbon-14. Production of substantial amounts of $^{14}C$ by neutron irradiation of nitrogen-14 in 60" Crocker cyclotron. Work with this long-lived isotope of carbon (half-life approx. 5000 years) changed the face of organic chemistry and biochemistry.

1941     RUBEN, RANDALL, KAMEN, and HYDE. Use of enriched oxygen to demonstrate oxygen evolution in photosynthesis from $H_2O$, not $CO_2$.

1946     CALVIN and CO-WORKERS. Use of $^{14}C$ in synthesis of labeled organic compounds; beginning of major synthetic work.

1947     KAMEN. Publication of "Radioactive Tracers in Biology", first edition (second edition, 1951; third edition, 1957).

1949     CALVIN and CO-WORKERS. Publication of "Isotopic Carbon".

1948–
1958     CALVIN and CO-WORKERS. Elucidation of the path of carbon in photosynthesis. (Path I to Path XXIII).

1957     BASSHAM and CALVIN. Publication of "The Path of Carbon in Photosynthesis".

1962     CALVIN. "The Path of Carbon in Photosynthesis" (Nobel Prize Address).

## CARBON-14 SYNTHETIC STUDIES AT BERKELEY

During the years after the discovery of carbon-14 in 1940, a great many researchers in organic and biochemistry realized the importance of this isotope in the synthesis of biologically-important compounds. The first definitive book on the subject was written by Martin Kamen in 1947.

At the University of California, Berkeley, Dr. Ernest O. Lawrence (Fig. 1) realized the importance of this isotope for chemistry, biology, and medicine. In 1945 he asked me to form a group within the radiation laboratory to synthesize carbon-14 labeled organic compounds for biological experiments, first for the medical studies of his brother, Dr. John H. Lawrence, who used the $^{14}$C-labeled compounds for the study of metabolic rates.

One of the early, purely chemical experiments with carbon-14 was to synthesize carboxyl-labeled malonic acid and search for the mass effect in the decarboxylation of malonic to acetic acid and $CO_2$. We were able to observe that the specific activity of the $CO_2$ which was produced upon decarboxylation was actually less than that of the $CO_2$ which was used in the synthetic procedure, indicating that the $^{14}C/^{12}C$ bond was broken slightly more slowly than the $^{12}C/^{12}C$ bond.

As our synthetic work with carbon-14 proceeded, we found ourselves making a wide variety of organic and biological compounds with specific carbon atoms labeled. This work is described in detail in "Isotopic Carbon", published in 1949 which became a laboratory manual for isotope synthesis with carbon-14 for many years.

Because the Berkeley group had most of the early radioactive $^{14}$C, we began supplying labeled compounds to many people throughout the country and throughout the world during the first years when this isotope was available. The original carbon-14 came out in the form of $CO_2$ and was precipitated as barium carbonate. The $^{14}$C was produced from the ammonium nitrate solutions used to absorb neutrons, stacked around the 60-inch cyclotron in the Crocker Laboratory. For some time we had almost the entire supply of the radioactive barium carbonate in the United States, and in those days we considered a millicurie of $BaCO_3$ to be priceless.

FIFTEEN CENTS

November 1, 1937

# TIME

## The Weekly Newsmagazine

*Color Photograph for TIME by Oliver Calvert Underhill*

Volume XXX

**ERNEST ORLANDO LAWRENCE**
*He creates and destroys.*
(See SCIENCE)

Number 18

Circulation Office, 330 East 22nd Street, Chicago.    (Reg. U. S. Pat. Off.)    Editorial and Advertising Offices, 135 East 42nd Street, New York.

Fig. 1

Subsequently, carbon-14 was produced from the reactors at Richland and Oak Ridge. Nitrogen, in its most concentrated form as beryllium nitride, was inserted into the reactors to make the carbon-14. At this point, the synthetic work at Berkeley gradually turned to preparing selected compounds for our own research purposes.

## THE PATH OF CARBON IN PHOTOSYNTHESIS

Ernest Lawrence's belief in the usefulness of carbon-14 has been borne out in all its aspects. In addition to using this isotope for the synthesis of labeled compounds, we began to use $^{14}C$ in the form of $^{14}CO_2$ to investigate the way in which plants absorb $CO_2$ and produce all of the organic compounds in them using the energy of the sun, i.e., the process of photosynthesis. The original work on the path of carbon in photosynthesis was done by Ruben and Kamen before World War II when only carbon-11 was available to them. (Although carbon-14 was actually discovered by Ruben and Kamen in 1940, they did not have an opportunity to explore the use of this isotope in their photosynthetic studies because of the war.) They showed that plants did indeed fix the $CO_2$ and that most of it, in the early stages at least, was found in a carboxylic acid group; this was determined by the decarboxylation reaction of the crude plant products. Because of the short life of carbon-11, Ruben and Kamen were limited in the chemistry that could be done with that isotope.

During the war years we were all occupied with direct applications of chemistry to the war effort, and Ruben was killed while working with phosgene.

Following the war, I picked up the work on the use of $^{14}C$ in photosynthesis and had the time to do the chemistry which was necessary to sort out the complex reactions in the plant. To do this work we assembled a group of chemists, biochemists and plant physiologists in the old radiation laboratory (Fig. 2), a "temporary" building constructed in the late 19th Century on the Berkeley campus which had been the home of the original 37-inch cyclotron designed by Ernest Lawrence.

Our principal technique to unravel the unknown path of carbon was to use radioactive $CO_2$ followed by the separation of the products by paper chromatography which had been developed for amino acids by Martin and Synge in England. Our first product separation, however, was done before paper chromatography was developed, using ion exchange

Fig. 2

resins. Because of the difficulties of removing the label from an anion exchange resin, we came to the conclusion that the first compound had at least two negative charges at two different points so that it was bound very tightly to the ion exchange resin. This turned out to be a correct assumption, and we were able to identify phosphoglyceric acid as the earliest product of photosynthesis. Later this was confirmed by paper chromatography.

The overall reaction of photosynthesis had been known for many years. Our general method was to expose plants, usually microalgae (although we also used weeds from outside the ORL as well as barley shoots) for limited periods of time in radioactive $CO_2$ in an apparatus called a "lollipop" (Fig. 3) and then extract the plant material in an organic solvent and chromatograph the extract in two dimensions on filter paper. We then exposed the paper to X-ray film, and depending on how long the paper was exposed to the film black spots appeared (Fig. 4) which were identified by various chemical methods. The identification of the various intermediates in the path of carbon was dependent upon our gradually accumulating knowledge of how the compounds behaved in two-dimensional chromatography since we had no measurable amount of material, only a radioactive spot.

The essential features of that identification involved an initial estimate of the nature of the compound from its position on the paper which had been calibrated with known compounds. We then extracted the compound from the paper, performed some chemistry on it and put it back on another piece of filter paper. It was the behavior of these two or more spots which allowed us to make an identification. The final step of co-chromatography with macroscopic amounts of the suspected compounds whose position on the paper had been established by color chemical reactions permitted us to identify the distribution of the colored chemical spots with the radioactive spot produced on X-ray film for final confirmation.

The overall work on the elucidation of the path of carbon on photosynthesis took ten years, from 1948-1958, and involved many collaborators: staff scientists from the Department of Chemistry and Lawrence Berkeley Laboratory; visiting postdoctoral fellows from the United States and all over the world; and graduate students. A group of these collaborators (Fig. 5), involving the disciplines of chemistry, biochemistry, cell biology, microbiology, is shown standing outside the old radiation laboratory. That was the nature of the work which led to the ultimate definition of the path of carbon in photosynthesis which is the

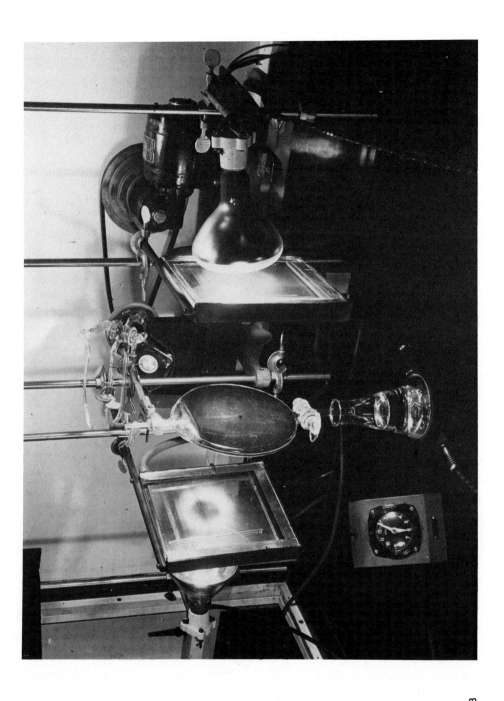

Fig. 3

12

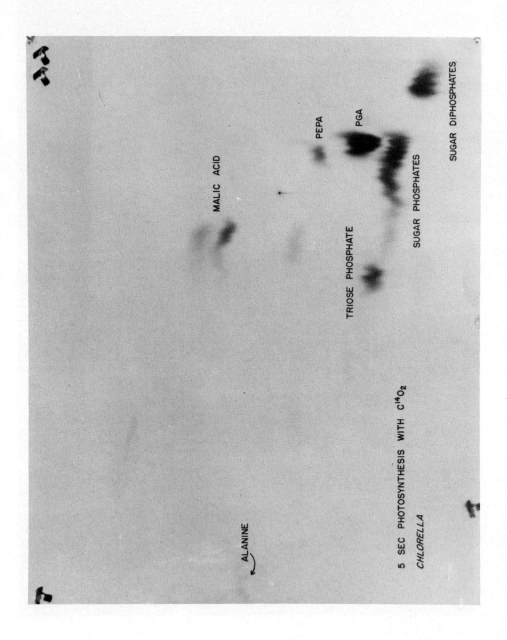

MALIC ACID

PEPA

PGA

TRIOSE PHOSPHATE

SUGAR PHOSPHATES

SUGAR DIPHOSPHATES

ALANINE

5 SEC PHOTOSYNTHESIS WITH C¹⁴O₂

CHLORELLA

Fig. 4

primary method of ultimately fixing carbon by all green plants.

At this meeting, I have heard dozens of different ways in which isotopes are being used. The number of different ways in which it is being used today were inconceivable forty years ago when we started this work. Now, we can look forward in the future to still newer ways of making use of the fact that the elements consist of many different isotopic forms. The people who are going to do it are you folks, and I look forward to seeing you at the next meeting.

14

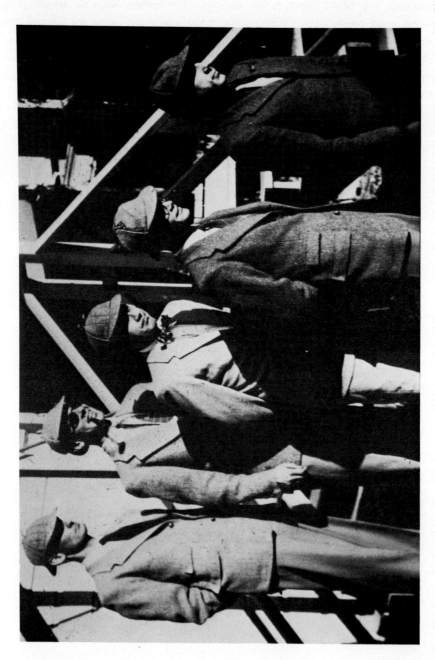

Fig. 5. Old Radiation Laboratory, 1954. J. Rodney Quale (vice-Chancellor, Univ. of Bath), Richard E. Norris, R. Clinton Fuller (Univ. of Massachusetts) Sir Hans Kornberg (Cambridge Univ.), Malcolm Thain (Tropical Products Institute, London), Melvin Calvin (UCB).

*Synthesis and Applications of Isotopically Labeled Compounds 1985.*
Proceedings of the Second International Symposium, Kansas City, MO, U.S.A.,
3—6 September 1985, R.R. Muccino (Ed.), 15—20
© 1986 Elsevier Science Publishers B.V., Amsterdam — Printed in The Netherlands

BACKGROUND AND PRESENT STATUS OF ISOTOPE APPLICATIONS IN CHINA

S.C. WANG and M.T. HUA

Capital Nuclear Medicine Center, Chinese Academy of Medical Sciences, Beijing
(China)

ABSTRACT

In China, isotopes have been used in medicine, agriculture and biological
research. In this report, production of isotopic products and nuclear equip-
ments, professional societies and journals related to the use of isotopes,
international scientific exchanges, popularization of technical knowledge, as
well as the history of development of isotope production and applications in
China are briefly described. Specific examples are also presented to illustrate
the applications of isotopically labeled compounds in various fields. Although
isotope applications in China have already made some progress, we still have a
long way to go to develop a program for using isotopes effectively.

INTRODUCTION

In China, the production and applications of isotopes and their labeled compounds began in the middle of 1950s. We now have more than 10,000 scientific
and technical staff working in this area and there are a certain number of organizations specialized in the research and production of isotopic products.
Historically, the following are some of the chief events: (1)establishment of
the Institute of Atomic Energy in 1950, (2)offering the first isotope training
course by the Chinese Academy of Medical Sciences (CAMS) in 1956, (3)inaugura-
tion of the first research laboratory for the use of atomic energy in agriculture in 1957, (4)operation of the first reactor, producing 33 radioactive
isotopes, in 1958, (5)establishment of the Shanghai Nuclear Institute in 1959,
(6)founding of the Institute of Radiation Research by CAMS in 1959, (7)setting
up an organization for the control of radiopharmaceuticals in 1961, (8)distri-
bution of the first batch of cyclotron-produced isotopes in 1963, (9)production
of tritium in 1964, (10)production of 99.8% enriched heavy water in 1965, and
(11)supply of Tc-99m and In-113m generators in 1972.


PRODUCTION OF ISOTOPIC PRODUCTS

The number of producers of isotopic products has increased recently to 21
and among them, the Institute of Atomic Energy is the largest. In comparison
with 1966, the number of isotopic products has increased from 33 to 600 in 1981
and the number of users from 70 to 1200. During this period the sales volume
has increased 58 times. We are gradually becoming capable of supplying most of
the common isotopic products needed in this country domestically.

In order to strengthen the production of isotopes and handle import and
export trade, China Isotope Corporation was founded in 1983. Since then, the
production of isotopes grew considerably. The sales volume of this Corporation
in 1983 and 1984 amounted to 7,410 and 8,125 thousand yuans respectively. It

is expected to exceed 10 million yuans this year.

The production of RIA kits has only 8 years' history. However, development in this field is very fast. In 1983 and 1984, the number of types of kits increased 3.5 and 4.4 times respectively when compared to 1980. There are 44 types of kits which are being produced and put on the market, although the total number of drugs and biologically active products assayed by this method exceeds 120 in our country.

There are 6 chief producers of labeled compounds in China: (1)Institute of Atomic Energy, (2)Shanghai Nuclear Institute, (3)Institute of Radiation Research, CAMS, (4)Institute for Application of Atomic Energy, Chinese Academy of Agricultural Sciences, (5)Shanghai Institute of Materia Medica, Academia Sinica and (6)Institute of Pharmacology and Toxicology, Chinese Academy of Military Medical Sciences. The total number of labeled compounds synthesized by these 6 organizations amounts to 644. As expected, H-3 and C-14 compounds top all other compounds.The majority of these products are metabolites, drugs and other biologically active compounds, of which at least one-tenth are new labeled products that have not been synthesized previously.


PROFESSIONAL SOCIETIES

The Chinese Nuclear Society (CNS) was founded in 1980. This Society has established 18 professional societies or branch societies, which cover the specialties such as Isotopes Separation Technology Isotopes, Nuclear Agronomy, Nuclear Automation Technology, Nuclear Chemical Engineering, Nuclear Chemistry and Radiochemistry, Nuclear Electronics and Nuclear Detection Technology, Nuclear Fusion and Plasma Physics, Nuclear Materials, Nuclear Medicine, Nuclear Physics, Nuclear Reactor Technology, Particle Accelerator Technology, Radiation Protection, Radiation Research and Technology, Uranium Geology, Uranium Mining and Milling Technology etc.

Of these societies some are led by other national societies in close relation to the specialty as well as by the CNS. For instance, the Society of Nuclear Medicine is a subsociety of CNS and also a subsociety of Chinese Medical Association.

Each professional society organizes its own scientific activity projects independently. For instance, more than 25 symposiums and seminars covering various subjects have been held in the last 5 years by the Society of Nuclear Agronomy. Some of the major meetings organized by the Chinese Society of Nuclear Medicine are: First National Conference (1980), Symposium on the Quality Control of Radionuclide Diagnosis (1982), Symposium on the Radioreceptor Assay (1982), Symposium on the Dynamic Imaging of Organs (1982), Conference on Electronics in Nuclear Medicine (1983), Symposium on the Application of Nuclear Techniques to Traditional Chinese Medicine (1983), Symposium on the Radionuclide Therapy (1983), Symposium on Radiopharmaceuticals (1984), Second National Conference (1984), Symposium on Nuclear Cardiology (1985), Second Conference on Electronics in Nuclear Medicine (1985), Symposium on Radiopharmaceuticals and Labeled Compounds (1985) and Third Symposium on In-Vitro Radioassays (1985).

Of course, members of one society usually may take interest in scientific meetings conducted by other societies. For example, members of our Society of Nuclear Medicine often attend conferences convened by other societies such as those concerning with Activation Analysis (1978, 1984), Stable Isotopes (1981, 1982, 1983, 1984,1985), Liquid Scintillation Counting (1982, 1985), Nuclear Electronics and Detection Technology (1979, 1984) etc.

PUBLICATIONS

Papers on the use of isotopes may occur in many kinds of journals, such as Chinese Journal of Biochemistry or Chinese Medical Journal.

During the period of "cultural revolution", practically all scientific activities were put aside in our country and the publication of all journals discontinued. Only after the end of that period, we started to publish our scientific journals all over again. At present we have more than 10 journals related to isotope applications: Nuclear Science and Technology (first published in 1975), Nuclear Techniques (1978-), Radiation Protection (1978-), Nuclear Chemistry and Radiation Chemistry (1979-), Application of Atomic Energy in Agriculture (1980 -), Chinese Journal of Nuclear Medicine (1981-), Journal of Stable Isotope (1981-), Nuclear Electronics and Detection Technology (1981-), Nuclear Instruments and Methods (1981-), Chinese Journal of Radiological Medicine and Protection (1981-), and Chinese Journal of Nuclear Science and Engineering (1981-).

Since 1983, the Chinese Journal of Nuclear Medicine has started to publish English abstracts. Now the editorial board has made exchange of this journal with 17 foreign journals in related fields. More exchanges are in expectation.

PRODUCTION OF NUCLEAR INSTRUMENTS

The China Nuclear Instrumentation and Equipment Corporation (CNIEC) was established in 1983. CNIEC, with a capital amounting to 220 million yuans, consists of a number of factories in Beijing, Shanghai and other cities. The corporation possesses more than 16,000 workers and staff including over 1800 technical and engineering personnel, among them over 1,100 are engineers.

The corporation mainly deals in nuclear radiation detection devices, radiation dosimeters, nuclear medical instruments, automatic fire alarm systems, systems for monitoring environmental radiation and special instruments for nuclear industry. The products developed by the corporation include liquid scintillation counters, gamma counters, minicomputerized multichannel analyzers, Moessbauer spectrometers, Ge(Li) and Si(Li) detectors.

INTERNATIONAL SCIENTIFIC EXCHANGES

Scientists from different countries have visited China. Among the distinguished visiters were Dr. Rosalyn Yalow, 7 former presidents of the Society of Nuclear Medicine of the United States and many others. On the other hand, Chinese scientists have also been invited to attend academic meetings and visit institutions abroad. Our president of the Society of Nuclear Medicine has been invited to attend the 27th annual meeting of the Society of Nuclear Medicine in Detroit by American colleagues and visit many American nuclear medicine centers. Three groups of scientists have been invited one after another to visit Japanese institutions using isotopes. Next year an International Symposium on Radiopharmaceuticals and Labeled Compounds will be held in Beijing. We welcome scientists from various countries to participate in this occasion.

On January 1, 1984, China officially became a member of the IAEA and began to participate in various activities held by the agency.

POPULARIZATION OF THE KNOWLEDGE OF NUCLEAR TECHNIQUES

Exhibitions of nuclear techniques and their applications have been held in Beijing and several other cities in 1972 and in 1984. These exhibitions have always attracted a big crowd of spectators. Video tapes, color slides, short films and models of human body or modernized machines accompanied by lectures or interpretations were shown so that even the laymen may understand and appreciate the items in display. A nationwide exhibition is scheduled for 1986.

Last month, high school students were invited to a summer camp organized by the CNS, where knowledge of and interest in the use of nuclear techniques were spread by contact with scientists, touring through laboratories and observing scientific demonstrations.

USE OF ISOTOPES IN BIOLOGICAL RESEARCH

The first successful total synthesis of insulin was accomplished in China in 1963. It became the first protein ever synthesized. In order to confirm the identity and purity of the synthetic insulin, ($^{14}$C)insulin was synthesized from ($^{14}$C)glycine. Paper chromatography and paper electrophoresis of the labeled crystalline preparation showed that the position of the peak of radioactivity coincided with the position of the spot revealed by Pauly reaction and that the rate of migration of the synthetic labeled product also agreed with that of the corresponding natural one. These furnish additional evidence for the successful total synthesis of crystalline bovine insulin (ref.1).

After 14 years' hard work, the Chinese biochemists have also synthesized yeast alanine transfer RNA. It has been claimed to be the first man-made RNA with full biological activities, which include both accepting and incorporation activities. Since the amount of the synthetic tRNA obtained is limited, an extremely sensitive method is required for the determination of the biological activity. So (T)alanine was used. tRNA accepted labeled alanine in the presence of rat liver aminoacyl-tRNA-synthetase. The efficiency of transferring alanine from the aminoacylated tRNA into the protein was determined in rabbit reticulocyte lysate cell-free protein-synthesizing system. Both accepting and incorporation activities could be determined in one assay with as little as 5-7 pmoles of tRNA (ref.2).

To study the mechanism of action of LHRH, a group of Chinese zoologists used mature female mud-carps and a synthetic LHRH analog labeled with I-125. By means of electron-microscopic autoradiography, they demonstrated that the labeled hormone was found not only in the cytoplasm of the gonadotrophs of the fish pituitary, but also in the nucleus, apparently via the nuclear pores. This suggests that the peptide hormone is capable of being internalized into the target cells, probably acting directly on the genome to regulate gene expression. This finding suggests a mechanism of peptide hormone action different from the generally accepted hypothesis of hormone receptors, which are assumed to be located on the cell membrane (ref.3).

AGRICULTURAL APPLICATIONS OF ISOTOPES

Isotopes and radiations are extensively used in agriculture. For examples, 165 new types of crops have been bred by using radiation such as Co-60 and widely grown in different parts of China, covering a total area of 23 million acres and producing an increase in yield of 6 billion catties, equivalent to an economic benefit of 4 billion yuans. Through field experiments with tracers, the farmers have learned how to use fertilizers properly and economically and have also become knowledgeable about the effectiveness of pesticides. Other major achievements made are (1)stimulation of the growth of certain beneficial insects and crops by radiation, (2)control of harmful insects by radiation sterilization, and (3)preservation of food and farm products by irradiation (ref.4).

# MEDICAL APPLICATIONS OF ISOTOPES

## The detection of liver cancer

The application of alpha fetoprotein (AFP) assay in China has greatly improved the detection rate of early cases of primary liver cancer. A mass survey has been carried out by AFP determination in high-risk primary liver cancer areas, involving a population of 3 million people. There were found 300 cases of liver cancer that would not have been revealed by other means. 45% of these, 134 cases, were asymptomatic. Hence many cases of subclinical tumors have been detected. By early surgical operation the survival rate was greatly increased, thereby saving the life of a lot of patients.

## Adrenal imaging

Since 1971 (19-$^{131}$I)iodocholesterol has been routinely used for adrenal scanning by the University of Michigan. In 1973 we tested (6-$^{131}$I)iodocholesterol, first synthesized by us in 1959, and found it to be a good adrenal cortical imaging agent too. One Chinese hospital alone has used this agent to image more than 650 cases of suspected adrenal diseases. In comparison with its 19-iodo isomer, it has certain advantages: (1)Synthesis is simpler and less time-consuming. (2)It is very stable chemically. (3)It is more adrenophilic.

## Radioimmunoimaging of cancers

Recently we have tried to use radiolabeled antibodies in the clinical diagnosis of various cancers. The distribution of the labeled antibodies was first studied in animal experiments. For instance, radioiodine labeled monoclonal anti-CEA antibody was injected intravenously to nude mice with human tumor xenografts. At 72 hours after injection, a clear image of the tumors was revealed. Satisfactory results have been obtained in the radioimmunoimaging (RII)of colonrectal carcinoma with this labeled antibody. Besides, polyclonal anti-AFP antibody has been used in the diagnosis of AFP-producing tumors such as endodermal sinus tumor of the ovary. We have also prepared an antiovarian cancer antibody by immunizing rabbits with intact living cells harvested from the fresh epithelial ovarian cancer cell culture. It seems that the RII may be a more sensitive indicator of the presence of tumors than other diagnostic methods such as the RIA of tumor associated antigen in blood and B ultrasonography. Both primary and metastatic lesions can be localized at the same time.

## Mechanism of action of Qinghaosu

Many herbal drugs produce a powerful pharmacological effect and are useful in treating certain diseases. For example, an effective antimalarial constituent was extracted from a medicinal herb in 1972. It was named Qinghaosu (QHS), which was found to be an antimalarial drug with rapid action and low toxicity. It is especially effective in treating cerebral malaria and in killing chloroquine-resistant parasites (ref.5). QHS labeled with H-3 was found to accumulate in infected RBC, especially in the parasite. QHS was also found to inhibit the incorporation of (T)hypoxanthine into the infected RBC. These tracer experiments suggest that this drug can act directly on the parasite and kill the pathogen inside the RBC, very likely by cutting off the supply of nucleic acid which is indispensable for the survival and growth of the malaria parasites.

## Study of gossypol

The discovery of gossypol by the Chinese as an antifertility agent for men aroused a great deal of interest around the world, because it is a new non-steroid drug which has been tested for more than 10,000 subjects and for a period of 8 years. Gossypol is a natural substance extracted from the cotton plant. It is cheap and its supply is abundant. It is safe, with an overall efficiency of 99%. In a study in our hospital, volunteers taking antifertility doses of gossypol showed no change in blood testosterone, LH and FSH level as measured by RIA. It is remarkable that with gossypol, it is possible to suppress sperm production without any effect on the hormone production. Testicular mitochondria have a high affinity for ($^{14}$C)gossypol, which bound most heavily to LDH-X and LDH-4, the mitochondrial marker enzymes of human spermatozoa. Gossypol also inhibited the incorporation of ($^{14}$C)lysine in the sperm cells. It is conceivable that gossypol inhibits spermatogenesis by binding with mitochondrial enzymes and interfering the protein synthesis (ref.6).

## How does acupuncture work?

The use of acupuncture therapy goes back several thousand years. It is safe, inexpensive and simple. Acupuncture analgesia (AA) was developed in China in 1958. A great deal of work has been done in the scientific study of acupuncture and more than 1000 papers have been published in the past five years (ref.7). Isotopic technique is an important tool in this field. Many Chinese scientists proved that serotonin, noradrenaline, beta-endorphine and met-enkephaline all participated in AA. The distributions of morphine-like receptors in the brain before and after acupuncture were observed. The transmission pathways of nervous inflow induced by acupuncture were traced. A new morphine-like substance which was increased markedly after acupuncture was isolated from the human cerebrospinal fluid. It was through the use of tracer experiments with labeled neuro-transmitters or labeled deoxyglucose, RIA, radioligand-binding assay of receptors and autoradiography respectively that the above-mentioned remarkable results were obtained.


## CONCLUSION

In conclusion, although the synthesis and applications of isotopically labeled compounds in China have already made some progress, when compared with advanced countries, we still have a long way to go. In order to accelerate the future development, the interflow of ideas and informations with experienced scientists abroad should be encouraged; cooperation and connections with foreign organizations should also be strengthened.

## REFERENCES

1 Y. Wang, et al, Acta Chim. Sin., 32 (1966) 284-291.
2 Q.X. Shen et al, Sci. Sinica, 26 (1983) 504-512.
3 X.G. Pan et al, Sci. Sinica, 24 (1981) 983-988.
4 G.R. Xu, Industrial Equipment and Materials, 6:4(1985) 92-94.
5 Qinghaosu Antimalaria Coordinating Research Group, Chinese Med. J., 92 (1979) 811-816.
6 S.P. Xue, in T.J. Lobl and E.S.E. Hafez (eds.), Advances in Reproductive Health Care, MTP Press, 1985, pp. 155-174.
7 Abstracts of the Second National Symposium on Acupuncture and Moxibustion and Acupuncture Anesthesia, All China Society of Acupuncture and Moxibustion, Beijing, 1984.

*Synthesis and Applications of Isotopically Labeled Compounds 1985.*
Proceedings of the Second International Symposium, Kansas City, MO, U.S.A.,
3—6 September 1985, R.R. Muccino (Ed.), 21—26
© 1986 Elsevier Science Publishers B.V., Amsterdam — Printed in The Netherlands

USE OF $^{15}$N IN THE FIELD OF AGRICULTURAL SCIENCE IN JAPAN

K. KUMAZAWA

Fac. Agri., Univ. of Tokyo, Bunkyo-ku, Tokyo (Japan)

ABSTRACT
$^{15}$N has been widely used in the research of agricultural and biological
sciences in Japan. Development of emission spectrometry has especially expanded
$^{15}$N use in biochemical studies. Problems on emission spectrometry including
sample preparation are discussed. Case studies on nitrogen absorption, distribution, assimilation and metabolic pathways in the plant, and on symbiotic
nitrogen fixation by soybean nodules, and on behavior of fertilizer nitrogen
in soils are described.

INTRODUCTION
$^{15}$N has been widely used in the research of agricultural and biological
sciences in Japan since 1947 when Dr. Nishina, a famous physicist, began to
produce heavy nitrogen for the study of "the application of heavy nitrogen for
agricultural science and technology". In 1955 a CEC21-201 mass-spectrometer
began to be used for routine analysis of $^{15}$N. It increased the accuracy of measurement and decreased the experimental cost, compared to the preceding experiments. Subsequently $^{15}$N tracer experiments for the evaluation of nitrogen fertilizers in the field increased in number and facilitated recommendations for
improvement of fertilizer N practice.

As the supply of high concentration of $^{15}$N-compounds increased, physiological
and biochemical studies using $^{15}$N as tracer began. However, the requirement for
high amounts of nitrogen for the analysis with mass spectrometer was a great
restriction to $^{15}$N use compared with radioisotopes.

During the last decade an analytical method for $^{15}$N based on emission spectrometry has been developed rapidly (ref. 1-4), and the use of $^{15}$N in the field
of biological sciences has been promoted.

DEVELOPMENT OF THE EMISSION SPECTROMETRIC ANALYSIS OF $^{15}$N
Spectroscopic measurement of the $^{15}$N abundance is based on the measurement
of the intensity ratio of the bandheads of $^{14}N_2$, $^{14}N^{15}N$ and $^{15}N_2$ molecules,
between the wavelengths of 297 and 299 nm, which correspond to the 2-0 transition of the second positive system in the nitrogen emission spectra.

A commercially available $^{15}$N analyzer was produced in 1968 by Isocommerz
GmbH, D.D.R., and in 1970 by Japan Spectroscopic Co. Ltd., Japan.

To prepare the discharge tube for the $^{15}N$ analyzer without contamination, a vacuum system which has various sizes of attachment to glass tubes and an inlet system for the gas mixture of He and Xe (10:2 v/v) is necessary. Introduction of noble gases is useful when analyzing very limited quantities of N (0.1 - 1 μg) (ref. 5).

The OH$^-$ of water and CO of carbon dioxide exhibit spectra near the band peak of $^{14}N^{15}N$ (ref. 3) and induce a systematic error when sample $^{15}N$ concentration is low. The preparation of discharge tube with Dumas combustion method sometimes introduces the $CO_2$ interference and results in unexpected higher values of $^{15}N$.

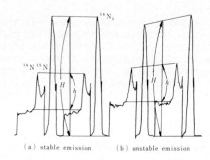

(a) stable emission      (b) unstable emission

Fig. 1. Measurement of peak heights of $^{14}N^{15}N$ (h) and $^{15}N_2$ (H)

However the contribution of $CO_2$ band at the shoulder point of $^{14}N^{15}N$ in its long wave length side, is almost the same as that of the peak head of $^{14}N^{15}N$. Therefore the author recommends the selection of the shoulder point as background for $^{14}N^{15}N$ (Fig. 1).

Standard procedure to make discharge tube by Dumas method

A piece of solid reaction reagent and a sample are put in a pyrex glass tube (o.d. 4 mm, length 20 cm). This solid reagent is prepared by compressing a 1:1 mixture of CuO powder and CaO powder and cutting the resultant solid into small square briquet, followed by heating at 650 °C before use. Usually the sample contains N in the range of 0.5 to 5 μg (Fig. 2).

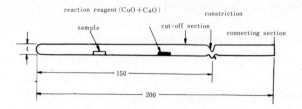

Fig. 2. Pyrex glass tube with sample and reagents (unit: mm)

A solution sample is put in the tube after having been taken into a pyrex glass capillary and dried. The glass tube is connected to a vacuum line to produce a vacuum below $10^{-4}$ torr, cut off by fusing at a point some 10 cm from the end, and heated at 650 °C from 2-6 hr to convert all N forms to $N_2$ in the discharge tube. When the sample to be analyzed is rich in oxygen, as in the case of $NO_3$, a reducing agent such as metallic copper should be used.

## Amino acids and amides separated with thin-layer chromatography

The amino acids and amides are separated with two dimensional silica gel thin-layer chromatography with phenol-water and butanol-acetic acid-water. After spraying ninhydrin solution, the central part of each colored spot is transferred into a glass tube along with the silica gel. Then each amino acid is eluted from the silica gel into another glass tube with 80% ethanol solution, and dried under low pressure below 40 °C. After that CuO powder is put in and the narrow point on which CaO briquet is put, is made 5 cm above the bottom. After evacuating the discharge tube to $10^{-4}$ torr, the noble gas mixture is introduced and the tube is sealed (Fig. 3).

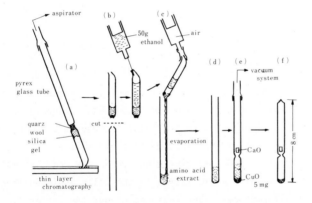

Fig. 3. Preparation procedure of discharge tube for $^{15}N$ analysis of amino acids.

## CASE STUDIES IN THE RESEARCH OF PLANT AND AGRICULTURAL SCIENCES USING $^{15}N$ EMISSION SPECTROMETRY

### Distribution of $^{15}N$ in plant tissues and organs

In studies on nitrogen uptake and transport in corn roots, we measured total N and $^{15}N$ in a small section of central cylinder and cortex tissues after feeding plants $^{15}NH_4^+$ and $^{15}NO_3^-$ (ref. 6). The $^{15}N$ analysis showed that ammonium-nitrogen was strongly absorbed from the elongation zone, while nitrate-nitrogen was absorbed from the elongation and root-hair zones.

In leaves of rice seedlings, it was shown that in the older leaf, less N was accumulated from $^{15}NH_4^+$ than from $^{15}NO_3^-$, while in the younger leaf the reverse was found (ref. 7).

## Assimilation of absorbed ammonium or nitrate in rice root

The time course of $^{15}N$ distribution in several soluble nitrogenous compounds was determined in rice roots after feeding $^{15}NH_4^+$ for 120 min, followed by a chase with $^{14}NH_4^+$ for 210 min (ref. 8). The $^{15}N$ atom % excess of ammonium began to increase in roots immediately after the plants were transferred to the $^{15}NH_4^+$ solution (I-phase) and decreased immediately when returned to the $^{14}NH_4^+$ solution (II-phase). The $^{15}N$ content of glutamine increased very rapidly in the I-phase and immediately fell in the II-phase. At the beginning of both phases there was no lag time. The $^{15}N$ of the amido- and amino-groups of glutamine were analyzed separately after feeding with $^{15}NH_4^+$. It became clear that the amide of glutamine was labeled more extensively with $^{15}N$ compared with its amino-group (ref. 9). In addition to the above results, an experiment using methionine sulfoximine, an inhibitor of glutamine synthetase, showed that the first step of ammonium assimilation was incorporation into the amido-group of glutamine. Then glutamic acid was formed from glutamine and 2-oxoglutaric acid by glutamate synthase (GOGAT) (ref. 10).

## Nitrogen metabolism in plant leaves

Amino acids synthesis in sunflower leaves was studied by a double labeled experiment with $^{14}CO_2$ and $^{15}NH_4^+$ (ref. 11). The results indicated that $NH_4^+$ incorporation into glutamic acid, nitrate reduction, and serine formation were remarkably dependent on light; and that alanine incorporated $NH_4^+$ by direct amination in addition to the transamination from glutamic acid.

Inhibitor experiment showed that glutamine synthetase and glutamate synthase pathways operated in ammonium assimilation in the cells isolated from spinach leaves, and that the former was light-independent but the latter light-dependent (ref. 12).

## Nitrogen fixation of soybean plant

Soybean nodules supplied with $^{15}N_2$ were macerated and separated into various nitrogenous fractions, which were subjected to the determination of total nitrogen and $^{15}N$.

Distribution of fixed nitrogen in cytosol amounted to 97 and 96% of the total nitrogen in the ethanol-soluble fraction after 5 and 10 min of $^{15}N_2$ exposure, respectively. This indicates that the nitrogenase is situated in the surface membrane of the bacteroid, and that most of the newly fixed nitrogen is transferred to cytosol soon after the fixation (ref. 13).

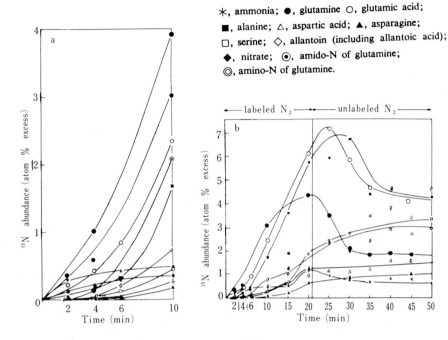

Fig. 4. The incorporation of $^{15}N$ into various nitrogenous compounds in the alcohol extract of soybean nodules after exposing $^{15}N_2$.

After feeding with $^{15}N$ the time course of $^{15}N$ incorporation into various soluble components in the nodules was measured (Fig. 4) (ref. 14). Initially the $^{15}N$ abundance of $NH_4^+$ increased rapidly. Among amino acids, glutamine accumulated the highest $^{15}N$ abundance through 10 min of $^{15}N_2$ supply. Again the amido nitrogen of glutamine showed much higher $^{15}N$ content than its amino nitrogen. Following glutamine, glutamic acid and alanine showed the highest $^{15}N$ abundances. It was noteworthy that allantoin showed a higher $^{15}N$ level than did serine, aspartic acid, and asparagine.

These results indicate that fixed ammonia is firstly incorporated into glutamine, especially the amido-N group, and secondly into glutamic acid by GS/GOGAT system rather than GDH. This hypothesis was proven using various kinds of inhibitors (ref. 15). The $^{15}N$ abundance of glutamine in bacteroids, separated after feeding of $^{15}N_2$ to intact nodules, was remarkably lower than that of glutamic acid or alanine, whereas glutamine content of $^{15}N$ was higher in the cytosol. This shows that the rapid formation of glutamine from the newly fixed nitrogen occurs in the cytosol region (ref. 13).

From the result that much higher $^{15}N$ abundance and total amount of allantoin was observed in the cytosol than in the bacteroid fraction, allantoin synthesis is presumed to be carried out mainly in the cytosol in connection with the formation and decomposition of purine. The fact that $^{15}$N abundance of allantoic acid is always lower than that of allantoin also shows that allantoin formation is through purine decomposition (ref. 14).

From the measurement of $^{15}$N values in nodules, roots, stems, and leaves of soybean plants treated with $^{15}$N$_2$ and $^{15}$NO$_3^-$, allantoin was found to be a characteristic compound involved in the transport of fixed nitrogen from the nodules to the shoots. A portion of the nitrate absorbed by the roots is transported as it is. Asparagine is formed from both nitrogen sources and transported to the upper-plant parts (ref. 16).

Nitrogen from $^{15}$N$_2$ preferentially distributes to the developing organs, young leaves, and developing pods, in comparison with that from $^{15}$NO$_3^-$. Nitrogen from $^{15}$NH$_4^+$ showed a distribution pattern similar to that from N$_2$ (ref. 17, 18).

## Efficiency of nitrogenous fertilizer

In order to evaluate nitrogenous fertilizers and improve their application methods to various kinds of crops and trees, $^{15}$N-labeled fertilizers are widely used. Many experiments have been carried out on rice, wheat, soybean, tobacco, tea, mandarin orange, apple, persimmon, pear, grape, peach and loquat etc..

## CONCLUDING REMARKS

$^{15}$N is a very useful tool in the agricultural sciences, including plants and soils. Development of instruments to measure $^{15}$N, and decreased costs for supply of various kinds of $^{15}$N-labeled compounds, are important factors which have accelerated the use of $^{15}$N and promoted the development of agricultural science and technology.

## REFERENCES

1  G. Meier and G. Muller, Isotopenpraxis, 1 (1965) 53-62.
2  H. Faust, Isotopenpraxis, 1 (1965) 62-65.
3  R. Fiedler and G. Proksch, Anal. Chem. Acta, 78 (1975) 41-62.
4  P. B. Vose, Introduction to nuclear techniques in agronomy and plant biology, Pergamon, 1980, pp. 151-176.
5  J. A. Goleb and V. Middelboe, Anal. Chem. Acta, 43 (1968) 229-234.
6  T. Yoneyama, K. Komamura and K. Kumazawa, Soil Sci. Plant Nutr., 21 (1975) 371-377.
7  T. Yoneyama and K. Kumazawa, J. Sci. Soil Manure, Japan, 43 (1972) 329-332.
8  T. Yoneyama and K. Kumazawa, Plant & Cell Physiol., 15 (1974) 655-661.
9  Y. Arima and K. Kumazawa, J. Sci. Soil Manure, Japan, 46 (1975) 355-361.
10 Y. Arima and K. Kumazawa, Plant & Cell Physiol., 18 (1977) 1121-1129.
11 O. Ito and K. Kumazawa, Soil Sci. Plant Nutr., 26 (1977) 365-372.
12 O. Ito, T. Yoneyama and K. Kumazawa, Plant & Cell Physiol., 19 (1978) 1109-1119.
13 T. Ohyama and K. Kumazawa, Soil Sci. Plant Nutr., 26 (1980) 205-213.
14 T. Ohyama and K. Kumazawa, Soil Sci. Plant Nutr., 24 (1978) 525-533.
15 T. Ohyama and K. Kumazawa, Soil Sci. Plant Nutr., 26 (1980) 109-115.
16 T. Ohyama and K. Kumazawa, Soil Sci. Plant Nutr., 25 (1979) 9-19.
17 T. Yoneyama and J. Ishizuka, Soil Sci. Plant Nutr., 28 (1982) 451-462.
18 T. Ohyama, Soil Sci. Plant Nutr., 29 (1983) 133-145.

*Synthesis and Applications of Isotopically Labeled Compounds 1985.*
Proceedings of the Second International Symposium, Kansas City, MO, U.S.A.,
3—6 September 1985, R.R. Muccino (Ed.), 27—31
1986 Elsevier Science Publishers B.V., Amsterdam — Printed in The Netherlands

RECENT ADVANCES IN THE CHEMISTRY OF POSITRON EMITTERS

ALFRED P. WOLF and JOANNA S. FOWLER

Chemistry Department, Brookhaven National Laboratory, Upton, NY 11973 USA

There are at present approximately 60 institutions world-wide equipped with some type of charged particle accelerator, preponderantly "small medical cyclotrons" associated with one or more positron emission tomographs (1,2). The use of positron emitters in labeled compounds for biomedical research all but disappeared post World War II, being displaced by carbon-14 and tritium in biochemical and biological research, and by the single photon emitters primarily iodine-131 and technetium 99m in biomedical research and clinical practice. Following the introduction of a "medical cyclotron" at Hammersmith Hospital in London a number of papers again began appearing utilizing simple oxygen-15 and carbon-11 labeled compounds. In 1966 a paper appeared which served as a renewed stimulus to considering positron emitters for research and clinical use (3). As the positron emission tomograph allowing quantitative determination of radionuclide (or positron emitter labeled compound) concentration in a given volume element of tissue in vivo became more readily available in the early and mid-seventies, the opportunity to use increasingly sophisticated labeled compounds and labeled biomolecules manifested itself. Compounds labeled with carbon-11, nitrogen-13 and fluorine-18 described in the literature prior to 1981 have been documented in a book on synthesis methods (4). Somewhat more recent reviews can be found in a number of book chapter (5a,b). However, no extensive review of new labeled compounds is available covering published work of the last three years. It is not the purpose of this short paper to present such a review but rather to present some of the more recent trends in labeling compounds with positron emitters.

Beginning with carbon-11 the traditional methods of preparing $^{11}C$-methanol from $^{11}CO_2$ and the use of the carboxylation of a Grignard with $^{11}CO_2$ have been applied with advantage in preparing a host of labeled ethers, alcohols, ketones and hydrocarbons for use in studying the relationship between lipophilicity and brain extraction (6).

New approaches to preparing amino acids with the label in the 3 position have been described by Langström and colleagues (7) by utilizing carbon-11. The use of chiral hydrogenation catalysts for the partial asymmetric synthesis of L-[3-$^{11}$C]phenylalanine (9) has also been reported by these authors. Another more recent approach to labeling amino acids is the further elaboration of the carboxylation of α lithioisocyanides by the Groningen group who have prepared DL[1-$^{11}$C]proline by the carboxylation of α lithio pyrrolidyl-N-tert-butylformamidine. These new and newly elaborated methods add to the amino acids accessible by the modified Bücherer-Strecker synthesis (cf. references in 4) described in the earlier literature. The importance of labeled amino acids is taking on added significance due to their more widespread use in a variety of tumor studies, a number of which are noted herein (10-13). Indeed the use of positron emitter labeled compounds for tumor detection and staging is becoming an increasingly important aspect of research and clinical application in PET. The extensive work of DiChiro and colleagues in utilizing $^{18}$F-FDG for brain tumor research is well known. Another example is the use of polyamines for example the use of N-[$^{11}$C]methylputrescine, spermine and spermidine for prostate tumor detection (14). More recently [1-$^{11}$C]putrescine has been prepared (15) and is under active investigation in our laboratory for the study of primary and metastatic brain tumors.

A trend which is becoming increasingly evident is the use of carbon-11 labeled methyl iodide. The organic chemistry of this labeling agent is well understood and it has been used to label amino acids (eg. methionine) and many different agonists and antagonists for brain receptor work an early example of which was the labeling of chlorpromazine (16). A more recent example of the continued use of [$^{11}$C]H$_3$I by this group in labeling psychoactive drugs involves the synthesis of a highly specific benzodiazepine receptor drug [RO 15.1788-$^{11}$C] (17). Other examples of methylation using [$^{11}$C]H$_3$I, of psychoactive drugs include the preparation of 3-N-[$^{11}$C]methylspiperone (18) (cf. the preparation of the $^{18}$F compound vide infra) and the opiate receptor binding agent, [$^{11}$C]carfentanil (19).

A new initiative is the development of probes for functional enzyme activity using suicide enzyme inhibitors labeled with carbon-11 via the N-methylation reaction with [$^{11}$C]H$_3$I (20,21).

A number of methods of preparation of [$^{11}$C]H$_3$I have been described. Three variations are in common use (22-24). Recently another variation using P$_2$I$_4$ as the agent to iodinate $^{11}$C-methanol has been described yielding a pure product in high yield (25).

[1-$^{11}$C]Ethyliodide as a labeling agent has also been utilized recently (26). Before leaving comment on some recent advances in carbon-11 labeling, it is worth stressing that facile labeling can also provide compounds which undergo facile metabolism of the labeled position in vivo. Thus demethylation of [$^{11}$C]methyl or decarboxylation of [$^{11}$C]carboxyl or indeed the labeling in any metabolically labile position with $^{11}$C can render the labeled compound less useful as a tracer than a synthesis leading to a label in a stable position. An exception, of course, is the use of [$^{11}$C]carboxyl labeled amino acids for the quantitative measurement of regional protein synthesis (27).

Increased emphasis on fluorine-18 fluoride ion as a labeling agent is becoming apparent in the more recent literature. While a large number of fluorine-18 precursors have been made, only two $^{18}$F-F$_2$ and $^{18}$F-F- (25) have enjoyed widespread use. Any number of syntheses of 18-FDG have appeared in the literature since its initial description in 1978 (29). Two recent syntheses (30,31) utilize [$^{18}$F]fluoride ion in the preparation of $^{18}$FDG. High yields of a pure product can be obtained. The Hamacher (31) synthesis may prove to be the more useful because of the ready availability of the precursor and the simplicity of the reaction steps.

The use of nucleophilic aromatic substitution as a labeling method was investigated (32,33) and then applied to the labeling of fluorinated butyrophenone compounds (34) and fluorine-18 labeled N-methylspiperone (35) (cf. [$^{11}$C]labeled compound reference). A comparative study of fluorination with [$^{18}$F]fluoride ion has also been recently reported (36). Fluorinated estrogens utilizing $^{18}$F fluoride ion have also been prepared (37).

Syntheses with nitrogen-13 and oxygen-15 are less common and will not be reviewed here.


CONCLUSION

With the increasing active interest in PET as a method for studying biochemistry in normal and pathological states in humans we can expect to see the development of new techniques for precursor preparation and synthesis. We have seen a doubling of the publication rate in the past three to four years over the previous three to four year period. As the need for these compounds, especially in the tumor and receptor areas, in a purely clinical setting, increases the trend towards true automation of production of the most needed compounds will accelerate. The cyclotron manufacturers all offer "black boxes" for synthesis but the optimum approach to user friendly automation yet needs to be defined.

I would again note that this paper was not intended as a comphrehensive review but rather my goal was to highlight just some of the exciting developments of the past several years. We are entering what may well be the most extensive and active period of research in the synthesis of positron emitter labeled compounds. If 1984-1985 is any gauge, many new methods and compounds will appear in the next several years.

## ACKNOWLEDGEMENT

This research was carried out at Brookhaven National Laboratory under contract DE-AC02-76CH00016 with the U. S. Department of Energy and supported by its Office of Health and Environmental Research.

## REFERENCES

1   A.P. Wolf and J.S. Fowler, "Radiopharmaceuticals and Labeled Compounds", Proceedings of an International Conference, IAEA Publication CN45/101, 1985, Vienna, Austria.
2   A.P. Wolf and J.S. Fowler, "Physics and Engineering of Medical Imaging", Proceedings of NATO ASI Series Robotics and Artificial Intelligence, M. Brady, L.A. Gerhardt and H.F. Davidson (Eds.), Springer-Verlag, 1984.
3   M.M. TerPogossian and H.N. Wagner, Jr., Nucleonics, 24 (1966) 50.
4   J.S. Fowler and A.P. Wolf, The Synthesis of Carbon-11, Fluorine-18 and Nitrogen-13 Labeled Radiotracers for Biomedical Applications, Nuclear Science Series, NAS-NS-3201, National Academy of Science N.R.C. published by Technical Information Center, U. S. Department of Energy, 1982, Springfield, VA., pp. 1-124.
5   (a)   A.P. Wolf and J.S. Fowler, Positron Emission Tomography, Chapter 3, A.R. Liss, Inc. Publishers, New York, 1985, pp. 63-80.
    (b)   J.S. Fowler and A.P. Wolf, Positron Computed Tomography, M.E. Phelps, J.C. Mazziotta, and H. Schelbert (Eds.), Raven Press, 1985, in press.
6   D.D. Dischino, M.J. Welch, M.R. Kilbourn, et al., J. Nucl. Med., 24 (1983) 1030.
7   C. Halldin and B. Langström, Int. J. Appl. Radiat. Isot., 35 (1984) 779.
8   C. Halldin and B. Langström, Acta Chem. Scand., B38 (1984) 1.
9   C. Halldin and B. Langström, Int. J. Appl. Radiat. Isot., 35 (1984) 945.
10  J.M. Bolster, N. TenHoeve, W. Vaalburg, et al., J. Appl. Radiat. Isot., 36 (1985) 339.
11  K. Kubota, K. Yamada, H. Fukada, et al., Eur. J. Nucl. Med., 9 (1984) 136.
12  K. Kubota, T. Matsuzawa and M. Ito, J. Nucl. Med., 26 (1985) 37.
13  G. Meyer, O. Schober and H. Hundeshagen, Eur. J. Nucl. Med., 10 (1985) 373.
14  M.J. Welch, R.E. Coleman, M.G. Straatmann, et al., J. Nucl. Med., 18 (1977) 74.
15  D.W. McPherson, J.S. Fowler, A.P. Wolf, et al., J. Nucl. Med., 26 (1985) 1186.
16  D. Comar, M. Maziere and C. Crouzel, Radiopharmaceuticals and Labeled Compounds, Vol. I, IAEA/SM-171/94, Vienna, 1973, pp. 461-469.
17  M. Maziere, P. Hantraye, C. Prenant, et al., Int. J. Appl. Radiat. Isot., 35 (1984) 973.
18  H.D. Burns, R.F. Dannals and B. Langström, J. Nucl. Med., 25 (1984) 1222.
19  R.F. Dannals, H.T. Ravert and J.J. Frost, Int. J. Appl. Radiat. Isot., 36 (1985) 303.
20  R.R. MacGregor, C. Halldin, J.S. Fowler, et al., Biochem. Pharmacol., 34 (1985) 3207.
21  K. Ishiwata, T. Ido, K. Yanai, et al., J. Nucl. Med., 26 (1985) 630.
22  B. Langström and H. Lundquist, Int. J. Appl. Radiat. Isot., 27 (1976) 357.
23  C. Marayama, M. Maziere, G. Berger, et al., Ibid., 28 (1977) 49.
24  R. Iwata, T. Ido, H. Saji, et al., Ibid., 30 (1979) 194.
25  F. Oberdorfer, M. Hanisch, F. Helus, et al., Int. J. Appl. Radiat. Isot., 36 (1985) 435.
26  E. Ehrin, L. Farde, and T. dePaulis, Int. J. Appl. Radiat. Isot., 36 (1985) 269.
27  C.B. Smith, L. Davidsen, G. Deibler, et al., Trans. Am. Soc. Neurochem., 11 (1980) 94.

28  Cf. some examples in R.A. Ferrieri and A.P. Wolf, Rad. Chim. Acta, 34
    (1983) 69.
29  T. Ido, C.N. Wan, V. Casella, et al., J. Label. Cmpds. Radiopharm., 14
    (1978) 175.
30  T.J. Tewson and M. Saderlind, J. Nucl. Med., 26 (1985) P129.   Cf.
    T.J. Tewson, J. Nucl. Med., 24 (1983) 718.
31  K. Hamacher, H.H. Coenen and G. Stöcklin, J. Nucl. Med., (1985) in press.
32  M. Speranza, R.A. Ferrieri, A.P. Wolf, et al., J. Label. Cmpds.
    Radiopharm., 19 (1981) 61.
33  M. Attina, F. Cacace and A.P. Wolf, J. Label. Cmpds. Radiopharm., 20
    (1983) 501.
34  C.-Y. Shiue, J.S. Fowler, A.P. Wolf, et al., J. Nucl. Med., 26 (1985) 181.
35  C.D. Arnett, J.S. Fowler, A.P. Wolf, et al., Life Sci., 36 (1985) 1359.
36  M.S. Berridge, C. Crouzel and D. Comar, J. Label. Cmpds. Radiopharm., 22
    (1984).
37  D.O. Kiesewetter, M.R. Kilbourn, S.N. Laudratter, et al., J. Nucl. Med.,
    25 (1984) 1212.

*Synthesis and Applications of Isotopically Labeled Compounds 1985.*
Proceedings of the Second International Symposium, Kansas City, MO, U.S.A.,
3—6 September 1985, R.R. Muccino (Ed.), 33—40
© 1986 Elsevier Science Publishers B.V., Amsterdam — Printed in The Netherlands

HOMOGENEOUS CATALYSIS OF HYDROGEN ISOTOPE EXCHANGE

E. BUNCEL[1] and J.R. JONES[2]

[1]Chemistry Dept., Queen's University, Kingston, Canada, K7L 3N6

[2]Chemistry Dept., University of Surrey, Guildford GU2 5XH, U.K.

ABSTRACT

Hydrogen isotope exchange reactions have in the past found many applications
(refs.1,2). Thus they have been used to estimate the kinetic and equilibrium
acidities of carbon acids (ref.3), the effects of ion association (ref.4), the
proton abstracting ability of highly basic media (ref.5), the effect of
complexation on reactivity (ref.6) and the relative reactivity of different
forms (protonated, neutral and anionic) of heterocyclic carbon acids (ref.7).
Nevertheless there are still some areas such as solvent effects which are
relatively unexplored. Work in the area of non-aqueous media opens up new
opportunities, e.g. it is possible to study the relative basicities of a large
number of amines and this in turn leads to the study of conformational effects.
A related area is the catalysis of hydrogen isotope exchange by amino-containing
polymers. Finally examples of stereoelectronic effects and steric strain in
aqueous conditions are discussed.

INTRODUCTION

Of all the reactions in organic chemistry few have stronger claims to being

recognised as the most important than hydrogen isotope exchange. It can be

catalysed by acids, bases, metals and radiation and has therefore played an im-

portant role in improving our understanding of carbanion and carbocation chem-

istry as well as in catalysis itself. Very frequently it represents an example

of a proton transfer reaction, one of the simplest of all reactions, and has

therefore been much used as a model for improving our understanding of reaction

kinetics in solution. Yet the study of solvent effects on proton transfer re-

actions is virtually a neglected area. In attempting to explain why this is so

one is led to the conclusion that this is because one of the most widely used

methods of studying these reactions in water, namely halogenation, can not be

readily adapted to non-aqueous conditions.

Before embarking on a study of hydrogen isotope exchange reactions in non-

aqueous media it is pertinent to mention some of the interesting features that

have come to light from studies carried out under aqueous conditions. Firstly

it is very frequently the case that the points for $H_2O$ and $OH^-$ catalysis are

displaced from the Brönsted plot generated by other catalysts, both being less

effective than anticipated. The extent of the deviation however seems to be a function of the substrate as can be seen in Table 1.  Secondly, the behaviour of

TABLE 1

Hydroxide-ion Catalysis and Deviation from the Brönsted Relationship (ref. 8)

| Reaction | $k_{obs}$ | $\log\{k_{obs}/k_{calc}\}$ |
|---|---|---|
| Iodination of acetone | $2.5 \times 10^{-1}$ | -3.54 |
| "     " monobromoacetone | $2.0 \times 10^{2}$ | -2.92 |
| Bromination of 1,1-dichloroacetone | $4.5 \times 10^{2}$ | -2.71 |
| Detritiation of phenylacetylene | $2.3 \times 10^{2}$ | -2.10 |
| "     " p-nitrobenzyl cyanide | $2.6 \times 10^{1}$ | -1.65 |
| Mutarotation of glucose | $6.4 \times 10^{1}$ | +0.71 |

carbon acids is greatly influenced by the nature of the activating groups, leading in some cases to charge delocalisation and consequent extensive solvent interaction whilst in other cases, the process of ionisation is a good deal more
straightforward.  In those cases where non-aqueous conditions have been employed
they serve to show the importance of the solvent.  Thus for proton transfer reactions of hydrocarbons in dimethyl sulfoxide and methanol (ref. 9) the reactions
approach diffusion controlled limits in both directions, but at much smaller
values of ΔpK in dimethyl sulfoxide than in methanol.  This solvent effect reflects the importance of reorganisation or breaking of solvent-solvent hydrogen
bonds in methanol.

In order that a study of solvent effects on hydrogen isotope exchange reactions be effective it is necessary that the experimental method be as versatile as possible.  Our detritiation method, first established for studies in
aqueous conditions, has now been modified so that it can be used under non-
aqueous conditions.  Taken together with the various radio-analytical techniques
that we have at our disposal (radio-thin layer chromatography, - gas chromatography,- high performance liquid chromatography, [3]H nuclear magnetic resonance
spectroscopy and liquid scintillation counting) it satisfies the above requirement and makes the way clear to study a range of carbon acids in a number of
solvents.

SOLVENT EFFECTS

We have concentrated our attention on the following six solvents - dimethyl
sulfoxide, sulpholane, hexamethylphosphoramide, dimethylformamide, acetonitrile
and tetrahydrofuran, all of which, with the exception of the last named, have
dielectric constants in the 30-50 range.  To study solvent effects one can either
measure enthalpies of activation and combine the information with thermochemical

measurements of heats of solution so that the overall effect can be divided into initial state and transition state contributions or alternatively one can study the reactions in mixed solvents. The reactions investigated are ones that have been studied by us previously in aqueous conditions, e.g. the detritiation of diethyl malonate. Our interest in heterocyclic carbon acids, particularly those containing an imidazole function, prompted an investigation into their base strengths and the results (Table 2) show with the exception of one result (that

TABLE 2
Relative Rates of Detritiation of Diethyl Malonate with imidazole catalysts in various solvents at $50^{\circ}$C.

| Base | Solvents | | | | | |
| | DMSO | DMF | THF | EtOH | Sulpholane | HMPT* |
|---|---|---|---|---|---|---|
| Imidazole | 1.00 | 1.00 | 1.00 | 1.00 | 1.00 | 1.00 |
| 1-Me Imidazole | 0.53 | 0.40 | 0.057 | 0.46 | 0.18 | 0.20 |
| 2-Me " | 7.5 | 6.68 | 7.43 | 4.5 | 7.10 | 8.11 |
| 2-Et, " 4-Me | 19.6 | 15.0 | 8.4 | 8.14 | 13.4 | 15.8 |

* at $25^{\circ}$C

of 1-methylimidazole in tetrahydrofuran) a relative behaviour which is remarkably consistent in marked contrast to e.g. the situation in water and methanol. For any of the catalysts used $k_{max}/k_{min}$ for the various solvents were in the range 4-7, the relative order more often than not being DMSO > HMPT... > sulpholane.

## BASICITIES OF AMINES IN NON-AQUEOUS MEDIA

Amines are amongst the most widely used of bases, partly because of the large number of structurally different compounds that are available. Thus sterically hindered tertiary amines such as 2,6-di-t-butyl pyridine, which show low nucleophilicity are widely used in organic synthesis; so also are hindered amidines although the stronger ones such as DBN (1,5-diazabicyclo-[4.3.0]non-5-ene) and DBU (1,8-diazabicyclo[5.4.0]-undec-7-ene) are rather easily alkylated. Derivatives of 1,8-diaminonaphthalene give very strong non-nucleophilic bases with, in appropriate examples, $pK_a$ values in excess of 16. Strong guanidine bases are also known although little work on the modification of their nucleophilic character by steric hindrance has been reported.

In contrast to carbon acidity where thanks to the efforts of Bordwell, Arnett and others there is a wealth of $pK_a$ data, in non-aqueous media such as DMSO there is little information on basicities. The main exception is the amines where a large number of $pK_a$'s have been determined in acetonitrile firstly by Hall (ref. 10) in a rather qualitative manner and secondly, and more quantitatively by Coetzee and Padmanabhan (ref. 11). These workers showed that the glass electrode responded reversibly to the activity of the hydrogen ion in acetonitrile. The $\Delta pK$ values ($pK_{CH_3CN} - pK_{H_2O}$) are close to 7.6 for a number of amines although there are some notable exceptions. Thus the conjugate acids of pyrrolidine, monoethanolamine and morpholine are significantly weaker acids in acetonitrile than would be predicted from their strengths in water. For the latter two stabilisation is derived from intramolecular hydrogen bonding. The monoprotonated diaminoalkanes are also weaker acids than would be predicted from the strength of n-propyl and n-butylammonium ions. This weakening is attributed to stabilisation of the species $H_2N(CH_2)_n\overset{+}{N}H_3$ with n = 3 and 4 by intramolecular hydrogen bonding, a reaction which is largely masked in water.

When the detritiation of acetophenone is investigated using $CH_3CN$ as solvent the rates increase with the base strengths of the amines although there are serious deviations from linearity in the log $k_B^T$ - $pK_a$ plot. This is most evident when the results for the diamines are included. When a comparison of the rates of detritiation in acetonitrile and DMSO are made (Fig. 1) it is found that an excellent correlation, covering more than $10^5$ in rates, exists. Only in the case of morpholine and ethanolamine do the points deviate significantly. The reaction is more sensitive to catalyst changes in $CH_3CN$ than in DMSO so that the most reactive bases DBN and DBU are only a factor of two less reactive in $CH_3CN$ than in DMSO. In the absence of $pK_a$ data hydrogen isotope exchange data of the kind mentioned serve a very useful purpose.

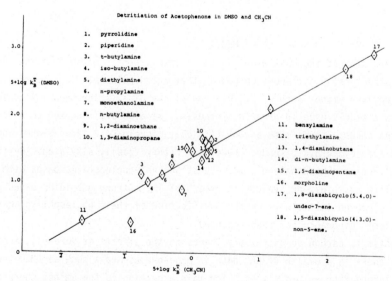

Detritiation of Acetophenone in DMSO and CH₃CN

1. pyrrolidine
2. piperidine
3. t-butylamine
4. iso-butylamine
5. diethylamine
6. n-propylamine
7. monoethanolamine
8. n-butylamine
9. 1,2-diaminoethane
10. 1,3-diaminopropane
11. benzylamine
12. triethylamine
13. 1,4-diaminobutane
14. di-n-butylamine
15. 1,5-diaminopentane
16. morpholine
17. 1,8-diazabicyclo(5.4.0)-undec-7-ene.
18. 1,5-diazabicyclo(4.3.0)-non-5-ene.

CONFORMATIONAL EFFECTS - CATALYSIS BY AMINO-ACIDS

Organic compounds are thought to be pure even though they may be a mixture of conformational isomers. This is because the conformers convert rapidly with each other at room temperature and their individual reactivities are little known. However, since conformational isomers are often diastereomers, their reactivities should be different in principle even under achiral conditions (ref. 12). As stated by the Curtin-Hammett principle the product ratio is governed by the rate constants for reaction of each isomer in addition to the equilibrium constant.

In recent years a number of examples showing different reactivity in conformational isomers have been reported. The difference in rates can amount to in excess of $10^4$. As an example (ref. 13), in the deprotonation of 9-(2-methyl-1-naphthyl)fluorene by butyl-lithium in benzene-hexane the respective pseudo-first-order rate constants at room temperature are

sp                              ap

$$k_{sp} = 3.6 \times 10^{-5} s^{-1} \qquad k_{ap} = 5.2 \times 10^{-6} s^{-1}$$

The 9-H in the ap conformation seems to be better protected by a methyl group than the 9-H in the sp conformation, which is protected by the π-system. For the corresponding 2-methoxy compound at 40°C the results (ref. 14) imply that the

sp                              ap

$$k_{sp} > 3 \times 10^{-2} s^{-1} \qquad k_{ap} = 7 \times 10^{-5} s^{-1}$$

oxygen atom assists lithiation, presumably through deaggregation of the butyl-lithium hexamer.

CATALYSIS BY POLYMERS

One of the great challenges of modern chemistry is for chemists to synthesise compounds that are able to reproduce the catalytic properties of enzymes. These are macromolecules which through binding to the substrate and provision of a molecular environment conducive to the chemical transformation are able to operate with high catalytic efficiency. One possible approach is to study hydrogen isotope exchange in the presence of a polymer containing basic groups and then to see how the rates are affected as a result of modifications to the polymer structure. For this to be effective one needs a polymer that can be readily synthesised, which has good solubility properties and can be easily modified. Klotz (ref. 15) has found that polyethylenimine (PEI) where 50% of the nitrogens are secondary amines, the rest being split equally between primary and tertiary, is a good choice. When the detritiation of acetophenone is studied in the presence of different solvents containing PEI one finds that the rate decreases in the order DMSO > EtoH > DMF. Equally interesting is the finding that the rate of the reaction is virtually independent of the molecular weight of the polymer. It will be of interest to see whether these characteristics are shared by other carbon acids, particularly those that can be tightly bound to the polymer.

STEREOELECTRONIC EFFECTS

A great deal of experimental evidence indicates that the geometry and reactivity of many organic molecules are controlled by stereoelectronic effects which arise as a result of the presence of non-bonded electron pairs on heteroatoms such as oxygen, nitrogen and sulphur and in particular by their orientation in space. One of the most challenging of current-day problems is to show how such effects may be applied to both rationalise and predict organic chemistry reactivity. Only then will it be possible to use stereoelectronic effects to design organic molecules having unusual reactivities and to develop new strategies in organic synthesis.

To date most of the experimental studies have been concerned with the hydrolysis of esters, acetals and amides and reactions at saturated carbon. In the few examples of hydrogen isotope exchange studies the substrates have been ketones (cyclic, bicyclic or steroidal). In the case of 4-t-butyl-cyclohexanone $k_{axial}/k_{equatorial}$ is ~ 5 but _ab initio_ calculations (ref. 16) suggest that much higher selectivities should be possible and this interpretation has recently received experimental support. Thus for 4',1"-dimethyl-1,2,3,4-dibenzcyclohepta-1,3-diene-6-one (ref. 17) hydrogen-deuterium exchange of its methylene protons in MeOD-OMe$^-$ proceeded with a stereoselectivity of 73:1. A kinetic selectivity of 290:1 was witnessed (ref. 18) in the base-catalysed exchange of the diastereotopic protons α to the carbonyl group in twistan-4-one. An example of another kind of carbon acid is the tetracyclic compound mianserin 1,2,3,4,10,14b-hexahydro-2-methyl-dibenzo[c.f]pyrazino[1,2-a]azepine, and here the value of $k_{axial}/k_{equatorial}$ which has been estimated at ~ 5 from deuteriation studies (ref. 19) has been confirmed by more detailed detritiation studies.

## STERIC STRAIN EFFECTS

Although the contribution of ring strain to reactivity is difficult to quantify there are now many examples (ref. 20) where considerable rate accelerations can be ascribed to this factor. It is probably a contributing factor in the pattern of reactivity witnessed in the detritiation of cyclopentanone, indanone, benz[e]indanone and dihydrocyclopenta[a]phenanthren-17-one (ref. 21). Addition of the first benzene ring leads to a four-fold acceleration of rate, which can probably be ascribed to the extra rigidity provided. The addition of a second benzene ring leads however to a two-fold reduction in rate, possibly because its addition causes a small deviation from planarity. Interestingly the addition of a further benzene ring brings with it a 60% increase in reactivity. Clearly the effect of additional benzene rings is not additive, rather does it imply that factors such as deviation from planarity, which in themselves are a cause of ring strain, are important. This view finds further support in the pattern of reactivity observed for a series of mainly methyl substituted dihydrocyclopenta [a]-phananthren-17-ones.

## SUMMARY

Hydrogen isotope exchange studies provide not only a route to the preparation of a range of deuteriated and tritiated compounds but also a very subtle means of studying mechanistic details. These have now been considerably widened now that it is possible to measure hydrogen isotope exchange reactions so conveniently in non-aqueous media.

## ACKNOWLEDGEMENTS

We are grateful to NATO for supporting a good deal of the work reported in this paper.

## REFERENCES

1   J.R. Jones, The Ionisation of Carbon Acids, Acad. Press, London, 1973 pp. 236
2   E. Buncel, Carbanions: Mechanistic and Isotopic Aspects, Elsevier, Amsterdam, 1975, pp 270.
3   J.R. Jones, Quart. Rev. Chem. Soc., 25 (1971) 365-378.
4   J.R. Jones, Progr. React. Kinetics, 7 (1975) 1-22.
5   E. Buncel and H. Wilson, Adv. Phys. Org. Chem., 14 (1977) 133-202.
6   R. Kluger and P. Wasserstein, J. Am. Chem. Soc., 95 (1973) 1071-1074.
7   J.R. Jones and S.E. Taylor, Chem. Soc. Revs., 10 (1981) 329-344.
8   A.J. Kresge, Chem. Soc. Rev., 2 (1974) 475-503.
9   C.D. Ritchie and R.E. Uschold, J. Am. Chem. Soc., 90 (1968) 3415-3418.
10  H.K. Hall jr, J. Phys. Chem., 60 (1956) 63-70.
11  J.F. Coetzee and G.R. Padmanabhan, J. Am. Chem. Soc., 87 (1965) 5005-5010.
12  M.Ōki, Acc. Chem. Res., 17 (1984) 154-159.
13  M. Nakamura, N. Nakamura and M.Ōki, Bull. Chem. Soc., Japan, 50 (1977) 1097-1101.
14  M. Nakamura and M.Ōki, Chem. Lett., (1975) 671-674.
15  I.M. Klotz, Adv. Chem. Phys., 39 (1978) 109-176.
16  S. Wolfe, H.B. Schlegel, I.G. Csizmadia and E. Bernardi, Can. J. Chem., 53 (1975) 3365-3370.
17  R.R. Fraser and P.J. Champagne, Can. J. Chem., 54 (1976) 3809-3811.
18  R.R. Fraser and P.J. Champagne, J. Am. Chem. Soc., 100 (1978) 657-658.

19  F.M. Kaspersen, J.S. Favier, G. Wagenaars, J. Wallaart and C.W. Funke, Recl.
    Trav. Chim. Pays-Bas, 102 (1983) 457-460.
20  C.J.M. Stirling, Chem. Rev., 78 (1978) 517-567.
21  J.A. Elvidge, J.R. Jones, J.C. Russell, A. Wiseman and M.M. Coombs, J.C.S.
    Perkin II (1985) 563-565.

*Synthesis and Applications of Isotopically Labeled Compounds 1985.*
Proceedings of the Second International Symposium, Kansas City, MO, U.S.A.,
3—6 September 1985, R.R. Muccino (Ed.), 41—46
© 1986 Elsevier Science Publishers B.V., Amsterdam — Printed in The Netherlands

HYBRIDIZATION HISTOCHEMISTRY - LOCATING GENE EXPRESSION

J.P. COGHLAN, P. ALDRED, I.A. DARBY, J. HARALAMBIDIS, J.D. PENSCHOW and
G.W. TREGEAR
Howard Florey Institute of Experimental Physiology and Medicine, University
of Melbourne, Parkville, Victoria 3052, Australia.

A technique has been developed based upon the intrinsic property of cDNA to
hybridize with its complementary mRNA. This technique has enabled the detection
of specific mRNA populations in specially prepared tissue sections, even
in tissue from very heterogeneous organs and multi-functional organs. The technique locates specific cell populations in which a particular gene is being
expressed.

In our studies we have used $^{32}$P labelled cDNA or synthetic oligonucleotide
probes. Whilst $^{32}$P labelling does not provide the resolution of $^{3}$H, $^{35}$S or
$^{125}$I labelling when steps are taken to minimize the problem of $^{32}$P adequate
resolution for our needs down to a single cell can be obtained.

$^{32}$P-labelling of probes

#### cDNA

. nick translation
. random primers
. riboprobe SP6

#### Synthetic DNA

. 5' with polynucleotide kinase
. DNA polymerase

DNA polymerase is used also to incorporate nucleotides labelled with $^{3}$H, $^{35}$S
and $^{125}$I.

The specific activities of probes/unit mass made by the various methods
finish up more or less of the same order in our hands. Whereas with a single
labelled nucleotide substitution, the nick translation and random primer methods
should give one nucleotide in four labelled and thus very high specific activity, the actual efficiency of labelling is far from ideal. This inefficient
labelling is probably due to variable chain lengths and difficulties arising
from competing strands and other problems. The theoretical advantage of the
riboprobe system in our experience has been offset by the high concentration of
reagents (lower initial specific activity) required for good efficiency with

RNA polymerase. Although the synthetic oligonucleotides when end labelled
have only one label per mole, the increased mass available for hybridization
histochemistry with this approach confers considerable advantages, and we would
consider this superior. The specific activities are of the order $1-6 \times 10^8$ cpm/
µg.

An outline of the procedure is set out in table I.

TABLE I

HYBRIDIZATION HISTOCHEMISTRY

DAY 1

1. Freeze tissue in hexane/dry ice at $-70^{\circ}$C.
2. Cut frozen sections.
3. Fix glutaraldehyde + ethylene glycol at $4^{\circ}$C.
4. Soak in hybridization buffer containing salt, DNA, formamide.
   denharts.
5. Rinse-ethanol
6. Apply $^{32}$P-labelled probe in hybridization buffer.
7. Incubate at $30-50^{\circ}$C (Depending on probe length homology)

DAY 2

8. Wash off probe in salt solutions at $30-50^{\circ}$C.
9. Rinse-ethanol.
10. Count sections with geiger counter.
11. Apply fast X-ray film. Expose 4-24 hours.
12. Develop film, evaluate result, estimate exposure time for emulsion.

DAY 3

13. Apply emulsion and/or high resolution X-ray film.
    Expose 1-21 days.

One considerable advantage of the use of $^{32}$P-labelled probes is the fact
that the hybridized sections can be previewed after exposure to fast X-ray film.
With experience these crude autoradiographs allow the prediction of the appropriate exposure time when using emulsion which reduces the wastage in time and
effort commonly associated with this type of autoradiographic end point. In
addition, failed experiments where labelling has not occurred or background is
too high can be aborted early. The fast X-ray film is also useful when screening large numbers of sections for the location of gene expression, for example,
in serial sections of the brain.

It is difficult to describe the technique and results without extensive illustrative material. However, a variety of cDNA probes were used to illustrate
the versatility of the technique. Sensitivity down to single cells can be
demonstrated for most probes, and illustrations of this degree of resolution
were shown using cDNA probes for human prolactin and human calcitonin.

The major thrust of the oral presentation was to illustrate the use of synthetic oligonucleotides in the procedure. The advantages of these are listed in table II, and some disadvantages in table III.

## TABLE II
### Synthetic DNA Probes

#### Advantages over Cloned Probes

1.  Probes can be made in a few days.
2.  They are much easier to prepare and label in ordinary laboratory.
3.  Overall better labelling of tissue results because unlimited amounts of probe available.
4.  Consistent specific activity of probes is more easily obtainable.
5.  Pure synthetic probes give lower backgrounds.
6.  Discriminating sequences for similar genes may be made.
7.  Known sequences may be altered for different species using preferred codons.
8.  In some cases probes may be synthesized from amino acid sequences when DNA sequence is unknown.
9.  Shorter probes may be more accessible to cellular mRNA.
10. Absence of poly(T) tails eliminates one source of background.
11. Bacterial sequences in cloned probes labelling gut or infected tissues no longer a problem.

## TABLE III
### Synthetic DNA Probes

#### Disadvantages over Cloned Probes

1.  Fewer labels available at the moment.
2.  Stability of probes yet to be fully explored.
3.  Establishment of optimal conditions for short probes.
4.  Cross species hybridizations more likely to be successful with longer probes.
5.  Typographical proof-reading or sequencing errors in published sequences lead to "wild goose chases".

Synthetic oligonucleotide probes have allowed the widest application of the technique. Synthetic probes can be constituted which allow differentiation to be made between expression of genes even within gene families, eg. between oxytocin and arginine vasopressin, or between members of the kallikrein family.

In figure 1 some illustrations are shown of the use of a synthetic probe for atrial natriuretic factor. The experiment is described in the figure legend. With the larger amounts of synthetic probes available, and where the mass can be accurately measured, dilutions to extinction of the probe provide a semi-quantitative measure of mRNA levels in different sections of tissue. Also in this case the cDNA probe was not available to us, but the synthetic probe could be made immediately based on the published cDNA sequence (11).

44

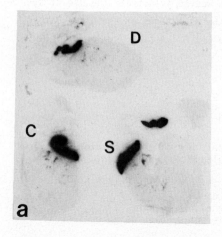

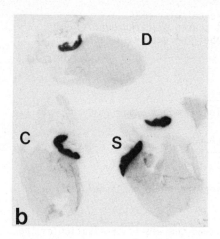

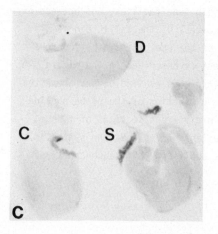

Fig. 1 Autoradiographs on X-ray film of hearts from female (D) dehydrated (48 hrs. without water), (S) sodium loaded (200mM sodium chloride to drink for 7 days) and (C) normal control rats after hybridization with a 30 mer synthetic oligodeoxyribonucleotide probe corresponding to amino acids 8-17 inclusive of rat atrial natriuretic factor (11) Mag. x 3

a) 10ng $^{32}$P-labelled DNA probes applied to sections.

b) 10ng $^{32}$P-labelled and 10ng unlabelled homologous DNA probe applied to sections.

c) 10ng $^{32}$P-labelled and 50ng unlabelled homologous probe applied to sections.

Our own papers in this field would provide information not possible to include in this brief survey (1-7). Coghlan et al (8) reviews the hybridization histochemistry field and includes better illustrative material. Varndell et al (9) have recently used a novel approach to the production and use of non-radioactively labelled probes. Uhl et al (10) have published recently their experiences with synthetic AVP probes.

Hybridization histochemistry has already proved a valuable technique for locating the sites of gene expression. Clearly it is a valuable research tool complementary to existing techniques such as immunohistochemistry. Its vast diagnostic potential is yet to be tapped in infectious disease, especially viral, in creating a new taxonomy of maligant tumours based on oncogene and growth factor expression and possibly even where parasitic vectors are involved.

This work was supported by grants-in-aid from the National Health and Medical research Council of Australia; the Myer Family Trusts; the Ian Potter Foundation; the Howard Florey Biomedical Foundation (USA).

REFERENCES
1.  P.J. Hudson, J.D. Penschow, J. Shine, G. Ryan, H.D. Niall and J.P. Coghlan, Hybridization Histochemistry, Proc. Endocrine Soc. of Aust., 1980, 23: 22
2.  J.P. Coghlan, A. Butkus, P.J. Hudson, H.D. Niall, J.D. Penschow, J. Shine, G. Ryan and J. Walsh, Hybridization Histochemistry: Use of Recombinant DNA as a "homing probe" for tissue localization of specific mRNA populations. Proc. Aust. Endocrine Soc., 1981, 24: 58.
3.  J.P. Coghlan, J.D. Penschow, P.J. Hudson and H.D. Niall, Hybridization Histochemistry: Use of Recombinant DNA for tissue localization of specific mRNA populations, Clin. and Exp. Hypertension (1984), A2, 63-78.
4.  P.J. Hudson, J.D. Penschow, J. Shine, G. Ryan, H.D. Niall and J.P. Coghlan Hybridization Histochemistry; Use of Recombinant DNA as a "homing probe" for tissue localization of specific mRNA populations. Endocrinology, (1981) 108: 353-356.
5.  J.W. Jacobs, E. Simpson, J.D. Penschow, P.J. Hudson, J.P. Coghlan and H.D. Niall. Characterization and localization of calcitonin mRNA in rat thyroid. Endocrinology (1983) 113; 1616-1622.
6.  J.P. Coghlan, J.D. Penschow, G.W. Tregear and H.D. Niall. Hybridization Histochemistry: Use of complementary DNA for tissue localization of specific mRNA populations, Receptors,Membranes and Transport Mechanisms in Medicine, F. Mendelsohn (ed). Excerpta Medica, Amsterdam, 1984 1-11.
7.  J.P. Coghlan, P. Aldred, A. Butkus, R.J. Crawford, I.A. Darby, R.T. Fernley, J. Haralambidis, P.J. Hudson, R. Mitri, H.D. Niall, J.D. Penschow, P.J. Roche, D.B. Scanlon, G.W. Tregear, R. Richards, B. Van Leeuwen, L. Rall, J. Scott and G. Bell. Hybridization Histochemistry. In Endocrinology (eds.) F. Labrie and L. Proulx,Elsevier Publishers, (1984) p16-24.
8.  J.P. Coghlan, P. Aldred, J. Haralambidis, H.D. Niall, J.D. Penschow and G.W. Tregear, Hybridization Histochemistry, Analytical Biochem. August 1985, 249.
9.  I.M. Varndell, J.M. Polak, K.L. Sikri, C.D. Minth, S.R. Bloom and J.E. Dinson. Visualization of mRNA directing peptide synthesis by in situ hybridization using a novel single stranded cDNA probe. Histochemistry, 1984, 81: 597-601.

10.   G.R. Uhl, H.A. Zingy and J.F. Habener. Vasopressin mRNA in situ hybrid-
      ization. Proc. Nat. Acad. Sci. 82; 5555-5559, 1985.
11.   Kinjo Kangawa, Yasunori Tawaragi, Shinzo Oikawa, Akira Mizuno, Yoi Sakura-
      gawa, Hiroshi Nakazato. Identification of rat atrial natriuretic polypep-
      tide and characterization of the cDNA encoding its precursor, Nature Vol.
      312, 152-155, 1984.

*Synthesis and Applications of Isotopically Labeled Compounds 1985.*
Proceedings of the Second International Symposium, Kansas City, MO, U.S.A.,
3—6 September 1985, R.R. Muccino (Ed.), 47—52
© 1986 Elsevier Science Publishers B.V., Amsterdam — Printed in The Netherlands

ANALYTICAL CONTROL OF TECHNETIUM-DIPHOSPHONATE COMPLEXES FOR RADIODIAGNOSTIC APPLICATIONS : REVIEW AND RECENT PROGRESS

P. OSINSKI

Catholic University of Louvain, Laboratory of Medicinal Chemistry,

Av. Emmanuel Mounier 73 - UCL 7340, 1200 Brussels, Belgium.

ABSTRACT

The last review of Tc-99m production, chemistry and applications appeared in 1982. Several general conclusions are apparent : 1) Complexity of Tc-chemistry, particularly of lower-valent states; 2) Paucity of fundamental data on the structure and biological behaviour of various radiopharmaceuticals; 3) Relative inadequacy of analytical control methods with regard to the intrinsic heterogeneity and diversity of formulations of various radiopharmaceuticals. Recent progress has established ion exchange HPLC as an advanced tool for the study of composition and charge of Diphosphonate-Tc complexes. Biodistribution data have shown the most adequate complexes for bone-imaging, in relation to preparative conditions. We have used the ion exchange HPLC multidetector system (U.V.; conductivity; radioactivity;) for the quantitation of various ionic species present in samples formulated as commercial kits and in genuine kits : methylenediphosphonate (MDP), MDP-Sn complex, several MDP-Tc complexes and the residual $TcO_4^-$, if present. The aim is to devise a general analytical method for the twofold purpose of control of kits in actual use and for the study of novel formulations with better bone-imaging properties.

Technetium, the first artificial, man-made element has been known for nearly 50 years. Since its development in the late 1950's, at Brookhaven National Laboratory of the $^{99m}$Tc-generator, this isotope has become a radiodiagnostic tool of choice (ref. 1). There is already a vast number of $^{99m}$Tc-labelled radiopharmaceuticals and the increasing usage is shown by the large number of publications appearing every year (ref. 2).

The history of this element and its application is the work of 3 distinct professional communities : 1) Inorganic and physical chemistry - fundamental studies; 2) Clinical medicine - radiodiagnostic applications; 3) Commercial sector - production of readily usable forms. In certain cases the weak interaction between these communities led to a situation, anomalous for the last quarter of this century of using routinely the variable mixtures of compounds of poorly known structure and hypothetical mode of action.

The usual labelling procedure involves the reduction of per-technetate $TcO_4^-$ to lower valences (I - V) in the presence of a ligand. The chemistry of reduced Tc is reputedly most complex, requiring for its elucidation a high degree of specialized know-ledge and sophisticated equipment (ref. 3,4). The task of an inor-ganic-physical chemist is further complicated by the probable interactions of these molecules with various components in vivo (ref. 5).

The medical profession greatly appreciates the Tc-labelled agents, mainly for its excellent nuclear characteristics, low dosage of labelled species and hence the virtual absence of side effects. Even while deploring the empirical character and variable results of some tests, this community has no means to bring forth the desired improvements.

The commercial sector, while producing "kits" under rigourous controls - usual practice for this industry - is not impelled toward change, neither by market forces nor by the available scientific expertise.

Technetium-labelled radiopharmaceuticals range from simple, well-defined compounds to macromolecular aggregates and cells. Our review will be focused on the calcified tissue imaging agents, diphosphonates (DiP). They have been in use for over 10 years and kits for clinical applications are produced by several firms in the U.S.A. and in Europe (ref. 6). Three substances are used most frequently: methylenediphosphonate, (MDP); ethylidenediphospho-nate, (EMDP); hydroxymethylidenediphosphonate, (HMDP).

Their history is quite illustrative of the situation described above. The physico-chemical interaction of DiP with calcium phos-phate crystals in vitro designates these substances as calcified tissue imaging agents (ref.7). Their relation to bone metabolism in vivo is, however, still speculative (ref. 8). The recent (5 years) studies of Tc-DiP complexes allow some provisional conclu-sions as to their structure and composition (ref. 9-17):
1) Tc-DiP preparations are heterogeneous mixtures of complexes of varying metal valency, metal to ligand ratio, charge and size (oligo- and polymeric polynuclear clusters);2) The composition of these preparations depends on several parameters : pH, reductant and ligand to total metal concentration ratios (i.e. quality and

age of the generator), time, presence of oxygen;3) The biodistribution of these components in the experimental animal is variable,
the lowest negative charge correlating with the highest bone uptake; 4) The main methodology used in these studies involved X-ray
crystallography, size exclusion chromatography, anion exchange
HPLC and biodistribution determinations.

The conclusions above are now confronted with the usual formulations of the clinical kits, on one hand, and with the current
methods of quality control, on the other. A) Stannous ion is used
throughout as reductant, variously expressed as weight of Sn or
$SnCl_2.2H_2O$. The fact of reductant being Sn-DiP complex of unknown
structure and electrochemical potential is not always acknowledged. B) Ligand quantity is expressed as weight of free acid
under various forms (sodium, di/tri-sodium salt). C) Ligand to
reductant ratios are often 10:1 with extremes of 35:1 and 5:1,
expressed as weight, not molar, ratios. D) The pH, generally
adjusted prior to lyophilization is stated within limits varying
between 0.2 to 3 pH units, and the contents of the vials are kept
in a nitrogen atmosphere. E) The kit is prepared by adding $^{99m}TcO_4^-$
solution from the generator, which contains variable amounts of
total Tc (99m + 99) and of dissolved oxygen. The final solution is
weakly buffered by DiP salts.

The significant control procedures according to recent Pharma-
copoeae (USP XXI and the projected European P.) are twofold: radiochemical purity and biological distribution. The former involves
2 solvent partitions on cellulose (paper) or silica gel, one with
an aqueous and one with an organic solvent. The residual unreduced
$TcO_4^-$ and species such as " hydrolysed, reduced Tc" and "Tc-Sn col-
loid" are thus quantitated. The acceptable pH values are spread
over the range of 3.5-4 pH units. The latter, while being the
ultimate index of the diagnostic agent performance, does not
necessarily match closely the conditions of routine clinical practice. Furthermore, the results obtained in the normal experimental
animal are considered as valid for the pathology of the human
patient. In our opinion, therefore, neither the criteria of formu-
lation and labelling procedure, nor the control methods are related meaningfully to the present state of knowledge, however
incomplete, of the structure and properties of DiP-Tc complexes.

The remedial action cannot be anything else than multidisciplinary, involving fundamental research, clinical practice and the

industrial establishment, in close collaboration.

Some short term changes are already apparent. Studies of labelling parameters are published, thanks to appropriate analytical
methods, indicating the conditions optimal for high yield of most
efficacious component. Results of Cincinnati group obtained in
preview through the courtesy of Dr. E. Deutsch have shown these
conditions to be high pH and high ligand concentration (i. e. high
ligand/metal ratio) promoting the predominance of oligomeric
rather than polymeric species (ref. 18, 19). The contribution of
our laboratory is focused on a general analytical method of determination of the relevant components: ligand, reductant, ligand-Tc
complexes, and the residual $TcO_4^-$. The experimental details and
complete results will be published elsewhere. We report only a
brief outline of methodology and a summary of significant data.

We are using ion exchange HPLC with Hewlett-Packard 1084 B
Liquid Chromatograph fitted with 3 detectors: variable wavelength
U.V.; conductivity and $\gamma$-radioactivity. The column is a Waters
IC-PAK anion exchange methacrylate-quaternary ammonium resin,
10 $\mu$m, 4.6 x 50 mm. 3 types of eluents have been tried :
borate-gluconate, 20 mM (isocratic); sodium acetate, 5-850 mM
(gradient); and trisodium citrate, 2-500 mM (gradient).

The results, some of them preliminary, are summarized as follows: 1) The borate-gluconate solvent allows the statistically
satisfactory quantitation of non-U.V. absorbing MDP by conductivity and of strongly absorbing Sn(II)-MDP complexes at 210 nm.
Sn(IV) is non-absorbing (Fig 1-2).

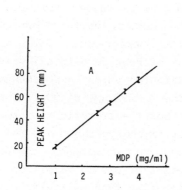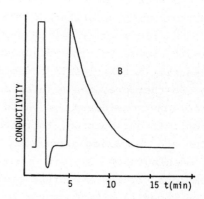

Fig 1. HPLC quantitation of MDP. A : Calibration, B : Conductivity

2) The Tc-MDP complexes are irreversibly adsorbed on this column in borate-gluconate system. The subsequent increase in any solvent concentration (gradient elution) does not reverse this phenomenon. Therefore, it is not possible to use a single solvent system and a single sample for all components. 3) The citrate eluent does separate adequately several components of Tc-MDP complexes, but there are strong indications of its interference as a chelator. 4) Sodium acetate with a molarity gradient 20-850 mM in 45 min separates Tc-MDP complexes into 3-4 components and allows also the quantitation of well-separated residual $TcO_4^-$.

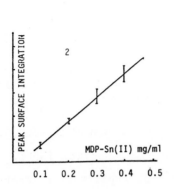 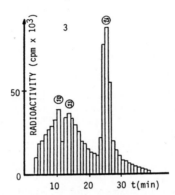

Fig 2. HPLC quantitation of MDP-Sn(II). Calibration.

Fig 3. HPLC Separation of MDP-Tc(Sn) complexes.

5) Work is in progress on re-chromatography and biological distribution of individual components. 6) There are, however, some indications that components separated from the excess of reductant and of ligand behave differently from the intact mixture.

Some aspects of these results, whether reviewed or reported, must be stressed : 1) The underlying structural data, while strongly indicative, are not very abundant and still await conclusive proof. 2) The results of optimization to be operative at all, must be translated into appropriate formulations, into relevant labelling procedures in clinical milieu and into an adequate official control methodology.

Long term projects are a matter of conjecture, but are nevertheless proposed as follows : 1) Reductants. Perhaps some substances will be found in the whole array of known inorganic and organic reductants, which will be better than stannous ion. Of particular interest are solid, porous polymers with reducing functional groups. Their electrochemical potential should yield one valency of Tc only and they might be easily removable prior to clinical use. 2) New ligands. The design of ligands with bone seeking properties might be considered in the light of presently accumulating data on structure - activity relationship. Such molecules should yield single, stable, non-polymeric complex with Tc reduced to an appropriate valency. They might be similar to known macrocyclic crown ethers.

The help of J. Adline and S. Carré is gratefully acknowledged.

## REFERENCES

1   W. D. Tucker, M. W. Greene, A. J. Weiss and A. P. Murenhoff, BNL 3746, Trans. Am. Nucl. Soc., 1 (1958) 160.
2   A. B. McIntyre, P. Paras and R. C. Grant, J. Nucl. Med., 21 (1980) 42.
3   A. G. Jones and A. Davison, Int. J. Appl. Radiat. Isot., 33 (1982) 867.
4   A. Davison and A. G. Jones, Int. J. Appl. Radiat. Isot., 33 (1982) 875.
5   W. C. Eckelman and W. A. Volkert, Int. J. Appl. Radiat. Isot., 33 (1982) 945.
6   Y. Yano, J. McRae, D. C. VanDyke and H. L. Anger, J. Nucl. Med., 14 (1973) 73.
7   M. D. Francis, D. L. Ferguson, A. J. Tofe, J. A. Bevan and S. E. Michaels, J. Nucl. Med., 21 (1980) 1185.
8   H. Shinoda, G. Adamek, R. Felix, H. Fleisch, R. Schenk and P. Hagan, Calcif. Tissue Int., 35 (1983) 87.
9   T. C. Pinkerton, W. R. Heineman and E. Deutsch, Anal. Chem., 52 (1980) 1106.
10  K. Libson, E. Deutsch and B. L. Barnett, J. Am. Chem. Soc., 102 (1980) 2476.
11  A. G. Jones and A. Davison, J. Nucl. Med., 23 (1982) 1041.
12  E. Deutsch, W. R. Heineman, J. P. Zodda, T. W. Gilbert and C. C. Williams, Int. J. Appl. Radiat. Isot., 33 (1982) 843.
13  T. C. Pinkerton, D. L. Ferguson, E. Deutsch, W. R. Heineman and K. Libson, Int. J. Appl. Radiat. Isot., 33 (1982) 907.
14  J. A. G. M. Van Den Brand, H. A. Das, B. G. Dekker, C. L. De Ligny and C. J. A. Van Den Hamer, Int. J. Appl. Radiat. Isot., 33 (1982) 917.
15  S. Tanabe, J. P. Zodda, E. Deutsch and W. R. Heineman, Int. J. Appl. Radiat. Isot., 34 (1983) 1577.
16  S. Tanabe, J. P. Zodda, K. Libson, E. Deutsch and W. R. Heineman, Int. J. Appl. Radiat. Isot., 34 (1983) 1585.
17  G. M. Wilson and T. C. Pinkerton, Anal. Chem., 57 (1985) 246.
18  J. P. Zodda, S. Tanabe, W. R. Heineman and E. Deutsch, in preparation. Personal communication of Dr. E. Deutsch.
19  D. L. Ferguson, K. Libson, W. R. Heineman and E. Deutsch, in preparation. Personal communication of Dr. E. Deutsch.

*Synthesis and Applications of Isotopically Labeled Compounds 1985.*
Proceedings of the Second International Symposium, Kansas City, MO, U.S.A.,
3—6 September 1985, R.R. Muccino (Ed.), 53—58
© 1986 Elsevier Science Publishers B.V., Amsterdam — Printed in The Netherlands

USE OF STABLE ISOTOPES FOR MECHANISTIC STUDIES OF CYTOCHROME P-450 AND EPOXIDE HYDROLASE

ROBERT P. HANZLIK, STEPHEN P. JACOBER, KAREN J. HAMRICK, JOSEPH B. MOON, KERSTIN HOGBERG AND CHARLES M. JUDSON

Department of Medicinal Chemistry, University of Kansas, Lawrence Kansas, 66045 (U.S.A)

ABSTRACT

The microsomal hydroxylation and chemical chlorination of $PhCH_2D$ (1) and $PhCHD_2$ (2) have been studied. For chlorination both primary (P = 5.0) and secondary (S = 0.85/d) deuterium isotope effects were determined, but during hydroxylation, H/D discrimination was different for 1 and 2 (P/S = 3.01 and 5.64, respectively), and values of P and S could not be defined. In addition, oxygen-18, carbon-13 and deuterium kinetic isotope effects have been measured for the enzymic hydration of R- and S-p-nitrostyrene oxide (PNSO), and for its reaction with methoxide and pyrrolidine. Transition state structures of these processes have been deduced.

INTRODUCTION

Our laboratory has been interested in using kinetic isotope effects (KIEs) to probe mechanisms of microsomal drug metabolizing enzymes. This report will summarize recent results obtained with cytochrome P-450 catalyzed hydroxylations, with microsomal epoxide hydrolase, and with related chemical models.

## Benzylic Functionalization of Toluene

Aliphatic hydroxylation by P-450 enzymes is thought to proceed via a two step sequence of H-abstraction by an oxo-iron (ferryl) form of the enzyme, followed by recombination of the intermediate carbon radical with OH from the heme iron. There have been many reports of primary deuterium KIEs associated with aliphatic hydroxylation, but secondary KIEs, which could provide information about the hybridization at carbon in the transition state for abstraction, have received much less attention. We sought to measure the secondary DKIE for benzylic hydroxylation of toluene, taking advantage of an "intramolecular" design that also allowed simultaneous determination of the primary DKIE. As a test of this approach the benzylic chlorination of $PhCH_2D$ (1) abd $PhCD_2H$ (2) was also studied.

Deuterated toluenes $PhCH_2D$ (1, 98.6 mol %-$d_1$) and $PhCHD_2$ (2, 97.6 mol %-$d_2$) were prepared (ref.1) by a sequence of reduction of methyl benzoate with LAH (LAD), treatment with HBr gas in anhydrous benzene, reduction of the benzyl bromide with $NaCNBD_3$ ($NaCNBH_3$) in HMPA, and bulb-to-bulb distillation for purification. They were separately subjected to free-radical chlorination as described by Fonouni et al. (ref. 2), and to microsomal hydroxylation as described by us previously (ref. 3). The deuterium contents of the resulting benzyl chlorides and benzyl alcohols are presented in Table 1.

Hydrogen abstraction from 1 or 2 is subject to the combined influence of primary (P) and secondary (S) DKIEs, as indicated in eq. (1) and (2). These equations (which assume the "rule of the geometric mean" applies) cannot be solved for P and S, but only for their ratio. However, as one test of their validity, one can compare the observed value of $r_1/r_2$ to the predicted value of 4.0. As seen from Table 1, the agreement in the case of the chlorination reaction is very good. With the additional information that the intermolecular isotope effect on chlorination (i.e. $r_3$) is 3.6, eq. (1)-(3) may be solved for explicit values of P and S. Thus for the chlorination of toluene P = 5.0 and S = 0.85 per deuterium.

$$r_1 = \frac{d_1}{d_0} = \frac{2(PhCHD-H)}{(PhCHH-D)} = \frac{2k_H^{HD}}{k_D^{HH}} = 2P/S \tag{1}$$

$$r_2 = \frac{d_2}{d_1} = \frac{(PhCDD-H)}{2(PhCHD-D)} = \frac{k_H^{DD}}{2k_D^{HD}} = P/2S \tag{2}$$

$$r_3 = \frac{d_0}{d_2} = \frac{(PhCHH-H)}{(PhCDD-D)} = \frac{k_H^{HH}}{k_D^{DD}} = PS^2 \tag{3}$$

The finding that P = 5.0 is reasonable, but the inverse secondary effect is contrary to expectation for a transition state in which $sp^2$-hybridized benzylic radical character is supposedly being developed. The reason for the apparent increase in restriction of out-of-plane C-H bending is not clear. Perhaps the chlorinating reagent approaches in such a way as to hinder the remaining hydrogens. Further studies of model reactions leading to the benzylic functionalization of toluene derivatives are currently under way in our laboratory.

As shown by the data in Table 1, there is considerable discrimination against D-abstraction in the microsomal hydroxylation of 1 and 2. However, the discrimination is much more marked with 2 (P/S = 5.64) than with 1 (P/S = 3.01).

Table 1. Hydrogen-Deuterium Discrimination During Microsomal Hydroxylation and Chemical Chlorination of $PhCH_2D$ and $PhCHD_2$.

| Reaction | from $PhCH_2D$ | | from $PhCHD_2$ | | |
|---|---|---|---|---|---|
| | mole% $PhCH_2X$ | $r_1$ | mole% PhCHDX | $r_2$ | $r_1/r_2$ |
| Chlorination (n=3) | 90.94 ± 0.08 | 11.87 ± 0.12 | 73.12 ± 4.06 | 2.96 ± 0.63 | 4.01 ± 0.07 |
| Microsomes (n=3) | 84.57 ± 3.97 | 6.03 ± 1.99 | 72.35 ± 4.06 | 2.82 ± 0.61 | 2.13 ± 0.84 |

Table 2. Kinetic Isotope Effects on Reactions of p-Nitrostyrene Oxide

| | Kinetic Isotope Effect ($^*k$ or $^*V_{max}$) | | | | |
|---|---|---|---|---|---|
| Reaction | $f_8$ | $8-^{13}C$ | $^{18}O$ | $7-d_1$ | $8,8-d_2$ |
| Methoxide, $^*k_8$ | 0.833 ± 0.003 | 1.082 ± 0.012 | 1.036 ± 0.024 | 0.922 ± 0.020[a] | 0.971 ± 0.026[a] |
| Pyrrolidine, $^*k_8$ | 0.895 ± 0.006 | 1.055 ± 0.016 | 1.014 ± 0.015 | 0.984 ± 0.021 | 0.946 ± 0.011 |
| MEH (S-PNSO), $^*V$ | 0.930 ± 0.01 | 1.118 ± 0.015 | 1.016 ± 0.018 | 1.034 ± 0.015 | 1.090 ± 0.020 |
| MEH (R-PNSO), $^*V$ | 0.924 ± 0.01 | 1.044 ± 0.013 | 1.044 ± 0.013 | 0.964 ± 0.008 | 1.095 ± 0.015 |

[a]Data from ref. 5.

Admittedly there is considerably more variance in the hydroxylation data than in the chlorination data, but this is not atypical with microsomal systems. Nevertheless, it is still quite apparent that the observed value of $r_1/r_2$ is quite different from 4.0. Since the heme iron in P-450 is paramagnetic, the possible intervention of a _magnetic_ isotope effect was considered, but the results of microsomal incubations conducted in the 18.8 kGauss field of a Bruker WP-80 NMR spectrometer were not significantly different (data not shown). The induction status of the microsomes also had no discernable effect on $r_1$ and $r_2$ (data not shown). We plan to perform similar experiments using purified reconstituted P-450 systems, as well as other toluene derivatives, in an attempt to discover the origins of this unexpected discrepancy between theory and experiment. Further discussion of possible reasons is given in ref. 1.

## Ring-Opening Reactions of p-Nitrostyrene Oxide

Microsomal epoxide hydrolase (MEH) is important in detoxifying epoxide metabolites of many unsaturated compounds. It hydrates mono-, 1,1-di-, and cis-1,2-disubstituted oxiranes with inversion of configuration and high regioselectivity for the least hindered carbon. There is good evidence for general base activation of water as a specific co-substrate, but as yet no compelling evidence for acid catalyzed epoxide activation. We have developed a continuous photometric assay for MEH based on p-nitrostyrene oxide (PNSO), and have used it to measure KIEs for enzymic hydration of R-(-)- and S-(+)-PNSO labeled with $^{18}O$, 8-$^{13}C$, 7-$d_1$, and 8,8-$d_2$. The assay has been described by us previously (ref. 4). In addition the regioselectivity and KIEs for reaction of PNSO with methoxide (1M in MeOH), and pyrrolidine (1M in EtOH) have been studied as model reactions. The results are reported in Table 2.

Nucleophiles can attack PNSO at the benzylic carbon (C-7) or the terminal carbon (C-8). Thus the total rate of reaction is $k_{obs} = k_7 + k_8$. The regioselectivity (i.e. the fraction of C-7 vs. C-8 attack) is defined as $f_7 = k_7/k_{obs}$ and $f_8 = k_8/k_{obs}$. HPLC quantitation of the isomeric products gives $f_7$ and $f_8$.

Methoxide reacts primarily at C-8 ($f_8 = 0.833$). The large $^{13}C$ effect on $k_8$ suggests appreciable $S_N2$ character in the transition state, and this is reinforced by the _inverse_ DIE at C-8 (crowding by the nucleophile). The $^{18}O$ effect suggests substantial cleavage of the C-O bond in the transition state, which is supported by an _inverse_ DIE at the "non-reacting" carbon (rehybridization of C-7 as the ring opens).

Pyrrolidine shows an even greater preference for reaction at C-8 ($f_8 = 0.895$). Close approach of the nucleophile is indicated by the _inverse_ DIE at C-8, while the large $^{13}C$-effect indicates strong $S_N2$ character (i.e. pentacoordinate carbon) at C-8 in the transition state. However, in contrast to methoxide, the $^{18}O$ effect and the DIE at C-7 are reduced, suggesting an earlier transition state with less ring opening.

The MEH-catalyzed hydration of R- and S-PNSO proceed via E-S transition states which are diastereomers of one another. Therefore each enantiomer displays different kinetic constants; for S-(+)-PNSO Km is 7.6 uM and Vmax is 116 nmol/min/mg protein, while for R-(-)-PNSO the values are 1.6 and 34, respectively. Correspondingly each enantiomer gives rise to similar but nonidentical patterns of KIEs on Vmax (Table 2). The large $^{13}C$ effect for S-PNSO, the "fast, loose-binding" enantiomer, and the large $^{18}O$ effect for R-PNSO, the "slow, tight-binding" enantiomer, indicate that the rate limiting step in turnover of each substrate is catalysis. Therefore all KIEs may be interpreted in terms of two diastereomeric transition states for hydration. Interestingly, both enantiomers are hydrated with the same regioselectivity.

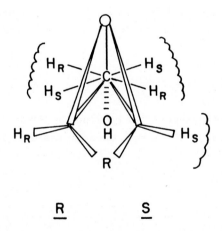

Figure 1. Enzymic hydration of PNSO.

For S-PNSO the large $^{13}C$ and small $^{18}O$ KIEs suggest an early transition state with strong $S_N2$ character and little ring-opening. For R-PNSO the larger $^{18}O$ and smaller $^{13}C$ KIEs suggest a later transition state with more ring opening and less penta-coordinate character at C-8. Curiously, in comparison to the model studies, the DIEs for enzymic hydration tend to be normal rather than inverse. One possible explanation for this apparent loosening of C-H bonding in the transition state is that in the ground state E-S complex (i.e. the Michaelis complex) there exist some steric compressions of these bonds which are released in the transition state. This is indicated diagramatically in Figure 1. Since the (water)O---C---O(oxirane) bond (and the aromatic substituent) are common to both transition states, these groups are assumed to be aligned for both substrates. This places the C-8 hydrogens of both enantiomers in virtually identical environments (and both give similar normal DIEs). In contrast the C-7 hydrogens are in very different environments (and the two enantiomers give very different DIEs). Taking the wavy lines in Figure 1 to represent E-S steric compressions in the Michaelis complex which are relieved in the transition states provides a reasonable explanation for the DIEs observed. It is especially interesting that the "fast, loose-binding" S-PNSO apparently develops more ground state strain than the "slow, tight-binding" R-PNSO. Thus the model in Figure 1 can account for the relative kinetic properties of the substrates as well as their associated patterns of isotope effects. It may be that relief of intermolecular ground state strain is a significant driving force for catalysis by MEH. If so it would perhaps explain why no strong experimental support for general acid catalysis on the part of MEH has yet been found.

ACKNOWLEDGEMENT

Financial support for these studies provided by the National Institutes of Health and the University of Kansas General Research Fund is gratefully acknowledged.

REFERENCES

1    R. P. Hanzlik, K. Hogberg, J. B. Moon and C. M. Judson, J. Amer. Chem. Soc., 107 (1985, in press).

2    H. E. Fonouni, S. Krishnan, D. G. Kuhn, and G. A. Hamilton, J. Amer. Chem. Soc., 105 (1983) 7672-7676.

3    R. P. Hanzlik, K. Hogberg and C. M. Judson, Biochemistry, 23 (1984) 3048-3055.

4    R. B. Westkaemper and R. P. Hanzlik, Arch. Biochem. Biophys., 208 (1981) 195-204.

5    R. P. Hanzlik and R. B. Westkaemper, J. Amer. Chem. Soc., 102 (1980), 2464-2467.

*Synthesis and Applications of Isotopically Labeled Compounds 1985.*
Proceedings of the Second International Symposium, Kansas City, MO, U.S.A.,
3—6 September 1985, R.R. Muccino (Ed.), 59—64
© 1986 Elsevier Science Publishers B.V., Amsterdam — Printed in The Netherlands

THE MECHANISM OF ACTIVATION AND COVALENT BINDING OF RONIDAZOLE (1-METHYL-5-NITROIMIDAZOLE-2-METHANOL CARBAMATE)

A. Y. H. Lu, J. S. Walsh, R. Wang, R. F. Alvaro, P. G. Wislocki, and G. T. Miwa, Department of Animal Drug Metabolism, Merck Sharp & Dohme Research Laboratories, Rahway, NJ 07065 (USA).

## ABSTRACT

Ronidazole is activated anaerobically to a reactive metabolite which covalently binds to liver proteins. Cysteine thiol groups are the primary targets for protein alkylation. Studies with ronidazole radiolabeled at various positions indicate that covalent binding occurs with retention of the entire carbon framework of the molecule but with loss of the carbamate and the proton at C-4. Direct evidence demonstrates the addition of a protein cysteine residue to the 2-methylene carbon. Based on these results, a mechanism for the metabolic activation of ronidazole is proposed.

## INTRODUCTION

Nitroimidazoles have been widely used as therapeutic agents to treat bacterial and parasitic diseases in both humans and animals. Although it is known that the reduction of the nitro group is essential for their biological and toxicological activities (1), the details of the metabolic activation mechanism are still unknown. In the last several years, our laboratory has studied the mechanism of activation of ronidazole, one of the most potent nitroimidazoles known. Covalent binding to liver microsomal proteins was used as an end-point measurement of the generation of a reactive intermediate during the activation of ronidazole. In this paper, we describe the mechanism involved in the formation of protein-bound ronidazole adducts.

## CHARACTERIZATION OF THE COVALENT BINDING SYSTEM

A series of studies establish that the covalent binding to proteins by a [14C]ronidazole metabolite is catalyzed most efficiently by rat liver microsomes, requires NADPH, and is inhibited by the presence of oxygen (2). Inhibition studies suggest that the cytochrome P-450-containing electron transport chain in liver microsomes is involved in the metabolic activation of ronidazole, but purified NADPH-cytochrome P-450 reductase by itself can carry out this reaction (3). Evidence also indicates that reduction of the nitro group is responsible for the generation of a reactive metabolite which is responsible for the covalent binding to proteins and that the cysteine thiol group in proteins is the major target of alkylation (2-4).

MECHANISM OF RONIDAZOLE ACTIVATION

The chemical reduction of the nitro group of ronidazole in aqueous solution is known to result in extensive hydrolytic fragmentation of the imidazole ring, producing simple molecules such as ammonia, carbon dioxide, cyanide, methylamine, and acetamide (5).  However, when ronidazole is reduced by dithionite in the presence of cysteine, the isolated cysteine adducts retain the intact imidazole nucleus (6).  To examine which part of the ronidazole molecule binds to the cysteine thiol groups of proteins during NADPH-dependent enzymatic reduction, studies were conducted with ronidazole radiolabeled at different positions (Table 1).  The covalent binding to liver microsomal proteins is identical in incubations with ronidazole labeled with [$^{14}$C] in the N-methyl, 2-methylene, or 4,5-ring positions, but greatly reduced with substrate labeled with [$^{14}$C] in the carbonyl group or with [$^{3}$H] at the C-4 position (Table 2).  These results establish that covalent binding occurs with retention of the carbon framework of the molecule but with loss of the carbamate and the proton at C-4.  Further studies using structural analogues, modified at the carbamate group, all result in low covalent binding, suggesting

TABLE 1

Ronidazole structure and position of radiolabels

| Compound | Position of Radiolabel |
|---|---|
| 1a | N-$^{14}$CH$_3$ |
| 1b | 2-$^{14}$CH$_2$ |
| 1c | 4,5-$^{14}$C$_2$ |
| 1d | $^{14}$C=O |
| 1e | 4-$^{3}$H |

TABLE 2

Relative protein-binding of specifically labeled ronidazoles
to rat liver microsomal proteins in vitro and to rat liver
proteins in vivo

| Compound | In Vitro Microsomal Protein Binding | In Vivo Liver Protein Binding |
|---|---|---|
| $^{14}C$:    1a | 1.00[a] | 1.00 |
| 1b | 0.99 | 1.17 |
| 1c | 1.09 | 1.00 |
| 1d | 0.15 | Not determined |
| $^3H$:    1e | 0.10 | 0.12 |

[a]Protein binding is expressed for each of the [$^{14}C$] and [$^3H$]-
labeled substrates relative to 1a.

that the carbamate group is necessary for the generation of reactive
metabolite to achieve maximum covalent binding to proteins.  In addition,
these structure-activity studies also suggest that the 2-methylene position is
the preferred site for cysteine alkylation since in the absence of a carbamate
group, alkylation to other positions of the molecule is much lower.  This
suggestion is confirmed by the isolation and identification of
$^{14}C$-carboxymethylcysteine from an acid hydrolyzed sample of 2-[$^{14}CH$]$_2$-
ronidazole covalently bound to microsomal proteins.

TABLE 3

Stoichiometry in NADPH-dependent, metabolism-mediated covalent
binding of ronidazole to microsomal proteins.

| Measurement | Ratio |
|---|---|
| Ronidazole metabolized/[$^{14}C$]-bound protein adduct | 22 |
| Total reactive metabolite formed/[$^{14}C$]-bound protein adduct | 18 |
| 4-[$^3H$] released/[$^{14}C$]-bound protein adduct | 17 |

In a series of experiments, the amount of ronidazole metabolized, total
reactive metabolite formed, and the amount of 4-[$^3$H] released were measured in
relation to the amount of [$^{14}$C] protein bound adduct formed. The quantity of
the total reactive metabolite formed was estimated by the amount of metabolite
bound to bovine serum albumin at infinite albumin concentration (4). As shown
in Table 3, a ratio of approximately 20 is observed for all three parameters
in relation to covalent binding. These results suggest that virtually all of
the ronidazole metabolized results in the formation of the reactive metabolite
via a mechanism involving the release of the 4-proton. However, for every 20
molecules of reactive metabolite formed, only one molecule alkylates microsomal proteins, whereas the other 19 molecules are presumably degraded in
water to generate ring fragmentation products.

When rats are dosed with ronidazole radiolabeled at various positions and
killed six hours after dosing, protein-bound adducts isolated from the liver
tissue retain the imidazole ring carbons but have eliminated the proton at C-4
(Table 1). Based on these multiple radiolabel experiments, radiochromato-
graphic profile after acid hydrolysis, and the identification and quantitation
of hydrolysis products (7), it is concluded that the liver protein-bound
adduct formed in vivo in rats is identical to that formed under anaerobic
incubations with liver microsomes.

Based on these data, a mechanism for ronidazole activation is proposed
(Fig. 1). In this scheme, ronidazole is shown to undergo 4-electron
enzymatic reduction to the hydroxylamine (II) which then activates the C-4
position to nucleophilic attack by either protein thiols or water to produce
IIIa and IIIb. Subsequent loss of the 4-proton and carbamic acid yields a
Michael-like acceptor capable of reacting with thiol nucleophiles at the
2-methylene position (Vb) or with water producing Va. The formation of Vb is
preferred since the expected product, carboxymethylcysteine, has been
identified from acid hydrolysates of the protein adduct. Even though the
addition of a protein cysteine residue to the 2-methylene carbon may represent
the major pathway for protein adduct formation, the extent of this pathway in
protein alkylation has not been established. In addition, although the
4-electron reduction product, hydroxylamine, is postulated to be the reactive
species reponsible for protein alkylation, other intermediates, such as the
nitrosoimidazole, cannot be ruled out at the present time.

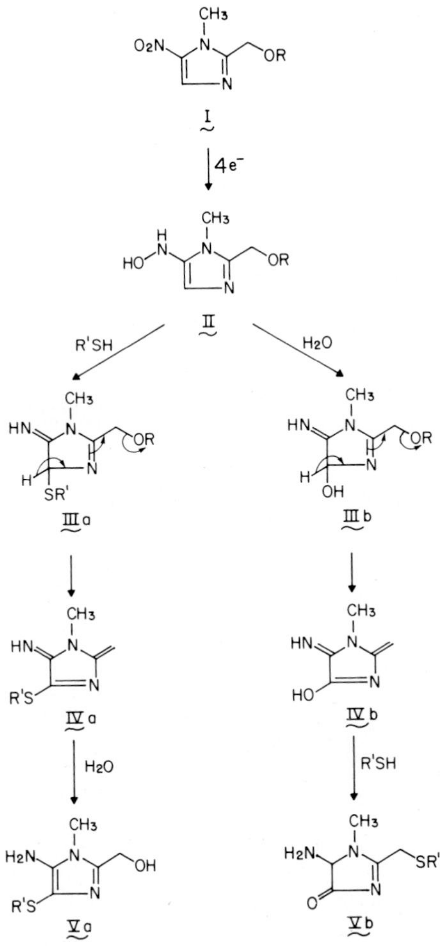

Fig. 1. Proposed mechanism for ronidazole activation.

ACKNOWLEDGEMENTS

We thank Dr. R. Ellsworth, Mr. G. Gatto, Dr. H. Mertel, Mr. S. O'Connor, and Dr. A. Rosegay for the synthesis of the radiolabeled ronidazoles. We also thank Mrs. Terry Rafferty for her assistance in the preparation of this manuscript.

64

REFERENCES

1  D. I. Edwards, Br. J. Vener. Dis. 56 (1980) 285-290.

2  S. B. West, P. G. Wislocki, K. M. Fiorentini, R. Alvaro, F. J. Wolf, and A. Y. H. Lu, Chem.-Biol. Interactions 41 (1982) 265-279.

3  S. B. West, P. G. Wislocki, F. J. Wolf, and A. Y. H. Lu, Chem.-Biol. Interactions 41 (1982) 281-296.

4  G. T. Miwa, S. B. West, J. S. Walsh, F. J. Wolf, and A. Y. H. Lu, Chem.-Biol. Interactions 41 (1982) 297-312.

5  R. P. Buhs, A. Rosegay, T. A. Jacob, N. A. Allen, and F. J. Wolf, Pharmacologist 21(1979) 232.

6  P. G. Wislocki, E. S. Bagan, W. J. A. VandenHeuvel, R. W. Walker, R. F. Alvaro, B. H. Arison, A. Y. H. Lu, and F. J. Wolf, Chem.-Biol. Interactions 49 (1984) 13-25.

7  G. T. Miwa, R. F. Alvaro, J. S. Walsh, R. Wang, and A. Y. H. Lu, Chem.-Biol. Interactions 50 (1984) 189-202.

*Synthesis and Applications of Isotopically Labeled Compounds 1985.*
Proceedings of the Second International Symposium, Kansas City, MO, U.S.A.,
3—6 September 1985, R.R. Muccino (Ed.), 65—68
© 1986 Elsevier Science Publishers B.V., Amsterdam — Printed in The Netherlands

ISOTOPIC STUDIES APPLIED TO THE MECHANISM OF ALKYLATION OF DNA BY ETHYLENE DIBROMIDE

F. PETER GUENGERICH, NOBUYUKI KOGA, PHILIP B. INSKEEP, and NAOKI OZAWA

Department of Biochemistry and Center in Molecular Toxicology, Vanderbilt University School of Medicine, Nashville, Tennessee 37232 (USA)

ABSTRACT

A number of modes of activation of haloalkanes are possible. Model studies suggested that oxygenation of iodo compounds can be catalyzed by the enzyme cytochrome P-450. However, such a mechanism is probably not a major pathway in the oxidation of ethylene dichloride and ethylene dibromide. Instead the major oxidation pathway probably involves direct $\alpha$-hydrogen abstraction and oxygen rebound to form haloacetaldehydes, which react rapidly with protein and non-protein thiols but not nucleic acids. The major route to formation of DNA adducts from ethylene dihalides involves enzymatic conjugation with glutathione (GSH) and reaction of the resulting S-(2-haloethyl)glutathione conjugates with DNA (via an episulfonium ion). GSH and ethylene dibromide are bound to DNA in a 1:1 ratio in rat hepatocytes or in the presence of purified GSH S-transferase. The major DNA adduct formed from ethylene dibromide $\underline{in}$ $\underline{vitro}$ and $\underline{in}$ $\underline{vivo}$ is S-[2-($N^7$-guanyl)-ethyl]glutathione.

INTRODUCTION

Halogenated chemicals are nearly ubiquitous today in our industrial society, and nearly all are potentially toxic. While many of these materials have direct pharmacological effects when people or experimental animals are exposed to high concentrations, another matter of concern is chronic exposure to low doses. Many of the effects of chronic low levels of halogenated hydrocarbons are the result of enzymatic bioactivation pathways operative in mammals. Different pathways are involved in the activation of various halogenated materials, including oxidation, reduction, conjugation, and dehydrohalogenation (ref.1). In this report we discuss our investigations of the activation of $\underline{vic}$ dihaloalkanes and how isotopically-labeled materials have been employed in the work.

METHODS

Conditions for the oxygen exchange between iodosylbenzene and iodobenzene have been reported elsewhere (ref.2), as have the methods used to measure rates of alkylation of macromolecules (ref.3), the metabolism of ethylene dichloride (ref.4), and the isolation of ethylene dibromide-DNA adducts (ref.5). S-[2-($N^7$-

guanyl)ethyl]glutathione was isolated from DNA using neutral thermal hydrolysis (ref.6), reverse phase high performance liquid chromatography (HPLC) (ref.5), and ion exchange HPLC (ref.7). $^1$H NMR spectra were obtained in $^2$H$_2$O with a Bruker AM-400 instrument using two-dimensional correlated spectroscopy (COSY) and the collaboration of Dr. T.M. Harris. Fast atom bombardment (FAB) mass spectra were obtained using glycerol as the matrix with a VG 70-250 system and the help of Drs. I.A. Blair and B. Sweetman.

RESULTS AND DISCUSSION

We considered the possible oxygenation of halogens by cytochrome P-450 (P-450). Few haloso compounds are stable, so we took advantage of the stability of iodosylbenzene and its ability to transfer an oxygen atom to P-450 to demonstrate the following reaction (ref.2)

$$\phi I=O \ + \ \phi^{125}I \ \rightleftharpoons \ \phi^{125}I=O$$

The relevance of such a reaction to the metabolism of ethylene dichloride was considered (Fig. 1). Several observations were consistent with such a reaction (ref.4). However, subsequent isotopic studies done using NADPH-fortified rat liver microsomes containing alcohol dehydrogenase and NADH to trap aldehydes

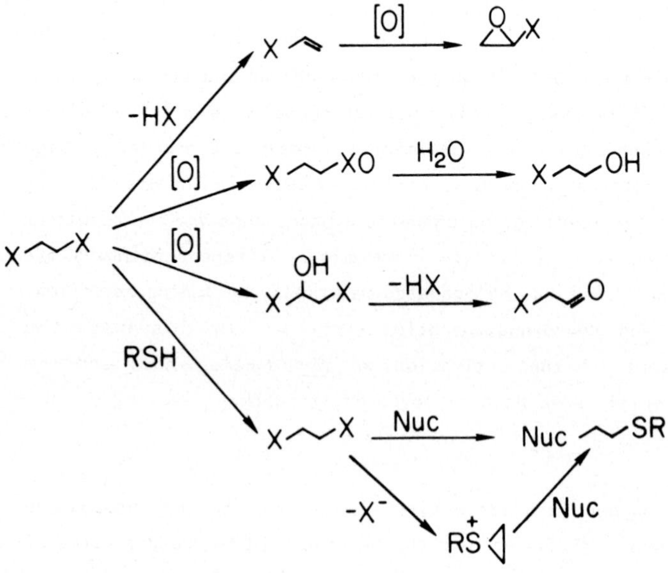

Fig. 1. Possible pathways of ethylene dihalide oxidation.

indicate that (1) $^2H_4$-ethylene dichloride yields $^2H_3$-chloroethanol and $^2H_4$- ethylene dibromide yields $^2H_3$-bromoethanol, but no $^2H_4$-haloethanol in either case, (2) oxygen from $^{18}O_2$, but not $H_2{}^{18}O$, is incorporated into chloroethanol, and (3) $^2H$ from $NAD^2H$ is incorporated into chloroethanol. Further, substantial intermolecular kinetic deuterium isotope effects ($k_H/k_D$ = 8.5) are seen in the formation of bromoethanol from ethylene dibromide. Dehydrohalogenation is also possible (Fig. 1) but ethylene dichloride did not form detectable amounts of vinyl chloride (ref.4). Thus, the major pathway of oxidation of ethylene dichloride and ethylene dibromide probably involves formal α-hydroxylation and spontaneous dehydrohalogenation to form the 2-haloacetaldehyes.

Several lines of investigation indicate that the oxidative pathway (vide supra) is the main route of formation of reactive metabolites that bind to protein and glutathione (GSH) (refs.4, 8, 9). The kinetics of binding of $^{14}C$-labeled bromoacetaldehyde and chloroacetaldehyde to protein were rapid but alkylation of DNA was quite slow (ref.3).

Previous biological and radioisotopic binding studies had indicted that cytosolic conjugation with GSH should be the major source of DNA adducts (ref.4). If the hypothesis of Rannug et al. (ref.10) is correct in this regard, then GSH and ethylene dihalide should both become attached to DNA in stoichiometric amounts. We demonstrated that this indeed was the case with $[1,2-^{14}C]$-ethylene dibromide and $^{35}S$-GSH or [glycine-$^3H$]-GSH in the presence of GSH S-transferase. Similar experiments were done in isolated rat hepatocytes after the endogenous pool of GSH was labeled with $^{35}S$-methionine. The stoichiometry of labeling of DNA indicated that this is the major pathway of DNA adduct formation with ethylene dibromide (ref.5).

$[1,2-^{14}C]$-Ethylene dibromide was used as a tracer to separate the DNA adducts formed in vitro and in vivo. The first deduction of the structure came after the conjugation was isolated from nuclease-digested DNA and reduced with a modified Raney nickel procedure to form $N^7$-ethylguanine (ref.5). Subsequently the intact adduct has been isolated and shown to be S-[2-($N^7$-guanyl)ethyl]glutathione (Fig. 2). The adduct can be released from DNA by neutral thermal hydrolysis and degraded by pronase or γ-glutamyl transpeptidase. Its molecular weight is 484 as judged by the molecular ions observed in positive and negative FAB mass spectrometry. The $^1H$ NMR COSY spectrum has been compared to those of GSH and oxidized GSH and is only consistent with the assigned structure. Chromatographic comparisons indicate that this is the only major DNA adduct formed in vivo from $[1,2-^{14}C]$-ethylene dibromide in rat liver and kidney. The biological half-life of this adduct is 70-100 h.

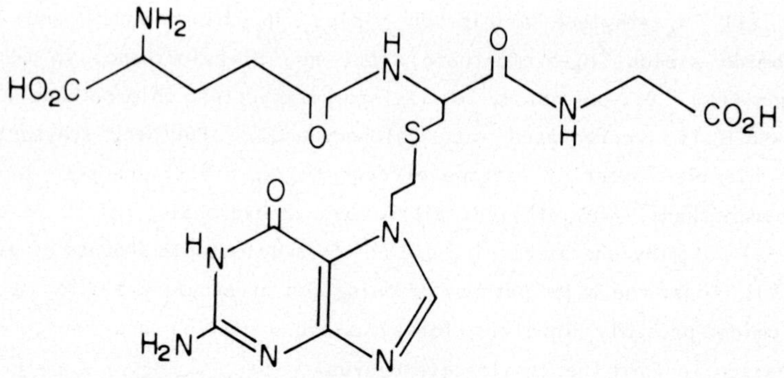

Fig. 2. S-[2-(N$'$-guanyl)ethyl]glutathione.


These studies describe the major routes of activation of ethylene dibromide. The results suggest that S-[2-(N[7]-guanyl)ethyl]glutathione is related to the formation of tumors but further biological evidence is lacking.


REFERENCES

1   T.L. Macdonald, CRC Crit. Rev. Toxicol., 11 (1982) 85-120.

2   L.T. Burka, A. Thorsen and F.P. Guengerich, J. Am. Chem. Soc., 102 (1980) 7615-7616.

3   F.P. Guengerich, P.S. Mason, W. Stott, T.R. Fox and P.G. Watanabe, Cancer Res., 41 (1981) 4391-4398.

4   F.P. Guengerich, W.M. Crawford, Jr., J.L. Domoradzki, T.L. Macdonald and P.G. Wanatabe, Toxicol. Appl. Pharmacol., 55 (1980) 303-317.

5   N. Ozawa and F.P. Guengerich, Proc. Natl. Acad. Sci. U.S.A., 80 (1983) 5266-5270.

6   P.B. Inskeep and F.P. Guengerich, Carcinogenesis, 5 (1984) 805-808.

7   D.J. Reed, J.R. Babson, P.W. Beatty, A.E. Brodie, W.W. Ellis and D.W. Potter, Anal. Biochem., 106 (1980) 55-62.

8   R.D. White, A.J. Gandolfi, G.T. Bowden and I.G. Sipes, Toxicol. Appl. Pharmacol., 69 (1983) 170-178.

9   R.D. Storer and R.B. Conolly, Toxicol. Appl. Pharmacol., 77 (1985) 36-46.

10  U. Rannug, A. Sundvall and C. Ramel, Chem.-Biol. Interactions, 20 (1978) 1-16.

*Synthesis and Applications of Isotopically Labeled Compounds 1985.*
Proceedings of the Second International Symposium, Kansas City, MO, U.S.A.,
3—6 September 1985, R.R. Muccino (Ed.), 69—75
© 1986 Elsevier Science Publishers B.V., Amsterdam — Printed in The Netherlands

APPLICATIONS OF OXYGEN-18 IN MECHANISTIC STUDIES OF DRUG METABOLISM

T. A. BAILLIE and K. S. PRICKETT

Department of Medicinal Chemistry, School of Pharmacy, BG-20, University of
Washington, Seattle, WA 98195, U.S.A.

ABSTRACT

The utility of oxygen-18 as a tracer for probing mechanistic questions in
drug metabolism is illustrated with examples drawn from recent work on the
pathways by which three analogs of 4-pentenoic acid are converted to substituted γ-butyrolactone derivatives in vitro. Despite marked similarities in the
structures of both substrates and products, $^{18}O$ labeling experiments revealed
significant differences in the biotransformation pathways followed for each
compound and afforded valuable information on the identities of enzyme systems
which participated in the respective multi-step sequences.

INTRODUCTION

Elucidation of the molecular processes by which drugs and other foreign compounds undergo biotransformation to either chemically-reactive intermediates or
stable end-products is a fundamental goal in modern drug metabolism studies.
Since the majority of metabolic reactions encountered both in vitro and in vivo
are oxidative in nature, the heavy isotope of oxygen, $^{18}O$, is especially well-
suited for use as a tracer in such investigations. As a consequence, applications of $^{18}O$ labeling techniques, in conjunction with sample analysis by gas
chromatography-mass spectrometry (GC-MS), have grown rapidly in recent years
and have provided, in many cases, detailed insight into the mechanism by which
a parent compound is converted to its terminal metabolite(s) (ref. 1).

As examples of the utility of oxygen-18 in such work, results are presented
from recent studies on the pathways by which three analogs of 4-pentenoic acid
are metabolized in vitro to substituted γ-butyrolactone derivatives. Despite
many similarities in the respective reaction sequences, subtle differences in
metabolic transformations were revealed which would have been difficult to detect by conventional methods. The three compounds of interest in this study
were 2-isopropyl-4-pentenamide (allylisopropylacetamide, AIA), 2-n-propyl-4-
pentenoic acid ($\Delta^4$-valproic acid, $\Delta^4$-VPA) and the ethyl ester of $\Delta^4$-VPA, the
structures of which are shown in Fig. 1.

Metabolism of AIA

The porphyrinogenic agent AIA has been the focus of widespread attention in
recent years in view of its ability to destroy hepatic cytochrome P-450 with

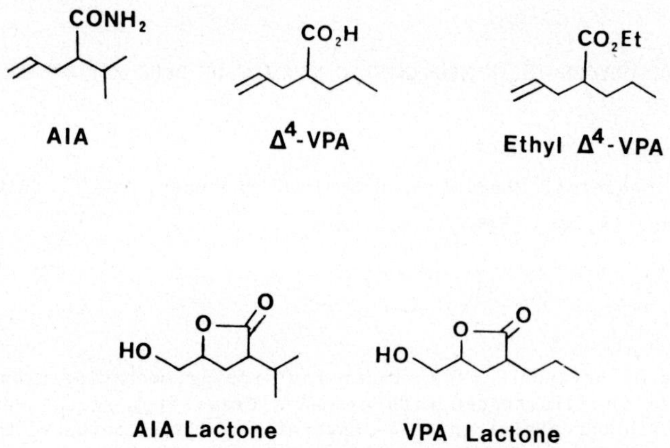

**Fig. 1**    Structures of the compounds referred to in the text.

the concomitant production of abnormal "green" pigments (ref. 2).  It is now known that destruction of cytochrome P-450 results from metabolic "activation" of AIA by the cytochrome P-450 system to a chemically-reactive intermediate, a fraction of which alkylates the prosthetic heme of the cytochrome.  Such alkylation, which takes place at the porphyrin nitrogen atoms, inactivates the enzyme irreversibly and produces the observed pigments (1:1 covalent AIA-heme adducts).  AIA is therefore classified as an enzyme-activated irreversible inhibitor ("suicide substrate" inhibitor) of cytochrome P-450 (ref. 3).  Detailed studies of the inactivation process have highlighted the importance of the terminal olefin group in AIA for suicide substrate activity and interest has focused, therefore, on studying the double bond oxidation pathway of AIA metabolism in order to provide information on the mechanism by which this compound is converted to reactive intermediates.

Cytochrome P-450-catalyzed metabolism of AIA in hepatic microsomal preparations yields 3-isopropyl-5-hydroxymethyltetrahydro-2-furanone (AIA lactone, Fig. 1) as the major product.  Although this compound clearly results from oxidation of the double bond, the precise mechanism by which it is produced from AIA is not known.  The electron impact (EI) mass spectrum of the trimethylsilyl (TMS) ether derivative of the lactone is shown in Fig. 2, which indicates the origin of three structurally-significant fragment ions, viz. m/z 215 ($[M-CH_3]^+$), which retains all 3 oxygen atoms in the metabolite, m/z 117, which retains only the alcohol and ether oxygen atoms, and m/z 103, which derives from the primary trimethylsilyloxy function and contains only the alcohol

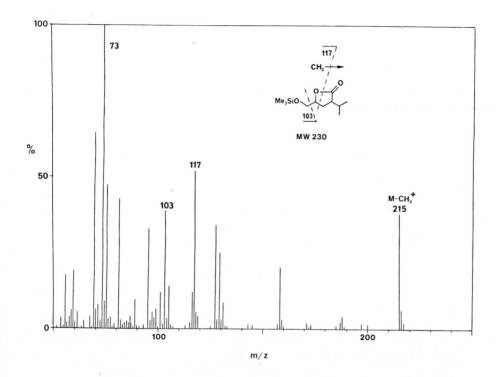

Fig. 2    Mass spectrum of the TMS derivative of the γ-lactone metabolite of AIA.

oxygen atom (ref. 4). These three diagnostic ions were of prime importance in this study because they provided the means whereby sites of oxygen-18 incorporation, resulting from metabolism of AIA in different labeled environments, could be established unambiguously. The $^{18}O$ labeling patterns, in turn, were to provide the key to the origin of this important AIA metabolite.

When AIA was incubated with hepatic microsomes under an atmosphere of $^{18}O_2$ gas, the lactone which was formed was found to have incorporated one atom of the heavy isotope. All three of the above diagnostic ions shifted 2 units to higher mass, indicating that the single atom of $^{18}O$ in this metabolite must be located at the terminal -OH position. Conversely, incubation in $^{18}O$-enriched water (50 atom % excess $^{18}O$), which again led to the incorporation of one atom of oxygen-18, gave a lactone whose mass spectrum exhibited a 1:1 doublet at m/z 217/219, but in which the fragment ions at m/z 103 and 117 were unaffected. This finding indicates that only the carbonyl oxygen of the lactone had become labeled in this incubation (ref. 4).

The results of these experiments using oxygen-18 are fully consistent with the metabolic pathway depicted in Fig. 3. Oxidation of the double bond by cytochrome P-450 generates, initially, an iron-coordinated free radical intermediate which is believed to be responsible for alkylation of the prosthetic heme and destruction of cytochrome P-450 (ref. 3). AIA epoxide, the product expected from successful completion of the double bond oxidation reaction, is proposed as the second intermediate in the pathway and undergoes facile intramolecular rearrangement to afford a protonated iminolactone; this species, in

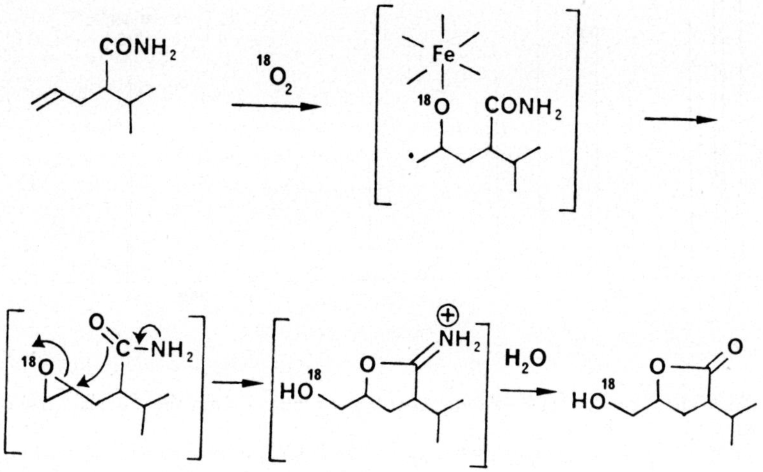

Fig. 3    Metabolic scheme for AIA in rat liver microsomes. Intermediates shown in brackets were not isolated. The sites of incorporation of oxygen from atmospheric $O_2$ are as indicated.

turn, is readily hydrolyzed to the stable $\gamma$-lactone. Since the oxygen inserted by cytochrome P-450 derives exclusively from atmospheric $O_2$, the label from the $^{18}O_2$ gas experiment should end up in the -OH group of the metabolite, while the oxygen atom from water should be present only at the carbonyl position. This is precisely what is found in practice. These results are of toxicological interest in that they demonstrate that three chemically-reactive, potentially toxic, intermediates are formed during the course of AIA metabolism, viz. the heme-bound free radical species, AIA epoxide and the protonated iminolactone.

## Metabolism of $\Delta^4$-VPA and ethyl $\Delta^4$-VPA

$\Delta^4$-VPA is a metabolite of the antiepileptic drug valproic acid and has been shown recently to be strongly hepatotoxic in rats (ref. 5). In light of evidence which suggests that $\Delta^4$-VPA undergoes metabolic activation in mammalian liver to produce toxic intermediates (ref. 6), it became of interest to study in detail the metabolic fate of this compound _in vitro_. Using an identical experimental approach to that described above for the AIA work, it was found that cytochrome P-450-catalyzed double bond oxidation was again the major route of metabolism in rat liver microsomes, the product of which was 3-_n_-propyl-5-hydroxymethyltetrahydro-2-furanone (VPA lactone, Fig. 1). The mass spectrum of the TMS derivative of this metabolite was very similar to that of the AIA lactone (Fig. 2) and the structurally-diagnostic ions at m/z 215, 117 and 103 were again present. Incubations under $^{18}O_2$ gas resulted in incorporation of label in VPA lactone at the -OH group, as they had done in the corresponding experiment with AIA, while no incorporation of heavy isotope occurred during incubation in $H_2^{18}O$. These results indicate that $\Delta^4$-VPA is metabolized by a pathway which is directly analogous to that followed by AIA, the reactive epoxide intermediate in this case being captured by the adjacent carboxylate anion to form the lactone product directly (Fig. 4). This finding suggested an additional experiment, in which an ester derivative of $\Delta^4$-VPA was employed as

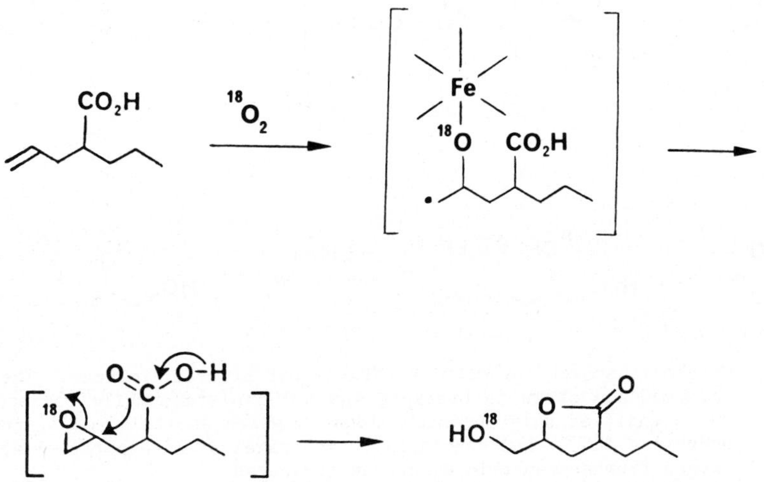

Fig. 4    Metabolic scheme for $\Delta^4$-VPA in rat liver microsomes. Intermediates shown in brackets were not isolated. The sites of incorporation of oxygen from atmospheric $O_2$ are as indicated.

substrate. The rationale for this experiment was that if oxidation of the terminal double bond were again to occur, intramolecular capture of the intermediate epoxide would not be possible since the carboxylate moiety in this substrate lacks an ionizable hydrogen; therefore, a product other than the lactone should result.

When the fate of ethyl $\Delta^4$-VPA in rat liver microsomes was examined, it was found that the major product was a dihydrodiol metabolite, resulting from hydrolytic opening of the epoxide intermediate (data not shown). Interestingly, however, VPA lactone was again formed and experiments with oxygen-18 were carried out in order to probe the mechanism underlying its production. Incubation of ethyl $\Delta^4$-VPA under an atmosphere of $^{18}O_2$ resulted in a lactone which was labeled in the ether oxygen of the ring, while the corresponding species formed in $H_2{}^{18}O$ contained one atom of $^{18}O$ at the -OH position. These results, which are different to those obtained with the free acid form of $\Delta^4$-VPA, show that ethyl $\Delta^4$-VPA is converted in microsomes to the 4,5-epoxide which is then hydrolyzed to the corresponding dihydrodiol (Fig. 5). This hydrolysis occurs via regiospecific attack of water at the terminal carbon of

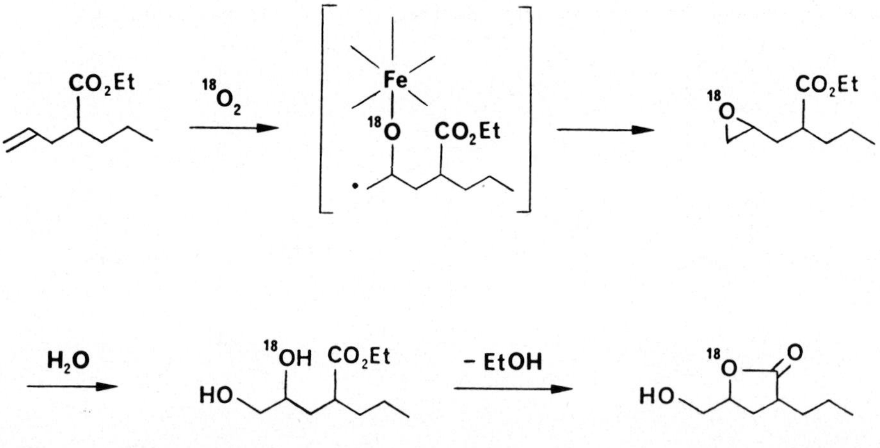

Fig. 5    Metabolic scheme for ethyl $\Delta^4$-VPA in rat liver microsomes. The intermediate shown in brackets was not isolated, while the epoxide was identified only in incubations to which an inhibitor of epoxide hydrolase (TCPO) had been added. The sites of incorporation of oxygen from atmospheric $O_2$ are as indicated.

the oxirane ring, a finding which is consistent with epoxide hydrolase-mediated ring opening of the intermediate, but which is not in accord with a purely chemical hydrolysis reaction which would have led to $^{18}O$ incorporation at both the terminal and internal positions (ref. 7). The dihydrodiol finally cyclizes slowly and spontaneously to yield the lactone as stable end-product. Thus, although both the free acid and ethyl ester forms of $\Delta^4$-VPA undergo metabolism in rat liver microsomes to yield a common product, VPA $\gamma$-lactone, the mechanisms involved are mechanistically quite distinct.

CONCLUSIONS

The examples presented in this paper illustrate the power of oxygen-18 labeling procedures, coupled to sample analysis by GC-MS techniques, for studies of mechanistic aspects of metabolic reactions and for the identification of short-lived, reactive intermediates formed during the course of drug metabolism. Information on the chemical structures of reactive intermediates, and on the nature of the enzyme systems responsible for both their generation and subsequent detoxification, is of paramount importance in gaining an understanding of drug-induced toxicities at the molecular level and in developing rational strategies to circumvent these adverse reactions. Tracer studies with oxygen-18 clearly have an important role to play in drug metabolism, and their use in the field of biochemical toxicology in particular seems certain to increase in future years (ref. 8).

ACKNOWLEDGEMENTS

We are indebted to Drs. P. R. Ortiz de Montellano (University of California San Francisco) and W. A. Garland (Hoffmann LaRoche, Inc.) for gifts of AIA, and to Mr. W. N. Howald for assistance with the mass spectrometry. These studies were supported by a research grant from the Epilepsy Foundation of America and by National Institutes of Health Research Grants GM 32165 and AM 30699.

REFERENCES
1   T. A. Baillie, Pharmacol. Rev., 33 (1981) 81-132.
2   P. R. Ortiz de Montellano and B. A. Mico, Arch. Biochem. Biophys., 206 (1981) 43-50.
3   P. R. Ortiz de Montellano and M. A. Correia, Ann. Rev. Pharmacol. Toxicol., 23 (1983) 481-503.
4   K. S. Prickett and T. A. Baillie, Biomed. Mass Spectrom., 11 (1984) 320-331.
5   J. W. Kesterson, G. R. Granneman and J. M. Machinist, Hepatology, 4 (1984) 1143-1152.
6   A. W. Rettenmeier, K. S. Prickett, W. P. Gordon, S. M. Bjorge, S.-L. Chang, R. H. Levy and T. A. Baillie, Drug Metab. Dispos., 13 (1985) 81-96.
7   R. P. Hanzlik, M. Edelman, W. J. Michaely and G. Scott, J. Amer. Chem. Soc., 98 (1976), 1952-1955.
8   S. D. Nelson, in W. P. Duncan and A. B. Susán (Eds.), Synthesis and Applications of Isotopically Labeled Compounds, Elsevier, Amsterdam, 1983, pp. 89-94.

*Synthesis and Applications of Isotopically Labeled Compounds 1985.*
Proceedings of the Second International Symposium, Kansas City, MO, U.S.A.,
3—6 September 1985, R.R. Muccino (Ed.), 77—82
© 1986 Elsevier Science Publishers B.V., Amsterdam — Printed in The Netherlands

THE USE OF DEUTERIUM LABELLING IN STUDIES OF PROTEIN AND DNA ALKYLATION

P.B. FARMER, I. BIRD and D.E.G. SHUKER

MRC Toxicology Unit, MRC Laboratories, Woodmansterne Road, Carshalton, Surrey,
SM5 4EF, England.

ABSTRACT

Deuterium labelling has been used to develop methods for monitoring exposure to genotoxic agents. In vivo protein modification (determined by levels of methylated amino acids in haemoglobin) and nucleic acid modification (determined by levels of urinary 7-methyl guanine) has been studied using trideutero-methylating agents or precursors. Deuterium labelled amino acids were used as internal standards in the GC-MS quantitation of modified residues in haemoglobin arising from exposure to alkylating agents such as ethylene oxide, propylene oxide and various methylating agents.

INTRODUCTION

A large proportion of environmental mutagens and carcinogens are alkylating agents, or are converted by metabolism in vivo to alkylating agents. These compounds yield covalently bound adducts with nucleophiles encountered within the cell. It is generally believed that alkylation of specific bases in DNA is responsible for the genotoxic lesion, although extensive alkylation of proteins also occurs. The study of alkylation of nucleic acids and proteins by alkylating carcinogens has been greatly aided by the use of isotopes, both radiolabelled and stable and, in particular, by the use of deuterated compounds.

One of the first reported applications of deuterium labelling in the study of carcinogen metabolism was that of Lijinsky et al[1], who investigated the in vivo interaction of the methylating carcinogen dimethylnitrosamine with DNA and RNA using the hexadeuterated analogue $(CD_3)_2NNO$ and found that the $CD_3$ group was transferred intact to the N-7 position of guanine in the nucleic acids. Sussmuth et al[2] and Nagasawa et al[3] showed similar reactions for N-methyl-N[1]-nitro-N-nitrosoguanidine and for 5-(3-methyl-1-triazeno) imidazole-4-carboxamide respectively. The mechanism of alkylation by the chemotherapeutic nitrogen mustards and nitrosoureas has also been studied with selectively deuterated compounds. For example the intermediacy of an aziridinium ion in the alkylation process by phosphoramide mustard has been demonstrated by studies of the reaction of selectively deuterated analogues with ethanethiol[4]. In some cases a deuterium-labelled carcinogen will interact with a nucleophilic target site at a lower rate than that for the unlabelled carcinogen. This occurs when a carbon-deuterium bond is broken in a rate-limiting metabolic step. For example, a reduction of carcinogenicity of at least 5-fold has been reported for $3,3,5,5-d_4$ 4-nitrosomorpholine as compared to the unlabelled material[5]. The demonstrated presence of such isotope effects on tumourigenic or mutagenic properties has provided powerful evidence for the importance of the metabolic activation processes for many carcinogens (e.g. dimethylnitrosamine[6] and 3-methylcholanthrene[7]). Similarly, isotope effects on the anti-tumour effects of deuterated analogues of the alkylating agent cyclophosphamide have aided identification of the metabolic step leading to the active alkylating species[8].

In addition to these uses of deuterium-labelled alkylating agents for studies of mechanism of action, the labelled analogues have been extensively used as internal standards for mass spectrometric quantification of the unlabelled compounds in biological fluids.

Examples of both of these applications of deuterated carcinogens, taken from our recent work, will be given in this paper. Quantification will be exemplified by our determinations of the reaction products of several simple carcinogens (e.g. ethylene oxide, dimethylnitrosamine and acrylamide) with amino acids in proteins, and mechanistic studies by our investigations of the production of methylating carcinogens by the in vivo nitrosation of N-methyl compounds (identified by the detection of stable isotope labelled methylation products on proteins and nucleic acids).

METHODS

Syntheses of deuterated carcinogen-amino acid adducts.

The intermediate benzyloxyacetic acid has proved to be extremely useful in our syntheses of deuterated carcinogen-amino acid adducts. Deuterium labels have been incorporated by exchange with sodium deuteroxide and/or by reduction with lithium aluminium deuteride/hydride (Scheme 1) to give appropriately labelled 2-benzyloxyethanol.

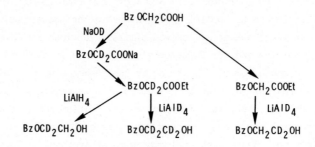

Scheme 1. Syntheses of deuterated 2-benzyloxyethanols.

These labelled precursors can be converted (Scheme 2) to N-(2-hydroxyethyl) histidine and S-(2-hydroxyethyl) cysteine (ethylene oxide-histidine and cysteine reaction products). Syntheses of S-(2-carboxamidoethyl) cysteine (acrylamide-cysteine reaction product) and S-(2-chloroethyl) cysteine (ethylene dichloride reaction product) are in progress.

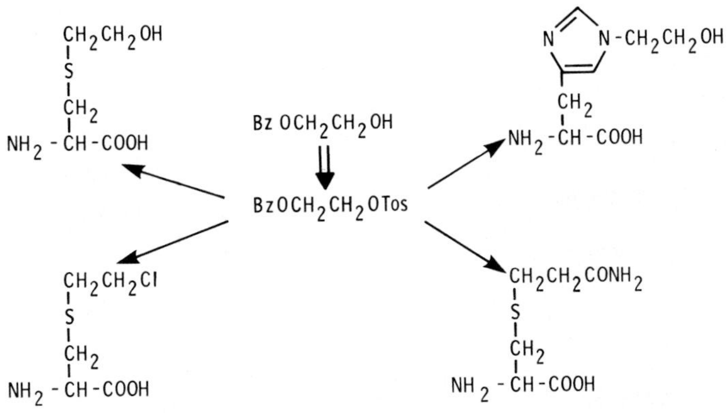

$$
\begin{array}{ccc}
\begin{array}{c}
CH_2CH_2OH \\
| \\
S \\
| \\
CH_2 \\
| \\
NH_2-CH-COOH
\end{array}
& Bz\,OCH_2CH_2OH &
\begin{array}{c}
\text{(imidazole)} N\!-\!CH_2CH_2OH \\
| \\
CH_2 \\
| \\
NH_2-CH-COOH
\end{array}
\\
& \Downarrow & \\
& BzOCH_2CH_2OTos & \\
\begin{array}{c}
CH_2CH_2Cl \\
| \\
S \\
| \\
CH_2 \\
| \\
NH_2-CH-COOH
\end{array}
& &
\begin{array}{c}
CH_2CH_2CONH_2 \\
| \\
S \\
| \\
CH_2 \\
| \\
NH_2-CH-COOH
\end{array}
\end{array}
$$

Scheme 2. Conversion of **2-benzyloxyethanol** into variously substituted alkylated amino acids.

Compounds containing the trideuteromethyl group

The structures of the $CD_3$-labelled compounds used in our studies are shown in Scheme 3. The syntheses of $d_3$-methylmethanesulphonate[9], $d_6$-aminopyrine[10], $d_3$-cimetidine[11] and $d_6$-pyrilamine[12] have been described in detail elsewhere.

Analytical methods

Genotoxic damage by alkylating carcinogens can be monitored either indirectly via determination of alkylated residues in proteins or more directly via levels of urinary purine adducts which may be, in part, derived from modified nucleic acids.

The monitoring of carcinogen-protein adducts is normally achieved with 10 mg samples of globin (blood concentration is ca.150 mg/ml in humans). Deuterated carcinogen-amino acid adduct is added as internal standard (25 ng - 1 µg, depending upon the analysis). The methods for determining methylated products have previously been reported [13], and these methods have now been developed further for the study of more complex alkyl groups (e.g. 2-hydroxyethyl, 2-carboxyethyl etc). An example of analytical reproducibility is $\pm$ 8% for 5 ng 2-hydroxyethylhistidine added to hydrolysed protein (10 mg).

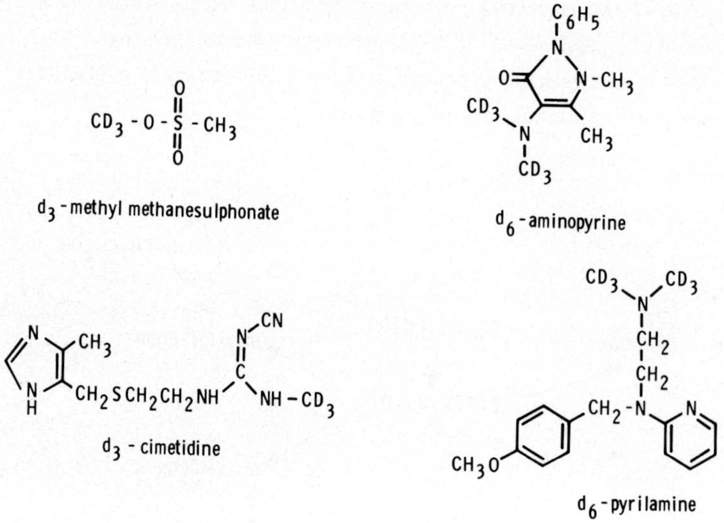

Scheme 3. Structures of $CD_3$-labelled compounds.

Details of the analysis of urinary 7-methyl guanine (7-MeG) have been described elsewhere[9].

Recently, studies have been initiated using a VG Analytical 70 MS-MS instrument, using direct insertion of the samples into the mass spectrometer source, and obtaining collision spectra of the alkylated products.

RESULTS AND DISCUSSION

As indicated in Table 1, dose-related production of haemoglobin adducts has been observed by our techniques following exposure of animals and/or humans to ethylene oxide, propylene oxide, acrylamide, and a variety of methylating agents. The limit of detection of the exposure determinations is frequently difficult to determine owing to the presence of background levels of naturally occurring alkylated amino acids.

The main advantage that we have observed for using labelled internal standards (as opposed to say homologues) is the greater linearity of calibration curves, as the deuterated analogue is presumably acting as a carrier for the unlabelled compound throughout the work-up procedure.

TABLE 1

Some examples of haemoglobin-carcinogen adducts studied by GC-MS selected ion monitoring.

| Carcinogen | Amino acid adduct | Reference |
|---|---|---|
| Ethylene oxide | $N^\tau$-(2-hydroxyethyl) histidine | 14 |
| Propylene oxide | $N^\tau$-(2-hydroxypropyl) histidine | 15 |
| Dimethyl nitrosamine. Methyl methane-sulphonate. | S-methylcysteine | 16 |
| Acrylamide | S-(3-amino-3-oxopropyl) cysteine | 17 |

In the case of urinary alkylated purines naturally occurring background levels are found e.g. 7-methyl guanine (ca. 100-150 µg/day in rats). An unambiguous identification of carcinogen-derived methylation products could be achieved by the use of stable isotope labels in the carcinogen methyl groups. We have adopted this approach with the compounds shown in Scheme 3 which are either directly acting methylating agents (methyl methanesulphonate) or compounds activated by nitrosation and/or metabolism (e.g. aminopyrine, cimetidine or pyrilamine). Determinations of the extent of formation of trideuteromethylated adducts have been made by determining the $d_3:d_0$ ratio (i.e. carcinogen induced:natural methyl adduct) and comparing this with the $d_3:d_0$. ratio obtained after addition of a known amount of $d_3$ or $d_0$-species. Solution of the resulting simultaneous equations yields the amount of the $d_3-$ and the $d_0-$ methylated adducts. We have confirmed the finding of Lijinsky et al[1] that $d_6$-dimethylnitrosamine (liberated in our case from $d_6$-AP and nitrite combinations) produces $d_3$-labelled adducts[9]. As indicated in the introduction our estimations of exposure to methylating agents activated by metabolism may be conservative when the deuterated analogues are studied, owing to possible isotope effects on the metabolism. For microsomal metabolism of $d_6$-dimethylnitrosamine isotope effects of 1.6 and 3.8 have been reported for the Michaelis constant and maximum velocity respectively.[18] However, it remains to be determined whether such an isotope effect manifests itself as a change in the cumulative amount of excreted alkylated purines in vivo.

Demonstration of deuterated protein or nucleic acid alkylation products following administration of a deuterated potential carcinogen is strongly indicative of the occurrence of genotoxic reactions. For the compounds in Scheme 3, we have demonstrated these reactions for $d_3$-methyl methanesulphonate and for $d_6$-aminopyrine (in combination with nitrite) but not for $d_3$-cimetidine or $d_6$-pyrilamine. Studies with human volunteers should be more ethically acceptable using deuterated analogues of potentially carcinogenic drugs than with radiolabelled compounds. In addition the use of stable isotope labelled precursors enables the unambiguous determination of products by mass spectrometry.

We intend to accelerate the analytical process by the use of MS-MS multiple selected daughter ion monitoring. Initial studies have demonstrated that urinary 7-methylguanine may be detected by daughter ion monitoring with minimal work-up, as compared to our standard procedure for isolation of the alkylated base from urine.

REFERENCES

1  W. Lijinsky, J. Loo and A.E. Ross, Nature, 218 (1968) 1174.
2  R. Sussmuth, R. Haerlin and F. Lingers, Biochem. Biophys. Acta, 269 (1972) 276.
3  H.T. Nagasawa, F.N. Shirota and N.S. Mizuno, Chem.Biol.Interactions, 8 (1974) 403.
4  M. Colvin, R.B. Brundrett, M.N. Kan, I. Jardine and C. Fenselan, Cancer Res., 36 (1976) 1121.
5  W. Lijinsky, H.W. Taylor and L.K. Keefer, J.Natl. Cancer Inst., 57 (1976) 1311.
6  L.K. Keefer, W. Lijinsky and H. Garcia, J. Natl.Cancer Inst., 51 (1973) 299.
7  E. Cavalieri, H. Garcia, P. Mailander and K. Patil, Chem.Biol.Interactions, 11 (1975) 179.
8  P.J. Cox, P. B. Farmer, A.B. Foster, E.D. Gilby and M. Jarman, Cancer Treat.Rep., 60 (1976) 483.
9  D.E.G. Shuker, E. Bailey, S.M. Gorf, J. Lamb and P.B. Farmer, Anal.Biochem.,140 (1984) 270.
10 D.E.G. Shuker, E. Bailey and P.B. Farmer, I.A.R.C. Scientific Publication No. 57, 'N-Nitroso Compounds: Occurrence, Biological Effects and Relevance to Human Cancer', 1984, 589.
11 P.B. Farmer, D.E.G. Shuker and I. Bird, submitted for publication.
12 I. Bird and D.E.G. Shuker, J. Labelled Cpd. and Radio-pharm., 22 (1985) 109.
13 P.B. Farmer, E. Bailey, J.H. Lamb and T.A. Connors, Biomed. Mass Spectrom., 7 (1980) 41.
14 S. Osterman-Golkar, P.B. Farmer, D. Segerback, E. Bailey, C.J. Calleman, K. Svensson and L. Ehrenberg, Teratogenesis, Carcinogenesis and Mutagenesis, 3 (1983) 395.
15 S. Osterman-Golkar, E. Bailey, P.B. Farmer, S.M. Gorf and J.H. Lamb, Scand.J. Work Environ.Health 10 (1984) 99.
16 E. Bailey, T.A. Connors, P.B. Farmer, S.M. Gorf and J. Rickard, Cancer Res., 41 (1981) 2514.
17 E. Bailey and P.B. Farmer, Human Toxicol., (1985) in press.
18 D. Dagani and M.C. Archer, J. Natl. Cancer Inst., 57 (1976) 955.

*Synthesis and Applications of Isotopically Labeled Compounds 1985.*
Proceedings of the Second International Symposium, Kansas City, MO, U.S.A.,
3—6 September 1985, R.R. Muccino (Ed.), 83—88

RACEMIC RADIOLABELS IN CHIRAL BINDING INTERACTIONS

M. SIMONYI

Central Research Institute for Chemistry, The Hungarian Academy of
Sciences, Budapest Pf 17, H-1525 (Hungary)

ABSTRACT
    In order to overcome difficulties arising from the lack of
labeled enantiomers, methods are presented for the demonstration
of enantioselectivity in the binding of racemic benzodiazepines to
human serum albumin. These include enantioselective labeling of
racemates by stepwise and stationary ultrafiltration, the combination of ultrafiltration with CD spectroscopy, and affinity chromatography. Spontaneously racemizing compounds can neither be
permanently resolved, nor be selectively labeled, still, their
chiral nature in binding interactions should be taken into account.

INTRODUCTION
    Chirality is a highly neglected property of pharmaceutical
agents. The negligence is reflected by the general omission of ($\pm$)
prefixes for racemic compounds listed in drug references. Hence,
generic and trade names do not discriminate an achiral structure
from a racemate. Since the occurrence of racemic agents is as
frequent as one drug out of every four (ref.1), all too often
compounds of racemic composition are applied in biological systems.
Without clear realization of the differential actions of enantiomers, studies with racemic drugs could give rise to "expensive
highly sophisticated pseudoscientific nonsense" (ref.2).
    The problem of detecting enantioselective action is substantial
if pure enantiomers are not available. This paper deals with
methods applicable to studying the stereoselective binding of
racemic benzodiazepines to human serum albumin (HSA).

STEREOSELECTIVE LABELING OF RACEMATES
    This method can be performed if both radiolabeled and
nonlabeled racemates are available. A further requirement is the
application of a chiral adsorbent (HSA) that stereoselectively
binds the enantiomers (ref.3).

Stepwise ultrafiltration
    In a solution of HSA and racemic oxazepam acetate ($rac$-OAc)
two binding equilibria are reached simultaneously for the
enantiomers. The fraction $\alpha$ of the ligand free at equilibrium is
then a composite quantity given by equation (1), where $c_f$ and $c_o$
are the free and total ligand concentrations, while $\alpha_l$ and $\alpha_d$

stand for unbound fractions of levo- and dextrorotatory enantiomers, respectively.

$$\alpha = \frac{c_f}{c_o} = \frac{\alpha_l + \alpha_d}{2} \tag{1}$$

In a simple ultrafiltration step protein and bound ligand are
concentrated while free drug is collected in the filtrate. $rac$-OAc
is partially resolved both in filtrate and retentate in
complementary extent; the racemic composition can be restored again
by simply combining filtrate and retentate in the ultrafiltration
cell.

In two parallel filtration experiments with racemic ligand and
protein solution of identical composition in equal volumes $(V_o)$
radioactive ligand is applied in one cell whereas the ordinary
isotopomer is in the other. After the collection of identical volumes
of the filtrates $(V_f)$ enantioselective labeling is easily achieved
by quantitative cross-mixing of radioactive filtrate with radioinactive retentate and $vice\ versa$ (ref.4). The enantiomer of lower
binding affinity has relatively higher specific radioactivity in
the cell containing the radioactive filtrate (filtrate line) and
the opposite is true for the other cell in which the radioactivity
comes from the retentate (retentate line).

The stereoselectivity of labeling is clearly manifested by a
subsequent ultrafiltration step with the same pair of cells. The
fraction of radioactivity appearing in the filtrate of the second
step will be different from that of the first, and characteristic
of each cell; the filtrate line is associated with a higher radioactive degree of dissociation, whereas the retentate line has a
lower radioactive fraction. The extent of stereoselectivity in
labeling can be improved in further subsequent ultrafiltration
steps. Keeping the filtrate volumes constant throughout the operation, the radioactive degrees of dissociation in the i-th step of
filtrate and retentate lines are given by equations (2) and (3),
respectively. For i = 1, both are reduced to equation (1).

$$\alpha_{i,f} = \frac{\alpha_l^i + \alpha_d^i}{\alpha_l^{i-1} + \alpha_d^{i-1}} \ ; \quad \lim_{i \to \infty} \alpha_{i,f} = \alpha_l, \text{ if } \alpha_l > \alpha_d \tag{2}$$

$$\alpha_{i,r} = \frac{\alpha_l q_l^{i-1} + \alpha_d q_d^{i-1}}{q_l^{i-1} + q_d^{i-1}}, \quad q_l = 1 - \alpha_l \frac{V_f}{V_o}, \quad q_d = 1 - \alpha_d \frac{V_f}{V_o} \tag{3}$$

$$\lim_{i \to \infty} \alpha_{i,r} = \alpha_d, \text{ if } \alpha_l > \alpha_d$$

The results of two four-step series (Table 1) represent the applicability of the method (ref.4). The enantiomeric α values indicate the binding strength of (+)OAc to HSA to be 5 to 6 times as high as that of the levorotatory antipode.

TABLE 1

Labeling of *rac*-oxazepam acetate by four-step ultrafiltration

| [*rac*-OAc](μM) | 73.0 | | 53.0 | |
|---|---|---|---|---|
| [HSA](μM) | 105.0 | | 45.5 | |
| α | 0.35 | | 0.55 | |
| | filtrate line | retentate line | filtrate line | retentate line |
| $\alpha_2$ | 0.50 | 0.24 | 0.62 | 0.49 |
| $\alpha_3$ | 0.59 | 0.21 | 0.70 | 0.46 |
| $\alpha_4$ | 0.57 | 0.17 | 0.73 | 0.42 |
| $\alpha_l$ | 0.59 | | 0.76 | |
| $\alpha_d$ | | 0.12 | | 0.34 |

## Stationary ultrafiltration

In the retentate line of the preceding method the ultrafiltration cell containing the radioactive retentate is fed by radioinactive filtrate. The stepwise process outlined above can be replaced by continuous operation (ref.5) if the feed solution entering the cell has the same composition (except for radioactivity) as the radioactive filtrate leaving the cell. The total (radioactive + radioinactive) ligand concentration is then constant throughout the experiment resulting in isotopic replacement of the ligand involved in stationary binding equilibria (ref.6). The concentration of radioactivity in the filtrate ($c_f^*$) for an achiral ligand is given by equation (4),

$$c_f^* = \alpha c_o \exp\left(-\frac{\alpha x}{V}\right) \tag{4}$$

where x is the volume of the filtrate and V is the volume of the cell. For a racemic ligand involved in simultaneous enantiomeric equilibria the radioactivity of the filtrate as a function of filtrate volume is expressed by a sum of exponentials:

$$c_f^* = \frac{c_o}{2}\left[\alpha_l \exp\left(-\frac{\alpha_l x}{V}\right) + \alpha_d \exp\left(-\frac{\alpha_d x}{V}\right)\right] \tag{5}$$

indicating the possibility of enantioselective labeling. When x/V is sufficiently high, the only term remaining in equation (5) contains the lower enantiomeric $\alpha$ value as a result of complete isotopic replacement for the enantiomer having lower binding affinity (i.e. higher $\alpha$ value). Hence, the radioactive degree of dissociation, $\alpha^*$ depends on the filtrate volume as given by equation (6),

$$\alpha^*(x) = \frac{\alpha_l \exp(-\frac{\alpha_l x}{V}) + \alpha_d \exp(-\frac{\alpha_d x}{V})}{\exp(-\frac{\alpha_l x}{V}) + \exp(-\frac{\alpha_d x}{V})} \tag{6}$$

which, for x = 0, becomes identical with equation (1). The least squares fit of experimental data to equations (5) and (6) provides the values of $\alpha_l$ and $\alpha_d$ (ref.7). This method indicated the binding of (+)OAc to be 6 times stronger than that of (-)OAc to HSA.

## ULTRAFILTRATION COMBINED WITH CD SPECTROSCOPY

The partial resolution of a racemate achieved by a single ultrafiltration step can be determined experimentally by measuring the optical activity of the ligand recovered from both filtrate and retentate (ref.8). Since ultrafiltrate is protein-free it contains the free ligand only whereas the bound drug present in the retentate is always contaminated with the unbound fraction. This is reflected by equations expressing the optical purity of filtrate ($\xi_f$) and of retentate ($\xi_r$) the latter only being dependent on filtrate volume (cf. equation 3):

$$\xi_f = \frac{\alpha_d - \alpha_l}{\alpha_d + \alpha_l} \quad ; \quad \xi_r = \frac{q_d - q_l}{q_d + q_l} \tag{7}$$

The basic equation of the method relates experimental parameters ($\alpha$, $\xi_f$ and $\xi_r$) to enantiomeric $\alpha$ values,

$$\alpha = \frac{\alpha_d + \alpha_l}{2} = \frac{V_o}{V_f} \frac{\xi_r}{\xi_r - \xi_f} \tag{8}$$

and offers three possibilities to determine $\alpha_d$ and $\alpha_l$ by using any pair of the three experimental parameters. The enantioselectivity obtained by this method for the binding of rac-OAc to HSA is 6 to 7 (ref.8) in agreement with the results of stereoselective labeling experiments.

## AFFINITY CHROMATOGRAPHY

Optical purity measurements require the CD spectral data of the
enantiomers, hence the resolution of the racemate proved unavoidable even for the application of the last method. The enantioselective binding affinity of HSA towards benzodiazepines makes
chromatographic resolution possible by the protein immobilized in
hydrophilic Sepharose gel (ref.9).

Several esters of oxazepam can be completely resolved yielding
both enantiomers in optically pure form (ref.10). Besides this
series of compounds (1) having the center of asymmetry at C-3,
other structures (2,3) could also be resolved on HSA-Sepharose
column (refs. 11-12).

| 1 | 2 | 3 |

It is, however, not always possible to separate structurally
related pharmacological entities of different binding ability
towards protein binding sites. A common example is oxazepam
(1, R = OH) itself subject to fast racemization in aqueous solution
(ref.13). Evidence for the enantioselective binding of short lived
enantiomers has been obtained by affinity chromatography (ref.10)
suggesting stability for the bound species. The resolution of
oxazepam enantiomers is transitory by this method since desorbed
molecules racemize again. It is the rate of racemization that
controls the detection of enantioselectivity. If chromatographic
separation can compete with racemization, the compound elutes in
the form of entirely separated fractions. This can be achieved for
oxazepam and related compounds by fast elution on a short column
(ref.14) but cannot be attained for diazepam the conformational
racemization of which is too fast to be intercepted by chromatography (ref.15).

The conformational inversion of the diazepine ring is, however,
not always as fast as in the case of diazepam. The interconversion
of the conformations of S-tofizopam is slow enough to be followed
by chromatography owing to the different binding strength of

$\underline{S}(-)$ and $S(+)$ conformers towards HSA (ref.16).

The minimum lifetime, allowing for the chromatographic detection of racemizing enantiomers or different conformers, can be estimated to be on the second to minute time scale. It is, of course, not possible to label selectively interconverting species. It is important, however, to consider their selective action in chiral environment, e.g. in binding interactions, when the free fraction of the drug is again a composite quantity.

$$\alpha = \frac{2\alpha_d \alpha_l}{\alpha_d + \alpha_l} \tag{9}$$

The neglection of chirality for ligands racemic by their chemical nature leads to an apparent binding constant which is erroneous by a factor of 2 in respect of the active enantiomer (ref.15).

REFERENCES

1. M. Simonyi, Med.Res.Rev., 4 (1984) 359-413.
2. E.J. Ariens, Eur.J.Clin.Pharmacol., 26 (1984) 663-668.
3. M. Simonyi, I. Fitos, I. Kovács and Zs. Tegyey, Hung, Patent No. 180.503, 1979.
4. M. Simonyi, I. Fitos and Zs. Tegyey, J.C.S.Chem.Comm., 1980, 1105-1106.
5. W.F. Blatt, S.M. Robinson and H.J. Bixler, Anal.Biochem., 26 (1968) 151-173.
6. M. Simonyi, I. Fitos, Zs. Tegyey and L. Ötvös, Biochem.Biophys. Res.Commun., 97 (1980) 1-7.
7. Stationary ultrafiltration, Program No. 04730D, Hewlett-Packard 67/97/41 Users'Library, 1982.
8. M. Simonyi, I. Fitos, J. Kajtár and M. Kajtár, Biochem.Biophys. Res.Commun., 109 (1982) 851-857.
9. C. Lagercrantz, T. Larsson and H. Karlsson, Anal.Biochem., 99 (1979) 352-364.
10. I. Fitos, M. Simonyi, Zs. Tegyey, L. Ötvös, J. Kajtár and M. Kajtár, J.Chromatogr. 259 (1983) 494-498.
11. I. Fitos and M. Simonyi, Experientia, 39 (1983) 591-592.
12. M. Simonyi, J. Visy, I. Kovács and M. Kajtár, in H.C. van der Plas, L. Ötvös and M. Simonyi (Eds.), Bio-Organic Heterocycles, Akadémiai Kiadó-Elsevier, Budapest-Amsterdam, 1984, pp.255-259.
13. M.Stromar, V.Sunjic, T.Kovac, L.Klasinc and F. Kajfez, Croat. Chem.Acta, 46 (1974) 265-274.
14. I. Fitos, Zs. Tegyey, M. Simonyi, I. Sjöholm, T. Larsson and C. Lagercrantz, Biochem.Pharmac., in press.
15. I. Fitos, M. Simonyi, Zs. Tegyey, M. Kajtár and L. Ötvös, Arch.Pharmazie, in press.
16. M. Simonyi and I. Fitos, Biochem.Pharmac., 32 (1983) 1917-1920.

*Synthesis and Applications of Isotopically Labeled Compounds 1985.*
Proceedings of the Second International Symposium, Kansas City, MO, U.S.A.,
3—6 September 1985, R.R. Muccino (Ed.), 89—94
© 1986 Elsevier Science Publishers B.V., Amsterdam — Printed in The Netherlands

EXTREME ISOTOPE EFFECTS AND REACTION BRANCHING IN STUDIES OF
REACTION MECHANISMS

P. AHLBERG[1] and A. THIBBLIN[2]

[1]Department of Organic Chemistry, University of Göteborg,
Kemivägen 3, S-412 96 Göteborg (Sweden)

[2]Department of Organic Chemistry, University of Uppsala,
P.O. Box 571, S-751 21 Uppsala (Sweden)

ABSTRACT

To differentiate between one-step reactions and stepwise processes is a common problem in reaction mechanistic studies. Under
certain conditions isotope effects offer a powerful tool to elucidate such questions. The method which is based upon reaction
branching allows us to differentiate between such mechanisms. For
instance, in reaction systems showing base-initiated elimination
reaction competing with base-catalyzed 1,3-hydron transfer unusually large ($k_H/k_D$ ~90) and small isotope effects have been observed in evidence of stepwise mechanisms. Thus not only tunneling
but also reaction branching may result in very large isotope effects. Large isotope effects reported in the literature and proposed to be due to tunneling are readily explained by the model.

Central in the study of reaction mechanisms is to find out if
a reaction makes use of a one-step mechanism (Scheme 1) or one
involving two or more steps (Scheme 2).

$$S \rightarrow P \qquad\qquad\qquad S \rightarrow I \rightarrow P$$

Scheme 1                             Scheme 2

This problem is a challenging one, in particular for reactions
whose potential intermediates are so short lived that they can
not be directly observed. Their presence on the reaction coordinate has to be inferred from indirect evidence. E.g. in solvolysis reactions it is common that two or more products are formed
from one substrate due to substitution, elimination and rearrangement reactions. The wish to account for observations by a mechanism as simple as possible and the relationship between these reaction products has led to the proposition of a mechanism with a

common carbocationic intermediate for the reactions (Scheme 3) rather than assuming that they are formed by parallel independent routes (Scheme 4). However, minor - if any - evidence really proves that the reactions are coupled by the very same cationic intermediate.

$$S \to I \to \begin{matrix} \nearrow P_1 \\ P_2 \\ \searrow P_3 \end{matrix} \qquad\qquad S \begin{matrix} \nearrow P_1 \\ \to P_2 \\ \searrow P_3 \end{matrix}$$

Scheme 3            Scheme 4

To be able to solve similar problems as the one just presented we have developed a novel reaction mechanistic tool by which it is possible to detect and study the role of short lived intermediates in the reactions. The method is based upon a combination of kinetic isotope effects and reaction branching. It was invented during investigation of mechanisms of base-initiated elimination reactions and the role of ion-pairs in such reactions (ref. 1).

In the following this novel method is described and some of the results that we have obtained so far are indicated. Other unusually large isotope effects which have been reported in the literature are conveniently explained within the theoretical framework of the method rather than being due to tunneling.

A reaction system has been designed in which the substrate has the possibility to undergo both base-promoted elimination and base-catalyzed 1,3-proton transfer (Scheme 5).

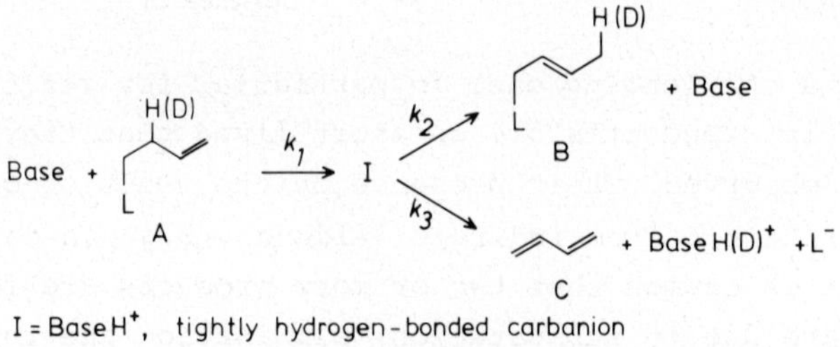

$$\text{Base} + \underset{A}{\overset{H(D)}{\Big|}} \xrightarrow{k_1} I \underset{k_3}{\overset{k_2}{\rlap{\diagup}\diagdown}} \underset{B}{\overset{H(D)}{\phantom{.}}} + \text{Base} \\ C + \text{Base H(D)}^+ + L^-$$

I = Base H⁺, tightly hydrogen-bonded carbanion

Scheme 5

In both of these reactions the 1-proton has to be abstracted. If
the two reactions are not coupled with common intermediates as in
Scheme 5, but are parallel reactions, we would expect a normal
hydrogen isotope effect for each of the reactions. However, if the
reactions are coupled, extreme hydrogen isotope effects may be observed, as will be indicated below.

According to the steady-state approximation applied to the intermediate in Scheme 5, the observed rate constant for the 1,3-
-proton transfer reaction ($k_{AB}$) depends on the mechanistic rate
constants, as in eq. 1.

$$k_{AB} = k_1 \frac{k_2}{k_2 + k_3} \tag{1}$$

For the observed deuterium isotope effect we obtain the expression
in eq. 2.

$$\frac{k_{AB}^H}{k_{AB}^D} = \frac{k_1^H}{k_1^D} \times \frac{k_2^H}{k_2^D} \times \frac{k_2^D + k_3^D}{k_2^H + k_3^H} \tag{2}$$

Thus, the observed rearrangement isotope effect is a product of
two primary isotope effects, $k_1^H/k_1^D$ and $k_2^H/k_2^D$, and a third factor,
the value of which depends on the relative importance of elimination from the hydrogen-bonded carbanions and the collapse of the
intermediate to rearranged material. If $k_3 \gg k_2$, this factor is expected to be close to 1, since there is no proton transfer in the
elimination of the hydrogen-bonded carbanion ion-pair, and thus
$k_3^H/k_3^D \sim 1$. Accordingly, as a consequence of coupling of the reactions in Scheme 5, we predict an extreme rearrangement isotope
effect, since it is the product of two primary isotope effects.
Similarly it is easy to show that the isotope effect on the elimination reaction $k_{AC}^H/k_{AC}^D$ may be unusually small as a consequence
of reaction branching.

The reactions of the allylic systems 1-(2-acetoxy-2-propyl)-
indene and $(1,3-{}^2H_2)$-1-(2-acetoxy-2-propyl)indene have been studied extensively in the solvents methanol, methanol-water and DMSO-
-water and with more or less sterically hindered tertiary amines

of varying basicity and with phenolates. Isotope effects $k_{AB}^H/k_{AB}^D$
ranging from ~7 to ~90 have been obtained. The results demonstrate the intermediacy of tightly hydrogen bonded intermediates. Internal consistency of the interpretation of the results demanded
the postulation of two intermediates in non-equilibrium with each
other. The ion-pair mechanisms and stereochemistry of the elimination reactions have been studied using threo- or erythro-1-(1-
-acetoxyethyl)indene (refs. 1 and 2).

Other isotope effects that we have obtained and which are conveniently explained by the model are in: sec. amidine catalyzed
1,3-hydron transfer of substituted propenes, acetic acid and sec.
amidine catalyzed rearrangement of $\beta,\gamma$ to $\alpha,\beta$-unsaturated ketones,
acid catalyzed $\alpha$-halogenation of amidines by tetrahalomethanes
(ref. 3c) and in some solvolysis reactions (ref.3d).

Cram and co-workers have in their studies of the mechanism of
the base catalyzed methylene-azamethine rearrangement observed a
deuterium isotope effect of 34±19 and 27, respectively (ref. 4).
These results are also easily understood using our model. Caldin
and co-workers found in their investigations of tunneling in proton transfer reactions of 4-nitrophenylnitromethane with bases
containing the imine group extreme deuterium isotope effects, e.g.
$k^H/k^D$ = 45 (ref. 5). However, their main origin appears to be reaction branching and not tunneling as proposed.

The probe has been generalized (ref. 2e). In Scheme 6 the intermediate (I) is assumed to be reversibly formed. The steady
state approximation leads to equations (3) and (4).

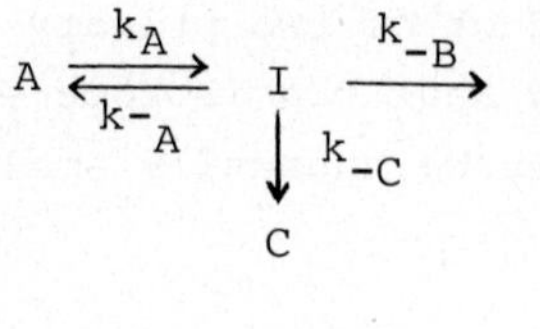

$$A \underset{k_{-A}}{\overset{k_A}{\rightleftarrows}} I \overset{k_{-B}}{\longrightarrow} B$$
$$\downarrow k_{-C}$$
$$C$$

Scheme 6

$$\frac{k_{AB}^{H}}{k_{AB}^{D}} = \frac{k_{A}^{H}}{k_{A}^{D}} \times \frac{k_{-B}^{H}}{k_{-B}^{D}} \times \frac{k_{-A}^{D} + k_{-B}^{D} + k_{-C}^{D}}{k_{-A}^{H} + k_{-B}^{H} + k_{-C}^{H}} \qquad (3)$$

$$\frac{k_{AC}^{H}}{k_{AC}^{D}} = \frac{k_{A}^{H}}{k_{A}^{D}} \times \frac{k_{-C}^{H}}{k_{-C}^{D}} \times \frac{k_{-A}^{D} + k_{-B}^{D} + k_{-C}^{D}}{k_{-A}^{H} + k_{-B}^{H} + k_{-C}^{H}} \qquad (4)$$

If $k_{-B}^{H}/k_{-B}^{D} > k_{-C}^{H}/k_{-C}^{D}$, then the following result is obtained:

$$\frac{k_{AB}^{H}}{k_{AB}^{D}} > \frac{k_{A}^{H}}{k_{A}^{D}} > \frac{k_{AC}^{H}}{k_{AC}^{D}}$$

Thus we conclude that competition between two processes having different isotope effects and which follow a common rate-limiting step sensitive to isotopic substitution results in an amplified observed isotope effect for the overall reaction which proceeds via the competing process with the largest isotope effect. The other overall reaction will show an attenuated isotope effect. If the isotope effect on the rate-limiting step is substantial, the amplification may yield an unusually large overall isotope effect. Reversibility, on the other hand, decreases the amplification and the attenuation.

There is controversy about the borderline between E2 and E1cB reaction mechanisms. What is the dependence of the mechanism on structure? Do base-promoted elimination reactions make use of both types of mechanisms or is there an exclusive switch of mechanism on crossing the borderline, i.e. do the mechanisms merge on the borderline? Using our probe we have found that also such a potent leaving group as Cl$^{-}$ may eliminate by an E1cB mechanism. We have studied the reaction system shown in Scheme 7 in which 1-(2-chloro--2-propyl)indene is reacted with pyridine in methanol. The base--catalyzed 1,3-proton transfer, i.e. the formation of $\underline{2}$-Cl, shows an unusually large kinetic deuterium isotope effect, $14.6 \pm 1.0$. The extreme deuterium isotope effect is proposed to originate from reaction branching, i.e. that the base-promoted elimination and

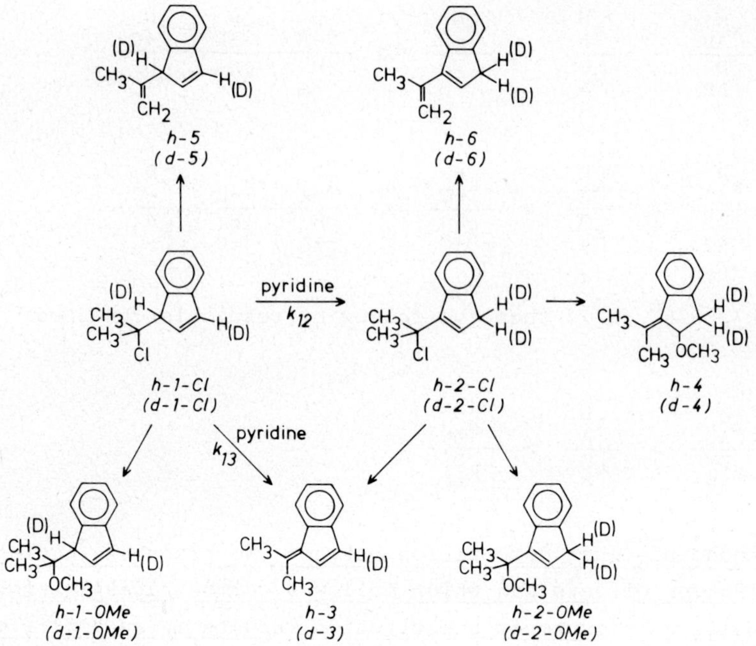

94

Scheme 7

the base-catalyzed rearrangement of <u>1</u>-Cl make use of at least one
common hydrogen-bonded carbanion intermediate (ref. 6).

References
1 (a) P. Ahlberg, Chem. Scr., 3 (1973) 183-189. (b) P. Ahlberg,
Ibid., 4 (1973) 33-39. (c) P. Ahlberg and S. Bengtsson, Ibid.,
6 (1974) 45-46.
2 (a) A. Thibblin and P. Ahlberg, Acta Chem. Scand., (B), 28 (1974)
818-820. (b) A. Thibblin and P. Ahlberg, Ibid., (B), 30 (1976)
555-561. (c) A. Thibblin, S. Bengtsson and P. Ahlberg, J. Chem.
Soc. Perkin Trans., 2 (1977) 1569-1577. (d) A. Thibblin and
P. Ahlberg, J. Am. Chem. Soc., 99 (1977) 7926-7930. (e) A. Thibblin and P. Ahlberg, J. Am. Chem. Soc., 101 (1979) 7311-7317.
(f) A. Thibblin, I. Onyido and P. Ahlberg, Chem. Scr., 19 (1982)
145-148. (g) A. Thibblin, Ibid., 22 (1983) 182-187. (h) A. Thibblin, Ibid., 105 (1983) 853-858. (i) A. Thibblin, Chem. Scr. 15
(1980) 121-127. (j) A. Thibblin, J. Chem. Soc. Chem. Commun.,
(1984) 92-93.
3 (a) M. Ek and P. Ahlberg, to be published. (b) H. Bivehed and
P. Ahlberg, to be published. (c) S. Löfås and P. Ahlberg, J. Am.
Chem. Soc., in press. (d) A. Thibblin, J. Chem. Soc. Perkin
Trans 2, in press.
4 R.D. Guthrie, D.A. Jaeger, W. Meister and D.J. Cram, J. Am. Chem.
Soc., 93 (1971) 5137-5153.
5 E.F. Caldin and S. Mateo, J. Chem. Soc., Faraday Trans. 1, 71
(1975) 1876-1904.
6 M. Ölwegård, I. McEwen, A. Thibblin and P. Ahlberg, J. Am. Chem.
Soc., in press.

*Synthesis and Applications of Isotopically Labeled Compounds 1985.*
Proceedings of the Second International Symposium, Kansas City, MO, U.S.A.,
3–6 September 1985, R.R. Muccino (Ed.), 95–100
© 1986 Elsevier Science Publishers B.V., Amsterdam — Printed in The Netherlands

ISOTOPE EFFECTS ON ISOTOPE EFFECTS:   NEW EXPERIMENTAL CRITERIA FOR TUNNELING
IN SLOW PROTON TRANSFERS[1]

W.H. SAUNDERS, JR.[1] RM. SUBRAMANIAN[2] and R.C. PRICE[1]

**1** Chemistry Department, University of Rochester, Rochester, New York 14627
**2** Chemistry Department, Washington University, St. Louis, Missouri 63130

ABSTRACT

   Secondary β-tritium isotope effects in E2 reactions are often larger than predicted from fractionation factors. Model calculations show that coupling of the bending motions of the non-transferred β-hydrogen with the stretching motion of the transferred β-hydrogen can lead to appreciable tunnel corrections to and abnormal temperature dependence ($A_H/A_T < 1$) of the secondary effect. Experiment confirms the prediction of abnormal temperature dependence. The contribution of tunneling to secondary β-tritium and primary β-carbon isotope effects is predicted to be less when deuterium rather than protium is transferred. Tunneling can cause deviations from the rule of the geometric mean.

SECONDARY β-TRITIUM ISOTOPE EFFECTS

   These effects were determined on 2-arylethyl derivatives tracer-labeled with tritium in the β-position. The following reactions are possible in this system:

$$ArCH_2CH_2X + OR^- \xrightarrow{2k_1} ArCH=CH_2 + ROH + X^- \tag{1}$$

$$ArCHTCH_2X + OR^- \xrightarrow{k_2} ArCH=CH_2 + ROT + X^- \tag{2}$$

$$ArCHTCH_2X + OR^- \xrightarrow{k_3} ArCT=CH_2 + ROH + X^- \tag{3}$$

The desired quantity, $(k_H/k_T)_{sec} = k_1/k_3$, which in turn can be calculated from the activity of the reactant and the activity of the styrene product at low conversions (ref.1).  The results are recorded in Table 1.

TABLE 1

Secondary isotope effects in E2 reactions of $PhCHTCH_2X$ at 50°C.

| Leaving group, X | Base, solvent | $k_1/k_3$[a] | $k_H/k_D$[b] |
|---|---|---|---|
| $NMe_3$ | $EtO^-$/EtOH | $1.259 \pm 0.010$ | 1.17 |
| $NMe_3$ | $OH^-$/30% $Me_2SO$ | $1.235 \pm 0.016$ | 1.16 |
| $NMe_3$ | $OH^-$/40% $Me_2SO$ | $1.250 \pm 0.023$ | 1.17 |
| $NMe_3$ | $OH^-$/50% $Me_2SO$ | $1.243 \pm 0.031$ | 1.16 |
| $NMe_3$[c] | $EtO^-$/EtOH | $1.284 \pm 0.030$ | 1.19 |
| $SMe_2$ | $EtO^-$/EtOH | $1.157 \pm 0.022$ | 1.11 |
| $SMe_2$ | $OH^-$/30% $Me_2SO$ | $1.119 \pm 0.023$ | 1.08 |
| $SMe_2$ | $OH^-$/40% $Me_2SO$ | $1.144 \pm 0.026$ | 1.10 |
| $SMe_2$ | $OH^-$/50% $Me_2SO$ | $1.134 \pm 0.026$ | 1.09 |
| OTs | $t\text{-}BuO^-$/t-BuOH | $1.239 \pm 0.023$ | 1.16 |
| Br | $EtO^-$/EtOH | $1.110 \pm 0.024$ | 1.08 |
| Br | $t\text{-}BuO^-$/t-BuOH | $1.071 \pm 0.026$ | 1.05 |

[a]Deviations are standard deviations.
[b]Calculated from $k_H/k_D = (k_1/k_3)^{1/1.44}$.
[c]For $p\text{-}ClC_6H_4CHTCH_2NMe_3^+$.

It is evident that the isotope effect varies considerably with the nature of the leaving group but very little with the nature of the solvent or base. A reasonable hypothesis would be that the isotope effect measures the extent to which the β-C-H bond has rehybridized from $sp^3$ to $sp^2$ in the transition state. The expected magnitude of such an effect can be reliably estimated from the fractionation factors of Hartshorn and Shiner (ref.2). From these factors the equilibrium constant for equation 4 is 1.124 at 25°C, or 1.11 at 50°C, which

$$CH_3CH_2CH_3 + CH_3CD=CH_2 \rightleftharpoons CH_3CHDCH_3 + CH_3CH=CH_2 \qquad (4)$$

corresponds to a tritium effect of 1.17. These are the values expected for complete rehybridization, and half of the values in Table 1 are significantly greater. We concluded that rehybridization could not be the only factor contributing to the isotope effect, and suggested that tunneling also contributed.

A contribution of tunneling to a secondary isotope effect may seem surprising, but it can easily occur if the mass of the nontransferred hydrogen contributes to the effective mass along the reaction coordinate. This is not at all unlikely, for the H-C-C bond angles at the β-carbon are changing from 109.5° $(sp^3)$ toward 120° $(sp^2)$ as the transferred hydrogen is removed. Coupling of the motions of the transferred and nontransferred hydrogens is thus to be expected.

Model calculations bear out this expectation (ref.3). The model for the transition state was 1̰ (L = H or D). The use of chlorine as leaving group was

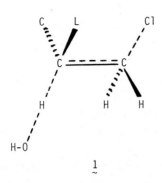

1̰

merely for calculational convenience, for earlier work showed the nature of the leaving group, other factors being equal, did not influence isotope effects at the β-position. Pertinent results are listed in Table 2 (temperature 45°C). Model 1 does not couple the bending motions of L with the stretching motions of the transferred H, while such coupling becomes increasingly important in models 3-5. In this and later tables, subscripts to k refer to the transferred and superscripts to the nontransferred hydrogen. $n_{OH}$ indicates the extent to which hydrogen transfer has progressed in the transition state. The isotope

TABLE 2

CCHDCH$_2$X + OH$^-$ $\longrightarrow$ CCD=CH$_2$ + X$^-$ + H$_2$O.

| Model | $n_{OH}$ | $k_H^H/k_H^D$ | $A_H^H/A_H^D$ |
|-------|----------|---------------|---------------|
| 1 | 0.5 | 1.053 | 0.981 |
|   | 0.9 | 1.113 | 0.963 |
| 3 | 0.3 | 1.069 | 0.938 |
|   | 0.5 | 1.088 | 0.945 |
| 4 | 0.3 | 1.184 | 0.587 |
|   | 0.5 | 1.197 | 0.663 |
| 5 | 0.3 | 1.270 | 0.284 |
|   | 0.5 | 1.267 | 0.440 |

effects include a tunnel correction calculated from the first term of the Bell equation.

The tunnel correction for model 1 is negligible, and $k_H^H/k_H^D$ is smaller than the larger experimental values in Table 2, even for a product-like transition state ($n_{OH}$ = 0.9). Model 4, which includes a substantial tunnel correction, comes closest to the larger values in Table 2. The last column of Table 2 lists the ratio of Arrhenius pre-exponential factors, obtained by fitting to the Arrhenius equation $k_H^H/k_H^D$ values calculated at 25-55°C. The ratio is close to unity in the absence of an appreciable tunnel correction (model 1), but can drop well below unity when the tunnel correction is important.

In order to test this prediction, we have determined the temperature dependence of the $k_H^H/k_H^T$ values for the reaction of $PhCHTCH_2NMe_3^+$ with ethoxide in ethanol over a temperature range of 29-65°C. While complete results are not in as of this writing, a value of $A_H^H/A_H^T$ of 0.779 ± 0.059 can be calculated from the data so far available. This is significantly below the values expected in the absence of tunneling, and strengthens our conclusion that tunneling contributes to observed $k_H^H/k_H^T$ values.

The success of the model in accounting for the above experimental facts encouraged us to use it to make additional predictions that could be tested experimentally, so as to provide new criteria for tunneling. First, the tunnel correction to the primary isotope effect is less when deuterium or tritium is transferred than when protium is transferred. It thus seemed that the tunnel correction to the secondary isotope effect should also be less when deuterium or tritium is transferred; i.e., $k_H^H/k_H^D > k_D^H/k_D^D > k_T^H/k_T^D$. Table 3 shows that this is indeed the case. The differences are insignificant for model 1, but

TABLE 3

$CCLDCH_2Cl + OH^- \longrightarrow CCD{=}CH_2 + Cl^- + LOH.$

| Model | $n_{OH}$ | $k_H^H/k_H^D$ | $k_D^H/k_D^D$ | $k_T^H/k_T^D$ |
|-------|----------|---------------|---------------|---------------|
| 1 | 0.3 | 1.027 | 1.031 | 1.033 |
|   | 0.5 | 1.053 | 1.059 | 1.063 |
| 4 | 0.3 | 1.184 | 1.104 | 1.083 |
|   | 0.5 | 1.197 | 1.134 | 1.123 |
| 5 | 0.3 | 1.270 | 1.129 | 1.099 |
|   | 0.5 | 1.267 | 1.161 | 1.135 |

substantial for models 4 and 5, for which tunneling is important. The temperature dependence likewise is more nearly normal for deuterium or tritium transfer ($A_L^H/_L^D$ closer to unity for L = D and T).

An experimental test of this prediction can be made by the same procedure as was used to obtain the data in Table 1. Using $PhCD_2CH_2X$ tracer labeled with tritium ($PhCDTCH_2X$) will give $k_D^D/k_D^T$. This can be compared to the experimentally determined $k_H^H/k_H^T$ via the relation (ref.4)

$$k_H^H/k_H^T = (k_D^D/k_D^T)^{3.26},$$

which should hold if only zero-point energy effects contribute to the isotope effect. In fact, the calculations predict that the $k_H^H/k_H^T$ calculated from $k_D^D/k_D^T$ should be <u>less</u> than the directly determined $k_H^H/k_H^T$ when tunneling is important. Typical values (for model 4, $n_{OH}$ = 0.3) are 1.147 and 1.266, respectively. Again, a more normal temperature dependence is predicted for the lower value.

We have shown in earlier experimental work that the β-carbon isotope effect on E2 reactions of $Ph^{14}CH_2CH_2NMe_3^+$ and its temperature dependence can be measured to good precision (ref.5). It should be a relatively simple matter to make analogous measurements on $Ph^{14}CD_2CH_2NMe_3^+$. Consequently, we included in our calculations β-carbon isotope effects when H and D are transferred. Table 4 lists the results.

TABLE 4

$C^{14}CL_2CH_2Cl + OH^- \longrightarrow C^{14}CL=CH_2 + Cl^- + LOH.$

| Model | $n_{OH}$ | $k_{H(12)}^H/k_{H(14)}^H$ | $k_{D(12)}^D/k_{D(14)}^D$ |
|---|---|---|---|
| 1 | 0.3 | 1.0008 | 1.0034 |
|   | 0.5 | 1.0229 | 1.0223 |
| 4 | 0.3 | 1.0509 | 1.0412 |
|   | 0.5 | 1.0765 | 1.0614 |
| 5 | 0.3 | 1.0727 | 1.0498 |
|   | 0.5 | 1.0960 | 1.0688 |

Just as was the case with the secondary isotope effects, the carbon isotope effect is smaller when deuterium is transferred than when protium is transferred, but only if tunneling is important -- there is little difference between $k_{H(12)}^H/k_{H(14)}^H$ and $k_{D(12)}^D/k_{D(14)}^D$ with model 1. The behavior of the temperature dependence is analogous to that for the secondary isotope effects. For example, $A_{H(12)}^H/A_{H(14)}^H$ is 0.825 but $A_{D(12)}^D/A_{D(14)}^D$ is 0.959 for model 4, $n_{OH}$ = 0.5, but they are almost the same for model 1, n = 0.5 (0.976 and 1.000, respectively).

Isotope effects for multiply labeled species can usually be considered to be cumulative, a principle often referred to as the rule of the geometric mean (ref.6). The present results show that this rule can be violated when tunneling is important. For example, the rule predicts that

$$k_H^H/k_D^D = (k_H^H/k_H^D)(k_H^H/k_D^H).$$

This can be true only if $k_H^H/k_H^D = k_D^H/k_D^D$, which Table 3 shows is <u>not</u> the case when tunneling is important.

In summary, we have shown that tunneling can affect not only the magnitude and temperature dependence of primary deuterium or tritium isotope effects, but also the following (1) the magnitude and temperature dependence of secondary deuterium or tritium isotope effects, (2) the relation between D/T and either H/D or H/T isotope effects, both primary and secondary, and (3) the magnitude and temperature dependence of carbon isotope effects for protium *vs.* deuterium transfer. We have tested experimentally the first of these sets of predictions, and plan to test the others.

REFERENCES

1  Rm. Subramanian and W.H. Saunders, Jr., J. Am. Chem. Soc., 106 (1984) 7887-7890.
2  S.R. Hartshorn and V.J. Shiner, Jr., J. Am. Chem. Soc., 94 (1972) 9002-9012; W.E. Buddenbaum and V.J. Shiner, Jr., in Isotope Effects on Enzyme-Catalyzed Reactions, W.W. Cleland, M.H. O'Leary and D.B. Northrop (Eds.), University Park Press, Baltimore, 1977, p. 11.
3  W.H. Saunders, Jr., J. Am. Chem. Soc., 107 (1985) 164-169.
4  L. Melander and W.H. Saunders, Jr., Reaction Rates of Isotopic Molecules, Wiley, New York, 1980, pp. 28-29, 143-144.
5  D.J. Miller, Rm. Subramanian and W.H. Saunders, Jr., J. Am. Chem. Soc., 103 ( 1981) 3519-3522.
6. J. Bigeleisen, J. Chem. Phys., 23 (1955) 2264-2267.

This work was supported by the National Science Foundation

*Synthesis and Applications of Isotopically Labeled Compounds 1985.*
Proceedings of the Second International Symposium, Kansas City, MO, U.S.A.,
3—6 September 1985, R.R. Muccino (Ed.), 101—106
© 1986 Elsevier Science Publishers B.V., Amsterdam — Printed in The Netherlands

# HEAVY-ATOM KINETIC ISOTOPE EFFECTS IN THERMAL AND PHOTOCHEMICAL MOLECULAR REARRANGEMENTS

HENRY J. SHINE, EWA GRUSZECKA, LIDIA KUPCZYK-SUBOTKOWSKA, EUN-SOOK RHEE AND WITOLD SUBOTKOWSKI

Chemistry Dept., Texas Tech University, Lubbock, TX 79409 (USA)

## ABSTRACT

Kinetic isotope effects (KIE) have been used in deducing the mechanisms of some acid-catalyzed and thermal benzidine rearrangements, as well as the photo-Wallach rearrangement. Both specifically-labeled and unenriched substrates were used, and KIE were calculated from isotope ratios obtained by combinations of whole-molecule-ion and isotope-ratio mass spectrometry ($^{13}C$, $^{15}N$, $^{18}O$) and scintillation counting ($^{14}C$).

## INTRODUCTION

The term heavy atom in the title refers to $^{13}C$, $^{14}C$, $^{15}N$ and $^{18}O$. Labeling with these atoms at bond-breaking and bond-forming sites in intramolecular rearrangements allows for the measurement of kinetic isotope effects (KIE) in the bond processes. This, in turn, allows us to decide whether or not bond-breaking and bond-forming occur in concert or in two separate steps. In the terminology of reaction mechanisms, the KIE measurements allow us to decide if an intramolecular rearrangement is a one-step, concerted process or if an intermediate is formed in one step and goes on to product in a second step. Furthermore, where a rearrangement is found to be a concerted process, it may be possible to deduce from the relative sizes of the bond-breaking and bond-forming KIE, and model calculations, by how much the extents of bond-breaking and bond-forming differ.

KIE for isotopes other than those of hydrogen are quite small, usually of the order of 1-5%. Consequently, it is not possible, because of low precision, to measure and compare rates of unenriched and specifically-enriched reactants separately. Instead, competitive methods must be used (ref. 1). The technique we have adopted is to allow a mixture of unenriched (R) and specifically-labeled reactant ($R^*$) to rearrange to product P and $P^*$ and to measure the ratio of masses $R/R^*$ or $P/P^*$ as reaction proceeds. Ordinarily we measure either $P/P^*$ at low and 100% conversions or $R/R^*$ at zero and high conversions. Measurements are made by multiscan, whole-molecule-ion mass spectroscopy with a quadrupole instrument (ref. 2,3). The mixtures (R + R$^*$) and (P + P$^*$) may be used themselves if they are suitable to mass spectrometer measurements. If not, a derivative is chosen, which must be not only suitable for mass measurements, but also be formed quantitatively (or without isotope fractionation).

Greater precision in mass ratio measurements is obtained by converting reactant or product into a low-molecular weight gas (N$_2$, CO$_2$) and measuring the isotope ratio (e.g., $^{28}$N$_2$/$^{29}$N$_2$) with an isotope-ratio mass spectrometer. The drawbacks to this method are the conversion techniques and also the relative scarcity of commerical isotope-ratio mass spectrometers. If this instrumental technique is available, though, an unenriched reactant is best used, or if a specifically-enriched reactant is used its concentration in the mixture (R + R$^*$) must be such that the atom-% content of heavy isotope is not too far from that of natural abundance.

Where $^{14}$C is used as the specific label, scintillation counting can be carried out on reactant and/or product as reaction proceeds, but here, of course, radioactive impurities (ref. 1) and quenching must be avoided.

We have used all of these techniques in measuring heavy-atom KIE. Our measurements have been particularly fruitful in clarifying the mechanism of benzidine rearrangements (refs. 4-6). In this symposium paper we describe some of our latest work in those rearrangements and in the photo-Wallach rearrangement.

REARRANGEMENT OF 2,2'-HYDRAZONAPHTHALENE (1) AND N-PHENYL-N'-2-NAPHTHYLHYDRAZINE (3)

Each of these compounds undergoes an acid-catalyzed o-benzidine rearrangement. That is, from 1 is obtained 2,2'-diaminobinaphthyl (2), while compound 4 is obtained from 3. Ortho-rearrangements are rare in the repertoire of benzidine rearrangements. Rearrangements of 1 and 3 are clean, however, so it was of particular interest to measure their KIE and to explore their mechanisms. Furthermore, 1 also rearranges into 2 when heated in solution, so it was attractive to be able to compare the thermal and acid-catalyzed rearrangements. This was done with [$^{15}$N,$^{15}$N']1 and [1,1'-$^{13}$C$_2$]1. The KIE (for two atoms) in the acid-catalyzed rearrangement were, respectively, 1.0904 and 1.0086, while in the thermal rearrangement the KIE were 1.0611 and 1.0182. These surprising results show that the rearrangements are concerted, but, moreover, have markedly unsymmetrical transition states. In Dewar's recent terminology (ref. 7) they are concerted but non-synchronous. We have interpreted the results as indicating that C-C bonding is much advanced by the time N-N bond breaking has its influence on the transition state. This difference in timing of C-C bonding and N-N bond breaking is greater in the acid-catalyzed than thermal rearrangement (ref. 8).

We were unable to work with the thermal rearrangement of **3**, but no problems were encountered with its acid-catalyzed rearrangement. This turned out to be also concerted and non-synchronous, but not so marked as in the rearrangement of **1**. In the case of **3** we used [$^{15}N,^{15}N'$]3 for measuring nitrogen KIE by whole-molecule-ion mass spectrometry (WMIMS) and [$2'$-$^{14}C$]3 for KIE by scintillation counting. We were also able to obtain both $^{13}C$ KIE and naturally-abundant $^{15}N$ KIE by working with specifically-labeled [$1$-$^{13}C$]3, and making measurements of the mass ratios of $^{44}CO_2/^{45}CO_2$ and $^{28}N_2/^{29}N_2$ by isotope-ratio mass spectrometry (IRMS) on the same samples.

The nitrogen KIE results were: for two $^{15}N$ atoms (WMIMS) 1.0434 and for one $^{15}N$ atom (IRMS) 1.0197. These results are in nice agreement, since $(1.0197)^2 =$ 1.0398. The carbon results were $k^{12}C/k^{14}C$ 1.0142 and $k^{12}C/k^{13}C$ 1.0042. From the $^{14}C$ result we would expect $k^{12}C/k^{13}C$ to be 1.0074. The difference in the two results may have been caused by errors in our $^{14}C$ measurements or in the difficulty in measuring the very small $^{13}C$ KIE. In any case, the overall results tell us again that the rearrangement is concerted and non-synchronous. We have argued that the transition state in the two-proton rearrangement of **3** is tighter than that in the one-proton rearrangement of **1** (ref. 9).

All mass and scintillation counting measurements in these two studies were made on the bis-trifluoroacetyl derivatives of the products, **2** and **4**.

## REARRANGEMENT OF HYDRAZOBENZENE

In our earliest benzidine work (ref. 4) we found that acid-catalyzed rearrangement of hydrazobenzene (**5**) into benzidine (**6**) was a concerted process, whereas concomitant rearrangement into diphenyline (**7**) was not concerted. We have been able to examine those rearrangements again, but with specific labeling in a different site. That is we have measured the $^{13}C$ KIE for forming **6** and **7** from 2,2',6,6'-[$^{13}C_4$]5. The KIE were obtained by WMIMS from the (M + 4)/M ratios in the bis-trifluoroacetyl derivatives of **6** and **7** and were, respectively, 0.9945 and 0.9953, (ref. 10). Although we do not know why each of these results is just under unity, there is no doubt that one does not differ from the other. Since the p-positions were not labeled there could be no carbon KIE in forming **6**. By analogy, although the o-sites were labeled, there is no KIE for forming **7**, and thus, again, C-C bonding is shown not to be part of the transition state in forming **7**.

## REACTIONS OF 4,4'-DICHLOROHYDRAZOBENZENE: DISPROPORTIONATION, o-SEMIDINE AND p-SEMIDINE REARRANGEMENTS.

Studies of KIE in benzidine rearrangements have taught us so far that these rearrangements comply with the Woodward-Hoffmann rules for sigmatropic shifts. Consequently, the study of an o-semidine rearrangement, which, according to the rules, cannot be concerted, became attractive. For reasons of ease in specific labeling and yield of o-semidine we chose to study 4,4'-dichlorohydrazobenzene (8). However, this undergoes not only o-semidine rearrangement (to 9) in acid solution but also p-semidine rearrangement with loss of a chlorine atom (to 10), and disproportionation (to 11 and 12). Limitations of space do not allow for a detailed description of our work (ref. 11), but we have been able to separate all products reasonably quantitatively and to use 9, 10 and 11 as their mono- or bis-trifluoracetyl derivatives for KIE measurements. In the case of 9 the product used was, however, 13. We were able to use $[^{15}N,^{15}N']$8 and WMIMS for nitrogen KIE in forming 10 and 11 but failed with 9 (non-reproducible WMIMS). We used $[2-^{14}C]$8 and measured $k^{12}C/k^{14}C$ for formation of 9 and 11; we used $[4-^{14}C]$8 and measured $k^{12}C/k^{14}C$ for forming each of 9, 10 and 11. Our attempts to measure $k^{12}C/k^{13}C$ by using $[4,4'-^{13}C_2]$8 and WMIMS failed, but we were able to obtain not only $k^{12}C/k^{13}C$ but also naturally-abundant $k^{14}N/k^{15}N$ for each product (9, 10 and 11) by using the $^{13}C$-enriched samples and IRMS. The $^{15}N,^{15}N'$ and $^{15}N$ KIE were in good agreement in the two cases (10 and 11) where both measurements were made. The single-atom $^{15}N$ KIE were for 9, 10 and 11, respectively, 1.0155, 1.0162 and 1.0141. As expected, there was no carbon KIE for forming 9 (a 1,3-sigmatropic shift). Much to our surprise, however, there was no carbon KIE in forming 10 and none in the disproportionation reaction, giving 11. We can rationalize these findings, of course, but they were surprising and differ from our earlier findings with other substrates (refs. 5,6). Disproportionation could, as Banthorpe has pointed out (ref. 12), involve the quinoidal precursor to 9, in which case a carbon KIE would not be expected. The bonding characteristics of the transition state in a concerted p-semidine rearrangement may be such as to obscure a carbon KIE. Apparently, we have more to learn yet about the transition states of benzidine rearrangements and the KIE to which they give rise.

## THE PHOTO-WALLACH REARRANGEMENT

KIE might be observed in photochemical rearrangements if there is an activation barrier in the electronically-excited state or in ground-state reactions which follow that excited state. To our knowledge, two attempts to measure heavy atom KIE in photochemical reactions are to be found in the literature (refs. 13, 14), and only in the second was one, an inverse $^{13}C$ KIE, found (ref. 14).

We have investigated the mechanism of the intramolecular photo-Wallach rearrangement, whose prototype is the rearrangement of 14 into 16. This rearrangement is believed to involve the formation and decomposition of intermediate 15. Working with $[^{15}N,^{15}N']$14, $[2'-^{14}C]$14 and $[^{18}O]$14, and with

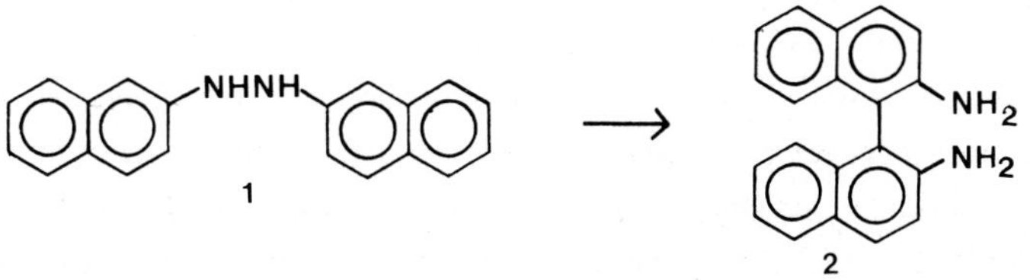

1 2

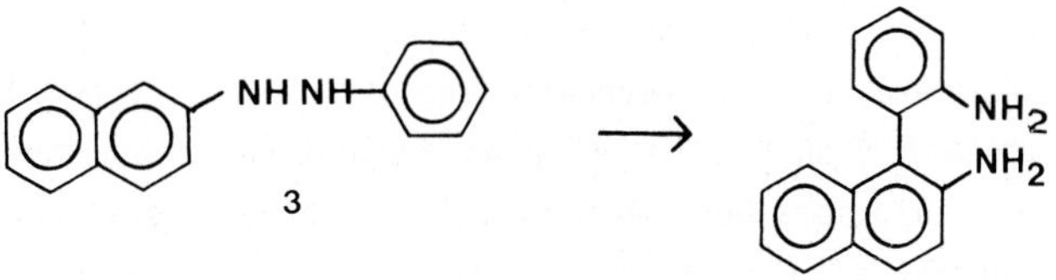

3 4

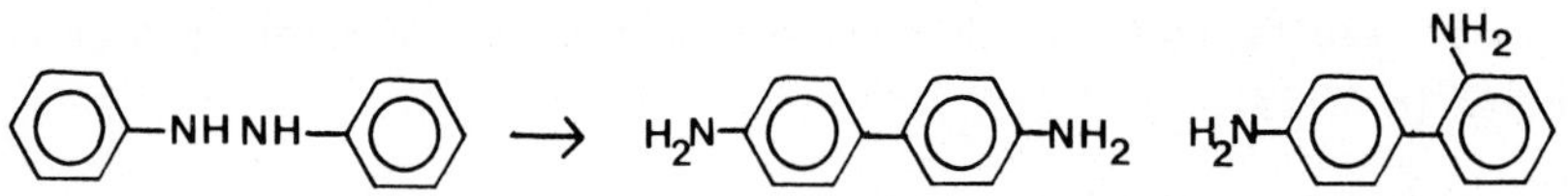

5 6 7

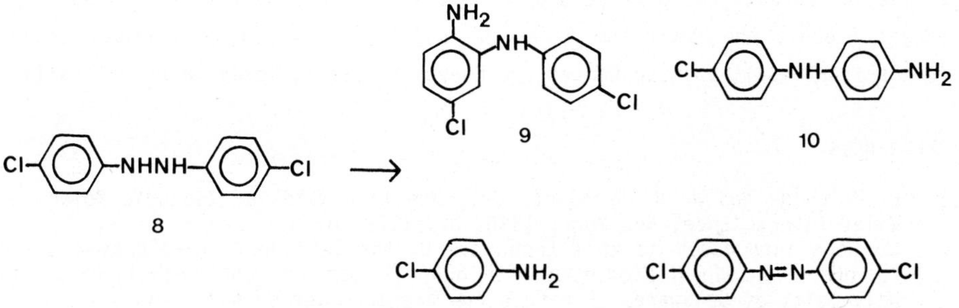

8 9 10 11 12

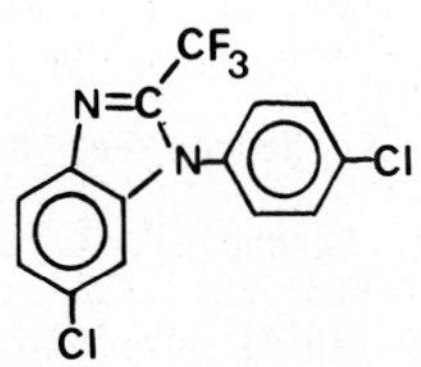

13

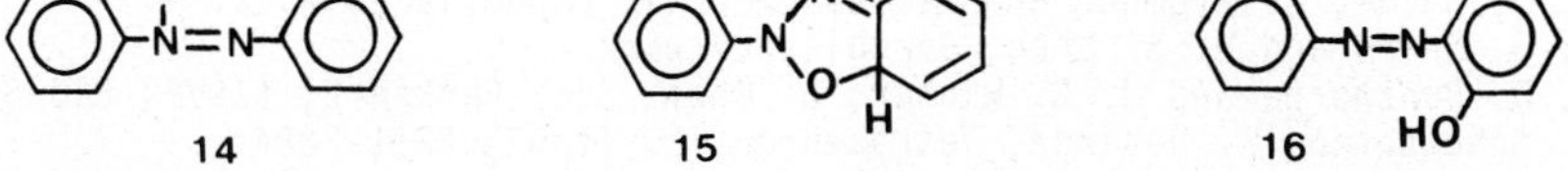

14 15 16

17 18

analogous $[^{15}N,^{15}N']17$ and $[1,1'-^{13}C_2]17$, our KIE results indicate that if there is an activation barrier in the rearrangement it is in the formation rather than decomposition of an intermediate such as **15**. Thus, we measured $k^{14}N/k^{15}N$ with both recovered **14** and isolated **16** and found, respectively 0.9991 ± 0.0038 and 1.0019 ± 0.0006. In the rearrangement of **17** we found (for product) $k^{14}N/k^{15}N$ 1.0011. These results suggest that N-O bond breaking is not part of the transition state in these rearrangements. The $^{18}O$ (product) and $^{14}C$ (substrate) KIE for rearrangement of **14** were, respectively, 0.9921 ± 0.0016 and 1.0036 ± 0.0015. There is an indication of an inverse oxygen KIE here, rationalizable in a bond-forming step. There appears to be no $^{14}C$ KIE. In the rearrangement of **17** the $^{13}C$ KIE was 1.0107, indicating that formation of the O-C bond is part of the transition state of the rearrangement. The summation of these results leads to the conclusion about the activation barrier stated earlier (ref. 15).

## ACKNOWLEDGEMENTS

The research work described has been supported by the National Science Foundation (Grants CHE-8026576 and CHE-8314947), the Robert A. Welch Foundation (Grant D-028), the Petroleum Research Fund of the American Chemical Society (Grant 15484-AC4), and the Center for Energy Research, Texas Tech University.

## REFERENCES

1   L. Melander and W. H. Saunders, Jr., Reaction Rates of Isotopic Molecules, Wiley-Interscience, New York, 1980, pp. 117-128.
2   We were introduced to this technique by the late Prof. Harold Kwart, who, to our knowledge, pioneered the general use of the technique at the University of Delaware. For this, we are for ever in his debt.
3   H. Kwart and J. J. Stanulonis, J. Am. Chem. Soc., 98 (1976) 4009-4010.
4   H. J. Shine, H. Zmuda, K. H. Park, H. Kwart, A. G. Horgan and M. Brechbiel, J. Am. Chem. Soc., 104 (1982) 2501-2509.
5   H. J. Shine, H. Zmuda, H. Kwart, A. G. Horgan and M. Brechbiel, J. Am. Chem. Soc., 104 (1982) 5181-5184.
6   H. J. Shine, J. Habdas, H. Kwart, M. Brechbiel, A. G. Horgan and J. San Filippo, Jr., J. Am. Chem. Soc., 105 (1983) 2823-2827.
7   M. J. S. Dewar, J. Am. Chem. Soc., 106 (1984) 209-219.
8   H. J. Shine, E. Gruszecka, W. Subotkowski, M. Brownawell and J. San Filippo, Jr., J. Am. Chem. Soc., 107 (1985) 3218-3223.
9   H. J. Shine, L. Kupczyk-Subotkowska and W. Subotkowski, unpublished work.
10  H. J. Shine, J. Zygmunt and W. Subotkowski, unpublished work.
11  H. J. Shine and E. S. Rhee, unpublished work.
12  D. B. Banthorpe and J. G. Winter, J. Chem. Soc. Perkin 2, (1972) 868-873.
13  L. Schutte and E. Havinga, Tetrahedron, 23 (1967) 2281-2284.
14  H. Kwart, D. A. Benko, J. Streith, and J. L. Schuppiser, J. Am. Chem. Soc., 100 (1978) 6502-6504.
15  H. J. Shine, W. Subotkowski and E. Gruszecka, unpublished work.

*Synthesis and Applications of Isotopically Labeled Compounds 1985.*
Proceedings of the Second International Symposium, Kansas City, MO, U.S.A.,
3—6 September 1985, R.R. Muccino (Ed.), 107—110
© 1986 Elsevier Science Publishers B.V., Amsterdam — Printed in The Netherlands

# SUBSTITUENT AND TEMPERATURE EFFECTS ON KINETIC ISOTOPE EFFECT IN OXIDATION REACTIONS

S. VENIMADHAVAN[1], S. SUNDARAM[1] and N. VENKATASUBRAMANIAN[2]

[1]Chemistry Dept., R.K. Mission Vivekananda College, Mylapore

Madras - 600 004 (India)

[2]IDL-Nitro Nobel Basic Research Institute (INBRI), P.B. No. 397, Malleswaram

Bangalore 560 003 (India)

ABSTRACT

The kinetics of the oxidation of benzhydrol, 4-methyl and 4-chloro benzhydrols and their corresponding $\alpha$-deuterated derivaties by bis(benzyltriethylammonium) dichromate (BATEADC) have been studied and the primary kinetic isotope effect $(k_H/k_D)$ evaluated. On the basis of (i) the magnitude of the kinetic isotope effect in relation to structure and (ii) its variation with the temperature, the structure and geometry of the transition state of these reactions have been delineated.

INTRODUCTION

Though kinetic isotope effect studies have been carried out in the oxidation of alcohols with conventional hexavalent chromium reagents (ref.1 and 2), detailed investigations have not been made with novel chromium reagents like bis (benzyltriethylammonium) dichromate (BTEADC). The temperature dependence of kinetic isotope effect (TDKIE) has been used as a valuable tool to understand the nature of the hydrogen transfer process involved in these reactions (ref. 3 and 4). The effect of substituents on the kinetic isotope effect has been gainfully employed to identify the nature of the transition state and the likely disposition of the various atoms therein (ref.5). Hence, a systematic kinetic study of the oxidation of a number of benzhydrols by BTEADC has been made with a view to understand the topology of the transition state of these reactions.

METHODS

BTEADC has been prepared by the method of Huang and Chan (ref.6). The $\alpha$-deuterated benzhydrols have been prepared by the reduction of the corresponding ketones by sodium brordeuteride.

RESULTS AND DISCUSSION

The oxidation reactions carried out in aqueous acetic acid (50-50% v/v) exhibit a first order dependence on both the oxidant and substrate concentrations and a dual order dependence of one and two on mineral acid concentrations. A rho value of -0.81 is obtained for the oxidation of several substituted benzhydrols. At a given temperature and mineral acid concentration, the isotope effect exhibited by the parent compound is maximum followed by 4-chloro and 4-methyl benzhydrols (Table 1).

TABLE 1

Effect of substituents and temperature on the kinetic isotope effect in the oxidation of benzhydrols by BTEADC[a].

| Substrate | Temp(°K) | $10^4 k_H(s^{-1})$ | $10^4 k_D(s^{-1})$ | $k_H / k_D$ |
|-----------|----------|--------------------|--------------------|-------------|
| 4-Cl | 303 | 3.52 ± 0.05 | 0.72 ± 0.02 | 4.89 |
|      | 313 | 7.25 ±0.06 | 1.67 ±0.03 | 4.34 |
|      | 323 | 13.8 ± 0.10 | 3.33 ± 0.05 | 4.14 |
| 4-H | 303 | 4.75 ± 0.05 | 0.92 ± 0.02 | 5.15 |
|     | 313 | 9.67 ± 0.08 | 2.02 ± 0.03 | 4.79 |
|     | 323 | 20.3 ± 0.20 | 4.50 ± 0.05 | 4.51 |
| 4-Me | 303 | 7.40 ± 0.06 | 1.75 ± 0.03 | 4.23 |
|      | 313 | 14.6 ± 0.10 | 3.58 ± 0.05 | 4.08 |
|      | 323 | 23.3 ± 0.20 | 6.17 ± 0.06 | 3.78 |

a    [ROH] = 2.01 x $10^{-3}$M    [BTEADC] = 1.67 x $10^{-4}$M

[HClO$_4$] = 0.8 M      solvent 50% HOAc - 50% H$_2$O

The TDKIE parameters, namely $[\Delta E_a]_D^H$ and $A_H/A_D$ have been evaluated for reactions (Table 2).

TABLE 2

TDKIE parameters for the oxidation of benzhydrols by BTEADC

| substrate | $[\Delta E_a]_D^H$ k.cal/M | $A_H/A_D$ |
|-----------|---------------------------|-----------|
| 4-Cl | 0.96 | 0.95 |
| 4-H | 0.96 | 1.06 |
| 4-Me | 1.14 | 0.83 |

A mechanistic sequence involving the initial fast equilibrium formation of the chromate esters followed by its rate limiting decomposition in which the secondary hydrogen is lost as a hydride ion to give the products can be proposed for this reaction (ref. 7). The $k_H/k_D$ value of 5.16 at 30°C exhibited by the parent benzhydrol is somewhat less than the maximum value of 6 to 7 expected for a centrosymmetric transition state (ref. 2). This is indicative of the fact that the transition state of the parent compound under these conditions has less of 'central character' with a leaning towards the products (ref. 3). A polar substituent like the 4-methyl group responds to the electron demand at the seat of the reaction, enhances the rate and displaces the transition state further to the right. In the case of the 4-chloro substituent, the cleavage of the C-H bond has just been initiated and as a consequence, the 4-chloro group not only lowers the rate but also pulls the transition state towards the left. The TDKIE parameters also serve as valuable diagnostic tools in identifying the nature of the hydrogen transfer process involved. The values of $[\Delta E_a]_D^H$ and $A_H/A_D$ obtained during the present investigation point unequivocally to a linear, symmetric hydrogen transfer process (Fig. 1).

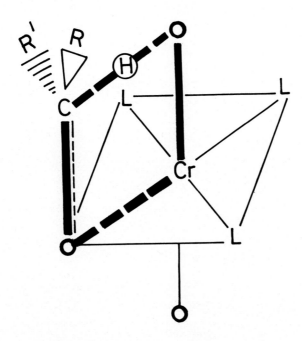

Fig. 1    The normal pericyclic transition state of hydrogen transfer. Critical bonds are represented by heavy lines

The two substituents viz., 4-chloro and 4-methyl groups perturb this situation towards either a 'reactant-like' or a more 'product-like' transition state respectively.

110

REFERENCES

1  K.B. Wiberg, Oxidation in organic Chemistry, Academic Press, New York, 1965.
2  F.H. Westheimer and N. Nicolaides, J. Amer. Chem. Soc., 71 (1949), 25.
3  H. Kwart and J.H. Nickle, J. Amer. Chem. Soc., 98 (1976), 2881.
4  H. Kwart, Acc. Chem. Res., 15 (1982), 401-408 and references therein.
5  N. Venkatasubramanian, Ind. J. Chem., 3 (1965), 225.
6  X. Huang and C. Chan, Synthesis, 12 (1982), 1091.
7  N. Venkatasubramanian, Proc. Ind. Acad. Sci., 50 (1960), 156.

*Synthesis and Applications of Isotopically Labeled Compounds 1985.*
Proceedings of the Second International Symposium, Kansas City, MO, U.S.A.,
3—6 September 1985, R.R. Muccino (Ed.), 111—112
1986 Elsevier Science Publishers B.V., Amsterdam — Printed in The Netherlands

BIOSYNTHESIS AND USES OF PER-DEUTERATED PROTEINS

H.L. CRESPI

Chemistry Division, Argonne National Laboratory, Argonne, Illinois, 60439, USA*

ABSTRACT

Fully deuterated microorganisms are a source of per-deuterated and isotope
hybrid proteins of utility in proton magnetic resonance spectroscopy, resonance Raman spectroscopy and neutron scattering analysis.

INTRODUCTION

Simple plant microorganisms have been cultured in 99.7 atom % D for a
number of years (ref.1), but more complex organisms do not survive such
extensive deuteration (see Table 1). Per-deuterated proteins are available
only from microalgae grown autotrophically in 99.7 atom % D and from heterotrophic microorganisms grown in algal-derived substrates (ref.2).

TABLE 1
Limits for survival in $D_2O$.

| 99.7 atom % D | 40-80 atom % D | 15-30 atom % D |
|---|---|---|
| Microalgae | Liverwort | Mammals |
| Bacteria | Higher Plants | |
| Cyanobacteria | Tissue Cultures | |
| Yeast and Molds | Protozoans | |

As described by Katz and Crespi (ref.3), per-deuterated proteins offer a
number of unique experimental possibilities. The slowly exchangeable amide
protons can be visualized by proton magnetic resonance (ref.4). The prosthetic group of many proteins can be chemically manipulated to give an isotope
hybrid material, such as [1]H-retinal ([2]H-bacterio-opsin) (ref.5). Such
materials find application in proton magnetic resonance spectroscopy, neutron
scattering analysis and resonance Raman spectroscopy. The isotopic composition of the amino acids of cellular proteins can often be controlled by
feeding [1]H amino acids to microorganisms growing in an otherwise fully
deuterated nutrient medium. Figures 1 and 2 show examples of this type of
experiment.

*Work performed under the auspices of the Division of Chemical Sciences,
Office of Basic Energy Sciences, U.S. Department of Energy.

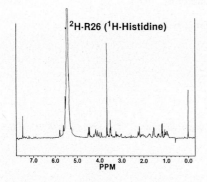

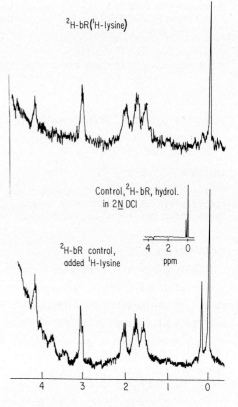

Fig. 1. DCl hydrolyzate of Rh.
sphaeroides R-26 cells grown in fully
deuterated nutrient medium except for
added ¹H-L-histidine. While there are
many proton lines upfield from the HOD
line at 5.4 ppm due to the metabolic
activity of histidine, there is only
the single histidine line in the
aromatic region. (Spectrum at 300 MHz)

Fig. 2. DC1 hydrolyzate of bacteriorhodopsin isolated from Halobacterium
halobium cells grown in fully deuterated nutrient medium with added
¹H-L-lysine. Lysine is the only amino acid containing significant amounts
of protons. (Spectrum at 80 MHz, scale in parts per million.)


Until recently, full deuteration was limited to proteins indigenous to

plant microorganisms. Now mammalian proteins are available from genetically

engineered microorganisms, which greatly widens the applicability of

per-deuteration to proteins of importance.


REFERENCES

1  J.J. Katz and H.L. Crespi, Science, 151 (1966) 1187-1194.
2  H.L. Crespi, in Stable Isotopes in the Life Sciences, International Atomic
   Energy Agency, Vienna, 1977, pp. 111-121.
3  J.J. Katz and H.L. Crespi, Pure Appl. Chem., 32 (1972) 221-250.
4  H.L. Crespi, A.G. Kostka and U.H. Smith, Biochem. Biophys. Res. Comm., 61
   (1974) 1407-1414.
5  A. Lewis, M.A. Marcus, B. Ehrenberg and H. Crespi, Proc. Nat. Acad. Sci.
   USA, 75 (1978) 4642-4646.

*Synthesis and Applications of Isotopically Labeled Compounds 1985.*
Proceedings of the Second International Symposium, Kansas City, MO, U.S.A.,
3—6 September 1985, R.R. Muccino (Ed.), 113—114
© 1986 Elsevier Science Publishers B.V., Amsterdam — Printed in The Netherlands

ISOTOPIC PROBES OF TRANSITION STATES IN THE ACYL TRANSFER FROM ARYL ACETATES TO
AMINES.[*]

I.M. KOVACH and R.L. Schowen

Chemistry Department, University of Kansas, Lawrence, KS  66045

ABSTRACT
     The reaction of phenyl acetate ($CH_3CO_2C_6H_5$ and $CD_3CO_2C_6H_5$) with methoxya-
mine at 25° in water exhibits β-secondary deuterium isotope effects $k_{3H}/k_{3D}$ =
0.857 ± 0.024 with $CH_3O_2CCH_2CH(CO_2CH_3)NH_3^+$ as general-acid catalyst and 0.867 ±
0.009 with $CH_3ONH_3^+$ general-acid catalyst. The reaction of phenyl acetate with
hydrazine with general-base catalysis by hydrazine gives $k_{3H}/k_{3D}$ = 0.972 ±
0.002.  The uncatalyzed reaction of 2,4-dinitrophenyl acetate with semicarbazide
has $k_{3H}/k_{3D}$ = 0.975 ± 0.009.

INTRODUCTION
     α-Deuterium (ref. 1-2) and β-deuterium (ref. 3-5) secondary isotope effects
(βDIE) are good measures of the degree of tetrahedral character in carbonyl
addition-elimination transition states.  This work illustrates their utility for
aminolysis reactions of esters that present a unique course of acyl transfer
with a number of viable tetrahedral intermediates of various charge density
along the reaction path.  By appropriate selection of general acid-base
catalysts, attacking and leaving groups, proton transfer between intermediates
can be slowed down to become rate limiting.  Structure-reactivity relationship
and kinetic solvent isotope effect results indicate (ref. 6) that methoxyaminolysis of phenyl acetate (PA) catalyzed by aspartic acid dimethyl ester conjugate
acid involve rate-limiting proton transfer by preassociation and the hydrazine
base catalyzed hydrazinolysis of PA (ref. 7) also takes place with some proton
transfer in the rate limiting step.  Since the transition states for these
reactions must be between two tetrahedral adducts, they themselves must also
have $sp^3$ character.

METHODS
     Spectroscopic monitoring of the appropriate phenol was carried out in an
excess of reagents under zero order conditions with methoxyamine and under
pseudo first order conditions with hydrazine and semicarbazide.  Protiated
and deuterated substrates were measured in alteration, in identical solutions.
Linear and nonlinear least squares techniques were used for data reduction.

*Supported by NIH-GMS through GM-20198

114

## RESULTS

TABLE OF βDIE. measure of tetrahedral structure in the transition state, and solvent isotope effects for ester aminolysis.

| Reaction | $k_{3H}/k_{3D}$ | $\hat{I}$ [a] | $k_{HOH}/k_{DOD}$ |
|---|---|---|---|
| PA + $CH_2ONH_2$ + $CH_3O_2CCH_2CH(CO_2CH_3)NH_3^+$ | $0.86 \pm 0.02$ | $1.08 \pm 0.15$ | $3.9 \pm 0.8$ |
| $CH_3ONH_3^+$ | $0.87 \pm 0.01$ | $1.00 \pm 0.12$ | $1.75 \pm 0.06$ |
| PA + $2N_2H_4$ | $0.97 \pm 0.01$ | $0.22 \pm 0.08$ | $1.45 \pm 0.02$ |
| DNPA[b] + $NH_2CONHNH_2$ | $0.975 \pm 0.009$ | $0.18 \pm 0.07$ | |

[a] Calculated from $k_{3H}/k_{3D} = (K_{3H}/K_{3D})^{\hat{I}}$, $K_{3H}/K_{3D} = 0.87 \pm 0.01$
[b] 2,4-dinitrophenyl acetate

## DISCUSSION

Results of the βDIE are converted to $\hat{I}$, the fraction of tetrahedral character at the transition state. They are calculated from $k_{3H}/k_{3D} = (K_{3H}/K_{3D})^{\hat{I}}$ (ref. 5), where $K_{3H}/K_{3D}$ is the limiting effect for complete conversion to a tetrahedral adduct taken as 0.87, the observed effect (corrected for 3D) for equilibrium hydration of 1,3-dichloroacetone. It was previously uncertain how accurately this limit could be applied to esters (ref. 5), but now this work confirms its correctness. Methoxyaminolysis ofP A catalyzed by both general acids proceeds through fully tetrahedral transition states with βDIE identical to those for ketone hydration. The solvent isotope effects in this work, in full agreement with the earlier report (ref. 6), show that a proton transfer to the rate limiting transition state takes place to a different degree in each case.

To the contrary, the hydrazine catalyzed hydrazinolysis transition state for PA is only 22% tetrahedral and the solvent isotope effect is also small. This is not consistent with rate limiting proton transfer to the zwitterionic intermediate as suggested for the analogous reaction of aryl acetates (ref. 7). A rate determining expulsion of phenol from PA through a more solvated trigonal transition state is a more probable model for this hydrazinolysis reaction, likewise for the reaction of semicarbazide with DNPA.

## REFERENCES

1. J.F. Kirsch, in W.W. Cleland, M. O'Leary, and D.B. Northrop, (Eds), Isotope Effects on Enzyme Catalyzed Reactions, University Park Press, 1977, Ch. 4.
2. L. do Amaral, et. al. J. Am. Chem. Soc. 101 (1979), 169.
3. J.L. Hogg, in R.D. Gandeour, and R.L. Schowen (Eds.), Transition States in Biochemical Processes, Plenium Press, New York, 1978, Ch. 5.
4. I.M. Kovach et. al. J. Am. Chem. Soc. 102 (1980) 1991.
5. I.M. Kovach, J.P. Elrod, and R.L. Schowen; J. Am. Chem. Soc. 102 (1980) 7530.
6. M.M. Cox and W.P. Jencks, J. Am. Chem. Soc. 103 (1981) 572.
7. A.G. Satterthwait and W.P. Jencks, J. Am. Chem. Soc. 96 (1974) 7018 and 7031.

*Synthesis and Applications of Isotopically Labeled Compounds 1985.*
Proceedings of the Second International Symposium, Kansas City, MO, U.S.A.,
3—6 September 1985, R.R. Muccino (Ed.), 115—120
© 1986 Elsevier Science Publishers B.V., Amsterdam — Printed in The Netherlands

PRINCIPLES OF NMR IMAGING AND SURFACE COIL APPLICATIONS

WILFRIED LOEFFLER

Siemens Medical Systems, Inc., 186 Wood Avenue South, Iselin, NJ
08830

MAGNETIC RESONANCE IMAGING

The phenomen of Nuclear Magnetic Resonance (NMR) has been
known since 1946 [1.2] and since then has found widespread
applications in physics, material science, and above all
analytical chemistry. In the 1970's it has been detected that
Magnetic Resonance Properties of cancerous tissue differ
significantly from that of healthy tissues [3]. This finding was
followed by the idea of using Nuclear Magnetic Resonance to
generate cross-sectional images of intact biological objects
[4]. In the years after these basic discoveries an increasing
number of research institutions and commercial companies started
constructing Magnetic Resonance Imaging (MRI) systems.
Instruments have been commercially available since 1982.

The physical principles of Magnetic Resonance Imaging have
been described in great detail in the literature [5, 6].
Therefore, only a very brief outline of the basic ideas will be
given here.

All nuclei with an odd number of neutrons or protons possess
an angular momentum and a magnetic moment. In an external
magnetic field these nuclei preferentially will align along the
direction of the external field. It is possible, therefore, to
detect an external macroscopic magnetic moment in samples
containing such nuclei. This macroscopic magnetization can be
understood as an average magnetic moment over a large number of
nuclei some of which are pointing into the preferential direction
along the external field. If the magnetization, for example by
means of a radio-frequency pulse, is tilted away from its
preferred direction along the external field, it will start to

precess about the direction of the external magnetic field like a
gyroscope precesses about the direction of the gravitational
field.  This motion can be detected by a pick-up coil surrounding
the sample.  The frequency $\nu$ of the precession is called Larmour
Frequency of NMR Frequency and is proportional to the external
magnetic field $B_o$:

$$\nu = \frac{\gamma}{2\pi} B_o$$

$\gamma$ depends on the type of nuclei involved and is called
gyromagnetic ratio.  For Hydrogen nuclei in a field of 1 Tesla
the resonance frequency is 42.57 MHz.

In imaging one makes use of the field dependence of the NMR
frequency.  To do so, additional spatially dependent magnetic
fields are superimposed on the static field $B_o$.  These fields
are called gradient fields and usually exhibit a linear
correlation between spatial position and field strength:

$$B = B_o + G_x \cdot x$$

In this case $G_x$ would be called a gradient along the
x-direction.  Similarly gradients along the other directions
(y and z) can be generated.  Because of the spatial dependence of
the magnetic field, the resonance frequency, of course, shows the
same dependence:

$$\nu = \frac{\nu}{2\pi} B_o + \frac{\gamma}{2\pi} G_x \cdot x$$

$$= \nu_o + \frac{\gamma \cdot G_x}{2\pi} \cdot x$$

Therefore, a simple frequency analysis of the resonance signal
will allow a localization of the sample along the x-direction.
By successively using magnetic field gradients along the x,y, and
z directions it is possible to localize the position of a sample
in three dimensions.  Or if an extended object is placed in the
NMR apparatus, one can determine the spatial origin of all
contributions to the NMR signal received.  An image then can be
created by plotting the intensity of the NMR signal over the

spatial location in two dimensions. It is possible to use a variety of different data acquisition and image reconstruction schemes. The two most common ones are the projection reconstruction method similar to x-ray Computed Tomography and the Fourier reconstruction method.

SPECTROSCOPY

If the nuclei under investigation are chemically bound to different compounds, the resonance frequencies show minor differences because of small variations in the local magnetic fields at the sites of the nuclei. This phenomenon is called chemical shift and can be used to chemically analyse the constitution of a sample or to reveal the structure of molecules. Certain imaging methods retain the chemical shift information and thus allow a chemical analysis of an intact extended object. These methods are called chemical shift imaging or spatially resolved spectroscopy.

Because of the high abundance in biological tissue and its high sensitivity, Hydrogen is almost exclusively used for Magnetic Resonance Imaging. All other nuclei with magnetic moments are much less abundant in the human body and also exhibit a much smaller NMR sensitivity than Hydrogen. Still it has been possible to acquire images or spatially resolved spectra from $^{13}C$, $^{23}Na$ and $^{31}P$ [7]. In order to acquire an NMR signal of sufficient strength it is necessary, however, to compromise the spatial resolution and use much larger volume elements or voxels than one is used from imaging with Hydrogen. The same sensitivity problems apply to the use of NMR for tracing isotopically labeled compounds in the human body. In principle it is possible to label metabolites or drugs with "NMR sensitive nuclei" and than trace these compounds in the body. The problem, however, is that a concentration close to a millimol is needed to reasonably apply NMR methods. Using radioactive labels and nuclear medicine methods, on the other hand, a concentration of $10^{-10}$ mol allows a safe localization of the labeled compounds. Therefore, if only spatial tracing of isotopic lables is required, nuclear medicine methods show by far a superior sensitivity. NMR, on the other hand, at least in principle allows not only a spatial tracing of labels, but also a determination of any chemical changes around the observed isotope.

USE OF SURFACE COILS

One way to overcome the inherent sensitivity problems in NMR to a certain extent is to use pick-up coils which are very closely matching the area of interest. One can show that the sensitivity of a coil increases approximately with the square of its inverse radius. Very small coils, therefore, show a superior sensitivity if they can be brought close enough to the area of interest. Applications are the investigation of surface close organs in the human body or even the invasive implantation of pick-up coils into the body. For spectroscopy using other nuclei than protons surface coils frequently are the only possible way to obtain reasonable results within an acceptable measurement time. For imaging with Hydrogen on the other hand one can make use of their superior sensitivity in a different way. Here the application of surface coils makes it possible to improve the spatial resolution of images by using higher field gradients or different acquisition schemes. Without surface coils this "zooming" of images can be done only to a very limited extend because of the associated decrease in the signal-to-noise ratio due to the decrease in picture element volume size. Figures 1-4 show high resolution MRI images of surface close areas obtained with surface coils.

REFERENCES

1 F. Bloch, W.W. Hansen, M.E. Packard, Phys. Rev. 69 (1946) 127.
2 E.M. Purcell, H.C. Torrey, R.V. Pound, Phys. Rev. 69 (1946) 37.
3 R. Damadian, Science, 171 (1971) 1151.
4 P.C. Lauterbur, Nature (London), 242 (1973) 190.
5 P. Mansfield, P.G. Morris, NMR Imaging in Biomedicine, Academic Press, New York-London, 1982.
6 T.L. James, A.R. Margulis (Ed), Biomedical Magnetic Resonance, Radiology Research and Education Foundation (Third and Parmassus Avenues - Suite C324, San Francisco, CA 94143).
7 Proceedings IV Annual Meeting Society of Magnetic Resonance in Medicine, London 1985 (SMRM, 15 Shattuck Square, Suite 204, Berkeley, CA 94704).

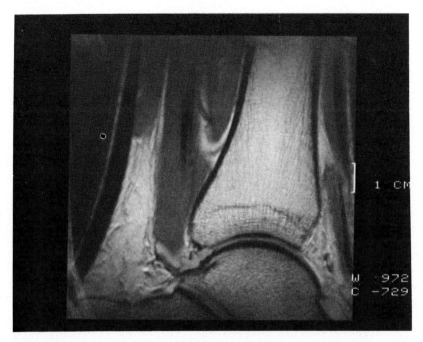

Fig. 1. High resolution surface coil image of the ankle

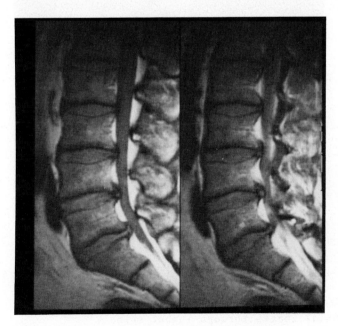

Fig. 2. Surface coil images of the lumbar spine

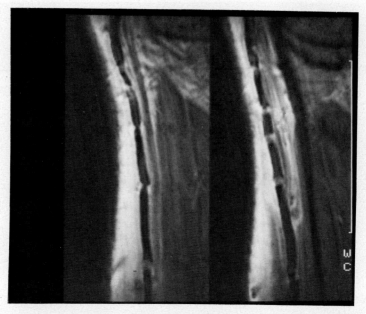

Fig. 3.   High resolution surface coil images of saphenous vein

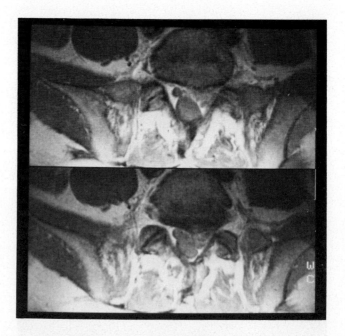

Fig. 4.   Axial images through lumbar spine

*Synthesis and Applications of Isotopically Labeled Compounds 1985.* 121
Proceedings of the Second International Symposium, Kansas City, MO, U.S.A.,
3—6 September 1985, R.R. Muccino (Ed.), 121—126
© 1986 Elsevier Science Publishers B.V., Amsterdam — Printed in The Netherlands

CLINICAL STUDIES WITH MAGNETIC RESONANCE IMAGING

W.A. Murphy, M.D.[1]
[1] Mallinckrodt Institute of Radiology, Washington University School of Medicine,
510 South Kinsghighway Boulevard, St. Louis, Missouri (U.S.A.) 63110

ABSTRACT

Magnetic Resonance Imaging (MRI), introduced in the early 1980's, was greeted with great enthusiasm. The several manufacturers now have a respectable installed base of equipment, and clinical experience is acruing rapidly. The recognized advantages of MRI over other techniques include: 1) high sensitivity to inherent differences among normal tissues and pathological conditions, 2) display of tissue differences as grey scale contrast, 3) capability to manipulate these tissue contrast differences, 4) ability to obtain images in nearly any plane through the human body, 5) absence of certain bone or metal derived artifacts that degrade computed tomographic (CT) images, and 6) freedom from ionizing radiation. MRI is finding application as a diagnostic imaging method in all regions of the human body.

INTRODUCTION

MRI has been rapidly accepted as an important new imaging method largely because it is sensitive to inherent differences among normal tissues and pathological conditions. MRI measures and displays differences in proton (hydrogen) distribution and environment. These differences are displayed as grey scale contrast that depends on the balance among 1) hydrogen (spin) density, 2) $T_1$ relaxation, 3) $T_2$ relaxation, and 4) blood flow. The contribution of each parameter as well as the signal intensity can be controlled to a certain degree by pulse sequence selection. In general, MR signal intensity is enhanced by greater hydrogen density, shorter $T_1$ relaxation rates, and longer $T_2$ relaxation rates. $T_1$ contrast is accentuated by saturation recovery, inversion recovery or spin echo (short TR, short TE) pulse sequences. $T_2$ contrast is accentuated by spin echo pulse sequences with long TR and long TE settings. Most investigators rely on spin echo pulse sequences. It is common to obtain images that emphasize $T_1$ contribution ($T_1$ - weighted), or $T_2$ contribution ($T_2$ - weighted), or proton density (spin density or balanced).

For the radiologist who must supervise an MR imaging examination, the potential number of imaging parameter combinations seems unmanageable. However, there are several general goals that limit the possibilities. First, a pulse sequence must be chosen that will provide adequate contrast among the normal tissues and pathological conditions that are likely to be present in the region of interest. Enough is known about the various tissues, fluids and conditions that their behavior with each pulse sequence choice is usually predictable. Second, the imaging plane must be chosen to best display the anatomy of interest. In addition to the three orthogonal planes (transaxial, sagittal and coronal), any oblique plane can also be obtained. The correct plane is dependent on the specific anatomic part. Finally, a coil must be matched with data acquisition parameters to ensure adequate signal strength. Having made these decisions, the physician is rewarded with an image of high signal having good spatial and contrast resolution, and showing anatomy and pathology oriented in a unique plane that best displays the region of interest.

For the patient, the examination is comfortable and safe. Currently there are no known biological hazards. Patients with cerebral aneurysm clips, cardiac pacemakers and neurostimulators are not examined. There is little indication for intravenous or oral contrast agents. In some cases, MRI can be substituted for uncomfortable tests such as myelograms or angiograms.

CLINICAL APPLICATIONS

Brain

MRI is an effective method for imaging the brain. One of the major advantages of MRI is the superb soft tissue differentiation that is inherent in the method. This results in an increased sensitivity of MRI for tumor detection when compared with CT. MRI is also superior to CT in the detection of white-matter abnormalities such as multiple sclerosis. MRI is particularly effective in the posterior fossa where spatial resolution is not degraded by bone artifacts as it is in CT studies. However, MRI is less specific than sensitive. Much overlap in relaxation times has been shown among various pathological conditions.

Contrast agents have been developed in an attempt to improve the sensitivity and specificity of brain MRI. Clinical trials are underway.

Sodium imaging is being developed as another MRI method for evaluation of neurological conditions. Early results show that tumors and cerebral infarctions have increased levels of sodium.

Spinal Cord

MRI is an exceptionally effective method for evaluation of the spinal cord because of its excellent contrast and spatial resolution, its capability to image in the sagittal plane and its noninvasive character. Surface coils are required for the greatest signal strength and spatial resolution. MRI has proven useful for evaluation of Chiari malformation, syringomyelia, arteriovenous malformation, tumor and extrinsic cord compression. It is likely that technological improvements will enhance the usefulness of

MRI for diagnosis of spinal cord conditions. Likewise, it is likely that MRI will replace an important fraction of myelography and CT studies of the spine.

## Chest

MRI of the mediastinum and lungs has been investigated as a method for demonstrating tumors, their local extent and their metastases to lymph nodes and lung parenchyma. It is clear that MRI can show tumors, local extent of disease and metastases. It has two clear advantages: 1) the ability to differentiate a mass or lymph node from a blood vessel without using an intravascular contrast agent and 2) the capability of directly obtaining an image in any plane through the body. Its relative disadvantages are: 1) inherent motion unsharpness, 2) insensitivity to calcification, 3) length of examination and 4) high cost.

Chest MRI has been compared with chest CT, the accepted standard for sectional imaging of the chest. The two methods have been shown to be nearly equal in their abilities to detect masses, local extent of disease and metastases, each having minor advantages over the other. Currently, CT is the method of choice for initial sectional imaging of the thorax because it has better spatial resolution, less motion unsharpness, lower cost and greater throughput. MRI is reserved for patients who have contrast allergies or for solving problems not resolved by CT.

Neither MRI nor CT is as yet tissue specific. MRI may have an advantage in differentiating collapsed lung from tumor and in separating fibrosis from tumor. MRI may eventually be able to quantitate lung water.

## Cardiovascular

MRI of the cardiovascular system can be divided into anatomic and physiological applications. The anatomic applications are more fully explored. The natural contrast between flowing blood and heart muscle is a great advantage. EKG triggering of the pulse sequence provides sharp images. Normal and pathological anatomy of pediatric and adult hearts is readily displayed. Congenital and acquired (cardiomyopathies and ischemic heart disease) conditions having anatomic abnormalities are regularly imaged.

Imaging of the great vessels (aorta, branches of the aorta and the vena cavae) is now well-accepted. Conditions such as coarctation, dissection, and aneurysm formation are commonly imaged.

Physiological information can also be derived from MR imaging. Regional myocardiac function, blood flow patterns and blood flow velocity are being studied.

MRI of the cardiovascular system compares well with other imaging tests such as angiocardiography, echocardiography, computed tomography and positron emission tomography. Each has its own strengths, and each will have an important position in cardiovascular diagnosis. The future of cardiovascular MRI is very great.

## Abdomen

MRI is capable of imaging the abdominal organs including the liver, spleen, pancreas, kidneys and adrenals. Solid masses, cystic lesions and diffuse conditions of these organs can ordinarily be detected. MRI is effective for analyzing the retroperitoneum, especially for detecting abnormalities of the iliopsoas muscle. It is not yet effective for imaging the gastrointestinal tract, primarily because of motion and the absence of a good MR gastrointestinal contrast agent.

Liver MR imaging is generally equivalent to CT, with MRI having advantages in distinguishing hepatic cavernous hemangioma from liver cancer, in detecting fatty infiltration of the liver and in detecting metastases to the liver. Proton spectroscopic imaging of the liver has improved MRI detection rate and specificity. MRI currently seems best utilized as a problem solving method following a nondiagnostic CT examination.

Renal MR imaging is generally equivalent to CT, with MRI being an accurate method of detecting and staging renal masses. MRI has the distinct disadvantage of being insensitive to most calcifications. However, it is effective for demonstration of renal vein and inferior vena cava involvement.

Adrenal MR imaging is an effective method of detecting normal and abnormal adrenal glands. Either MRI or CT can detect adrenal lesions, but neither is tissue specific. MRI seems effective for solving problems not resolved by CT.

Lymph nodes can be detected by MRI with approximately the same sensitivity as by CT. Neither test is tissue specific. It is easier to differentiate lymph nodes from blood vessels by MRI than by CT.

## Pelvis

MRI has real potential advantages in the pelvis because of its excellent contrast resolution and multiplanar capability. Studies are progressing in an effort to determine the role of MRI in detection and staging of tumors arising from the ovary, uterus, prostate and urinary bladder.

## Musculoskeletal

MRI of bones, joints and soft tissues is effective at detecting and localizing masses. Compared with CT, bone tumors, both benign and malignant, are detected as well or better by MRI. MRI seems better than CT at determining the extent of bone tumors and at detection and documentation of extent of disease for soft tissue masses. MRI has advantages in the demonstration of bone infarcts, ligament and tendon injury and muscle diseases. Because of good spatial resolution, excellent contrast resolution and multiplanar capability, MRI will be an important musculoskeletal imaging procedure.

## Breast

MRI of the breast has been shown to be capable of detecting normal tissue, cysts, fibroadenomas and cancers. Surface coil technology is necessary to obtain the best spatial resolution. Even with good spatial resolution and well-chosen pulse sequences, it may not be possible to confidently differentiate benign from malignant lesions. It is not yet clear what fraction of cancers can be detected by MRI. However, it is known that small calcifications are not detected by MRI. At this time, it is clear that MRI is not a replacement for mammography. The role of MRI in the analysis of breast diseases is yet to be determined.

## CLOSING COMMENTS

It must be recognized that clinical studies of magnetic resonance imaging are still in their infancy. Only small populations have been studied and only a basic understanding of clinical applications has been acquired. This is complicated by the fact that MRI hardware and software technology are not yet mature. Future technological improvements will impact clinical applications in ways we can not yet predict.

Other important clinical applications are either entering clinical testing or have not yet reached sufficient technological maturity for real clinical testing. These include in vivo imaging and spectroscopic applications of other nuclides such as sodium, phosphorus, carbon and fluorine. It is possible that important clinical applications will develop from among these investigations.

Finally, there are three important clinical realities that must be acknowledged. First, MRI is a method with a largely incompletely defined clinical role. Second, the method is expensive and is likely to become more expensive rather than less. Third, reimbursement for the clinical applications of MRI is uncertain, and will probably remain so for a prolonged period of time.

## REFERENCES

### Brain
1. W.G. Bradley Jr., V. Waluch, R.A. Yadley, R.R. Wycoff, Radiology, 152 (1984) 695-702.
2. R.C. Brasch, D.E. Nitecki, M. Brant-Zawadzki, D.R. Enzmann, G.E. Wesbey, T.N. Tozer, L.D. Tuck, C.E. Cann, J.R. Fike, P. Sheldon, AJNR 4 (1983) 1035-1039.
3. R. Felix, W. Schorner, M. Laniado, H-P. Niendorf, C. Claussen, W. Fiegler, U. Speck, Radiology 156 (1985) 681-688.
4. B.D. Flannigan, W.G. Bradley Jr., J.C. Mazziotta, W. Rauschning, J.R. Bentson, R.B. Lufkin, G.B. Heishima, Radiology 154 (1985) 375-383.
5. S.K. Hilal, A.A. Maudsley, J.B. Ra, H.E. Simon, P. Roschmann, S. Wittekoek, Z.H. Cho, S.K. Mun, J Comput Assist Tomogr 9 (1985) 1-7.
6. B.O. Kjos, M. Brant-Zawadzki, W. Kucharczyk, W.M. Kelly, D. Norman, T.H. Newton, Radiology 155 (1985) 363-369.
7. B.C.P. Lee, J.B. Kneeland, M.D.F. Deck, P.T. Cahill, Radiology 153 (1984) 137-143.
### Spinal Cord
8. G. DiChiro, J.L. Doppman, A.J. Dwyer, N.J. Patronas, R.H. Knop, D. Bairamian, M. Vermess, E.H. Oldfield, Radiology 156 (1985) 689-697.

126

9.  B.C.P. Lee, R.D. Zimmerman, J.J. Manning, M.D.F. Deck, AJR 144 (1985) 1149-1156.
10. M.T. Modic, W. Pavlicek, M.A. Weinstein, F. Boumphrey, F. Ngo, R. Hardy, P.M. Duchesneau, Radiology 152 (1984) 103-111.
11. M.T. Modic, M.A. Weinstein, W. Pavlicek, F. Boumphrey, D. Starnes, P.M. Duchesneau, AJR 141 (1983) 1129-1136.

Chest
12. F.E. Carroll Jr., J.E. Loyd, K.B. Nolop, J.C. Collins, Invest Radiol 20 (1985) 381-387.
13. D.M. Epstein, H. Kressel, W. Gefter, L. Axel, D. Thickman, J. Aronchick, W. Miller, J Comput Assist Tomogr 8 (1984) 670-676.
14. H.S. Glazer, J.K.T. Lee, J.P. Heiken, D. Ling, W.G. Totty, D.M. Balfe, B. Emani, T.H. Wasserman, W.A. Murphy, Radiology 156 (1985) 721-726.
15. R.G. Levitt, H.S. Glazer, C.L. Roper, J.K.T. Lee, W.A. Murphy, AJR 145 (1985) 9-14.
16. N.L. Muller, G. Gamsu, W.R. Webb, Radiology 155 (1985) 687-690.
17. W.R. Webb, B.G. Jensen, R. Sollitto, G. de Geer, M. McCowin, G. Gamsu, E. Moore, Radiology 156 (1985) 117-124.

Cardiovascular
18. L. Axel, AJR 143 (1984) 1157-1166.
19. W.G. Bradley Jr., V. Waluch, Radiology 154 (1985) 443-450.
20. C.B. Higgins, Radiology 156 (1985) 577-588.
21. C.B. Higgins, B.F. Byrd II, M.T. McNamara, P. Lanzer, M.J. Lipton, E. Botvinick, N.B. Schiller, L.E. Crooks, L. Kaufman, Radiology 155 (1985) 671-679.
22. H. Hricak, E. Amparo, M.R. Fisher, L. Crooks, C.B. Higgins, Radiology 156 (1985) 415-422.
23. J.K.T. Lee, D. Ling, J.P. Heiken, H.S. Glazer, G.A. Sicard, W.G. Totty, R.G. Levitt, W.A. Murphy, AJR 143 (1984) 1197-1202.
24. G.M. Pohost, A.V. Ratner, JAMA 251 (1984) 1304-1309.

Abdomen
25. P.L. Choyke, H.Y. Kressel, H.M. Pollack, P.M. Arger, L. Axel, A.C. Mamourian, Radiology 152 (1984) 471-477.
26. G.C. Dooms, H. Hricak, M.E. Moseley, K. Bottles, M. Fisher, C.B. Higgins, Radiology 155 (1985) 691-697.
27. J.P. Heiken, J.K.T. Lee, H.S. Glazer, D. Ling, Radiology 156 (1985) 423-427.
28. H. Hricak, B.E. Demas, R.D. Williams, M.T. McNamara, M.W. Hedgcock, E.G. Amparo, E.A. Tanagho, Radiology 154 (1985) 709-715.
29. J.K.T. Lee, J.P. Heiken, W.T. Dixon, Radiology 156 (1985) 429-433.
30. J.K.T. Lee, J.P. Heiken, D. Ling, H.S. Glazer, D.M. Balfe, R.G. Levitt, W.T. Dixon, W.A. Murphy Jr., Radiology 153 (1984) 181-188.
31. A.W.-L. Leung, G.M. Bydder, R.E. Steiner, D.J. Bryant, I.R. Young, AJR 143 (1984) 1215-1227.
32. C.L. Schultz, J.R. Haaga, B.D. Fletcher, R.J. Alfidi, M.A. Schultz, AJR 143 (1984) 1235-1240.
33. D.D. Stark, R.C. Felder, J. Wittenberg, S. Saini, R.J. Butch, M.E. White, R.R. Edelman, P.R. Mueller, J.F. Simeone, A. M. Cohen, T.J. Brady, J.T. Ferrucci Jr, AJR 145 (1985) 213-222.
34. J.C. Weinreb, J.M. Cohen, K.R. Maravilla, Radiology 156 (1985) 435-440.

Pelvis
35. H. Butler, P.J. Bryan, J.P. LiPuma, A.M. Cohen, S. El Yousef, J.G. Andriole, J. Lieberman, AJR 143 (1984) 1259-1266.
36. P.Y. Poon, R.W. McCallum, M.M. Henkelman, M.J. Bronskill, S.B. Sutcliffe, M.A.S. Jewett, W.D. Rider, A.W. Bruce, Radiology 154 (1985) 143-149.

Musculoskeletal
37. M. Reiser, N. Rupp, H.-J. Heller, B. Allgayer, P. Lukas, J. Lange, K. Pfafferott, U. Fink, Europ J. Radiol 4 (1984) 288-293.
38. W.G. Totty, W.A. Murphy, W.I. Ganz, B. Kumar, W.J. Daum, B.A. Seigel, AJR 143 (1984) 1273-1280.
39. D.A. Turner, C.C. Prodromos, J.P. Petasnick, J.W. Clark, Radiology 154 (1985) 717-722.
40. W.D.Zimmer, T.H. Berquist, R.A. McLeod, F.H. Sim, D.J. Pritchard, T.C. Shives, L.E. Wold, G.R. May, Radiology 155 (1985) 709-718.

*Synthesis and Applications of Isotopically Labeled Compounds 1985.*
Proceedings of the Second International Symposium, Kansas City, MO, U.S.A.,
3—6 September 1985, R.R. Muccino (Ed.), 127—132
© 1986 Elsevier Science Publishers B.V., Amsterdam — Printed in The Netherlands

DIRECT FLOW/MOTION, COILS, AND FIELD STRENGTH CONCERNS IN MRI

Paul R. Moran, Ph.D.

Department of Radiology, Bowman Gray School of Medicine, 300 S. Hawthorne
Road, Winston-Salem, North Carolina (U.S.A.)

ABSTRACT

Specific flow/motion bipolar phase-gradient encodings are interlaced into
MR sequences for direct NMR imaging of motion quantities, velocity,
acceleration, etc. This allows evaluation of the functional properties of
tissue, blood flow, heart-wall velocity, vortical-eddies in vascular disease,
and perfusion assessment. Attention to fundamentals and basics is important
in designing successful flow/motion imaging sequences.

INTRODUCTION

Magnetic resonance images (MRI) reflect subject anatomy, but the
image-values and contrasts represent more, or at least should. They should
help evaluate physiology and, we hope, even functional status of tissues. It
is better here to attack one sub-topic of the oral version, detailing
fundamentals and some practicalities, than to attempt all topics with
certainty of doing three very poor jobs.

BASICS OF MR IMAGING

Figure 1 shows an NMR-imaging cycle. The basics of data strategies,
etc., have been described elsewhere (1). In the initial free-induction-decay
(FID) signal, spin-excitation phases begin evolving in the magnetic field
gradient modulation, (gamma) $(G.r)t$, and $FID(t) = M_{ex}(r) \times \exp[\ 2(PI)\ (q\ .
r)]$. Wavevector "q" is a Fourier Transform encoding variable, $q = INTGRL
(T_B ---> t_c):[\ F\ dt']$. The spin frequency gradient, F, is caused by G. The
evolution FID-time is $t = (t_c - T_{BO})$; that is, $q = (F\ t)$.

The system demodulates phase-coherently, and stores, as digitized-data,
the phase-gradient evolution of the magnetization, for which we use $F(t_c)$. In
the example of Fig. 1, when a subsequent rf-180°-echo pulse occurs, it rotates
excitation phases immediately after the 180° rf-echo-pulse into the negative
of their value immediately before. That is why the F modulations invert
before the 180°-rf-pulse with respect to the G modulations. The F graph shows

128

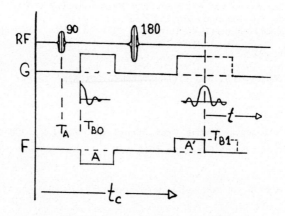

Fig. 1:  A single echo sequence.

physically why an echo-signal occurs in Fig. 1 at $T_{B1}$; the phase-gradient
modulations for all spins accumulated under the A lobe become reversed under
the A' lobe.  When the area under A' precisely cancels the area under A, then
the spin phases everywhere return to zero; the modulation-integral zero-point
defines $T_{B1}$, and a new FID recurs.  With $t = (t_c - T_{B1})$ we again have FID(t) =
$M_{ex}(r)$ exp [ 2(PI)i (q . r)].  The "free-induction-anti-decay" preceeding $t_c$ =
$T_{B1}$, expressed in time from echo-center, t, is a "mirror" FID running to the
negative time variable.  In terms of the Fourier variable, q, the double-sided
FIDs(t) trace out both the negative and positive domains of q.  There is an
empirical method to determine $T_{B1}$ precisely.

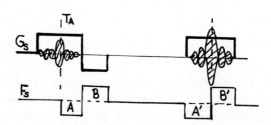

Fig. 2:  Slice-select for 2DFT.

NMR excitation may be confined to a slice with the perpendicular
gradient, $G_s$, shown in Fig. 2.  The modulations at both the 90 and the 180
rf-pulses return to the phase-zero condition.  Using rf-180°-echo pulses,
rather than reversing gradient coil currents, echoes any static off-resonance

effects back to $T_{B1}$-points also as phase-zeroes (the Hahn-point). A different slice-select, in Fig. 3, has the B-lobes from Fig. 2 extended as shown in cross-hatching; now A and B do not cancel. However, when the B'A' lobes occur at the 180-rf-pulse, we regain the phase-zero situation since A cancels A' and B cancels B'.

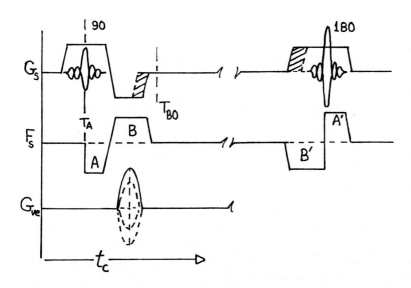

Fig. 3:  The zero-dipole slice-select and discrete-pulse "view-encoding".

The fundamental theorem of MRI is this:  the encoding to variable "q" from variable "r", of the distribution $M_{ex}(r)$, yields the <u>Fourier Transform</u> of $M_{ex}(r)$: FID-signals(q) $\equiv$ {FT(q):$M_{ex}$}. A computer Fourier Transform algorithm (of various types) reconstructs from these data the in-phase and the quadrature-phase image-arrays numerically depicting $M_{ex}(r)$. Conversion of numerical values to intensity in a video-monitor gives the displayed image. In the "2DFT" mode, one dimension of "r" encoding is done by the "view encoding" gradient, $G_{ve}$. The $G_{ve}$ amplitude increments from cycle to cycle. The $F_r$ modulation encodes the remaining Cartesian spatial dimension into the readout wavenumber $q_r$. The resulting data set is the two dimensional FT of $M_{ex}(R_{ve}, R_r)$, the two dimensional slice distribution:  FID-cycled-set = {FT($Q_{ve}$(n):{ FT($q_r$):$M_{ex}$ } }.

BIPOLAR PHASE-GRADIENT MODULATIONS

We described above the encodings of first echo-FIDs when the molecules

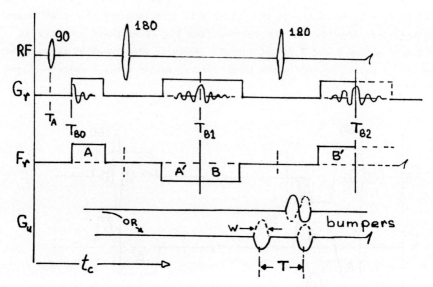

Fig. 4: A two-echo sequence with second-echo-FIDs "bumper" velocity-encoders.

possessing the NMR moments are motionless. Figure 4 shows a sequence with second echo-FIDs signals. In uniform motion at elapsed time "t", from a base-starting time, $r(t) = ( r(0) + v \, t)$. For "t" starting at the FID position $T_{B2}$, $r(0)$ is the average position the molecule actually had at the time of encoding. The effect of velocity "v" during this readout can be shown to give the molecule's image blurred out over the range it traversed while being measured; physically a very sensible result. In a stream of transport, no "motion during readout" effects occur.

We showed that the phase-gradient modulation integrals MUST return to the phase-zero condition for any constant position variable. We next, however, determine the overall phase-gradient modulation for a constant velocity in the interval. For a given echo-FID, that time interval extends from the excitation time, $T_A$, to the begin-FID time, $T_B$ (i.e., the q = 0 point), for the echoes in question. For any origin of time, "(v t)" is a pure temporal-dipole operator. It enters the phase-integral as $[F(t).v \, t]$ and produces an additive velocity-dependent phase-shift, $\exp[ 2(PI)i \, (u \, . \, v)]$. The Fourier variable "u" is the full temporal dipole-moment of the phase-gradient in the full interval; $u = INTGRL:\{F(t) \, t \, dt\}$. The operator (v t), however, projects onto any unipole modulation, such as the view-encoding pulse of Fig. 3, with exactly zero result.

The bipolar phase-gradient modulations (BPGM) on the $F_r$ timing diagram of

Fig. 4 show that the BPGM dipole AA' cancels BB'. That is why one chooses second-echoes. The single unipolar pulses, $G_{ve}$, give no velocity phase-integral, and we compensate all the slice-select modulations, as shown in Fig. 3, so that the select-direction BPGM-dipole vanishes also. For the second echo-FIDs there is no inherent F(t) dipole; we can control velocity encoding by the "bumpers" indicated. For example, u = $(G_{u0}$ T W); now we have FID2-Signal(t) = "sum total of" $M_{ex}(r)$ x exp[ 2(PI)i (q . r)] x exp[ 2(PI)i (u . v)]. Thus the velocity at any point is encoded to "u" just as position in space "r" was encoded to "q". The full data set therefore is a multi-dimensional Fourier encoding, {FT(u):FT(q):$M_{ex}$}, and we can fully reconstruct (from a complete data set) the distribution $M_{ex}(r)$ $D_r(v)$.

PRACTICALITIES

For useful information, it is unnecessary to reconstruct fully the velocity-spectrum, $D_r(v)$. But, there is an important and misunderstood point; within any spatially resolvable volume there is not a unique velocity, but rather a distribution $D_r(v)$ of molecular velocities, for which "v" is encoded into "u". Practitioners of Fourier space data-collection use well-known simplifications for restricted encodings, but one must obey the fundamental rules of this game. We have used the <u>average</u> velocity (v) in the form of flow-density $M_{ex}$ (v) for a displayed quantity.

Among many pitfalls for the inexperienced researcher, an example is that the dipole of the BPGM-AA' is huge on the first-echo FID's (Fig. 1 or Fig. 4). Slice-select dipoles, Fig. 2, can also cause an unmanageably large $u_s$. One must obey the Nyquist-condition: the minimum "u" applied must be smaller than the reciprocal of the maximum "v" encountered. Recent literature shows that forgetting these dipole-offsets, results in scans with a number of bizarre, but perfectly predictable, motion "artifacts".

A flow/motion sequence we favor extends the select-gradient compensations of Fig. 3 to a <u>single</u> rf-180-echo pulse sequence wherein we obtain <u>three</u> echo-FID readouts. This is a trivial rearrangement of the example we used in a 1982 publication (2) first proposing the theory and method for BPGM phase-modulated direct NMR-imaging of flow/motion.

Variations are obvious, but when the timings are set carefully to the scale illustrated in the timing-diagram (Fig. 5) we obtain some remarkable properties:

    - We get three echoes, two in gradient-reversal mode and a "Hahn" echo.
    - The third echo-FIDs at $T_{B3}$ have a zeroed read-gradient dipole moment.
    - By staggering the $G_r$ modulations slightly "downstream" we can align the

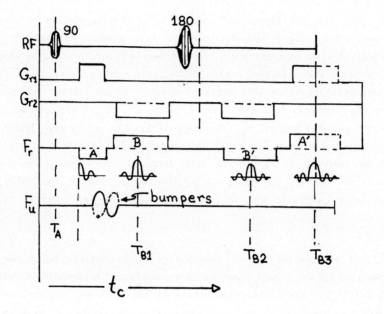

Fig. 5:   Single rf-echo pulse sequence with three echo-FIDs, dipole-zeroed at
          the third-FID time, $T_{B3}$.

Hahn-echo point precisely on the gradient-modulation echo-point, $T_{B3}$.

    - All quadrupole moments of the BPGM vanish for the $T_{B3}$ signals, thus
avoiding "acceleration" confusions for very fast curved flow.

    - We use the analog of this compensating procedure for the slice-select
gradients (see Fig. 3) if we wish to run in slice-select 2D MRI modes.

    - Moreover, the $T_{B1}$-data have a large $u_r$, the $T_{B2}$-data are negative of
that value, and the $T_{B3}$ data initially have a zero value; these give an
efficient spanning of wide "velocity dynamic range".   A complement-set of
"u's" (1st and 2nd echo of Fig. 5) are important in perfusive flow imaging.
Or, we can get three separate encodings in $u_r$, condensed into a single
composite cycle.

    - We get flexibility in secondary modulation with the bumper-BPGM pulses.

REFERENCES

1    King KF and Moran PR, A unified description of NMR imaging,
    data-collection strategies, and reconstruction.   Med Phys, 11 (1983)
    1-14.
2    Moran PR, A flow zeugmatographic interlace for NMR imaging in humans.
    Magn Reson Imaging, 1 (1982) 197-203.

*Synthesis and Applications of Isotopically Labeled Compounds 1985.*
Proceedings of the Second International Symposium, Kansas City, MO, U.S.A.,
3—6 September 1985, R.R. Muccino (Ed.), 133—138
1986 Elsevier Science Publishers B.V., Amsterdam — Printed in The Netherlands

THE SYNTHESIS OF RADIOLIGANDS FOR BINDING STUDIES

Louis PICHAT

DIRECTOR OF RESEARCH AT CEA. CEN SACLAY 91191 GIF/YVETTE CEDEX (FRANCE)

RECEPTOR SITE  ANALYSIS IN PHAMACOLOGICAL SCIENCES

Simple binding studies with high specific activity tritium labeled ligands
are widely used in basic and applied research (1). They contribute to the localization of classesand subclasses of various biological receptors as already reported in the literature (2). Various speakers at this session will also illustrate this point. They allow the quantitative assay of the affinity of many drugs
to these receptors. Receptor  site analysis will help the screening of biologically potent chemicals and eventually lead to the discovery of new drugs with
high therapeutic specificity, fewer side effects and devoid of addiction properties (1) (3). Radioligands are necessary tools for the drug design by the method
of receptor fit (4). Measurement of drug activity in receptor-binding experiments
offers definite advantages since for most receptors up to 100 chemicals in a day
can be screened (1) with the further advantage that only one milligram of chemical is used for screening. One single rat brain will suffice for several thousands
binding experiments (1). The gathering of data can be  sped up further by the use
of automated Robotics (5) or an automated harvester (6). Binding experiments also
help to evaluate the extent of  agonist, antagonist, mixed agonist + antagonist
properties of drugs. They provide valuable data very rapidly for systematic structure activity analysis. It is obvious that these in vitro results have to be substantiated by in vivo studies. In spite of its lack of specificity, the radioreceptor assays of drugs in plasma appear promising in pharmacology (7). Binding
assays will also contribute to the isolation and purification of biological receptors and a detailed description of the regional distribution of specific receptors in healthy and diseased subjects. It is likely that binding experiments will
lead to the identification of previously unrecognized endogenous agonist in living subjects. Permeation or trapping of ligands is sometimes a serious problem
which can give the illusion of specific binding. This pitfall in binding studies
should be given due consideration (8).

From this necessarily short review it is certain that the binding assays to membranes of radioactive ligands is a valuable technique in pharmacological sciences.
The papers to be presented at this session will further demonstrate its usefulness.

SOME RECENT SYNTHESES OF $[^3H]$ LIGANDS FOR THE ANALYSIS OF BIOLOGICAL RECEPTORS

The number of $[^3H]$ ligands commercially available is increasing rapidly. New
ligands believed to be better  will replace older ones.

In this field it is difficult to keep up to date. My purpose, at the      begin
ning of this session is to describe very briefly some synthesis of high specific
activity $[^3H]$ ligands which were carried out in the CEA laboratories.

Catalytic direct exchange tritium labeling procedures ($CH_3CO_2T-T_2O$-Pt or Pd)
($T_2$-PdO) rarely give the sufficiently high specific radioactivity required for
binding studies (minimum 20 Curies/mM).

The method of choice is the catalytic saturation with tritium of double or
triple bonds of appropriate precursors in which all the other functional groups

134

are already present :

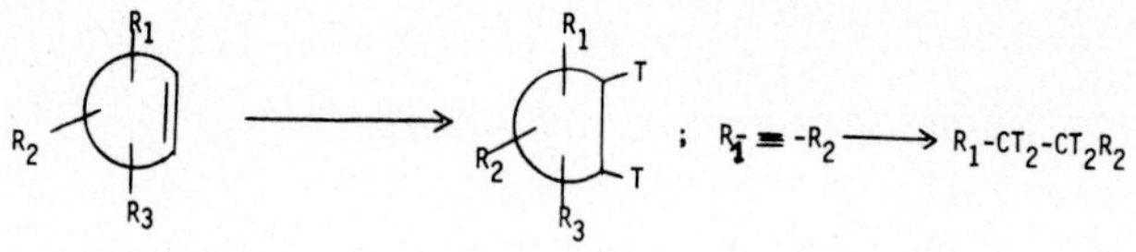

$; \quad R_1 = -R_2 \longrightarrow R_1-CT_2-CT_2R_2$

The synthesis which will be outlined here will illustrate this principle. Bin-ding receptors assays being carried out essentially "IN VITRO", on isolated mem-branes, the label may be placed on metabolically unstable positions (N-methyl, O-methyl, N-propyl etc...). Many commercially available [³H] ligands such as the benzodiazepines are N-methyl labeled.

(±) WB 4101 : 5 a selective in vitro and in vivo antagonist of $\alpha_1$ adrenorerecep-tors (9-12) was used for some years and was commercially available although its synthesis was not described. Recently (13), we gave the full details of the prepa-ration of [2,3-³H-benzodioxanyl] WB 4101 at specific activity 50-60 Ci/mM, based on the catalytic reduction of precursor 5 with ³H in presence of Wilkinson's ca-talyst in benzene. ³H-NMR was also reported (scheme 1) :

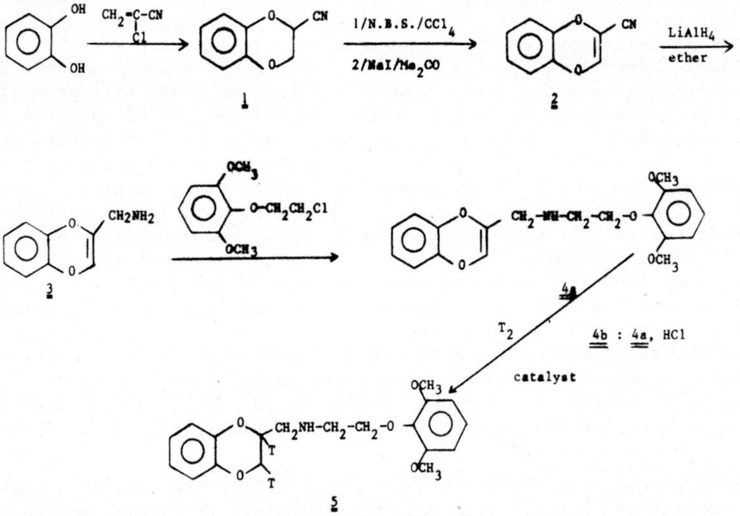

Scheme 1

(±) RX-78-1094 : 2-(2-imidazolinyl)-1,4-benzodioxan a selective $\alpha_2$ adrenorecep-tor : 7.

The $\alpha_2$-adrenoreceptors are likely to play a very important physiological ro-le (14). RX-78-1094 is an $\alpha_2$-adrenoreceptor antagonist with a selectivity $\alpha_2/\alpha_1$, for the adrenoreceptors superior to that of yohimbin or rauwolscine (15-17). The direct preparation of 7 by the catalytic reduction of 6 could not be attempted since all our efforts to synthesize : 6 failed (18).

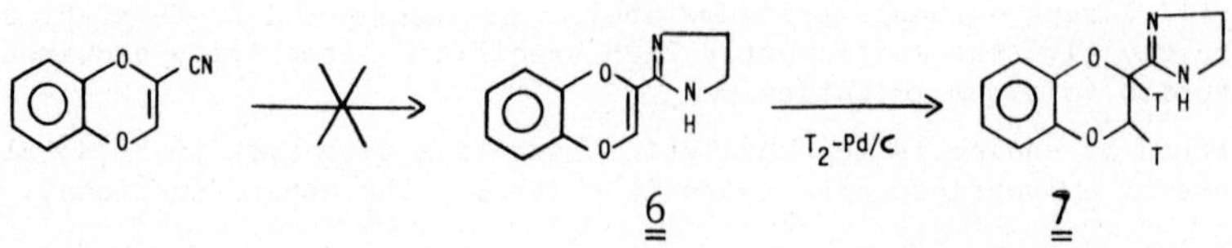

We (19) had to resort to more circuitous routes (scheme 2), involving more technical skill, based on the ring closure of α-aminocarboxamides (routes B,$C_1$, $C_2$, $C_3$) to 2-imidazolines by $Me_3$ Al (20).

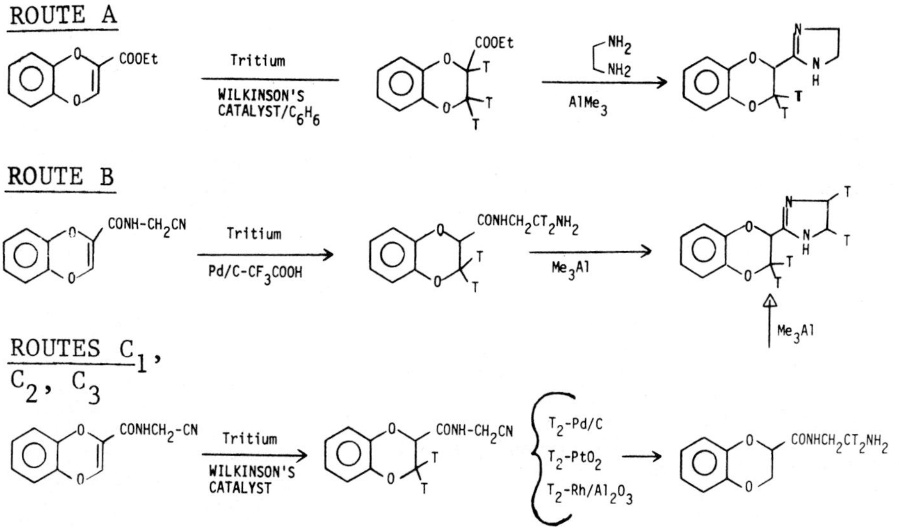

## ROUTE A

## ROUTE B

## ROUTES $C_1$, $C_2$, $C_3$

Scheme 2

The results of these methods are recorded in table 1. Specific activities varied (35.5 —— 44 Ci/mM) according to the route used. Table 1 also reports the tritium distribution measured by $^3$H.NMR (21).

| Méthod | A | B | $C_1$ | $C_2$ | $C_3$ |
|---|---|---|---|---|---|
| Specific activity Ci/MMole | 44 | 35,5 | 41,5 | 39 | 39 |
| $^3$H-NMR | B : 50% C : 50% | B : 17,5% C : 17,5% I : 65 % | B : 31% C : 31% I : 38% | B : 38% C : 38% I : 24% | B : 40% C : 40% I : 20% |

Table 1

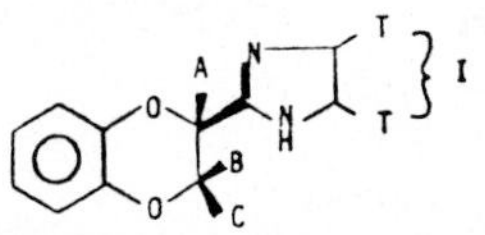

[$^3$H-n-Propyl]-8-Hydroxy-PAT : 8-Hydroxy-Di-($^3$H-n-Propyl)-2-amino tetraline : 8 5-HT-Agonist.

5-HT-agonists are of interest for the development of drugs with antidepressive activity and devoid of hallucinogenic properties, and for the evaluation of the role of 5-HT in sleep, body temperature, pain, and sexual behavior (22).

Arvidsson and al. (23) had shown that 8-hydroxy-2-di-(n-propyl)aminotetralin : 8 is a centrally acting 5-hydroxytryptamine receptor agonist while the 5,6,7 hydroxy isomers : 9 are centrally acting DA receptor agonists.

Comparison of 5-HT and 8-hydroxy-PAT as well as superposition of these structures clearly show their analogy :

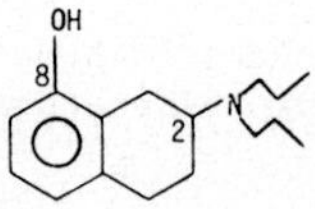

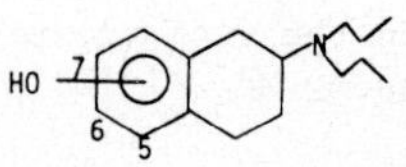

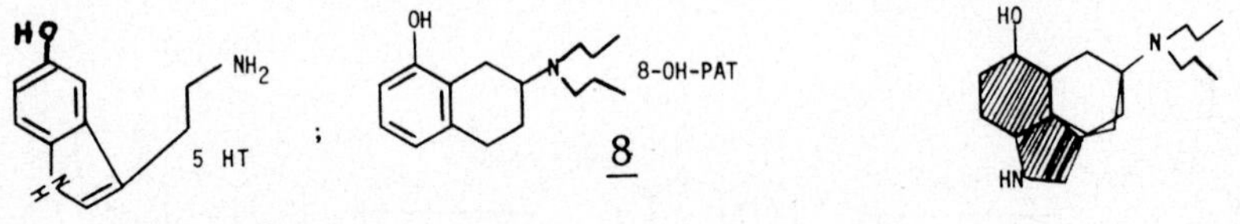

M. Hamon and his coworkers have established in very recent papers (24-26)
that [3H]-8-OH PAT is a good tool for the labeling of HT$_1$ sites, demonstrating
the heterogeneity of 5-HT$_1$ receptors, labeling in striatum the presynaptic receptors, and studying the 5-HT$_1$ pre and postsynaptic autoreceptors. Being fairly stable to self radiolysis [3H]-8-OH PAT does not require repurifications as
frequently as 5 HT. It was prepared at specific activities > 100 Ci/mM according
to scheme 3.

ROUTE A

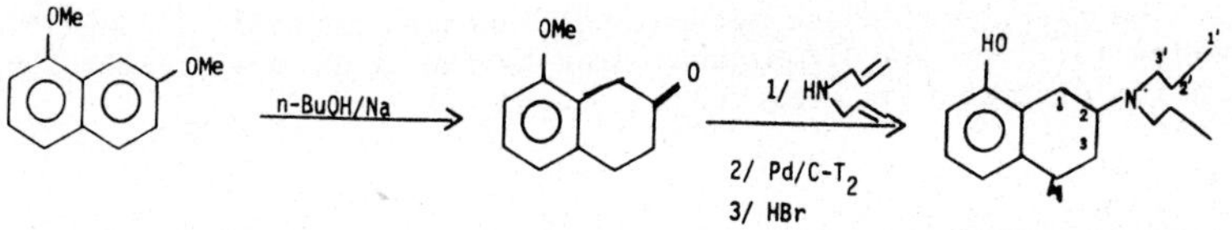

$^3$H distribution ($^3$H-NMR) : 1 + 4 : 12% - 2 : 6% - 1' : 37% - 2' : 31% - 3' :
14%.

ROUTE B

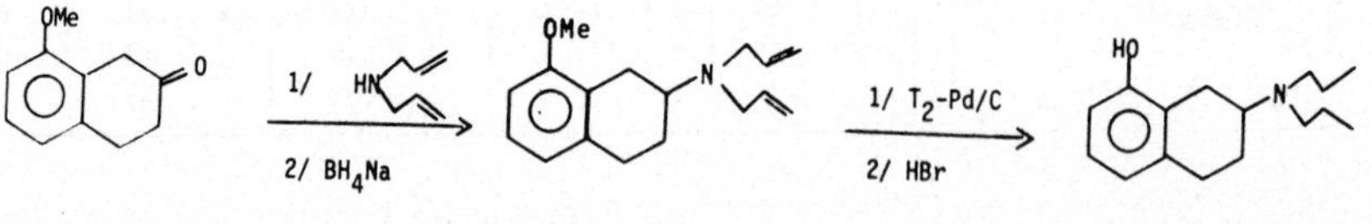

Scheme 3
3-(3-HYDROXYPHENYL)-n-Propyl Piperidine "3-PPP" DA AGONIST : 9

According to Arvidsson and al. (27) 3-PPP (9) is a DA autoreceptor agonist ;
it labels the pre and postsynaptic DA receptors. M. Hamon (27) as well as Dutch
researchers(28) reported that [3H] 3-PPP does not in fact allow the caracterisa-
tion of DA-autoreceptors.

[3H]-3-PPP was prepared at spec. act. 100 Ci/mM as shown in scheme 4.

1-(2-Chlorophenyl)-N-Methyl-N(1-methyl)[3H]propylisoquinoline carboxamide :
[3H]PK 11195 :  peripheral benzodiazepin receptor :  10

Chemically unrelated to benzodiazepines this isoquinoline has a high affinity for the peripherial type binding sites for benzodiazepines (29,30). Its preparation by the catalytic reduction of the unsaturated precursor : 10 was straightforward (31). Spec. act. was 50 Ci/mM.

N-1-[2-Thienyl]cyclohexyl[3H-3,4]piperidine :[3H] TCP for the phencyclidine
(PCP) receptors  :  13

TCP : 13 a thienyl analogue of PCP was found (32) to have a high affinity for PCP sites. The use of [3H] TCP has three main advantages over [3H] PCP : i) it dissociates slowly from its binding sites, ii) it has a better affinity for PCP binding sites than PCP itself, iii) the non specific binding obtained with [3H] TCP is much lower than that found with [3H] PCP.

Catalytic reduction of the tetrahydropyridine : 12 (33) provided easily [3H] TCP at specific activity > 50 Ci/mM.

138

REFERENCES

1  - S.H. Snyder. J. Med. Chem. 26 (1983) 1667-1672.
2  - H. Gozlan, S. El Mestikawy, L. Pichat, J. Glowinski, M. Hamon. Nature 305, (1983) 140-142.
3  - D. Bidet, J.C. Gaignault. L'Actualité Chimique (1984) 17-29.
4  - P.J. Goodford. J. Med. Chem. 27 (1984) 557-564.
5  - Zymark Corp. Technical Brief 109 (1984).
6  - Brandel- Cat. No-M 12R-No M 24R - (1983).
7  - G. Perret, P. Simon. J. Pharmacol. (Paris) 15 (1984) 256-286.
8  - J.M. Maloteaux, A. Gossuin, C. Waterkeyn, P.M. Laduron Biological Pharmacology 32 (1983) 2543-2548.
9  - M. Butler, D.H. Jenkinson, J. Pharmacol 52 (1978) 303.
10 - D.C. Prichard, S. Snyder Life Sciences 24 (1979) 79.
11 - G.M. Grew. Naunyn-Schmiedeberg's Arch. Pharmacol. 319 (1982) 222.
12 - R.R. Rufolo Jr., W.L. Nelson, E.Y. Yaden Archives of Pharmacology, 322 (1983) 93.
13 - G. Guillaumet, G. Coudert, M. Ponchant, J.P. Beaucourt, L. Pichat J. Labeled Compounds and Radiopharmaceuticals 21 (1984) 161.
14 - P.B. Timmermans, P.A. Van Zanten. J. Med. Chem. 25 (1982) 1389.
15 - C.B. Chapleo and al. J. Brit. Pharmacol. 842P (1981).
16 - H. Schmitt and al. C.R. Acad. Sciences 290D (1983) 1553.
17 - C. Pimoule, C. Scatton, S.Z. Langer. Eur. J. Pharmacol 95 (1983) 79.
18 - G. Couderc, G. Guillaumet, M. Clement, M. Tostain, L. Pichat - unpublished
19 - P. Ponchant, L. Pichat, G. Couderc, G. Guillaumet - unpublished.
20 - G. Neef, U. Eder, G. Sauer - J. Org. Chem. 46 (1981) 2824-2826.
21 - L. Sergent, J.P. Beaucourt - unpublished.
22 - L.E. Arvidsson and al. J. Med. Chem. 27 (1984) 921-923.
23 - L.E. Arvidsson and al. J. Med. Chem. 24 (1981) 921-923.
24 - H. Gozlan, S. El Mestikawy, L. Pichat, J. Glowinski, M. Hamon - Nature 305 (1983) 140.
25 - M. Hamon, H. Gozlan, M.D. Hall, S. El Mestikawy, M.B. Emerit, L. Pichat. Regulation of transmitter Function-Proc. 5th Meeting Eur. Soc. Neurochem. E.S. Vizi and K. Magyar (eds) 1984.
26 - M.D. Hall, S. El Mestikawy, M.B. Emerit, L. Pichat, M. Hamon, H; Gozlan J. of Neurochemistry 1985, 1685-1696.
27 - M. Hamon - Unpublished - Personnal Communication.
28 - Th. de Buer, J. Van Dertogt, F. Nefkens. Dutch Federal meeting. April 1985.
29 - G. Le Fur and al. Life Sciences 32 (1983) 1839.
30 - J. Benavides and al. Arch. Int. Pharmacodyn. 266 (1983) 38.
31 - G. Gueremy. Pharmuka-R.P. provided Compound 10.
32 - J. Vignon, R. Chicheportiche, M. Chicheportiche, J.M. Kamenka, P. Geneste, L. Lazdunski. Brain Research 280 (1983) 194-197.
33 - J.M. Kamenka kindly supplied compound 12.

ACKNOWLEDGMENTS

Besides the already quoted co-authors, M. Audinot, G. Chatelain, Ph. Donie, M. Herbert, P. Parent, P. Ponchant contributed to the synthesis described in this lecture. Melle F. Guyard typed the slides and the proceedings.

*Synthesis and Applications of Isotopically Labeled Compounds 1985.*
Proceedings of the Second International Symposium, Kansas City, MO, U.S.A.,
3—6 September 1985, R.R. Muccino (Ed.), 139—144

THE CONTRIBUTION OF LIGAND BINDING STUDIES TO THE PRESENT KNOWLEDGE

OF SEROTONIN RECEPTORS IN BRAIN


M. HAMON[1], H. GOZLAN[1], M.B. EMERIT[1], M.D. HALL[1] and L. PICHAT[2]

[1]INSERM U288, CHU Pitié-Salpêtrière, 75634 Paris cedex 13 (France)

[2]CEA, 91191 Gif-sur-Yvette (France)


ABSTRACT

An abundant literature on central serotonin receptors has been
published during the last ten years owing to the development of
ligand binding studies with radioactive agonists and antagonists.
Membrane labelling by $^3$H-agonists such as $^3$H-serotonin itself,
$^3$H-8-OH-DPAT and $^3$H-LSD has led to the discovery of three distinct
classes of specific sites : two at the postsynaptic level, $5\text{-HT}_{1A}$
and $5\text{-HT}_{1B}$, and the third one, $5\text{-HT}_3$, on presynaptic serotoninergic terminals. Another postsynaptic site called $5\text{-HT}_2$ has been
identified using radioactive antagonists such as $^3$H-spiperone, $^3$H-
ketanserin, $^3$H-metergoline and 125-I-LSD. The possible correspondence of these binding sites with 5-HT receptors characterized by
other (electrophysiological, behavioural, biochemical) approaches
is the subject of current investigations.


INTRODUCTION

Although serotonin (5-hydroxytryptamine, 5-HT) has been proposed as being a neurotransmitter in the central nervous system
(CNS) more than 30 years ago, studies on its receptors, i.e. the
structures mediating its neurotransmitter function on target cells,
really began only in 1974 with the development of appropriate receptor binding techniques (ref.1). Beforehand, mainly indirect
methods were used such as the measurement of central 5-HT turnover
in rats, with the postulate that the administration of a 5-HT antagonist should increase the turnover rate whereas an agonist should
reduce it. However, this rule does not apply in all cases, and for
instance, the antagonists acting on the $5\text{-HT}_2$ receptor class (see
below) have been shown recently to produce no alteration of central 5-HT turnover (ref.2).

During the last ten years, not only ligand binding techniques,
but also appropriate direct biochemical methods have been developed which led to the discovery of various 5-HT receptor classes
such as those coupled to adenylate cyclase or controlling

phosphatidylinositol turnover (ref.3). However, the ligand binding technique is undoubtedly the most convenient for rapid and reliable investigations of central neurotransmitter receptors, and for 5-HT, its application has led to the first clearcut classification of its various receptor classes in the CNS. Schematically, radioactive agonists appear to label preferentially the receptor class called $5-HT_1$ and the radioactive antagonists the $5-HT_2$ class, and this short review on the labelled ligands presently used for the characterization of 5-HT receptor binding sites is thenceforth also a brief comment on these two main classes of central 5-HT specific sites.

COMMENTS ON THE LIGAND BINDING TECHNIQUE

Classically, the ligand binding technique is applied *in vitro* and consists of incubating brain membranes with the radioactive agonist or antagonist until equilibrium is reached ; then membranes are collected by rapid filtration through a glass-fiber filter, and the entrapped radioactivity is counted. The "specific" binding is defined as the binding component which disappears when the receptors are occupied by a "cold" agonist or antagonist. The portion of specific binding must correspond at least to 50 % of total binding for quantitative reliable assays, and promising $^3H$-ligands such as $^3H$-quipazine (an agonist) and $^3H$-methiothepin (an antagonist) could not be used because of their high levels of nonspecific binding, notably to membrane lipids (refs.3,4).

However, even with $^3H$-molecules unsuitable for *in vitro* binding assays, another technique can be attempted : it consists of the *in vivo* binding which is simply the measurement of radioactivity accumulated in various brain regions a short time period after the peripheral administration of a labelled ligand. As under *in vitro* conditions, prior occupancy of 5-HT receptors by the administration of a large dose of a "cold" antagonist prevents the specific binding of the $^3H$-ligand and results in a significant reduction in the radioactivity accumulated in tissues. This is notably the case with $^3H$-methiothepin since the prior administration of another 5-HT antagonist, metergoline (10 mg/kg i.p.), reduced by half the subsequent accumulation of this labelled ligand in the cerebral cortex of rats (unpublished observations). In this particular case, the regional distribution of specific $^3H$-methiothepin accumulation corresponded exactly to that of $5-HT_2$ binding sites further confirming that these sites are selectively labelled by 5-HT antagonists (ref.3).

## THE RADIOACTIVE LIGANDS CURRENTLY USED FOR THE IDENTIFICATION OF CENTRAL 5-HT RECEPTORS

### Radioactive agonists

$^3$H-5-HT. The $^3$H-derivative of 5-HT itself is a satisfactory ligand, particularly since it is commercially available with a specific radioactivity regularly higher than 20 Ci/mmol. The specific sites labelled by $^3$H-5-HT are abundant in the hippocampus where non specific binding represents less than 15 % of total binding (ref.5). The distribution of these high affinity sites (Kd $\#$ 3 nM) exhibits no correlation with that of presynaptic serotoninergic terminals in any brain region, suggesting that they are located exclusively on postsynaptic target cells. In agreement with this view, convergent reports mentioned that the selective lesion of serotoninergic neurones by 5,7-dihydroxytryptamine does not reduce the density of $^3$H-5-HT binding sites in brain (refs.3, 5).

As expected for 5-HT receptors, the most efficient drugs to displace specifically bound $^3$H-5-HT are known 5-HT agonists and antagonists previously characterized by appropriate behavioural tests or pharmacological assays. Furthermore, agents modulating neurotransmitter receptors such as guanosine-triphosphate and divalent cations (particularly $Mn^{2+}$) are also extremely potent to reduce and enhance respectively $^3$H-5-HT binding to brain membranes (ref.6). Although the possible coupling of these binding sites to adenylate cyclase has been the subject of numerous reports, no convincing evidence has been provided yet for the involvement of this signal transducing system. However, high affinity $^3$H-5-HT binding sites are undoubtedly functional since they can exhibit down- and up-regulation as a consequence of their chronic hyper- and hypo-stimulation respectively *in vivo*.

$^3$H-LSD. Historically, the first radioactive agonist which has been used for ligand binding studies with the rapid filtration method is $^3$H-lysergic acid diethylamide ($^3$H-LSD, ref.1). However this drug is only a partial agonist and binds in fact to an heterogeneous population of sites in rat brain membranes. In addition to that already identified by $^3$H-5-HT, another category of sites is recognized by $^3$H-LSD : that labelled also by nanomolar concentrations of $^3$H-antagonists (see below). These observations led

Peroutka and Snyder (ref.7) to call the class selectively labelled by $^3$H-5-HT, 5-HT$_1$, and the other labelled by $^3$H-LSD and $^3$H-antagonists, 5-HT$_2$.

$\underline{^3\text{H-8-OH-DPAT.}}$  Recently, another $^3$H-agonist has been developed for the study of central 5-HT receptors (ref.8) : $^3$H-8-hydroxy-(di-n-propylamino)tetralin or $^3$H-8-OH-DPAT, with a specific radioactivity regularly higher than 100 Ci/mmol. Studies on the regional distribution of $^3$H-8-OH-DPAT binding indicated similarities but also striking differences compared to $^3$H-5-HT binding, therefore providing evidence for the heterogeneity of 5-HT$_1$ sites in the rat brain (ref.9). Thus, postsynaptic sites labelled by $^3$H-8-OH-DPAT correspond to a subpopulation of 5-HT$_1$ sites called 5-HT$_{1A}$ which are particularly abundant in limbic structures (hippocampus, septum, amygdala etc..). The other subpopulation labelled by $^3$H-5-HT only is called 5-HT$_{1B}$, and is present notably in extrapyramidal structures (globus pallidus, caudate nucleus, substantia nigra).

Extensive studies of $^3$H-8-OH-DPAT binding to various brain regions revealed another category of 5-HT sites, which, in contrast to 5-HT$_1$, disappear following the selective degeneration of serotoninergic neurones (refs.8,10). Because of this presynaptic location, such sites called 5-HT$_3$ may well correspond to the presynaptic autoreceptors controlling 5-HT release from nerve terminals. However, further investigations are necessary in order to prove definitively this hypothesis (ref.10).

As for 5-HT$_{1A}$ and 5-HT$_{1B}$ sites, the main pharmacological property of 5-HT$_3$ sites is a higher affinity for agonists than for antagonists (refs.3,8).

Radioactive antagonists

Originally, it was from a careful examination of the pharmacological properties of the specific binding of a putative dopamine-related ligand, $^3$H-spiperone, to cortical membranes that Leysen *et al.* (ref.11) discovered that this molecule binds also to 5-HT-related sites. Then, other radioactive molecules with 5-HT antagonist properties have been devised : $^3$H-metergoline (ref.12), $^3$H-ketanserin (ref.13), $^3$H-mianserin (ref.14), and more recently 125-I-LSD (ref.15). Of these ligands, $^3$H-ketanserin is more frequently used for several reasons : non specific binding is low compared notably to that of $^3$H-metergoline ; $^3$H-ketanserin binding sites correspond exactly to the 5-HT$_2$ sites previously identified with $^3$H-spiperone, whereas those labelled by $^3$H-mianserin are not similar, and may be only modulatory subsites of the functional 5-HT$_2$ receptors (ref.14).

The regional distribution of 5-HT$_2$ sites is clearly distinct from that of 5-HT$_1$ sites, with the frontal cortex being the richest region in $^3$H-ketanserin specific binding (refs.3,13). Furthermore, striking differences were also noted about their respective pharmacological properties since, in contrast to that observed for 5-HT$_1$ sites (see above), 5-HT$_2$ sites have much higher affinity for antagonists than for agonists including 5-HT itself Ki # 5 μM). The fact that the selective degeneration of serotoninergic neurones does not induce up-regulation of 5-HT$_2$ sites might indicate that they are not functional receptors but only recognition sites in brain membranes. However, this seems unlikely since the pharmacological profile of 5-HT$_2$ sites is positively correlated with that of 5-HT receptors mediating various behaviours and controlling phosphatidylinositol turnover (in blood platelets, ref.16). Furthermore, apparent down-regulation of 5-HT$_2$ sites has been reproducibly found following chronic antidepressant treatment in rats (but this change may be largely artefactual, see ref.3).

CONCLUSION

In addition to the 5-HT receptors identified owing to various behavioural, electrophysiological and biochemical investigations, three classes of high affinity sites for 5-HT, two : 5-HT$_{1A}$ and 5-HT$_{1B}$, being located postsynaptically, and the other, 5-HT$_3$, being presynaptic, have been detected in brain membranes using the ligand binding technique with radioactive 5-HT agonists. In addition, the use of radioactive antagonists has led to the discovery of another category of sites, 5-HT$_2$, with only μM affinity for 5-HT and related agonists. The main problem at present concerns the possible coincidence of these binding sites with 5-HT receptors characterized by other means. Recent autoradiographic investigations provided evidence for the identity of 5-HT autoreceptors controlling the nerve impulse flow within serotoninergic neurones in the dorsal raphe nucleus with 5-HT$_{1A}$ sites (ref.17). But, in most cases, the problem is far than being solved.

Undoubtedly, the development of new radioactive probes with higher degree of selectivity for the various classes of 5-HT sites already identified would be of great help for searching possible correlations between the pharmacological profiles of these sites and those of authentic 5-HT receptors identified by various behavioural, electrophysiological and biochemical approaches.

## ACKNOWLEDGEMENTS

This research has been supported by grants from INSERM and CNRS (ATP). Corresponding studies were performed when M.D. Hall was in receipt of a Royal Society European Exchange Fellowship.

## REFERENCES

1  J.L. Bennett and G.K. Aghajanian, Life Sci., 15 (1974) 1935-1944.
2  J.E. Leysen, W. Gommeren, P. Van Gompel, J. Wynants, P.F.M. Janssen and P.M. Laduron, Mol. Pharmacol., 27 (1985) 600-611.
3  M. Hamon, S. Bourgoin, S. El Mestikawy and C. Goetz, in A. Lajtha (Ed.), Handbook of Neurochemistry, 2nd Ed., Plenum Press, New York, 1984, pp. 107-143.
4  D.L. Nelson, A. Herbert, L. Pichat, J. Glowinski and M. Hamon, Naunyn-Schmiedeberg's Arch. Pharmacol., 310 (1979) 25-33.
5  D.L. Nelson, A. Herbert, S. Bourgoin, J. Glowinski and M. Hamon, Mol. Pharmacol., 14 (1978) 983-995.
6  M. Hamon, C. Goetz and H. Gozlan, in P. Mandel and F.V. de Feudis (Eds.), CNS Receptors - from Molecular Pharmacology to Behaviour, Raven Press, New York, 1983, pp. 349-359.
7  S.J. Peroutka and S.H. Snyder, Mol. Pharmacol., 16 (1979) 687-699.
8  H. Gozlan, S. El Mestikawy, L. Pichat, J. Glowinski and M. Hamon, Nature (Lond.), 305 (1983) 140-142.
9  M. Marcinkiewicz, D. Vergé, H. Gozlan, L. Pichat and M. Hamon, Brain Research, 291 (1984) 159-163.
10  M.D. Hall, S. El Mestikawy, M.B. Emerit, L. Pichat, M. Hamon and H. Gozlan, J. Neurochem., 44 (1985) 1685-1696.
11  J.E. Leysen, C.J.E. Niemegeers, J.P. Tollenaere and P.M. Laduron, Nature (Lond.), 272 (1978) 168-171.
12  M. Hamon, M. Mallat, A. Herbert, D.L. Nelson, M. Audinot, L. Pichat and J. Glowinski, J. Neurochem., 36 (1981) 613-626.
13  J.E. Leysen, C.J.E. Niemegeers, J.M. Van Nueten and P.M. Laduron, Mol. Pharmacol., 21 (1982) 301-314.
14  O. Gandolfi, M.L. Barbaccia and E. Costa, Life Sci., 36 (1985) 713-721.
15  P.R. Hartig, M.J. Kadan, M.J. Evans and A.M. Krohn, Europ. J. Pharmacol., 89 (1983) 321-322.
16  D. de Chaffoy de Courcelles, J.E. Leysen, F. De Clerck, H. Van Belle and P.A.J. Janssen, J. Biol. Chem., 260 (1985) 7603-7608.
17  D. Vergé, G. Daval, A. Patey, H. Gozlan, S. El Mestikawy and M. Hamon, Europ. J. Pharmacol., 113 (1985) 463-464.

*Synthesis and Applications of Isotopically Labeled Compounds 1985.*
Proceedings of the Second International Symposium, Kansas City, MO, U.S.A.,
3—6 September 1985, R.R. Muccino (Ed.), 145—150
© 1986 Elsevier Science Publishers B.V., Amsterdam — Printed in The Netherlands

TRITIUM-LABELLED HEMICHOLINIUM-3 ([3H]HC-3): MEMBRANE BINDING PROPERTIES AND POTENTIAL USES FOR A NOVEL PRESYNAPTIC MARKER IN CHOLINERGICALLY-INNERVATED TISSUES |

THOMAS W. VICKROY[1], MARK WATSON,[2] WILLIAM R. ROESKE[2] and HENRY I. YAMAMURA[2] *

[1]Abbott Laboratories, Neuroscience Research Area, Dept. 47H Bldg. AP10 LU8, Abbott Park, IL 60064

[2]Dept. of Pharmacology, Univ. of Arizona Health Sciences Center, Tucson, AZ 85724

ABSTRACT

Sodium-dependent high-affinity choline uptake (SDHACU) is the primary regulatory step in acetylcholine biosynthesis and subserves an essential function in cholinergically-mediated neurotransmission. Recent studies (refs. 1-5) with [3H]hemicholinium-3 ([3H]HC-3), a potent competitive inhibitor of SDHACU, reveal that closely associated membrane sites mediate high-affinity [3H]HC-3 binding and SDHACU. In this report, supportive evidences for this association are presented and potential uses of [3H]HC-3 are outlined for studies of disorders that involve cholinergic nervous system dysfunction.

INTRODUCTION

Acetylcholine (Ach)-containing neurons and their projections are located throughout the central nervous system (CNS) and undoubtedly influence and/or subserve a variety of centrally-mediated processes. By comparison to other putative neurotransmitters, the steady-state levels of Ach are more rigidly controlled and its overall rate of turnover is much greater (ref. 6). However, since the cholinergic synthetic enzyme choline acetyltransferase (ChAT, EC 2.3.1.6) apparently does not provide ample control to account for this efficient metabolic regulation, investigators have focused their attention upon alternative processes which may represent the principle mechanism(s) for the control of Ach biosynthesis and subsequent cholinergic neurotransmission.

Within the CNS, Ach is derived from two precursor molecules (acetyl coenzyme A or AcCoA and choline) through the action of ChAT. While nervous tissues readily synthesize the former compound from glucose and pyruvate (its immediate precursor), their inability to synthesize adequate amounts of

* Address correspondence to Dr. Henry I. Yamamura

choline (refs. 7-9) makes its necessary for neurons to accumulate this nutrient from peripheral sources.  It is now well-recognized that two choline
accumulation mechanisms (a low-affinity transport and a sodium-dependent high-
affinity transport) are present within nervous tissue and that the latter
process (SDHACU) is uniquely associated with neurons which synthesize and
release Ach (refs. 10-17).  Subsequent studies of the structure-activity
relationships among substrates and inhibitors of SDHACU (ref. 18) have revealed that hemicholinium-3 (HC-3), a synthetic bis-quaternary amonium compound containing two choline-like moieties (see Fig. 1), is an extremely
potent and competitive inhibitor of SDHACU (refs. 11, 13, 14).  This discovery
in combination with earlier observations that HC-3 toxicity (ref. 19) was
well-correlated with its ability to block central (refs. 20, 21) and peripheral (refs. 20, 22) Ach synthesis, has fostered the current hypothesis that
SDHACU represents the rate-limiting step in neuronal Ach formation and is
integrally associated with the functional status of cholinergic nerve terminals (refs. 15, 23-25).  In view of this, it is apparent that HC-3 should be a
useful molecular probe for SDHACU and more generally the biochemical regulation of cholinergic neurotransmission.

METHODS

    All of the procedures described here have been outlined in detail else-
where.  The reader is directed to refs. 1, 2, 4 and 5 for methodological
descriptions pertinent to the results described below.  [3H]Hemicholinium-3
(120-141 Ci/mmol) was obtained from DuPont/New England Nuclear (Boston, MA).

RESULTS AND DISCUSSION

    Prior to our attempts to characterize the membrane binding properties of
[3H]HC-3, preliminary studies were carried out in order to determine the
suitability of this compound as a radioligand.  In short, the only significant

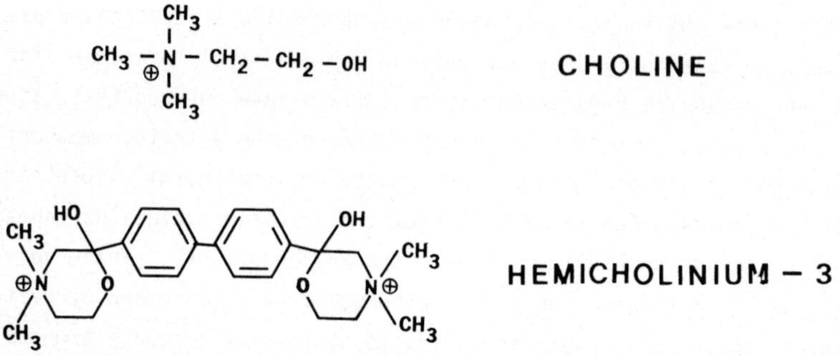

Fig. 1.  Chemical Structures of Choline and Hemicholinium-3.

problems that were encountered (HC-3 displaceable binding of [3H]HC-3 to glass fiber filters and adherence of [3H]HC-3 to certain types of plastic pipette tips) could largely be remedied by pretreatment with 0.1 percent polyethylenimine (filters) or the siliconizing agent Sigmacote (plastic tips) (see ref. 2 for details).

The membrane binding properties of [3H]HC-3 were initially characterized in a phosphate-buffered medium and displayed remarkable similarities to synaptosomal SDHACU (ref. 2). For washed membranes from the corpus striatum, [3H]HC-3 binding was saturable, high-affinity (apparent $K_d$ = 1-3 nM), sodium-dependent ($EC_{50}$ for NaCl = 30-50 mM) and temperature-sensitive. In addition, the regional distribution of [3H]HC-3 binding site densities was highly correlated with other cholinergic markers (SDHACU, ChAT activity and postmortem Ach levels) in several brain areas. Subsequent studies by light microscopic autoradiography (refs. 3, 4) with [3H]HC-3 have provided better resolution of the binding site distribution and indicate that [3H]HC-3 specific sites are selectively associated with cholinergic nerve terminal fields (such as the amygdala) which are devoid of cholinergic perikarya (refs. 26, 27). While these data have provided indirect evidence for the selective association of [3H]HC-3 binding sites with SDHACU carriers on cholinergic nerve terminals, lesion studies with selective neurotoxins have provided strong confirmatory evidence for this relationship.

Ibotenic acid, a neurotoxin, destroys perikarya proximal to the injection site but spares fibers (axons and dendrites) of passage. Stereotaxic injection of ibotenic acid into the nucleus basalis magnocellularis (nbm), a region rich in cholinergic nerve cell bodies, has previously been reported to reduce ChAT activity (refs. 28, 29) and SDHACU (ref. 30) in the frontal cortex where nbm cholinergic axons terminate. Our studies also indicate that bilateral injection of ibotenic acid into nbm produces an identical reduction (approximately 40 percent) in the density of anterior cerebral cortical [3H]HC-3 binding sites (ref. 1). Likewise, well-correlated changes in SDHACU, ChAT, and [3H]HC-3 binding are observed in the hippocampal region of rats following intracerebroventricular administration of the putative cholinergic neurotoxin ethylcholine mustard aziridinium ion (AF64A) (refs. 5, 28-30). Since these AF64A-induced neurochemical changes are accompanied by deficits in cognitive behavioral tasks (refs. 31, 32), it is apparent that central administration of this neurotoxin has both neurochemical and functional ramifications. However, additional studies must be undertaken in order to firmly establish a cause-effect relationship between these alterations and central cholinergic neurons.

FUTURE DIRECTIONS

While Ach was the first mammalian neurotransmitter to be identified, our understanding of the cholinergic nervous system is in many respects less complete than that of more recently discovered neurotransmitter systems. The limited number of highly-specific cell markers and probes for Ach-containing neurons has thwarted histochemical mapping studies, and attempts to understand the role of the cholinergic nervous system in CNS disorders such as Alzheimer's disease, schizophrenia, depression and Huntington's chorea have been hindered. However, several developments within the past five years have yielded some promise that significant progress can be made. First, the development of specific cholinergic neurotoxins should greatly expand our capabilities to determine the role of Ach in brain function and to develop animal models of central cholinergic dysfunction (both regional and global). Toward this end, much attention has been given to the putative selective cholinergic neurotoxin AF64A (ref. 33) although its specificity has recently become a controversial issue (refs. 34-37). Another advance in studies of the cholinergic nervous system has been realized through studies of the membrane receptors which mediate the cellular actions of Ach. The discovery and subsequent use of compounds which selectively interact with pharamcologically distinct subpopulations of the muscarinic cholinergic receptor (reviewed in ref. 38) have indicated that drugs may be developed which could mimic or antagonize the actions of acetylcholine within discrete areas of the nervous system. Finally, the initial studies outlined here indicate that [$^3$H]HC-3 may represent another important discovery for cholinergic nervous system research since its interaction with presynaptic SDHACU sites makes this marker unique among cholinergic probes.

If our current hypothesis regarding the selective association between [$^3$H]HC-3 binding sites and cholinergic neurons is correct, what are the potential uses for this or some structurally related compound? From a basic scientific viewpoint, [$^3$H]HC-3 has great potential for mapping cholinergic nerve projections and determining the plasticity of the cholinergic system in response to chronic drug treatment (especially regimens which produce cholinergic side effects), lesions and changes associated with development and aging. In addition, studies will need to be carried out to determine whether [$^3$H]HC-3 can be used as a _functional_ probe, since SDHACU is recognized to be tightly coupled with the functional activity of cholinergic neurons. Also, there is some possibility of developing an irreversible (alkylating) derivative of [$^3$H]HC-3 which could be used to provide a more selective model of cholinergic nervous system dysfunction. Finally, there are potential clinical diagnostic uses for HC-3 or some functionally-related derivative. Positron-emission tomography (PET) has recently evolved as a powerful clinical diagnostic procedure for studying the biochemical function of tissues, including the brain, in vivo (refs. 39, 40). Although HC-3 does not readily penetrate the blood-brain barrier, it may be possible to design a structural analogue of HC-3, which when labelled with a positron emitting isotope of a basic element (carbon-11, nitrogen-13, oxygen-15, fluorine-18), would provide a useful basic probe for PET studies. Such a procedure might facilitate the early noninvasive detection of central or peripheral cholinergic dysfunction that appears to be involved in the etiology of certain pathological conditions. While these uses of HC-3 are as yet unproven, this compound presently has great promise as a highly useful cholinergic probe for basic and clinical studies.

REFERENCES

1  T.W. Vickroy, H.C. Fibiger, W.R. Roeske and H.I. Yamamura, Eur. J. Pharmacol., 102 (1984) 369-370.
2  T.W. Vickroy, W.R. Roeske and H.I. Yamamura, Life Sci., 35 (1984) 2335-2343.
3  T.C. Rainbow, B. Parsons and C.M. Wieczorek, Eur. J. Pharmacol., 102 (1984) 195-196.
4  T.W. Vickroy, W.R. Roeske, D.R. Gehlert, J.K. Wamsley and H.I. Yamamura, Brain Res., 329 (1985) 368-373.
5  T.W. Vickroy, M. Watson, S.M. Leventer, W.R. Roeske, I. Hanin and H.I. Yamamura, J. Pharmacol. Exp. Ther., in press (1985).
6  D.J. Jenden, in A. Barbeau, J.H. Growden and R.J. Wurtman (eds.), Nutrition and the Brain, Raven Press, New York (1979), pp. 13-24.
7  R.I. Birks and F.C. MacIntosh, Can. J. Physiol. Pharmacol., 47 (1961) 127-143.
8  J. Bremer and D.M. Greenberg, Biochim. Biophys. Acta, 46 (1961) 205-216.
9  G.B. Ansell and S. Spanner, J. Neurochem., 14 (1967) 873-885.
10  H.I. Yamamura and S.H. Snyder, Science, 178 (1972) 626-628.
11  T. Haga and H. Noda, Biochim. Biophys. Acta, 291 (1973) 563-575.
12  M.J. Kuhar, V.H. Sethy, R.H. Roth and G.K. Aghajanian, J. Neurochem., 20 (1973) 581-593.
13  P. Guyenet, P. LeFresne, J. Rossier, J.C. Beaujouan and J. Glowinski, Mol. Pharmacol., 9 (1973) 630-639.
14  H.I. Yamamura and S.H. Snyder, J. Neurochem., 21 (1973) 1355-1374.
15  J.R. Simon, S. Atweh and M.J. Kuhar, J. Neurochem., 26 (1976) 909-922.
16  R.S. Jope, Brain Res. Rev., 1 (1979) 313-344.
17  M.J. Kuhar and L.C. Murrin, J. Neurochem., 30 (1978) 15-21.
18  F. Batzold, R. DeHaven, M.J. Kuhar and N. Birdsall, Biochem. Pharmacol., 29 (1980) 2413-2416.
19  F.W. Schueler, J. Pharmacol. Exp. Ther., 115 (1955) 127-143.
20  F.C. MacIntosh, R.I. Birks and P.B. Sastry, Nature, 178 (1956) 1181-1182.
21  J.F. Gardiner, Biochem. J., 81 (1961) 297-303.
22  R.I. Birks and F.C. MacIntosh, Can. J. Biochem. Physiol., 39 (1961) 787-827.
23  J.R. Simon and M.J. Kuhar, Nature, 255 (1975) 162-163.
24  A. Nordberg and A. Sundwall, Biochem. Pharmacol., 25 (1976) 135-140.
25  J.V. Nadler, D.L. Shelton and C.W. Cotman, Brain Res., 164 (1979) 207-216.
26  T. Nagai, P.L. McGeer and E.G. McGeer, J. Neurosci., 2 (1982) 513-520.
27  C.B. Saper and A.D. Loewy, Brain Res., 197 (1980) 297-317.

28  J. Lehmann, J.I. Nagy, S. Atmadja and H.C. Fibiger, Neuroscience, 5 (1980) 1161-1174.
29  M.V. Johnston, M. McKinney and J.T. Coyle, Proc. Nat'l. Acad. Sci. (U.S.A.), 76 (1979) 5392-5396.
30  F. Pedata, G. Lo Conte, S. Sorbi, I. Marconcini-Pepeu and G. Pepeu, Brain Res., 233 (1982) 359-367.
31  T.J. Walsh, H.A. Tilson, D.L. DeHaven, R.B. Mailman, A. Fisher and I. Hanin, Brain Res., 321 (1984) 91-102.
32  L.E. Jarrard, G.J. Kant, J.L. Meyerhoff and A. Levy, Pharmacol. Biochem. Behav., 21 (1985) 273-280.
33  A. Fisher, C.R. Mantione, D.J. Abraham and I. Hanin, J. Pharmacol. Exp. Ther., 222 (1982) 140-145.
34  A. Levy, G.J. Kant, J.L. Meyerhoff and L.E. Jarrard, Brain Res., 305 (1984) 169-172.
35  M.R. Kozlowski and R.E. Arbogast, in I. Hanin (ed.), Dynamics of Cholinergic Function, Plenum Press, New York (in press).
36  P. Kasa and I. Hanin, Fed. Proc., 44 (1985) 896.
37  P.E. Potter, L.G. Harsing Jr., I. Kakucska, G. Gaal, E.S. Vizi, A. Fisher and I. Hanin, Fed. Proc., 44 (1985) 897.
38  A.S.V. Burgen, Trends Pharmacol. Sci., (suppl.) (1984) 1-3.
39  K.L. Leenders, J.M. Gibbs, R.S.J. Frackowiak, A.A. Lammertama and T. Jones, Prog. Neurobiol., 23 (1984) 1-38.
40  M.E. Phelps and J.C. Mazziotta, Science, 228 (1985) 799-809.

*Synthesis and Applications of Isotopically Labeled Compounds 1985.*
Proceedings of the Second International Symposium, Kansas City, MO, U.S.A.,
3—6 September 1985, R.R. Muccino (Ed.), 151—152
© 1986 Elsevier Science Publishers B.V., Amsterdam — Printed in The Netherlands

SYNTHESIS AND INTRACELLULAR DELIVERY OF DIHYDROPYRIDINE COUPLED RADIO-
IODINATED AROMATIC AMINES FOR EVALUATION OF CEREBRAL AND MYOCARDIAL BLOOD
PERFUSION

PREM C. SRIVASTAVA,[1] MARVIN L. TEDJAMULIA,[2] and FURN F. KNAPP, JR.[1]

[1]Nuclear Medicine Group, Oak Ridge National Laboratory (ORNL), Oak Ridge,
Tennessee 37831

[2]The Upjohn Company, La Porte, Texas 77571

ABSTRACT

The model pyridinium and the corresponding dihydropyridine coupled radioiodinated compounds were synthesized for tissue distribution studies in rats.
The data indicate that the dihydropyridine compounds are transported to the
brain where they are oxidized to the corresponding non-lyophilic pyridinium
form and remain trapped. The technique may have potential application for the
measurement of cerebral blood perfusion.

INTRODUCTION

A unique approach for the delivery of radiopharmaceuticals to the brain for
measurement of cerebral blood perfusion has been evaluated in rats. The
approach involves the synthesis and transformation of the quaternary pyridium
form of a radiolabeled agent (*IP$^+$) to the reduced lipid soluble
dihydropyridine form (*IHP) which is administered intravenously and readily
crosses the blood:brain barrier. Within the brain the (*IP$^+$) form is
regenerated and trapped. The new compounds, 1-methyl-3-[N-[β-(4-[$^{125}$I]iodo-
phenyl)ethyl]carbamoyl]-1,4-dihydropyridine ([$^{125}$I]9) and 1-methyl-3-[N-
[β-(4-[$^{125}$I]-iodophenyl]carbamoyl]-1,4-dihydropyridine ([$^{125}$I]10) have been
prepared by reduction of the corresponding radioiodinated pyridinium
precursors, [$^{125}$I]7, and [$^{125}$I]8, respectively. Formation of [$^{125}$I]7
involved coupling of para-aminophenylethylamine with N-succinimidyl(1-methyl-
pyridinium iodide)-3-carboxylate (4) followed by transformation to the
corresponding piperidinyl or diethylamino triazines which were converted to
[$^{125}$I]7 by treatment with HI. [$^{125}$I]8 was prepared by conversion of
4-aminophenylmercuric acetate to 4-iodoaniline by treatment with I$_2$ and then
coupling with (4). As expected, the quarternary products, [$^{125}$I]7 and
[$^{125}$I]8 showed insignificant brain uptake, whereas the corresponding reduced

152

SCHEME 1

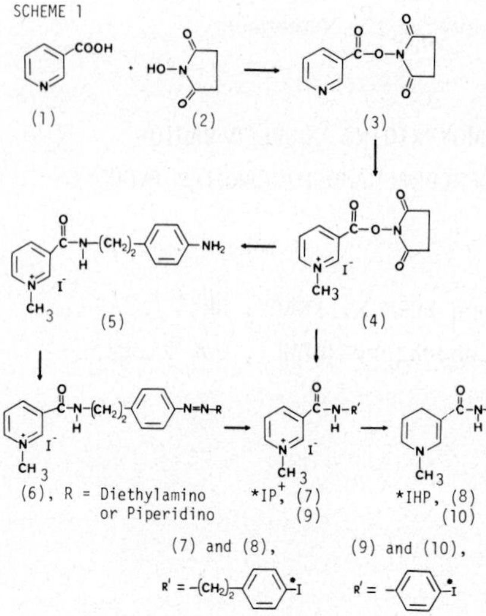

(1)　　　　　(2)　　　　　(3)

(5)　　　　　(4)

(6), R = Diethylamino
　　　or Piperidino

*IP,⁺ (7)　　　*IHP, (8)
　　(9)　　　　　(10)

(7) and (8),　　　(9) and (10),

R' = -(CH₂)₂-⟨⟩-*I　　R' = -⟨⟩-*I

TABLE 1

The distribution of radioactivity in tissues of
Sprague-Dawley rats following intravenous administration
of iodine-125-labeled compounds 7-10[a]

| Compound | Time after Injection | Mean percent injected dose/gm Tissue | | | |
|---|---|---|---|---|---|
| | | Brain | Blood | Liver | Heart |
| [$^{125}$I]7 | 5 min | 0.03 | 0.39 | 8.03 | 0.25 |
| | 15 min | 0.03 | 0.36 | 4.33 | 0.26 |
| | 60 min | 0.02 | 0.27 | 0.93 | 0.20 |
| [$^{125}$I]8 | 5 min | 1.03 | 0.42 | 3.09 | 3.60 |
| | 30 min | 1.24 | 0.36 | 2.34 | 4.02 |
| | 60 min | 0.96 | 0.29 | 1.66 | 2.89 |
| [$^{125}$I]9 | 5 min | 0.06 | 1.11 | 1.18 | 0.83 |
| | 30 min | 0.04 | 0.75 | 0.71 | 0.68 |
| | 60 min | 0.04 | 0.67 | 0.49 | 0.67 |
| [$^{125}$I]10 | 5 min | 1.14 | 0.37 | 1.65 | 2.86 |
| | 30 min | 1.01 | 0.38 | 1.18 | 2.18 |
| | 60 min | 1.12 | 0.31 | 0.82 | 1.88 |

[a]The percent dose/gm data are the mean for five rats.
The distribution for kidneys and lungs was also
determined.

analogues, [$^{125}$I]9 and [$^{125}$I]10, showed relatively high brain uptake (60 min, 1.0 and 1.1% dose/gm), good brain:blood ratios, (3.2 and 3.5) and good brain retention in rats (Table 1). Apparently, according to a previous report (ref.1) the lipid soluble (*IHP) is transported into the brain where it is oxidized to the non-lypophilic form (*IP⁺) and retained. The *IP⁺ is washed out from other tissues, however, giving good brain:blood ratios. These data demonstrate that the approach may be useful for the measurement of cerebral blood perfusion. In addition, radioiodinated 9 and 10 show high heart uptake (30 min, 4.02 and 2.18% dose/gm), and high heart:blood ratios (11 and 6) and may be potentially useful for the measurement of myocardial blood perfusion. Mechanistic studies of brain and heart uptake and retention of these new agents are in progress.

REFERENCES

1 N. Bodor and H. F. Hassan, Science, 214 (1981) 1370-1372.

ACKNOWLEDGEMENT

Research supported by the Office of Health and Environmental Research, U.S. Department of Energy, under contract DE-AC05-840R21400 with Martin Marietta Energy Systems, Inc.

*Synthesis and Applications of Isotopically Labeled Compounds 1985.*
Proceedings of the Second International Symposium, Kansas City, MO, U.S.A.,
3—6 September 1985, R.R. Muccino (Ed.), 153—154
© 1986 Elsevier Science Publishers B.V., Amsterdam — Printed in The Netherlands

# SYNTHESIS AND EVALUATION OF NEW IODOBUTYROPHENONES AS POTENTIAL RECEPTOR BINDING RADIOTRACER

I. Nakatsuka[1], H. Shimizu[1], F. Shono[1], A. Yoshitake[1], H. Saji[2], T. Tokui[2], U. Kuge[2], A. Yokoyama[2] and K. Torizuka[2]

[1]Takarazuka Research Center, Sumitomo Chemical Co., Ltd., Takarazuka, 665 (Japan)
[2]Faculty of Pharmaceutical Sciences and School of Medicine, Kyoto University, Kyoto, 606 (Japan)

ABSTRACT

The three new iodobutyrophenones (2-iodohaloperidol, 2-iodotrifluperidol, 2-iodospiroperidol) have been synthesized, and tested for the dopamine receptor binding affinity in vitro. Among them, 2-iodospiroperidol showed the highest affinity for the dopamine receptor with approximately four times more potency than that of haloperidol. [I-125]-2-iodospiroperidol binding was characterized by saturation analysis yielding $K_D$ = 0.25 nM and Bmax = 210 fmol/mg protein. The tissue distribution study of [I-125]-2-iodospiroperidol showed a high striatum-to-cerebellum ratio of 13.5 at 120 min after injection. These results suggest that radiolabeled 2-iodospiroperidol would be an excellent radiotracer for the study of dopamine receptors in vitro and in vivo.

Several neuropsychiatric diseases such as schizophrenia, Huntington's chorea and Parkinson's disease are thought to be associated with abnormalities of the dopamine receptor in the brain (ref. 1-4). Since butyrophenones have high affinities for the dopamine receptor there have been many attempts to label the butyrophenones with short-lived radionuclides for the external measurement of the dopamine receptors in the brain (ref. 5-9). We planned to label the butyrophenones with radioiodine to develop more practical radiotracers for the study of dopamine receptors.

Non-radioactive 2-iodobutyrophenones were synthesized from the cyclopropyl phenyl ketone derivative via eight steps by applying our previous method (ref. 10). The structures of the iodides were confirmed by their IR, NMR and mass spectra. In vitro binding studies were carried out according to the method of Seeman (ref. 11). Relative affinities determined from the inhibition of [$^3$H]-spiroperidol binding to the dopamine receptor by 2-iodobutyrophenones are summarized in Table.

[$^{125}$I]-Labeling of 2-iodospiroperidol has been achieved by two methods (carrier-added by exchange reaction, and no-carrier-added by direct [$^{125}$I]-iodination of the diazo intermediate). Radiochemically pure [$^{125}$I]-2-iodospiroperidol was obtained in 30-40% yield after purification by HPLC.

154

For in vivo evaluation, the tissue distribution of $[^{125}I]$-2-iodospiroperidol in mice was determined at intervals from 5 min to 120 min after injection. The striatum-to-cerebellum ratios observed at 60 min and 120 min after injection were 6.0 and 13.5, respectively. Its ease of preparation, high affinity to the dopamine receptor and high selective striatum uptake makes 2-iodospiroperidol a promising candidate for evaluation as a dopamine receptor imaging agent.

Table    Potency of 2-iodobutyrophenones in the inhibition of $[^3H]$-spiroperidol binding to the dopamine receptor

$$F-\text{⟨⟩}-COCH_2CH_2CH_2-R$$
X

| Compounds | X | $R^{a)}$ | Ki (nM) mean ± S.E.M. | Relative Potency, % of Haloperidol |
|---|---|---|---|---|
| Haloperidol | H | $R_1$ | $5.10 \pm 0.30 \times 10^{-9}$ | 100 |
| 2-Iodohaloperidol | I | $R_1$ | $3.40 \pm 0.20 \times 10^{-8}$ | 15 |
| 2-Iodotrifluperidol | I | $R_2$ | $5.08 \pm 0.16 \times 10^{-8}$ | 10 |
| 2-Iodospiroperidol | I | $R_3$ | $1.30 \pm 0.11 \times 10^{-9}$ | 390 |
| Spiroperidol | H | $R_3$ | $3.64 \pm 0.18 \times 10^{-10}$ | 1400 |

$R_1$: , $R_2$: , $R_3$:

REFERENCES

1  T.D. Reisine, J.Z. Fields and H.I. Yamamura, Life Sci., 21 (1977) 335-344.
2  T.D. Reisine, J.Z. Fields, L.Z. Stern, P.C. Johnson, E.D. Bird and H.I. Yamamura, Life Sci., 21 (1977) 1123-1128.
3  I. Lee, P. Seeman, W. Tourtelotte, I.J. Farley and O. Hornykeiwicz, Nature, 274 (1978) 897-900.
4  F. Owen, T.J. Crow, M. Poulter, A.J. Cross, A. Longden and G.J. Riley, Lancet, 2 (1978) 223-225.
5  G.A. Digenis, S.H. Vincent, G.S. Kook, R.E. Reiman, G.A. Russ and R.S. Tilbury, J. Pharm. Sci., 70 (1981) 985-988.
6  M.J. Welch, M.R. Kilbourn, C.J. Mathias, M.A. Mintum and M.E. Raichle, Life Sci., 33 (1983) 1687-1693.
7  H.N. Wagner Jr., H.D. Burns, R.F. Dannals, D.F. Wong, B. Langstrom, T. Duelfer, J.J. Frost, H.T. Ravert, J.M. Links, S.B. Rosenbloom, S.E. Lukas, A.V. Kramer and M.J. Kuhar, Science, 221 (1983) 1264-1266.
8  C.-Y. Shiue, M. Watanabe, A.P. Wolf, J.S. Fowler and P. Salvadori, J. Label. Compds. Radiopharm., 21 (1984) 533-547.
9  A.L. Gundlach, B.L. Largent and S.H. Snyder, Life Sci., 33 (1984) 1981-1988.
10  I. Nakatsuka, K. Kawahara, T. Kamada and A. Yoshitake, J. Label. Compds. Radiopharm. 16 (1979) 407-414.
11  P. Seeman, T. Lee, M. Chau-Wong and K. Wong, Nature, 261 (1976) 717-719.

*Synthesis and Applications of Isotopically Labeled Compounds 1985.*
Proceedings of the Second International Symposium, Kansas City, MO, U.S.A.,
3—6 September 1985, R.R. Muccino (Ed.), 155—156
© 1986 Elsevier Science Publishers B.V., Amsterdam — Printed in The Netherlands

TRITIUM LABELING USING ADSORBED TRITIUM AND CATALYTIC SURFACES

C.T. PENG

Department of Pharmaceutical Chemistry, School of Pharmacy, University of
California, San Francisco, CA 94143

ABSTRACT

Tritium adsorbed on supported metal catalysts can be used for tritium
labeling of organic compounds. The radiochemical yield and specific activity
of the labeled compound are dependent upon the nature of the substrate and the
catalytic surfaces on which tritium is adsorbed. The surfaces can also offer
selectivity in labeling and protection against degradation. Compounds containing hydrogen-sensitive groups that are reducible by catalytic hydrogenation may be directly labeled intact with tritium by this method.

INTRODUCTION

Tritium labeling of organic compounds is often carried out by synthesis
and catalytic exchange using tritium gas plus catalyst. For compounds
containing hydrogen sensitive groups that cannot stand the severe conditions
of catalytic hydrogenation, labeling is difficult by these methods. We
introduced the adsorbed tritium on catalytic surfaces as a mild agent for
direct labeling of iodobenzene (ref.1). This method has been extended to the
labeling of other compounds (refs.2,3), and some of its unique characteristics
are briefly discussed here.

DISCUSSION

Table 1 lists the tritium labeled products from reactions of benzene and
toluene with activated and adsorbed tritium . Activated tritium represents
the active tritium species formed by microwave discharge activation of tritium
gas, whereas the adsorbed tritium refers to tritium on catalytic surfaces
after the supported metal catalyst has been exposed to the activated
tritium. It is apparent that the adsorbed tritium has the ability to yield
practically pure labeled benzene and toluene without radioactive side products
and is superior to the activated tritium in that respect. Table 2 shows
reactions of sensitive bonds towards adsorbed tritium in comparison with
tritium gas in the presence of catalyst. These reactions demonstrate the mild
nature of the adsorbed tritium in reaction. Reactions between isolated −C=C−
bond and adsorbed tritium were studied with cyclohexane which readily

dimerizes to yield [$^3$H]tricyclo[6,4,0,0$^{2,7}$]dodec-3-ene (ref.3). The yield of the dimerized product varies with the metal and the support in the supported metal catalyst. With Pd on alumina or silica-alumina, the adsorbed tritium can yield labeled cyclohexene with no or minor dimerization.

The specific activity of the supported metal catalyst is determined by the metal, the support and the activated tritium. Of the transition metals studied, Ni was found to be the most reactive and form a large number of side products; Pt, Pd and Rh were less reactive than Ni but more selective; Ru and Co were the least reactive. LaNi$_5$ has approximately the same order of reactivity as Ni. The supports studied were alumina, silica-alumina, activated carbon and molecular sieves. The alumina and silica-alumina were found to be more reactive than other supports. These supports alone can also adsorb tritium and effect tritium labeling. A reaction mechanism was postulated (ref. 2) to involve metal-ligand binding with the ligands in the proximity of the adsorbed tritium on metal clusters, thus greatly facilitating T-for-H substitution and also protecting the molecules from degradation and the hydrogen-sensitive groups from reduction.

Impurities in tritium gas can adversely affect the yield decreasing the efficiency of the catalyst. Side products containing extraneous hydroxyl and methyl groups have also been detected (ref.3).

The labeled substrate is not carrier-free but the side products are. The adsorbed tritium can label substrate to a specific activity in the range of multi GBq per mmole. In spite of our lack of understanding regarding the reactive sites, the nature of tritium species on the supported catalyst, their lifetime or the transfer of label, the method is very useful for tritium labeling of compounds, especially those containing hydrogen-sensitive groups. (Research support from NIH CA 33437-04 is gratefully acknowledged.)

TABLE 1. Labeled products from adsorbed and activated tritiums

| Compound | Adsorbed tritium | Activated tritium |
|---|---|---|
| Benzene | [$^3$H]Benzene | [$^3$H]Cyclohexane + [$^3$H]Benzene (< 5%) |
| Toluene | [$^3$H]Toluene | [$^3$H]Methylcyclohexane + [$^3$H]Toluene (< 5%) |

TABLE 2. Reactions of tritium towards sensitive chemical bonds

| Bond | Adsorbed tritium | T$_2$ gas + catalyst |
|---|---|---|
| C-X (x=Cl,Br,I) | Intact | + C-T |
| C=O | Intact | + CT-OT |
| C=C | Dimerization | + CT-CT |
| C-NO$_2$ | Intact | + C-NT$_2$ |

REFERENCES

1  G.Y. Cao and C.T. Peng, Trans. Am. Nucl. Soc. 45 (1983) 18.
2  C.T. Peng and O. Buchman, Tetrahedron Lett. 26(11) (1985) 1375.
3  C.T. Peng, G.Y. Cao and O. Buchman, to be published.
4  C.T. Peng and O. Buchman, Int. J. Appl. Radiat. Isot. 36(5) (1985) 414.

*Synthesis and Applications of Isotopically Labeled Compounds 1985.*
Proceedings of the Second International Symposium, Kansas City, MO, U.S.A.,
3—6 September 1985, R.R. Muccino (Ed.), 157—158
© 1986 Elsevier Science Publishers B.V., Amsterdam — Printed in The Netherlands

CONTROL OF REGIOSELECTIVITY IN THE ISOTOPIC EXCHANGE OF FUNCTIONALISED
AROMATICS OVER GROUP VIII METALS

W.J.S. LOCKLEY

Metabolic Studies Department, Fisons plc, Pharmaceutical Division, R & D
Labs, Bakewell Road, Loughborough, Leics LE11 0RH, England. Tel. 0509266361

ABSTRACT
    Control over the site of labelling of organic molecules with isotopic
hydrogen is usually achieved by employing specific precursor molecules, e.g.
unsaturated or halogenated derivatives.  An alternative approach is described
for the highly regioselective deuteration of aromatic carboxylates by
exchange with deuterium oxide over palladium catalysts.  In this case,
control over the regioselectivity of the labelling process is achieved by
exploitation of steric and associative factors in the catalyst-substrate
interaction

INTRODUCTION
    Metal-catalysed isotopic exchange is widely utilised for the preparation
of tritiated or deuterated aromatic compounds (Refs. 1,2).  With
non-functionalised aromatics the procedures usually demonstrate a low order
of regioselectivity.  However, with functionalised aromatic systems, the
specific interactions of associative substituent groups with the catalytic
metal-centre can produce site-selective exchange, by enhancing the exchange
rates of adjacent (e.g. ortho) sites over those of more distant sites
(Fig. 1).  Examples of this process are known where the metal-centre
constitutes part of a heterogeneous (Ref. 3,4) or homogeneous (Ref. 5)
catalyst.  Alternatively, steric inhibition by a bulky non-associative group
can severely inhibit exchange at adjacent sites (Refs.  6,7,8), leading to
selective labelling of more distant sites (Fig. 2).

Fig. 1

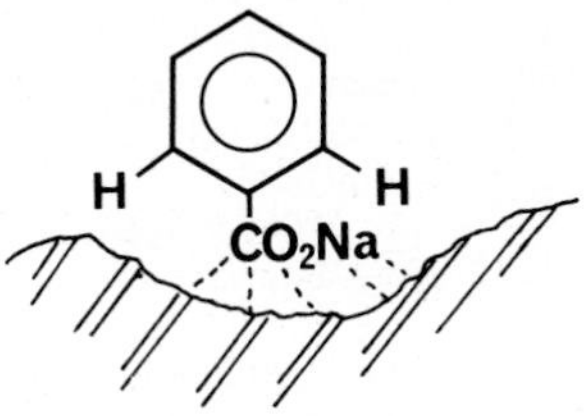

Fig. 2

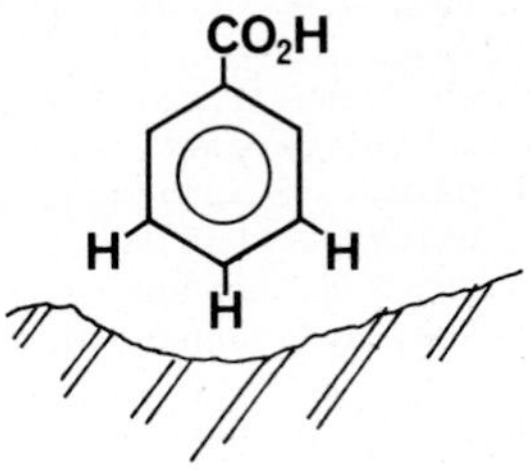

This paper describes the exploitation of these interactions to prepare selectively 2,6-$^2$H- or 3,4,5-$^2$H-labelled aromatic carboxylates.

Based upon the above considerations, selective 2,6-labelling of aromatic carboxylates should result from maximisation of the associative interaction between the carboxylate group and the catalyst. Alternatively, 3,4,5-labelled compounds should result from minimising such associative behaviour, whilst maximising the steric ortho-deactivation (Ref. 9) associated with the group. To explore this approach various aromatic carboxylates were deuterated by palladium-catalysed exchange under conditions promoting both associatively-directed 2,6-labelling, i.e. maximum substrate ionisation, strongly adsorptive carbon support, or sterically-directed 3,4,5-labelling, i.e. carboxyl group ionisation suppressed, absence of adsorptive support. The results obtained were consistent with expectations. Thus, labelling of sodium benzoate over commercial 1% palladium on carbon at 145° for eighteen hours yielded, after acidic work-up, [2,6-$^2$H]benzoic acid with ca 99% regioselectivity. Deuteration was 70% complete at both the 2- and 6-positions. Similar regioselective ortho-deuteration was observed with the sodium salts of 2-OMe, 2-Me, 3-Me, 4-Me and 4-Cl substituted benzoic acids. Conversely, labelling of benzoic acid over commercial palladium black in the presence of heptafluorobutyric acid and deuterium oxide at 145° for eighteen hours yielded [3,4,5-$^2$H]benzoic acid in which the regioselectivity of labelling was 97%. Deuteration was 40% and 60% complete at the 3,5- and 4- positions respectively. Similar regioselective labelling of positions remote from the substituent groups was observed for 2-methoxybenzoic acid (positions 4 and 5), 2-methylbenzoic acid (positions 4,5 and methyl), furan-3-carboxylic acid (position 5) and N-benzoylglycine (positions 3,4 and 5).

## REFERENCES

1  J.R. Jones in 'Isotopes: Essential Chemistry and Applications', eds J.A. Elvidge, J.R. Jones, Spec. Publ. No. 35, The Chemical Society, London (1979) p370.
2  L.A. Neiman, Russ. Chem. Rev., 50 (1981) 196.
3  G.E. Calf, J.L. Garnett, J. Chem. Soc., Chem. Commun., (1967) 306.
4.  C.G. McDonald, J.S. Shannon, Tetrahedron Lett., (1964) 3351.
5  W.J.S. Lockley, J. Lab. Comp. Radiopharm., 21 (1984) 45.
6  R.R. Fraser, R.N. Renaud, J. Amer. Chem. Soc., 88 (1966) 4365.
7  J.A. Elvidge, J.R. Jones, M. Saljouhian, J. Pharm. Pharmacol. 31 (1979) 508.
8  M.A. Long, J.L. Garnett, P.G. Williams in 'Synthesis and Applications of Isotopically Labelled Compounds', eds W.P. Duncan, A.B. Susan, Elsevier (1983).
9  J.L. Garnett, Catal. Rev., 5 (1971) 229.

*Synthesis and Applications of Isotopically Labeled Compounds 1985.*
Proceedings of the Second International Symposium, Kansas City, MO, U.S.A.,
3—6 September 1985, R.R. Muccino (Ed.), 159—160
© 1986 Elsevier Science Publishers B.V., Amsterdam — Printed in The Netherlands

ASYMMETRIC REDUCTION OF DEHYDROAMINO ACIDS AS A STRATEGY FOR THE SYNTHESIS OF
LABELLED PEPTIDES

HOWARD PARNES AND EMMA J. SHELTON

Institute of Organic Chemistry, Syntex Research, 3401 Hillview Ave. Palo Alto,
CA 94304

ABSTRACT

The unnatural labelled amino acids N-acetyl-D-(2,3-$^3$H)-3-(2-naphthyl)
alanine and N-acetyl-D-(3-$^{14}$C)-3-(2-naphthyl)alanine were synthesized by
asymmetric reduction of their respective dehydro analogs using the homogenous
chiral catalyst (S,S)BPPMRh$^+$. These products were obtained at 44 Ci/mmol
and 53 mCi/mmol respectively and in 97% optical yield. Each labelled amino
acid was used to prepare the two LHRH analogs (D-Nal)$^6$LHRH and (N-Ac-D-Nal$^1$,
D-p-Cl-Phe$^2$, D-Trp$^3$, D-hArg (Et$_2$)$^6$, D-Ala$^{10}$)LHRH in both tritium and
C-14 labelled form. L-(3-$^{14}$C)Phe was obtained in 95% optical yield in a
similar reduction of its dehydro analog using (R)PROPHORSRh$^+$.

INTRODUCTION

Analogs of LHRH (<Glu-His-Trp-Ser-Tyr-Gly-Leu-Arg-Pro-GlyNH$_2$) containing
unnatural hydrophobic residues often exhibit greater potency and longer
duration of action than the native hormone (ref. 1). Such compounds are,
therefore, of great interest as potential therapeutic agents for the treatment
of certain steroid mediated disorders. The clinical development of these and
other peptides requires a convenient source of labelled analogs for use in
absorption, distribution, and metabolism studies. To this end we undertook
the development of methodology which would be versatile and suitable for the
preparation of both tritium and C-14 labelled D and L-amino acids. This
objective could be realized by selection of dehydroamino acids as precursors
to the desired labelled compounds. Such precursors can be readily prepared
(ref. 2) by condensation of N-acetylglycine azlactone with the appropriate
aldehyde. The aldehyde may be C-14 labelled if this is the isotope desired in
the product. If tritium is the required isotope, the unlabelled aldehyde is
used. The dehydroamino acids thus obtained can then be reduced with hydrogen
or tritium as desired. The labelled amino acid thus obtained can be used in a
standard solution phase peptide synthesis. The critical aspect of this
approach is the hydrogenation step.

DISCUSSION AND METHODS

In a recent report (ref. 3) we described the synthesis of N-acetyl-D-3-(2-naphthyl)-(2,3-$^3$H)alanine at 45 Ci/mmol ($^3$H-Nal), $\underline{1}$, by reduction of 2-N-acetylamino-3-(2-naphthyl)acrylic acid, $\underline{2}$, with tritium and Wilkinson's catalyst. The initially obtained racemic product was resolved with subtilisin to give optically pure $\underline{1}$. Because of the large amount of radioactivity usually incorporated in a double bond reduction with tritium, the fifty percent loss incurred in the resolution step could be tolerated. Such a loss would, however, be unacceptable in a $^{14}$C synthesis. In order to avoid this loss we examined the reduction of $\underline{2}$ with tritium in the presence of the homogenous chiral catalyst (S,S)BPPMRh$^+$ (Ref. 4). Under these conditions $\underline{1}$ was obtained in 98% optical yield directly at a specific activity of 44 Ci/mmol (identical to the Wilkinson's catalyst reduction).

This methodology was successfully extended to the synthesis of N-acetyl-D-(3-$^{14}$C)Nal, $\underline{3}$. Thus naphthaldehyde-$^{14}$C was prepared in 92% yield from Ba$^{14}$CO$_3$ (1. ΦBr,n-BuLi, $^{14}$CO$_2$,H$^+$; 2. BH$_3$-Me$_2$S; 3. m-IO$_2$-Φ-CO$_2$H (ΦSe)$_2$).

Condensation of $\underline{4}$ with N-acetylglycine azlactone followed by hydrolysis (aq. acetone) afforded 2-N-acetylamino-3-(2-naphthyl)-(3-$^{14}$C)acrylic acid, $\underline{5}$, in 70% yield. Hydrogenation in the presence of (S,S)BPPMRh$^+$ gave $\underline{3}$ in 97% optical yield (identical to the tritiation result) at 52 mCi/mmol. Optical purities were determined by HPLC analysis of the GITC-Nal diastereomers (ref. 5).

Both $\underline{2}$ and $\underline{5}$ were used <u>without dilution</u> to synthesize their respective $^3$H and $^{14}$C labelled analogs of the decapeptides (D-Nal)[6] LHRH and (N-Ac-Nal[1], D-p-Cl-Phe[2], D-Trp[3], D-hArg(Et$_2$)[6], A-Ala[10])LHRH. These peptide syntheses were accomplished using standard solution phase techniques. Purifications were achieved by preparative HPLC.

More recently we have prepared L-(3-$^{14}$C)Phe in 95% optical yield by reduction of the correspsonding dehydro substrate in the presence of (R)PROPHOSRh$^+$ (ref. 6).

The methods described here offer complete versatility as to choice of label, optical isomer, and amino acid structure. In addition, the specificity of the label is guaranteed.

REFERENCES

1. J.J. Nestor, T.L. Ho, R.A. Simpson, B.L. Horner, G.H. Jones, G.I. McRae, B.H. Vickery, J. Med. Chem. 25 (1982) 795-801.
2. A. Vogel, Practical Organic Chemistry, 3rd ed., Longmans Group Ltd., London, (1956) pp. 907-910.
3. H. Parnes and E.J. Shelton, J. Labelled compds. Radiopharm., 21 (1984) 263-284.
4. K. Achiwa, J. Am. Chem. Soc., 98 (1976) 8265-8266.
5. T. Kinoshita, Y. Kashara, N. Nimura, J. Chromatog. 210 (1981), 77-81.
6. M.D. Fryzuk, B. Bosnich, J. Am. Chem. Soc., 100 (1978) 5491-5494.

*Synthesis and Applications of Isotopically Labeled Compounds 1985.*
Proceedings of the Second International Symposium, Kansas City, MO, U.S.A.,
3—6 September 1985, R.R. Muccino (Ed.), 161—162
© 1986 Elsevier Science Publishers B.V., Amsterdam — Printed in The Netherlands

# THE PREPARATION OF MULTIDEUTERATED RACEMIC ALPHA-TOCOPHERYL ACETATE

Y.-Y. LIU, G.J. BADER AND C.W. PERRY

Chemistry Dept., Hoffmann-La Roche Inc., Nutley, N.J. 07110 U.S.A.

ABSTRACT

A new synthetic method was developed for the preparation of gram quantities
of d,1-$\alpha$-tocopheryl acetate (6) labeled with deuterium to $d_6$ and $d_{11}$. Mannich
reaction of phenol provided (1) which was converted to the corresponding acetate (2) and bromide (3). Reduction with $D_2$ afforded deuterated 2,4,6-tri-
methylphenol (4) which provided the key intermediate (5, trimethyl hydroquinone)
on oxidation. Subsequent reactions to the desired product were carried out
following literature procedures (ref. 1-3). A second procedure using the less
expensive $LiAlD_4$ was also developed in which the ester (7) was eventually converted to TMHQ-$d_6$.

INTRODUCTION

d,1-$\alpha$-Tocopheryl acetate labeled with deuterium in the ring structure or the
ring methyl groups was required for use in human studies on the rate of its uptake and distribution into tissues. We were unable to obtain deuterium labeled
2,4,6-trimethyl phenol in reasonable yield from available starting materials
under a number of conditions attempted and this led to the development of a new
procedure which successfully produced the necessary starting materials and the
desired products on a large scale.

METHODS

Product labeled to $d_{11}$ was prepared starting with the reaction of $(DCDO)_n$
and $(CH_3)_2ND \cdot DCl$ on sodium phenoxide to yield (1) which was converted to (2)
with acetic anhydride. Subsequent conversion to (3) with HBr then deuterium
exchange followed by base hydrolysis yielded (4) as expected. Oxidation and
rearrangement provided TMHQ-$d_9$ (5). This was reacted with isophytol-$d_2$ followed by acetylation to give d,1-$\alpha$-tocopheryl acetate-$d_{11}$ (6, 96% $d_{11}$, mass
spectrum).

A second procedure was developed using $LiAlD_4$ as the starting label for the large scale preparation of $d_6$ product. The ester (7) was prepared as described (ref. 4) and $LiAlD_4$ reduction gave (8) which was converted first to the bromide then catalytically hydrogenated with $D_2$ and finally $BBr_3$ treatment gave (9). Oxidation provided TMHQ-$d_6$ (10, 96.9% $d_6$). This was treated with isophytol and the product acetylated to yield the hexadeuterated product (11, 100% $d_6$).

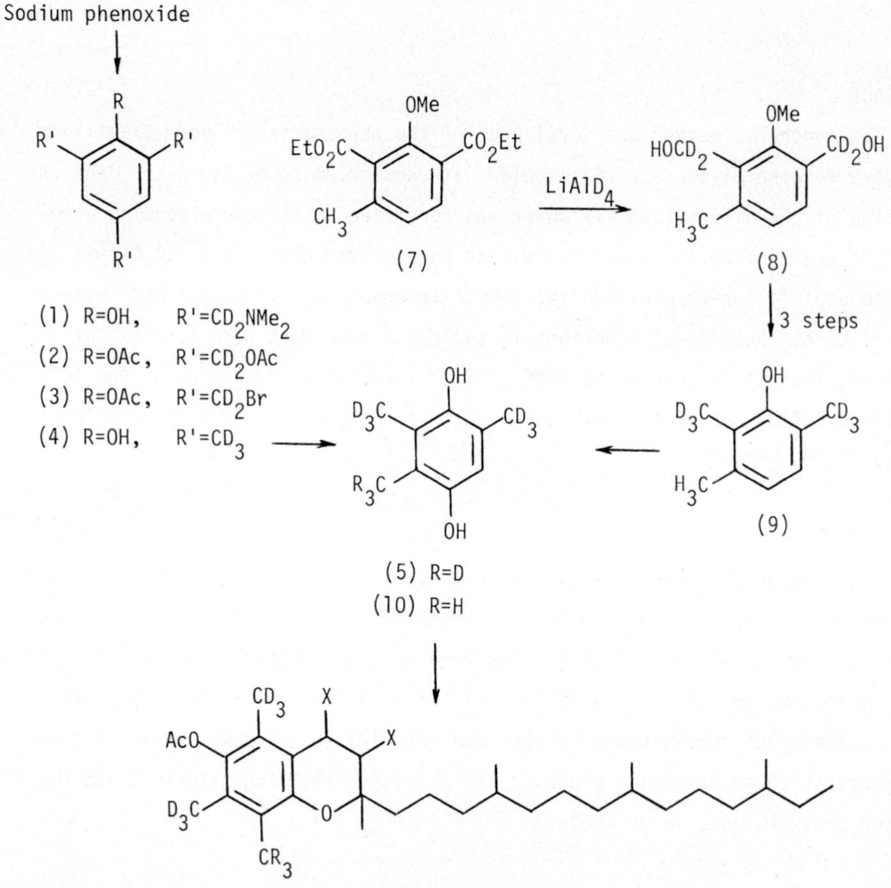

Sodium phenoxide
R
R'
R'
R'
(1) R=OH, R'=CD2NMe2
(2) R=OAc, R'=CD2OAc
(3) R=OAc, R'=CD2Br
(4) R=OH, R'=CD3
OMe
EtO2C
CO2Et
CH3
(7)
LiAlD4
OMe
HOCD2
CD2OH
H3C
(8)
3 steps
OH
D3C
CD3
R3C
OH
(5) R=D
(10) R=H
OH
D3C
CD3
H3C
(9)
CD3
X
AcO
X
D3C
O
CR3

(6) R=X=D

(11) R=X=H

REFERENCES


1 French Patent 25409-044-A (1985) Rhone-Pulencsante.

2 E. Bamberger and A. Rising, Ber., 23 (1900) 3600.

3 N. Cohen, R.J. Lopresti and G. Saucy, J. Am. Chem. Soc., 101 (1979) 6710.

4 V. Prelog, O. Metzler and O. Jeger, Helv. Chim. Acta, 30 (1947) 675.

*Synthesis and Applications of Isotopically Labeled Compounds 1985.*
Proceedings of the Second International Symposium, Kansas City, MO, U.S.A.,
3—6 September 1985, R.R. Muccino (Ed.), 163—164
© 1986 Elsevier Science Publishers B.V., Amsterdam — Printed in The Netherlands

SYNTHESIS OF TWO TRITIUM-LABELED DERIVATIVES OF A VASOPRESSIN ANTAGONIST PEPTIDE

S.W. LANDVATTER and J.R. HEYS

Smith Kline & French Laboratories, Philadelphia, PA 19101

ABSTRACT

SK&F 101926, a potent vasopressin antagonist, has been tritium labeled in
the tyrosine residue via exchange followed by solid phase coupling to a
hexapeptide. The peptide thus obtained was subsequently coupled with a PMP
residue, cleaved from the resin with HF, oxidized by ferricyanide and purified
by HPLC giving the desired cyclic peptide. Alternatively, a labeled PMP
residue can be prepared via reduction starting from phenol. Conversion of the
labeled cyclohexanone to PMP followed by solid phase coupling to a heptapeptide
can then afford PMP labeled peptide.

INTRODUCTION

SK&F 101926 [1-($\beta$-mercapto-$\beta$, $\beta$-cyclopentamethylenepropionic acid),
2-0-ethyl-D-tryosine,4-valine,8-arginine,9-desglycine]vasopressin (1) is a

potent vasopressin antagonist. It was of interest to obtain tritium labeled

peptide with the label in either of the unnatural amino acid residues:
0-ethyl-D-tyrosine or $\beta$-mercapto-$\beta$, $\beta$-cyclopentamethylenepropionic acid (PMP).

TYROSINE LABELING

The tyrosine labeling was readily achieved via catalyzed exchange (ref. 1)
of BOC-protected 0-ethyl-D-tyrosine in ethyl acetate solution, with tritium gas
over 5% Pd/BaSO$_4$. This method afforded material with a specific activity of
up to 7 Ci/mmole. Tritium NMR shows that at least 75% of the label resides as
expected in the benzylic position, with less than 0.5% in the aromatic and
$\alpha$-positions. The labeled residue is then incorporated via solid phase peptide
synthesis into the appropriate resin-bound hexapeptide. Subsequent coupling of
the PMP residue followed by cleavage of the peptide from the resin with
anhydrous HF, oxidation to the cyclic disulfide with ferricyanide and HPLC
purification affords tritium labeled SK&F 101926 in 3-4% overall radiochemical

yield and a specific activity of up to 4.35 Ci/mmole.

Typically we have employed excess peptide in order to maximize the use of labeled residue. High specific activity SK&F 101926 was obtained by acetylating the excess peptide with DCC and acetic acid following coupling of labeled tyrosine; and low specific activity material, by coupling excess unlabeled tyrosine instead.

Investigations have been made to determine the cause of the low yields usually obtained (ca. 1/3 that of similar synthesis with unlabeled materials). Generally, the specific activity of the final product is lower than that of the starting tyrosine, even though there is no stage at which exchange of label obviously occurs. However, the major source of product loss is the irreversible absorption of label onto resin. The effect of this phenomenon is reduced by the use of higher proportions of labeled amino acid to resin.

## PMP LABELING

A simple four-step labeling procedure was used to obtain tritium-labeled PMP. Phenol was reduced with tritium gas over 5% Pd/C in hexane to give tritiated cyclohexanone (ref. 2). This was directly treated with methyl

diethylphosphonoacetate to give an ethyl [G-$^3$H]cyclohexylidene acetate. Conjugate addition of 4-methylbenzyl mercaptan followed by enzymatic ester hydrolysis (porcine liver esterase I, pH 8) (ref. 3) gives exclusively the protected PMP labeled in the cyclohexyl ring. Other aqueous hydrolysis methods which were tried resulted in concurrent thiol elimination, giving mainly unsaturated acid. The desired product, S-(4-methylbenzyl)-[G-$^3$H]PMP, may then be introduced into the peptide via the methodology described above.

## REFERENCES

1. E.A. Evans, H.C. Sheppard, J.C. Turner, D.C. Warrell, J. Label. Comp. Radiopharm. 10(1974) 569-587.
2. P. Rylander, in "Catalytic Hydrogenation in Organic Syntheses," Academic Press: New York, 1979, pp 193-195.
3. a). F.C. Huang, L.F.H.Lee, R.S.D. Mittal, et. al., J. Am. Chem. Soc. 97(1975) 4144-4145. b). M. Schneider, N. Engel, H. Boensmann, Angew. Chem. Int. Ed. Engl. 23(1984)66.

*Synthesis and Applications of Isotopically Labeled Compounds 1985.*
Proceedings of the Second International Symposium, Kansas City, MO, U.S.A.,
3—6 September 1985, R.R. Muccino (Ed.), 165—166
© 1986 Elsevier Science Publishers B.V., Amsterdam — Printed in The Netherlands

SYNTHESIS OF (±)-7-CHLORO-8-HYDROXY-3-METHYL-1-PHENYL-2,3,4,5-TETRAHYDRO-1-$\underline{H}$-3-[9-$^3$H(n)]BENZAZEPINE (SCH23390)

STEVEN D. WYRICK[1] and RICHARD B. MAILMAN[2]

[1]Division of Medicinal Chemistry and Natural Products, School of Pharmacy,
University of North Carolina, Chapel Hill, N.C. 27514 (USA)

[2]Departments of Psychiatry and Pharmacology, Biological Sciences Research Center,
School of Medicine, University of North Carolina, Chapel Hill, N.C. 27514 (USA)

ABSTRACT

Once thought to be the first selective $D_1$ dopamine antagonist, the antipsychotic drug SCH23390 now shows evidence of producing its effect by interaction with receptors which may be a subpopulation of the $D_1$ dopamine receptors. SCH23390 has been tritium labelled in our laboratory by palladium catalyzed reduction of a brominated precursor with tritium gas to afford the product with a specific activity of 5.6 Ci/mmole.

INTRODUCTION

Most of the actions of antipsychotic drugs may be due to blockade of post-synaptic dopamine receptors which consist of the $D_1$ and $D_2$ classes (ref. 1). Experimental data indicated that interaction primarily with the $D_2$ class mediated both antipsychotic effects and antidopaminergic behavioral effects in man (ref. 2-6). The antipsychotic drug SCH23390 has been shown to be the first known selective $D_1$ antagonist.

However, Mailman et al (ref. 7,8) have demonstrated that SCH23390 has potent activity in inhibiting behaviors induced by dopamine agonists. It may be possible that this drug is interacting with a $D_1$ subpopulation of dopamine receptors.

Since labelling of the N-CH$_3$ of SCH23390 is undesirable for <u>in vivo</u> studies due to almost certain metabolic removal, we decided to tritium label the drug on the benzazepine ring.

DISCUSSION

An initial attempt to label the drug via reduction of the corresponding enamine from a Leonard oxidation (ref. 9) was abandoned due to the inaccessibility of the enamine. Therefore, aryl labelling was selected. Preliminary studies indicated complete resistance of the aryl chlorine to reductive dechlorination by H$_2$ under labelling conditions. Therefore, the 9-bromo derivative was prepared and subjected to palladium catalyzed reductive debromination with deuterium gas to afford the 9-deuterated SCH23390 as a tritiation model. Under similar conditions using carrier free tritium gas, the tritiated product was obtained at a specific activity of 5.6 Ci/mmole (19.4 mCi/mg).

## METHODS

### (±)-9-Bromo-SCH23390 (2) (ref. 10)

SCH23390 (1) (700 mg) was treated with 1.1 equivalents of bromine in acetic acid at room temperature. After evaporation of the volatiles, the solid residue was converted to free base (NaHCO$_3$) and recrystallized from ethanol-THF to afford 423 mg (47%) of yellow solid; mp = 220-221°C. Anal. C,H,N Theory C = 55.69, H = 4.64, N = 3.82; Found C = 55.74, H = 4.80, N = 3.64.

### (±)-[9-$^3$H(n)] SCH23390 (3) (ref. 10)

Compound (2) (22 mg, 0.06 mmol) was exposed at room temperature to 5.0 Ci of tritium gas in the presence of 5% Pd/C, Et$_3$N and THF for 4 h. Workup and purification by PTLC on silica gel (CH$_2$Cl$_2$-MEOH-NH$_4$OH 95:5:1) afforded the labelled product in 28% yield (94.3 mCi). The specific activity as determined by liquid scintillation counting and GC was 5.6 Ci/mmole (19.4 mCi/mg).

## ACKNOWLEDGEMENTS

This work was supported by National Institutes of Health grants ES01104, HD16834 and HD03110.

## REFERENCES

1  J.W. Kebabian and D.B. Calne, Nature 277 (1979) 93.
2  D.B. Calne, Trends Pharmacol. Sci. 3 (1980) 412.
3  I. Creese and S.E. Leff, J. Clin. Psychopharm. 2 (1982) 329.
4  I. Creese, D.R. Sibley, M.W. Hamblin and S.E. Leff, Annu. Rev. Neurosci. 6 (1983) 43.
5  I. Creese, A.L. Morrow, S.E. Leff, D.R. Sibley and M.W. Hamblin, Intl. Rev. Neurobiol. 23 (1982) 255.
6  J. Costentin, I. Dubuc and P. Protais, CNS Receptors: From Molecular Pharmacology to Behavior. Raven Press, New York, 1983, pp. 289-297.
7  R.B. Mailman, H. Rollema, D.W. Schulz, D.L. DeHaven and M.H. Lewis, Fed. Proc. 43 (1984) 1095.
8  R.B. Mailman, D.W. Schulz, M.H. Lewis, L. Staples, H. Rollema and D.L. DeHaven, Eur. J. Pharmacol. 101 (1984) 159.
9  N.J. Leonard and R.R. Sauers, J. Am. Chem. Soc. 79 (1957) 6210.
10  S.D. Wyrick and R.B. Mailman, J. Lab. Compds. 22 (1985) 189.

*Synthesis and Applications of Isotopically Labeled Compounds 1985.*
Proceedings of the Second International Symposium, Kansas City, MO, U.S.A.,
3—6 September 1985, R.R. Muccino (Ed.), 167—168
© 1986 Elsevier Science Publishers B.V., Amsterdam — Printed in The Netherlands

AN APPROACH TO THE SYNTHESIS OF DEUTERIUM LABELLED PIPERIDINE TYPE PHENOTHI-
AZINE ANTIPSYCHOTIC AGENTS

T. MOHAMMAD, K. K. MIDHA and E. M. HAWES

College of Pharmacy, University of Saskatchewan, Saskatoon, Saskatchewan,

Canada, S7N 0W0

ABSTRACT

A synthetic route was developed to thioridazine, mesoridazine and sulforidazine, which allows for the incorporation of up to four deuterium atoms in the
N-10 ethyl side chain. The dideuterated analogues of these piperidine type
phenothiazine antipsychotic agents were synthesised.

The most commonly encountered piperidine type phenothiazine antipsychotic
agents are thioridazine (5a, R=H; Mellaril[®], U.S.) and its metabolites resulting
from oxidation of the methylthio group, namely mesoridazine (5b, R=H; Serentil[®],
U.S.) and sulforidazine (5c, R=H; Inofal[®], FRG). Deuterium labelled analogues
of these marketed drugs were needed for metabolic and pharmacokinetic studies
and as true internal standards for GC-MS assays (ref.1). Whereas, there are
reports to the synthesis of deuterium labelled analogues of aliphatic (ref.2)
and piperazine (ref.3,4) type phenothiazine antipsychotic agents, there are no
such literature reports for the piperidine type of compound. This paper reports the development of a synthetic route to thioridazine, mesoridazine and
sulforidazine, which allows for the incorporation of up to four deuterium atoms
in the relatively non-metabolisable N-10 ethyl side chain.

The route which was envisaged for the synthesis of $[^2H_2]$- and $[^2H_4]$-(±)-
thioridazine, mesoridazine and sulforidazine incorporated a conventional sequence to increase the chain length of ethyl 1-methyl-2-piperidinecarboxylate
(1) by one carbon atom. The two key reactions involve lithium aluminum hydride
reduction of this starting ester 1, as well as its homologue, to the corresponding carbinols. The route has been successfully adopted for obtaining
piperidine type phenothiazine antipsychotic agents with two deuterium atoms at
position 1 of the N-10 ethyl side chain (5, R=$^2$H). Thus, commercially available ethyl ester 1 was reduced with lithium aluminum hydride to the primary
carbinol. This on treatment with thionyl chloride provided the chloro compound,
which in turn by reaction with potassium cyanide in dimethyl sulfoxide, was
converted to the unreported nitrile 2. The nitrile was hydrolysed with

methanolic hydrogen chloride to the methyl ester, which was reduced with lithium aluminum deuteride to the dideuterated carbinol. This was transformed to the chloro compound 3 (R=$^2$H). N-10 Alkylation of the appropriate phenothiazine 4 (a and b were gifts, c was synthesised in these laboratories) with synthon 3 (R=$^2$H), using sodium hydroxide as base in refluxing anhydrous toluene, afforded [1,1-$^2$H$_2$]-(±)-thioridazine (5a, R=$^2$H), mesoridazine (5b, R=$^2$H) and sulforidazine (5c, R=$^2$H) in good yields. The isotopic purities of 5, as determined by a single ion monitoring technique, were found to be >99%.

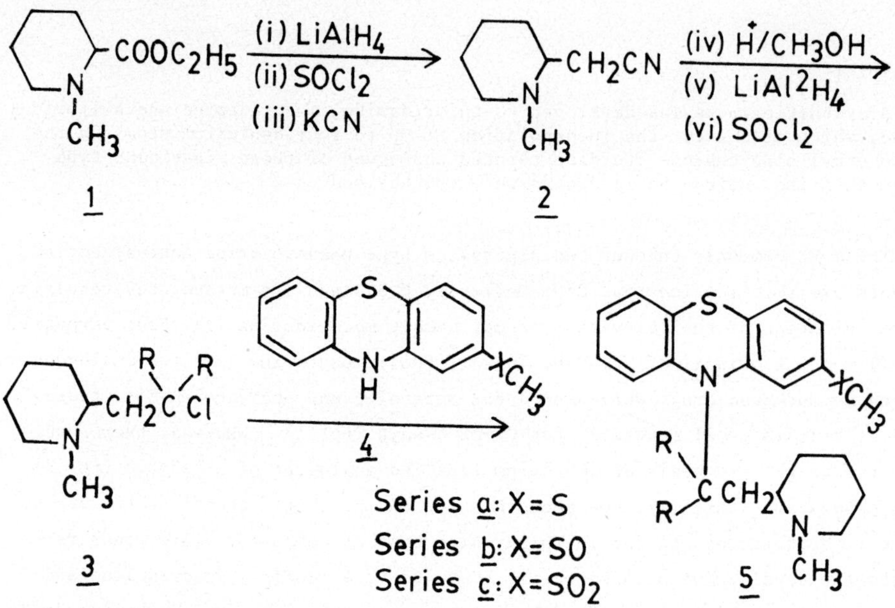

ACKNOWLEDGEMENTS

Financial support from the Medical Research Council of Canada (Grants MA-6767 and PG-34) and the gifts of 4a and 4b from Sandoz, Inc., East Hanover, NJ, are gratefully acknowledged. The authors would also like to thank Dr. G. McKay and Mr. R. W. Edom for the mass spectra.

REFERENCES

1  E.M. Hawes, G. McKay, H.U. Shetty and K.K. Midha, in D.D. Breimer and P. Speiser (Eds.), Topics in Pharmaceutical Sciences 1985, Elsevier Science Publishers, Amsterdam, in press.
2  J.C. Craig, L.D. Gruenke and S.-Y.C. Lee, J. Labelled Compd. Radiopharm., 15 (1978) 31-40.
3  H.U. Shetty, E.M. Hawes and K.K. Midha, J. Pharm. Sci., 73 (1984) 87-90.
4  H.U. Shetty, E.M. Hawes and K.K. Midha, J. Labelled Compd. Radiopharm., 18 (1981) 1633-1640.

*Synthesis and Applications of Isotopically Labeled Compounds 1985.*
Proceedings of the Second International Symposium, Kansas City, MO, U.S.A.,
3—6 September 1985, R.R. Muccino (Ed.), 169—170

SYNTHESIS OF CERTAIN DEUTERATED ORGANIC
COMPOUNDS FOR SPECTROSCOPIC STUDIES

L.C. LEITCH
Department of Chemistry, University of Ottawa
Ottawa, Ontario, Canada

ABSTRACT
The synthesis of heptadecane-1,1,1,17,17,17-$d_6$,n-octadecanol-5,5-$d_2$ and
D,L-malic-2,3,3-$d_3$ acid is described.

METHODS

Heptadecane-1,1,1,17,17,17-$D_6$, $CD_3(CH_2)_{15}CD_3$

The usual method of converting a carbethoxy group into a trideuteromethyl group involves reduction of the ester with lithium aluminum deuteride
to the glycol, conversion of the latter into the tosylate or the bromide and
treatment again with LAD in three steps. In the present work the title
deuterated hydrocarbon is prepared by a so-called "one pot" synthesis. After
reducing the diethyl pentadecanedioate-1,15 the product is decomposed by
careful addition of 57% deuteriohydriodic acid (prepared by adding iodine to
a suspension of red phosphorus in deuterium oxide). The solvent (ether) is
removed by distillation and the reaction mixture is heated six hours to
convert the glycol into the di-iodide. Granulated zinc is then added and
refluxing is resumed for ten hours, or until an aliquot shows absence of
glycol. The reaction mixture is then extracted with pentane. The product is
purified by bulb-to-bulb distillation under reduced pressure. The yield of
hydrocarbon is 30-40% overall, neglecting some dimer formed during reductive
dehalogenation.

The procedure is not applicable to ketones because the secondary
alcohols give mixtures of halides which result in a hydrocarbon containing
CHD groups besides the desired $CD_2$ group. In these cases, recourse must be
had to the tosylate.

Octadecanol-5,5-$d_2$, $CH_3(CH_2)_{12}CD_2(CH_2)_3CH_2OH$

The use of ethylene and trimethylene oxides as chain extension reagents
is well known. Octanols labelled on the 3 and 4 carbon atom chain were
prepared earlier by us in this manner. In the preparation of the title
compound, this would involve two chain extensions with ethylene oxide or one
with formaldehyde and one with trimethylene oxide.

It occurred to us that it might be possible to extend the chain in 1-bromotetradecane-1,1-d$_2$ in one step with tetrahydrofuran at high temperature. The Grignard reagent from 0.05 mole 1-bromotetradecane-1,1-d$_2$ was prepared directly in anhydrous THF in a thick-walled (Carius) tube which was then cooled in dry ice, carefully sealed and heated for 2 days at 275°. The tube was then cooled again in dry ice, opened and the contents were poured onto dilute hydrochloric acid. Work-up as usual gave a mixture of hydrocarbon and octanol-5,5-d$_2$ which was separated by chromatography on silica gel. The hydrocarbon was eluted with pentane and the alcohol with ethyl ether. The yield of alcohol is only 15-20% but the saving in time is considerable.

### D,L-Malic-2,3,3-d Acid, $HO_2CCD_2CD(OH)CO_2H$

Previously reported syntheses of malic acid were found to be unsuitable for the preparation of the deuterium labelled acid. Thus, the synthesis reported by McKenzie and Plenderleith[1] from chloral and malonic acid requires $CCl_3CDO$ which is difficult to obtain. Raney nickel catalyzed exchange of oxaloacetic acid in deuterium oxide resulted in total loss of the acid, possibly due to decarboxylation according to Koch[2].

Deuterated aspartic acid appeared to be a likely candidate for the synthesis of the title compound by deamination in aqueous solution with sodium nitrite. Subsequent evaporation under reduced pressure left a residue of sodium malate which crystallized. The acid was liberated on adding the calculated amount of sulfuric acid in methanol. Sodium sulfate was removed by filtration and the filtrate was heated under reflux for several hours to esterify the acid. Methanol was removed under reduced pressure and the residue was taken up in absolute ether in which it nearly all dissolved except for a small amount of gum. Evaporation of the filtered ether solution left an oil which was purified by bulb-to- bulb distillation under 20 μ pressure. The yield of deuterated dimethyl malate from 10.0 g. of aspartic acid was 5.2 grams. IR: 3500 cm$^{-1}$ (OH), 1730 cm$^{-1}$ (C=O); b.p. 90-94°/20 μ.

The ester was hydrolyzed on the steam bath in 12 ml. of 6 N HCl in one hour. The solvent was removed under reduced pressure; last traces of water were removed on the vacuum line to induce crystallization. The crude acid was purified by recrystallization from ethyl acetate in the presence of norit. Yield of product, m.p. 125-6°, is 3.5 grams.

REFERENCES

[1] McKenzie, E. and Plenderleith, L., J. Chem. Soc. 123, 1090 (1923).
[2] Koch, H., Unpublished work.

*Synthesis and Applications of Isotopically Labeled Compounds 1985.*
Proceedings of the Second International Symposium, Kansas City, MO, U.S.A.,
3—6 September 1985, R.R. Muccino (Ed.), 171—176
© 1986 Elsevier Science Publishers B.V., Amsterdam — Printed in The Netherlands

SYNTHESIS AND USE OF TRITIUM-LABELLED BIOLOGICALLY ACTIVE

COMPOUNDS IN THE USSR

N.F.Myasoyedov

Institute of Molecular Genetics, USSR Academy of Sciences

The production of organic compounds labelled with various
radionuclides began in the USSR in 1948. By the end of the
first decade about 200 different compounds were produced.
At that time the technologies existed for the labelling of
inorganic compounds, key compounds for the synthesis of organic substances and some preparations for medical use. By the
late sixties the number of labelled compounds approached 600,
and by mid-seventies the supply was sufficient to meet the
needs of the national market and the Comecon.

The recent advances of the natural sciences and the
development of molecular biology, molecular genetics, bio- and
immunochemistry, experimental medicine call for the study
of compounds such as proteins and amino acids, nucleic acids
and their components, various fat-like substances (lipids), and
carbohydrates. These past years have seen an upsurge of interest
in the low-molecular bioregulators, such as prostaglandins, peptides, steroids, pheromones, neurotoxins, etc. Hence there is
a growing demand for physiologically active compounds labelled
with radionuclides of biogenic elements: tritium, carbon-14,
phosphorus-32, 33, sulfur-35, iodine-125.

### Nucleic Acid Components

Tritium-labelled nucleic acid components - nitrous bases,
nucleosides and nucleotides - are extensively used for biological and medical research. Catalytic dehalogenation is the most

suitable labelling reaction for nucleic acid components. As a
rule it is used for incorporating the tritium label in nitrous
bases         to obtain /5,6-$^3$H/uracil, /methyl-$^3$H/thymine,
/2,8-$^3$H/adenine, /2,8-$^3$H/hypoxanthine, etc. Catalytic dehalogenation can be used for labelling nucleosides and nucleotides
with different degrees of phosphorylation.     In this way the
label is incorporated at position 5 in pyrimidines and at position 8 in purines.

The tritium-labelling of the nucleic acid components often
involves enzymic reactions. They enable nucleotides with different degrees of phosphorylation to be obtained from nitrous
bases in one step.         In the case of tritium-labelled D-ribose
one can get compounds with the label in the nitrous base and in
the sugar part of the molecule. The labeling of the carbohydrates
usually involves metal reduction by labelled hydrides or heterogeneous isotopic exchange with gaseous tritium.     In the latter
case one normally gets carbohydrates with a molar radioactivity
of 5-15 Ci/mmol, carrying the label at carbon 1. Nucleosides
and nucleotides with different degrees of phosphorylation can be
obtained from labelled nitrous bases and D-ribose.     By using
CTP-synthetase one can obtain cytidine triphosphate from labelled
uridine triphosphate, and appropriate nucleotide diphosphate re-
ductases make it possible to get deoxyribonucleotides from ribo-
-derivatives.     Deoxynucleotides carrying a multiple tritium
label in the heterocyclic nucleus and at 2$^1$-deoxyribose residue
can be obtained by an enzymic transfer of the labelled deoxyri-
bose residue from /2$^1$/deoxy2$^1$-$^3$H/uridine to the appropriate labelled base .

## Amino Acids and Peptides

Tritium-labelled amino acids are used in studies of the
structure and functions of proteins, polypeptides and low-molecular peptides. The synthesis of high-activity D,L - amino acids
is based on the tritium- hydrogenation of the appropriate precursors: oxime-   -ketoacids, azlactones and  -substituted-   -acy-

laminoacrylic acids .                 This method enables the
tritium label to be incorporated at positions 2 and/or 3 of the
amino acids.

At present there is a growing need for peptides labelled
with radioactive isotopes, particularly tritium, so that one
must develop and improve the procedures for their synthesis.
The most popular methods include catalytic dehalogenation by
tritium of the halogen-derivative or the halogen-phenylalanine
residues, heterogeneous catalytic exchange with tritium-containing
solvents or gaseous tritium, and hydrogenation of unsaturated
proline analogues .

## Prostaglandins

Prostaglandins are increasingly used in medicine and agriculture. As a rule the tritium label is introduced into prostaglandins by heterogeneous isotopic exchange       or by selective
hydrogenation of the double or triple bonds .

It is an important advantage of the heterogeneous catalytic exchange method that the label is introduced directly into
the desired compounds whether their structure is natural or not.
For example, we have successfully used this technique to label
prostaglandins $E_2$ (1.74 Ci/mmol), $F_2$  (1.60 Ci/mmol) and $F_1$
(1.85 Ci/mmol), and the biologically interesting 15-fluoro-15-deo-
xyprostaglandin $F_2$  (2.50 Ci/mmol). The main drawback of the
isotopic method consists in the low molar activity of the resulting compounds .

Molar radioactivities of the order of tens of Ci/mmol can
be obtained by selective hydrogenation of tertiary butyl dimethyl
silyl derivatives of 2d series prostaglandins to 1st series
prostaglandins (using homogeneous catalysts $(Ph_3P)_3RhCl$. This
technique has been used to obtain labelled prostaglandin $E_1$ (20)
(52 Ci/mmol) and 15-fluoro-15-deoxyprostaglandin $E_1$ (30 Ci/mmol).

8,11,14-eicosatrienic and arachidonic acids with a high
molar radioactivity were obtained by selective catalytic tritium hydrogenation of the appropriate acetylenic analogues. The
selective hydrogenation of these acetylenic acids was performed
on a catalyst deactivated by lead diacetate without deactivating
amines. The yield of tritium-labelled 8,11,14-eicosatrienic and
arachidonic acids was 65% and 60% resp. Their respective molar
radioactivities were 120 Ci/mmol and 176 Ci/mmol.

/$^3$H/arachidonic acid was turned by biosynthesis into prostaglandins $E_2$ and $F_2$ (46% and 35% yield; 150 Ci/mmol and
165 Ci/mmol respectively).

Many multiply labelled prostaglandins can be obtained with
a higher yield not by biosynthesis from polyenic acids but by
chemical methods from the biosynthetic multiply labelled prostaglandin $E_2$.

In this way, using sodium borohydride, we obtained $PGF_2$
(58% yield, 149 Ci/mmol) and $PGF_2$ (40%, 149 Ci/mmol); using
alkaline treatment of $PGE_2$ we got $PGB_2$ (85%, 105 Ci/mmol), using
acid treatment of $PGE_2$ we got $PGA_2$ (50%, 119 Ci/mmol).

## Lipids

Lipids are a large class of organic compounds that enter
into cell membranes and other structural elements of the cell
and are essential to its functioning. Heterogeneous catalytic
isotopic exchange with gaseous tritium is the method, apart
from the biosynthetic and microbiological techniques, that is
most often used for labelling lipids.

The reduction of double bonds, cis-trans isomerization and
double-bond migration create certain difficulties in the use
of this method for tritium-labelling. However, these difficulties can usually be overcome by high-efficiency chromatography.

The molar radioactivity of the labelled compounds largely
depends on the conditions of the isotopic exchange (medium, cata-

lyst, temperature). For example, the maximum radioactivity for lipids is usually obtained in dioxane. For dioxane-insolvent substances one can use methanol, chloroform, ethyl acetate or a mixture thereof. With 5% Pd/BaSO$_4$, for catalyst the best results are attained in chloroform, while with Lindlar catalyst acceptable radioactivities are obtained in chloroform-free solutions. As a rule, with palladium catalysts an increase in the degree of isotopic exchange is coupled with increased tritium hydrogenation at multiple bonds.                     We can see that in the synthesis of fatty acids and prostaglandins the yield is 30% and the molar radioactivity is about 1 Ci/mmol. After a partial reduction of double bonds by tritium, when the physiological properties of the compounds are not yet affected, for instance in the case of sphingo- and phospholipids, the yield can be 50% and the molar radioactivity can reach 10 Ci/mmol. For gangliosides (G$_1$ and G$_2$) the molar radioactivities are 4.3 and 2.9 Ci/mmol respectively. Thus, the level of molar radioactivity obtained by the method is quite acceptable for most metabolic and biochemical studies of this class of compounds.

Heterogeneous isotopic exchange with gaseous tritium has proved an effective technique for obtaining a number of physiologically active compounds, from pheromones (bombicol) to biogenic amines  and the some toxins (tetrodotoxin, batracho-toxin), the former of which was obtained through a selective reduction of the precursor's nitrile group by gaseous tritium .

Summing up, I have tried to outline the major trends in the synthesis of tritium-labelled compounds. Although my paper is based on the results obtained at the Institute of Molecular Genetics, USSR Academy of Sciences, it reflects the general situation in the study and production of tritium-labelled compounds in the USSR.

N.F.Myasoedov, O.B.Kuznetsova, O.V.Petrenik, V.I.Davankov, Yu.A.Zolotarev - "Resolution of tritium-labelled amino acid racemates by ligand-exchange chromatography. Part 1. Method for obtaining L - and D - $^3$H valine using a polystyrene resin with L-hydroxyproline grouping" - J. of Labell. Comp.,17, N3, p.439-452 (1980)

I.A.Yamskov, B.B.Berezin, V.A.Davankov, Ya.A.Zolotarev, I.N.Dostavalov, N.F.Myasoedov - "Ligand-exchange chromatography of amino acid racemates on separon gels containing L-proline or L-hydroxyproline groupings"- J. of Chrom., 217, p.539-593 (1981)

E.A.Evans, H.C.Sheppard, J.C.Turner, D.C.Warrell." - A new approach to specific labelling of organic compounds with tritium: catalysed exchange in solution with tritium gas" - Journal of Labelled Compounds, 10, N4, p.569-587 (1974)

H.R.Warner - "Propeties of Ribonucloside Diphosphate Reductase in Nucleotide-Permeable Cells" - J.Bacteriology, 1, N5, p.18-22 (1973) C.W.Long, A.B.Pardee - "Cytidine Triphosphate Synthetase of Escherihia coli B" - The J. of Biol.Chem., 242, N20, p.4715-4721 (1967)

Yu.A.Zolotarev, N.F.Myasoedov, V.J.Penkina, O.R.Petrenik, V.A.Davankov - "Ligand-exchange chromatography of racemates. XIII Micropreparative resolution of L,D-liucine"- J. of Chrom., 207, p.63-68 (1981)

Shevchenko V.P., Myasoedov N.F. J.Labelled Compnds.Radiopharm. 1982, vol.19, N1, p.95

*Synthesis and Applications of Isotopically Labeled Compounds 1985.*
Proceedings of the Second International Symposium, Kansas City, MO, U.S.A.,
3—6 September 1985, R.R. Muccino (Ed.), 177—182
© 1986 Elsevier Science Publishers B.V., Amsterdam — Printed in The Netherlands

USE OF RADIOACTIVE MATERIALS IN RECOMBINANT DNA RESEARCH

R. HIRSCHBERG

School of Basic Life Sciences, University of Missouri-Kansas City, Kansas City,

MO 64110 (USA)

ABSTRACT

Radioactively labeled compounds are used extensively in recombinant DNA work. The use of labeled compounds allows for great sensitivity of detection, essential for techniques such as DNA sequencing and genomic Southern hybridizations. DNA and RNA can be labeled to high specific activities using in vitro enzymatic reactions, and are useful in many procedures. $^{32}P$, $^{35}S$, $^{125}I$, and $^{3}H$ are the isotopes which are most often used in recombinant DNA studies.

THE NATURE OF RECOMBINANT DNA TECHNOLOGY

The development and application of recombinant DNA techniques in the last decade has led to a revolution in modern biology. It is now possible to identify and isolate virtually any procaryotic or eucaryotic gene; as a result studies of gene structure and regulation have advanced at a remarkable pace. The impact on eucaryotic molecular biology has been particularly dramatic. Gene families, mRNA splicing, oncogenes, rearrangement of antibody genes-- all were discovered with the use of these techniques. Fundamental, new ideas about gene regulation, the molecular basis of disease, and evolution have developed from recombinant DNA studies. Genetic engineering has also made possible the large scale production of proteins with practical applications in human and veterinary medicine, in agriculture, and in industry. Human insulin, human growth hormone, and the subunit vaccine for foot and mouth diaease are well known examples, and dozens of additional products are currently being developed.

Recombinant DNA technology is actually a group of experimental techniques that were made possible by technical advances in several different areas of microbiology and biochemistry during the 1960's and early 1970's. These include studies of restriction-modification and nucleic acid biosynthesis which have given us an understanding of restriction endonucleases, ligases, DNA and RNA polymerases, and other enzymes involved in nucleic acid metabolism; these studies have also made commercial production of these enzymes possible. Interestingly, some of these enzymes are now being produced by recombinant DNA techniques.

Genetic and biochemical studies of bacteriophages and plasmids have led to development of vectors for cloning and expression of genes. Improvements in DNA-DNA and DNA-RNA hybridization, in electrophoresis of nucleic acids, in autoradiography, and in nucleic acid chemistry have also been very important. Using automated, solid phase chemical synthesis oligonucleotides and even whole genes with defined sequences can be made. The availability of enzymes, vectors, and synthetic or analytical techniques led to what is now known as recombinant DNA technology, or genetic engineering. It is important to note that most of these critical advances came from basic research, not from studies intended to have direct practical consequences.

## IMPORTANCE OF RADIOACTIVE ISOTOPES IN RECOMBINANT DNA TECHNIQUES

Radioactive compounds are used extensively in recombinant DNA work. As is often the case with biological applications of isotopes, this is primarily because isotopes allow for great sensitivity of detection. Alternate detection techniques such as spectrometry, chromatography, or visualization by staining often require orders of magnitude more material, and would make procedures such as DNA sequencing technically impractical. DNA-DNA hybridizations performed with radioactively labeled probes permit detection of single copy human genes in as little as 5 ug of total genomic DNA; this corresponds to detection in the 1-10 pg range. Detection of low abundance gene transcripts and DNA sequencing also require sensitivity in this range.

Although several isotopes are useful for labeling compounds used in recombinant DNA studies, $^{32}$P-labeled compounds have been used more extensively than others. The short half-life of $^{32}$P (14.3 days), its abundance in nucleic acids, and the availability of very high specific activity nucleic acid precursors largely account for this. As a result, very high specific activity $^{32}$P-labeled DNA and RNA can be produced. Recently, however, $^{35}$S-labeled nucleotide analogs are being used as an alternative with increasing frequency in several applications. Specific activities of $^{35}$S-labeled are nearly as high, and the lower energy level of $^{35}$S (0.16 MeV vs. 1.71 for $^{32}$P) combined with its somewhat longer half-life (87.4 d) can be very desirable. $^{35}$S-labeled amino acids have, of course, been used for many years in procedures such as in vitro translation. The low energy level (0.019 MeV) and long half-life (12.28 y) of tritium make it suitable for techniques which involve micro-autoradiography, as well as for those requiring long-lived compounds. Finally, in applications requiring in vitro labeled proteins, $^{125}$I is often used. Other isotopes are seldom used in recombinant DNA studies.

# IN VITRO LABELING OF NUCLEIC ACIDS

Most applications of isotopically labeled compounds in recombinant DNA research involve the use of in vitro labeled macromolecules (nucleic acids or proteins). Several approaches are used to synthesize such compounds, the choice depending on the intended application and the type of molecule. Almost all involve the use of purified enzymes and radio-labeled nucleotide substrates. In these reactions alpha labeled nucleotide triphosphates (or analogs) may be incorporated throughout a growing nucleic acid chain as it is synthesized, or a pre-existing chain may be end labeled by transfer of gamma phosphate groups or other labeled groups from a nucleotide substrate.

Nick translation and various end labeling procedures have been employed extensively for many years. The former uses alpha labeled nucleotide triphosphates (commonly $^{32}$P-labeled dCTP or dATP) and DNA polymerase I holoenzyme to effect replacement synthesis on double stranded DNA templates [1]; specific activities in the range of $10^8$ dpm/ug of DNA can be obtained. 5' end labeling of single or double stranded DNA or RNA can be performed using polynucleotide kinase and gamma $^{32}$P ATP [2]; this technique is particularly useful for labeling small DNA fragments, RNAs, and oligonucleotides. Specific activities vary with the length of the molecule labeled and can approach $10^8$/ug with short fragments. Alternatively, terminal deoxynucleotidyl transferase and alpha $^{32}$P dATP or ddATP can be used to label 3' ends of DNA [3]; RNA can be 3' end labeled using T4 RNA ligase and $^{32}$P-labeled cytidine 3',5'-bis(phosphate) [4].

Radio-labeled cDNA probes can be synthesized from mRNA templates using reverse transcriptase and alpha $^{32}$P dNTPs in the presence of a suitable primer [5]. More recently techniques have been developed that make it possible to synthesize single stranded DNA or RNA molecules from DNA templates. For example, this can be done using phage vectors such as M13 and DNA polymerase Klenow fragment [6]. Alternatively, plasmid vectors containing SP6 or T7 promoters and SP6 or T7 RNA polymerase can be used to incorporate alpha $^{32}$P ribonucleotides into labeled RNA [7]. Single stranded molecules are useful for DNA sequencing and for hybridizations where an opposite strand control probe is desirable; in addition, probe reannealing is eliminated. RNA probes are also advantageous because they form more stable hybrids and can be synthesized without a primer. Specific activities approaching $10^9$/ug can be obtained. For an overall discussion of these enzymes and details of the labeling procedures consult reference 8.

SPECIFIC APPLICATIONS

Hybridization probes

The use of radiolabeled nucleic acids as hybridization probes is one of the most common applications. Hybridization techniques are, of course, based on the ability of homologous (or nearly homologous) complementary, single stranded regions of DNA and RNA to form stable double stranded hybrids when incubated under suitable conditions. The kinetics of reassociation (under conditions where the target sequences are immobilized on a solid support) is dependent on the probe concentration, the molecular complexity of the probe, probe length, temperature, ionic strength, viscosity, and pH. Since hybrid formation is reversible, it is possible to obtain information about the extent of homology by varying the temperature and/or the salt concentration (9). In practical terms, given a suitable probe, hybridization provides a means of obtaining information about specific nucleic acid sequences which are present in a large mixture of unrelated sequences. Hybridization techniques are useful for identifying and characterizing specific genes and DNA fragments as well as for monitoring gene expression. Formation of hybrids can be monitored optically or by fractionation on columns, but the use of radioactive probes permits the use of very small amounts of material and is particularly convenient for detection of hybrids immobilized on solid supports, such as nitrocellulose, by autoradiography.

Plaque or colony hybridizations are used for identifying the small fraction of clones that contain a specific gene in genomic or cDNA libraries (10, 11). DNA from clones is transferred and fixed to nitrocellulose, or other, fileters, and hybridized with a labeled, specific DNA or RNA probe; only clones containing the desired sequence, or closely related sequences (depending on the stringency of the hybridization conditions) will hybridize. Once purified cloned DNA is available, various applications of Southern hybridization (12) allow the structure, organization, and relatedness of genes and other DNA sequences to be determined. In this procedure, restricted DNA fragments are separated by size on agarose gels, transferred to filters, and hybridized to a labeled probe. Northern and dot blot hybridizations (13) use RNA as the target nucleic acid; in the Northern procedure, RNAs are separated according to size by electrophoresis, transferred to filters, and hybridized to a suitable probe. Both qualitative and quantitative information about transcription, RNA processing, and regulation of gene expression can be obtained. Dot blots involve spotting of RNA directly on filters, and are particularly useful for quantitating levels of specific gene transcripts. The probes for such experiments are prepared from cloned genes or fragments and labeled as described in previous sections.

Most of these applications are employed in basic research. Gene probes are also being developed for clinical use in the diagnosis of infectious diseases as

well as genetically determined diseases (14). Another recently developed area
is in situ hybridization techniques (15) which permit studies of genes and gene
expression at the single cell level. $^3$H-labeled probes are used in conjunction
with micro-autoradiography for detection.

## Mapping and sequencing cloned DNA fragments

Two procedures that permit direct determination of DNA base sequence in
large DNA fragments (single genes or larger regions) were developed in the mid
1970's. Both are based on electrophoretic separation sets of DNA fragments that
all originate at the same base and terminate randomly at every possible position
of the four bases. The procedures are such that the relative length of each
fragment and the base with which it terminates is known. Thus, the base
sequence can easily be determined from the positions of the fragments in the
gel. The two approaches differ in how the sets of DNA fragments are generated,
but both require the use of radiolabeled DNAs for detection of the fragments.
The Maxam-Gilbert technique (16) uses 5' end labeled fragments which are cleaved
at specific bases chemically. The Sanger technique (17) uses DNAs labeled
during synthesis from an appropriate template using chain terminating dideoxy
nucleotides in base specific reactions.

Labeled fragments can also be used for determining restriction endonuclease
maps using techniques such as the Smith-Bernsteil procedure (18) and the
Southern Cross technique (19).

## Immunological screening for clones

When a suitable nucleic acid probe is not available for screening a library
with hybridization techniques, it may be possible to identify desired clones by
looking for those which produce the protein product of the gene. Such
procedures use vectors, such as lambda gt11 (20), which are designed to permit
expression of the cloned gene in bacteria. The protein is then detected by
immunologically using antibodies prepared against purified protein. In order to
detect reaction of the antibody with the protein, $^{125}$I-labeled antibodies are
used. Iodination is accomplished chemically and has been used for many years in
other fields.

## CONCLUSION

The previous sections briefly outline many of the applications of
isotopically labeled compounds in recombinant DNA studies. The discussion
should not be taken as complete, however, either in scope or in depth. In
particular, techniques that have been widely used in molecular biology and
biochemistry prior to recombinant DNA techniques have not been given much

consideration. Nevertheless, the point should be clear. Recombinant DNA technology has throughout its short history been dependent on the use of radioactive isotopes. Although efforts to replace radiolabeled compounds with alternative detection systems have met with some success, it is unlikely that the use of radioactive isotopes will be eliminated in the forseeable future.

REFERENCES

1 P. W. J. Rigby, M. Dieckmann, C. Rhodes, and P. Berg, J. Mol. Biol. , 113 (1977) 245.
2 A. M. Maxam and W. Gilbert, Proc. Natl. Acad. Sci., 74 (1977) 560.
3 C.-P. D. Tu and S. N. Cohen, Gene, 10 (1980) 177.
4 A. Sugino, H. M. Goodman, H. L. Heyneker, J. Shine, H. W. Boyer, and N. R. Cozzarelli, J. Biol. Chem., 252 (1977) 3987.
5 I. M. Verma, Biochim. Biophys. Acta, 473 (1977) 3987.
6 K. Itakura and A. D. Riggs, Science, 209 (1980) 1401.
7 D. A. Melton, P. A. Krieg, M. R. Rebagliati, T. Maniatis, K. Zinn, and M. R. Green, Nucl. Acids Res., 12 (1984) 7057.
8 T. Maniatis, °E. F. Fritch, and J. Sambrook, Molecular Cloning, Cold Spring Harbor Laboratory, Cold Spring N. Y., 1982, 545 pp.
9 J. Meinkoth and G. Wahl, Anal. Biochem., 138 (1984) 267.
10 M. Grunstein and D. Hogness, Proc. Natl. Acad. Sci., 72 )1975) 3961.
11 W. D. Benton and R. W. Davis, Science, 196 (1977) 180.
12 E. Southern, J. Mol. Biol., 98 (1975) 503.
13 P. S. Thomas, Proc. Natl. Acad. Sci., 77 (1980) 5201.
14 S. Chou and T. C. Merigan, New Engl. J. Med., 308 (1983) 921.
15 K. H. Cox, D. V. DeLwon, L. M. Angerer, and R. C. Angerer, Dev. Biol. 101 (1984) 485.
16 A. M. Maxam and W. Gilbert, Meth. Enzymol., 65 (1980) 499.
17 M. D. Biggin, T. J. Gibson, and G. F. Hong, Proc. Natl. Acad. Sci. 80 (1983) 3963.
18 H. O. Smith and M. L. Bernsteil, Nucl. Acids Res., 3 (1976) 2387.
19 H. Potter and D. Dresser, submitted for publication.
20 R. A. Young and R. W. Davis, Proc. Natl. Acad. Sci. 80 (1983) 1194.

*Synthesis and Applications of Isotopically Labeled Compounds 1985.*
Proceedings of the Second International Symposium, Kansas City, MO, U.S.A.,
3—6 September 1985, R.R. Muccino (Ed.), 183—188
© 1986 Elsevier Science Publishers B.V., Amsterdam — Printed in The Netherlands

# USE OF $^{35}$S NUCLEOTIDES IN SANGER DIDEOXY SEQUENCING

Maurice A. Kashdan and Deborah L. Ornstein

E. I. DuPont de Nemours and Co./NEN Research Products, 549
Albany Street, Boston, MA 02118, (617)-350-9616.

ABSTRACT

Sequencing DNA using the Sanger Dideoxy Chain Termination Method and $^{35}$S-labeled deoxyribonucleotide analogs represents the current "state-of-the-art" in gene sequencing technology. The application of $^{35}$S-nucleotides has many significant advantages over older radiolabeling methods that use $^{32}$P-nucleotides. The lower emission energy and longer half life of $^{35}$S (87 days vs. 14 days for $^{32}$P) provide greater convenience and flexibility since no special shielding is necessary, and greater economy since waste due to radioactive decay is kept to a minimum. The lower β emission energy of $^{35}$S produces sequencing autoradiograms with sharper bands and greater clarity, so that more useable sequence information can be gathered from each experiment. Labeling with $^{35}$S improves the stability of DNA, which results in lower autoradiographic background, especially in labeled DNA samples that are not used immediately.

With the advent of rapid sequencing techniques (1-3), sequencing DNA fragments has become a common technique in most molecular biology laboratories. Although the original development work in sequencing technology was performed using $^{32}$P-nucleotides, sequencing with $^{35}$S-nucleotides has become increasingly popular. This paper will describe the advantages of using $^{35}$S in place of $^{32}$P-nucleotides for Sanger dideoxy DNA sequencing.

In Sanger dideoxy sequencing, there are five essential components, a primer, template, DNA polymerase, radioactive nucleotide mixtures, and chain terminators which are usually 2',3'-dideoxynucleotides. To sequence DNA fragments using this technique, a short single-stranded primer (usually 15-20 nucleotides in length) is annealed to the DNA template to be sequenced (see figure 1). Usually, the template DNA is single stranded, having been produced via bacteriophage m13, a popular cloning system that produces single stranded DNA as part of its life cycle (4). Double stranded DNA can be used as a template, if a primer complementary to the template can be produced. Annealing of primer to template can be achieved via displacement of the

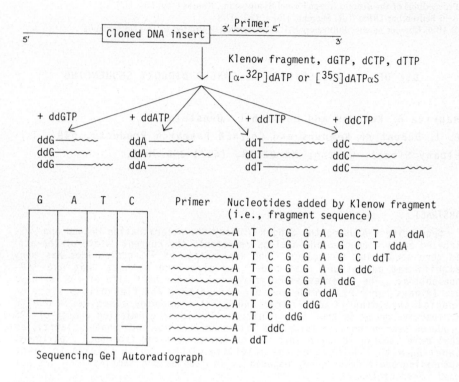

Fig. 1. Diagram of Sanger Dideoxy Sequencing. Four separate elongation reactions are performed with different dideoxynucleotide chain terminators. Fragments generated are separated on the basis of increasing size on 8% polyacrylamide sequencing gels and autoradiographed. The DNA sequence can be deduced from the banding pattern within the autoradiograph.

complementary strand at elevated temperatures. When an appropriate primer is annealed to the template strand, elongation of the primer with nonradioactive nucleotides (dGTP, dCTP and TTP) and a radioactive derivative of dATP can be catalyzed by E. coli DNA Polymerase I-large fragment (Klenow fragment). Nucleotides lacking a free 3'-hydroxyl group (dideoxynucleotides) can be incorporated, and will terminate chain elongation, since a free 3'-hydroxyl group is necessary for phosphodiester bond formation. If the concentration of dideoxynucleotides is limiting, then chain terminations will occur randomly, and at every nucleotide, so that every possible chain length will be represented in the population. The use of base specific chain terminators (ddATP, ddGTP, ddCTP, and ddTTP) and polyacrylamide gels capable of single base resolution allow the separation of all fragments within the population, and detection of these fragments within the gel is easily accomplished by autoradiography. As shown in figure 1, the DNA sequence can be easily determined from the resulting autoradiograph.

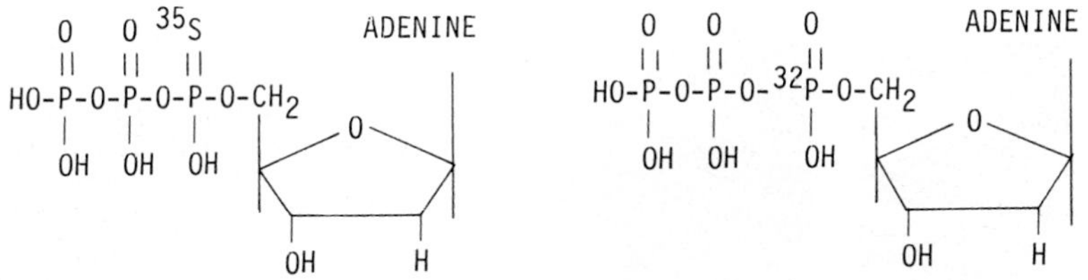

Fig 2.   Structures of [35S]dATPαS (left) and [α-32P]dATP (right).

Figure 2 shows the structure of [35S]2'-deoxyadenosine 5'-(α-thio)-triphosphate ([35S]dATPαS), the most common 35S-nucleotide used in Sanger dideoxy sequencing.  In comparison to [α-32P]dATP, an oxygen at the α-phosphate is replaced by an atom of 35S.  The resulting phosphorothioate derivative can still be recognized by either E. coli DNA polymerase I or AMV reverse transcriptase (sometimes used in place of Klenow fragment, ref. 5), and is easily incorporated into newly synthesized strands of DNA during sequencing reactions, without radically altering the physical properties of DNA (6).  One of the major advantages of using [35S]dATPαS in place of [α-32P]dATP is the longer half-life of the former (87 days vs. 14 days).  The increase in half life is advantageous, since [35S]dATPαS can be used for at least two months when stored at -80°C and handled carefully.  Figure 3 shows the autoradiographs of two sequencing gel patterns derived using fresh [35S]dATPαS (right) and a lot of [35S]dATPαS that was two months old (left).  No discernable differences in activity or sequence fidelity could be observed with 2 month old [35S]dATPαS.  With [α-32P]dATP, the typical shelf-life for use in Sanger Sequencing is generally about four weeks.  For many investigators, the greater shelf-life of 35S-Nucleotides vs. 32P-Nucleotides provides an economic advantage, since less product is lost as a result of radioactive decay.

The emission energy of β particles is ten fold lower with 35S than with 32P (0.167 MeV vs. 1.71 MeV).  In sequencing, the weaker emission has a practical advantage since less band scattering is seen in autoradiographs. This is particularly important in sequencing larger DNA fragments (>250 bases) on 40-80cm long gels, because the distance between adjacent bands is small, so that band sharpness is critical for making unambiguous base assignments.  A comparison is shown in figure 4.  The closely spaced bands within

186

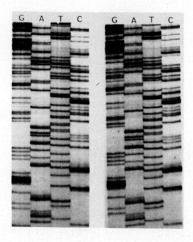

Fig. 3. Phage m13 DNA was sequenced with [35S]dATPαS (DuPont/NEN Products NEG-034S @ 500Ci/mmol) using the Sanger method (1,3) and exposed to film overnight without enhancement. The left sequence was generated with a sample of [35S]dATPαS that was stored at -80OC for 8 weeks. The sequence on the right was generated from 1 day old [35S]dATPαS.

35S-labeled samples are more easily resolved, due to the superior clarity of sequence data generated from [35S]dATPαS. Improved resolution of higher molecular weight fragments increases the number of nucleotides that can be read in each sequencing experiment. The weaker emission of 35S is an important health physics consideration for labs that sequence DNA routinely, since no lead shielding is required.

DNA labeled with 35S appears to be more stable than DNA labeled with 32P. An example of this phenomenon is shown in figure 5. Sequencing reactions performed with either [35S]dATPαS or [α-32P]dATP were stored at -20OC for two weeks and subsequently run on 8% sequencing gels. The 32P-labeled fragments had degraded during storage, but the reactions labeled with 35S were still intact, with very little background smearing from DNA degradation. The increased stability of these 35S-labeled DNA fragments is probably due to several factors, including the weaker emission energy of the sulfur nuclide, and the lack of a radioactive atom linked within a phosphodiester bond. Phosphorothioate internucleotidic linkages are resistant to many nucleases and phosphodiesterases, which can also account for their stability (7-9). The ability to freeze reaction mixtures without increasing autoradiographic background or sacrificing sequence fidelity is important to investigators who do not have the time to electrophorese sequencing reactions immediately. The reduction of autoradiographic background caused by degradation of DNA fragments is beneficial in improving the readability of sequencing gels.

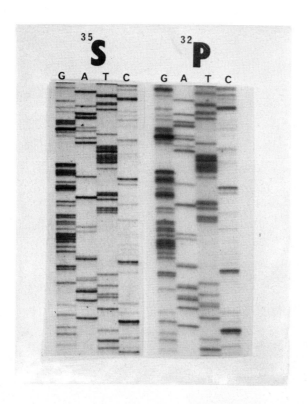

Fig. 4 Autoradiographs of sequences generated using [$^{35}$S]dATPαS (left, DuPont/NEN Products NEG-034S @ 500Ci/mmol) or [α-$^{32}$P]dATP (right, DuPont/NEN Products NEG-012A @ 500Ci/mmol). Phage m13 DNA was sequenced using the Sanger method (1,3) and separated on 8% polyacrylamide gels. Film exposures were obtained without enhancement. Total activity in each lane was 1 μCi. Exposure time: 4 hrs. for $^{32}$P, 10 hrs. for $^{35}$S.

CONCLUSION

The use of $^{35}$S for Sanger Dideoxy Sequencing has many advantages over sequencing with $^{32}$P. Using [$^{35}$S]dATPαS is more convenient than sequencing with [α-$^{32}$P]dATP, since no lead shielding is required, and the useable shelf life of the product is longer. Sequences generated with $^{35}$S show greater clarity and lower autoradiographic background, due to the enhanced stability of $^{35}$S-labeled DNA.

REFERENCES

1 F. Sanger, S. Nicklen, and A. R. Coulson, Proc. Natl. Acad Sci. U.S.A., 74 (1977) 5463-5468.
2 A. Maxam and W. Gilbert, Methods Enzymol., 65 (1980) 499-560.
3 M. D. Biggin, T. J. Gibson, and G. F. Hong, Proc. Natl. Acad. Sci. U.S.A., 80 (1983) 3963-3965.

188

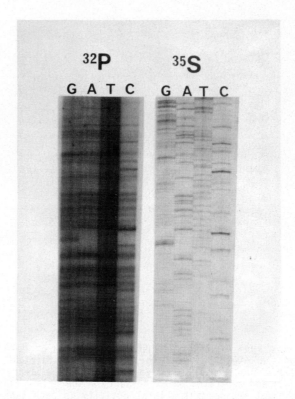

Fig. 5. Stability of m13 DNA labeled with either [32]P or [35]S. DNA was labeled using Sanger Dideoxy sequencing reactions (1,3) and frozen at -20°C. After 2 weeks, reactions were thawed, run on 8% polyacrylamide gels (40cm long) and autoradiographed.


REFERENCES (con't.)

4   J. Messing, Methods in Enzymol., 101 (1983) 20-78.
5   A. S. H. Smith, Methods Enzymol., 65 (1980) 560-580.
6   H-P. Vosberg and F. Eckstein, Biochemistry, 16 (1977) 3633-3640.
7   P. M. J. Burgers and F. Eckstein, J. Biol. Chem., 254 (1979) 6889-6893.
8   R. S. Brody and P. A. Frey, Biochemistry, 20 (1981) 1245-1252.
9   T. A. Kunkel, F. Eckstein, A. S. Mildvan, R. M. Koplitz, and L. Loeb, Proc. Natl. Acad. Sci. U.S.A., 78 (1981) 6734-6738.

*Synthesis and Applications of Isotopically Labeled Compounds 1985.*
Proceedings of the Second International Symposium, Kansas City, MO, U.S.A.,
3–6 September 1985, R.R. Muccino (Ed.), 189–194

189

RECENT DEVELOPMENTS IN AUTORADIOGRAPHY

Catherine A. Phillips[1], Alex G. Smith[2] and Edward J. Hahn[3]

[1]Central Research and Development Dept., E. I. du Pont de Nemours and Co.,
Inc., 500 S. Ridgeway Ave., Glenolden, PA  19036

[2]Dept. of Astronomy, 211 Space Sciences Research Bldg., University of Florida,
Gainesville, FL  32611

[3]Eastman Kodak Company, 343 State St., Rochester, NY  14650

ABSTRACT

Hypersensitization, a technique commonly used by astronomers, can also be
used by biochemists to increase the sensitivity and reliability of x-ray film
used for fluorography. Preexposure treatment with a safe mixture of hydrogen
and nitrogen at 65°C, results in a 2- to 8-fold increase in the detection
capability of Kodak X-Omat AR and Kodak SB films as compared to the untreated
films.

INTRODUCTION

Fluorographic methods have dramatically increased the ability of x-ray film
to detect weak beta-particles, eg. $^3$H. However, often long exposure times are
still required to achieve an adequate response. (For a review of basic
principles of autoradiography see ref. 1.)

X-ray films fail to record properly during long exposures at low light
levels (low intensity reciprocity failure, LIRF) (ref. 2). This inefficiency
is due to unstable latent image formation; that is, not enough photon-hits
accumulate in a given time on a silver grain to render the latent image
stable, and therefore developable (ref. 3). Procedures that stabilize latent
image formation have been described in the biochemical literature--for
example, low temperature exposure (ref. 4,5) and preexposure flash (ref. 6,7).
These methods are not generally applicable to all experimental or recording
situations (eg., those that involve low signal-to-noise ratio)(ref. 8-11).

Previously we have evaluated several standard astronomical techniques for
hypersensitizing Kodak X-Omat AR (XAR) and Kodak SB (SB) films (ref. 2, 12).
The best results were obtained by baking in pure hydrogen or 8% hydrogen in
92% nitrogen (forming gas).

Hypersensitization eliminated low intensity reciprocity failure, and increased the film speed to 3.4 times that of untreated SB film in an experiment where the fluor emissions were simulated by a filtered light source (ref. 2).

In this communication we demonstrate the effect of hypersensitization on the detection capability of film in an actual fluorographic recording situation.

## MATERIALS AND METHODS
### Hypersensitization

Two films, Kodak X-Omat AR and Kodak SB (Eastman Kodak Co., Rochester, NY), commonly used for autoradiography were used in these studies. Both films are blue-sensitive; XAR has emulsion coated on both sides, whereas, SB is coated on only one side. The baking box and internal rack used in these studies were borrowed from Kitt Peak National Observatory, Tucson, AZ (D27726 Case Assembly, Zero Manufacturing Corp., Burbank, CA)(Fig. 1).

The film to be hypersensitized was loaded into a rack (Fig. 2) with two sides made of plastic circuit board holders that could accommodate 16 8 x 10-inch film sheets. The rack was then placed into the box (Fig. 2b), and the cover clamped down. With the inlet and outlet valves open, the box was placed in a preheated (65°C) force-draft laboratory oven with a 75%-blowout back panel (Allied Fisher Scientific, modified by Du Pont, Wilmington, DE) (Fig. 3a). During the treatment, 8% forming gas (Keen Compressed Gas Co., Wilmington, DE) flowed through the box at the rate of 0.5 cuft/h after being preheated in the copper coil attached to the outside of the box (Fig. 3b). The optimum baking time for XAR was previously determined to be 5h, whereas 7h was required for SB (ref. 2). The hypersensitized films will be referred to as XARH and SBH. The treated film was used immediately or stored at -80°C in an evacuated Vac-U-Pak cassette (E-Z-EM Co., Westbury, NY). Under these conditions there is a minimal loss of speed (ref. 2).

### Exposure conditions and film processing

Both treated and untreated films were exposed to the test strips or gel in a Kodak X-Omatic cassette C-2 or in an evacuated Vac-U-Pak cassette at -80°C. After an exposure, the cassette(s) were allowed to come to room temperature before opening. All films were handled and processed in total darkness (ie., no safelight); hypersensitized films are easily fogged even under Kodak-recommended safelights. XAR and XARH films were processed using a Kodak RP X-Omat processor Model M7B containing DuPont HSD Developer and Kodak rapid fixer. SB and SBH were manually processed by developing for 5 min at 20°C in (preseasoned by developing several films) Kodak Industrex manual developer and replenisher. Very gentle agitation at 1-minute intervals was used to ensure uniform development. The films were rinsed 30s in running water, fixed for 4 min. in Kodak rapid fixer, agitated at 1-minute intervals, and air-dried.

Preparation of radioactive test strips and two-dimensional gels.

A series of binary dilutions of $^3$H-methionine (DuPont-New England Nuclear, Boston, MA) were applied to dried silica-gel-coated thin-layer chromatography sheets (Kodak Chromagram sheet 13179). The $^3$H-dose in dpm/mm$^2$ varied from approximately 40,000 to 0.08. The strips were impregnated with scintillation-grade, 2,5-diphenyloxazole (PPO, Fisher Scientific Products, Pittsburg, PA) by dipping in a 20% w/v solution of PPO in toluene, air-dried and maintained in total darkness.

$^{35}$S-labeled hydrophobic membrane proteins (ref. 13) from human peripheral blood lymphocytes were separated by two-dimensional electrophoresis (ref. 14) using a 3-9.5 pH-gradient in the isoelectric focusing and a 10% gel (Integrated Separation Systems, Newton, MA) for the second dimension. The gel was prepared for fluorography by impregnating with PPO by the method of Laskey and Mills (ref. 4) and dried onto a 3mm-Whatman paper (Whatman Ltd., England).

RESULTS AND DISCUSSION

The $^3$H-test strips exposed to SB and SBH for 2h and 35h at -80°C are shown in Fig. 4. The SBH image demonstrates increased detection capability and increased ease of detection as compared to the SB. Small black dots mark the last spot detectable by eye (if not by standard photographic printing methods). In the 2h and 35h exposures the SBH is 8-fold (3 spots) more sensitive than the SB film.

A two-dimensional gel of $^{35}$S-labeled proteins was first exposed to XAR for 48h at -80° and then to XARH for 48h at -80°C (Fig. 5). Even though the exposure procedure should favor detection with XAR, the XARH image contains much more information. To ensure unbiased detection of proteins, a uniform acrylamide concentration was used in the second dimension and the gels were not stained (ref. 15).

Hypersensitization can greatly increase the detection capability of both XAR and SB in a fluorographic exposure for weak to moderate β-emitters. The speed increases which result from this method are higher than would have been predicted from our previous studies with light alone. To detect 30 dpm/mm$^2$ in 24h with preexposure flash, an increase of 0.4-0.8 fog density over that of unexposed film was required (ref. 6); to achieve the same detection in this same time with hypersensitization required increases of only 0.06 for SBH and 0.10 for XARH over that of the untreated film (data not shown). Laskey's results (ref. 6) are comparable to ours because Kodak RP Royal X-Omat Medical x-ray film (discontinued) and XAR are coated with the same emulsion.

Hypersensitization is an effective preexposure treatment which reduces LIRF and increases speed for _all_ classes of signal-to-noise ratio recording situations. However, preexposure flash is _only_ appropriate for those recording situations in which a high signal-to-noise ratio exists (ref. 9). When in doubt, use hypersensitization and not preexposure flash to increase the detection capability of x-ray film.

## ACKNOWLEGEMENTS

This work was partially supported by NIH grant AI 17935 to C.A.P., and by NSF grants AST-8203926 and AST-8400208 to A.G.S. We would like to thank Elaine White and Cheral Canna for technical assistance, the Creative Communications Studio of Du Pont for photographic assistance, and W. Schoening for valuable discussions, and Eileen Freas for her assistance in manuscript preparation.

## REFERENCES

1  E.J. Hahn, American Laboratory 15 (1983) 64-71.
2  A.G. Smith, C.A. Phillips and E.J. Hahn, J. Imaging Tech. (1985) 27-32.
3  B.H. Carroll, G.C. Higgins and T.H. James, Introduction to Photographic Theory. John Wiley and Sons, New York, 1980, pp. 117-118, 137-138.
4  R.A. Laskey and A.D. Mills, Eur. J. Biochem 46 (1974) 83-88.
5  U. Luthi and P.G. Waser, Nature(London) 205 (1965) 1190-1191.
6  R.A. Laskey and A.D. Mills, Eur. J. Bioch. 56 (1975) 335-441.
7  R.A. Laskey, Meth. in Enzymology 65 (1980) 363-371.
8  H.D. Ables, A.V. Hewitt and K.A. James, AAS Photo-Bulletin 3 (1971) 18-22.
9  T.A. Babcock, AAS Photo-Bulletin 13 (1976) 3-8.
10  M.E. Sim, in R.M. West and J.-L. Heudier (Eds.), Astronomical Photography, European Southern Observatory Proceedings, 1977, pp. 23-41.
11  W.C. Miller, Astronomical Soc. of the Pacific Publ. 76 (1964) 328-349.
12  A.G. Smith, C.A. Phillips and E.J. Hahn, AAS Photo-Bulletin 39 (1985) 8-15.
13  C. Bordier, J. Biol. Chem. 256 (1981) 1604-1607.
14  P.H. O'Farrell, J. Biol. Chem. 250 (1975) 4007-4021.
15  C.R. Harding and I.R. Scott, Anal Biochem. 129 (1983) 371-376.

## FIGURES

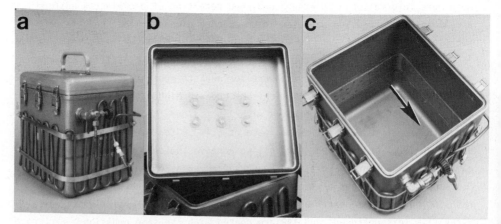

Fig. 1. Metal baking box for hypersensitization (a) assembled box with top clamped to bottom and coiled copper tubing banded to outside (b) detail of cover of baking box (c) inside of box; an arrow shows gas entry into box.

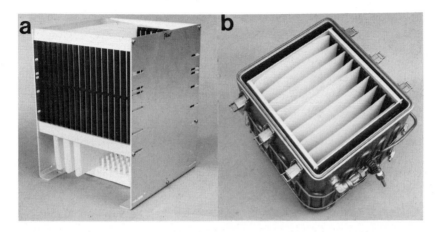

Fig. 2. Rack for holding film during hypersensitization (a) rack loaded with 8x10-inch sheets of XAR film; (b) placement of rack into baking box.

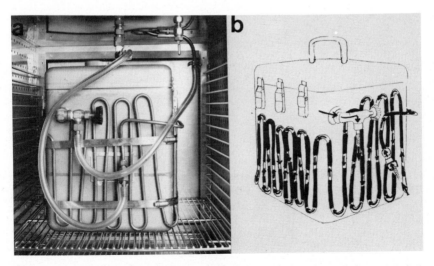

Fig. 3. Orientation of baking box during hypersensitization (a) Baking box in oven (b) flow of forming gas through copper coil and box.

194

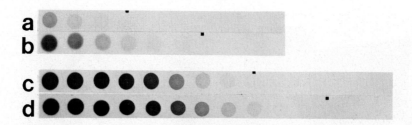

Fig. 4. Autoradiograms of $^3$H-test strips exposed to SB (a and c) and SBH (b and d) for either 2h (a and b) or 35h (c and d) at -80°C in a Vac-U-Pak cassette.

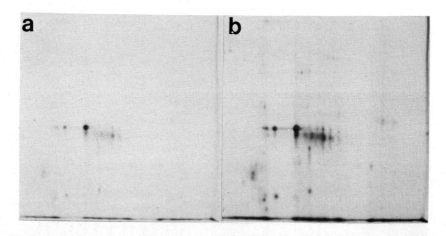

Fig. 5. Autoradiograms of $^{35}$S-proteins separated by 2-D gel electrophoresis and exposed for 48h in a Kodak C-2 cassette on (a) XAR and (b) XARH.

*Synthesis and Applications of Isotopically Labeled Compounds 1985.*
Proceedings of the Second International Symposium, Kansas City, MO, U.S.A.,
3—6 September 1985, R.R. Muccino (Ed.), 195—200
© 1986 Elsevier Science Publishers B.V., Amsterdam — Printed in The Netherlands

Radioimmunodetection of Human Cancer with Indium-111 Labeled
Monoclonal Antibodies

SAMUEL E. HALPERN, PHILLIP L. HAGAN, JAMES M. FRINCKE, RICHARD M.
BARTHOLOMEW, DENNIS J. CARLO, IVOR ROYSTON, and ROBERT O. DILLMAN

San Diego Veterans Hospital, San Diego (SH, PH, IR, RD) and
Hybritech, Inc., San Diego, California (JF, RB, DC)

ABSTRACT

Antibodies have been labeled with 111In and 113mIn using a
bifunctional chelation method. This technique produces a stable
complex which has the same in vivo distribution as endogenously
labeled antibodies. Animal models indicate tumor uptake of 111-
In monoclonal antibodies (MoAb) to be higher than 125-I labeled
MoAbs. Modifications of the bifunctional chelation technique
were also used for 90Y labeling of polyclonal and monoclonal
antibodies for radioimmunotherapy. 111-In murine IgG and human
IgM MoAbs have been studied in patients with melanoma, colon
carcinoma, prostate carcinoma, breast carcinoma, and T-cell
lymphoma. The results have been encouraging.

INTRODUCTION

Concerted efforts toward radioimmunodetection and radioimmunotherapy began with the work of David Pressman (ref.1). This
investigator was able to show that radiolabeled antibodies with
some specificity for murine tumors concentrated more of the
radiopharmaceutical than did radiolabeled nonspecific antibodies.
Since that time multiple efforts have been made in both animal
models (ref.2-4) and in humans (ref.5-7) which indicate that the
technology will work.

With the advent of monoclonal antibodies (ref.8) it became
possible to work with antibodies of much higher specificity and
affinity. Work by our group indicated that the iodination
procedures used to label these antibodies produced a complex that
resulted in removal of variable amounts of the iodine from all
tissues including tumor (ref.9-10). Because of this we chose to
label the antibodies with 111In (ref.11-14) and have proven them
to have the same distribution in animal models as in endogenously
labeled antibody (ref.11). The following summarizes our imaging
efforts in humans using 111In anti-tumor MoAbs and our work

toward the preparation of 90Y derivatives for radioimmunotherapy.

METHODS

All of the MoAbs used in this study were prepared by the Hybritech Corporation of La Jolla, California. The MoAbs have, in general, affinities of greater than $10^9$ moles per liter and with the exception of the melanoma MoAbs, show an immunoreactivity of 70% or greater. Two anti-melanoma MoAbs were utilized, the 96.5 which targets a 97 kilo dalton glycoprotein on the surface of the melanoma cell, and ZME-018 which targets the KD-240 "high molecular weight" antigen.

The anti-CEA MoAb used is designated ZCE-025 and was originated from a clone provided by J-P. Mach. Two antiprostate MoAbs have been studied, PAY-276, an anti-prostatic acid phosphatase, and PSA-399, a prostate specific MoAb.

The anti-T65 MoAb(T-101) targets T-cells and was used to study T-cell lymphoma patients.

The human IgM MoAbs target breast cancer.

All the MoAbs used in this study were labeled with 111In by the bifunctional chelation technique (ref.14).

Labeling has also been achieved with 113mIn via this same technique and a similar method was used for Yttrium labeling. Both polyclonal and monoclonal antibodies have been found to retain their affinity and immunoreactivity after labeling.

The 111In MoAbs were administered intravenously to the patients either mixed with unlabeled MoAb or preceded by unlabeled MoAb. In all cases 1 mg of the MoAb was labeled with from 3-5 mCi of 111In. The absolute dose of MoAb administered to the patients ranged from 0.5 mg to 21 mg. Imaging was begun immediately following administration and repeated at 4, 24, 48, 72, and as late as 168 hours post-administration. Blood was drawn at multiple time periods for toxicity studies and for determining changes in serum 111In kinetics.

The validation of the 90Y radiopharmaceutical was tested by administering it to mice simultaneously with the 111In labeled preparation. 88Y was used as a substitute for 90Y in order to do gamma counting. Following this, the animals were sacrificed at a variety of time periods. This type of validation has been performed for polyclonal anti-ferritin and multiple MoAbs.

RESULTS

The distribution of the IgG MoAbs is such that the target organs are the liver, spleen, G.I. tract, and bone marrow. Approximately 10% of the radiopharmaceutical is acquired and (mostly) remains in the liver. An increase in the quantity of MoAb injected results in a prolongation of the serum half-time and appears to improve lesion detection. Approximately 60% of

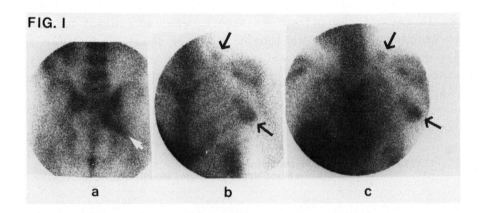

FIG. I

a          b          c

the lesions are detected by this method. Figures 1a and 1b are scans performed 48 hours after the administration of ZME-018, while Figure 1c was taken at 120 hours. This antibody has a slightly different distribution than the 96.5 and changes in its body distribution are highly dependent upon antibody mass. It does however detect lesions with 60-70% sensitivity. It must be noted however that occasionally it will detect inflammatory tissue as well as tumor.

Our results with ZCE-025 has had over a 70% detection rate. It has imaged lesions as small as 1 cm at depth. Elevated CEA values (5000 ng/ml) did not result in the radiopharmaceutical being removed from the vascular compartment by the liver; however, it was not possible to find the primary lesion under those circumstances. Tumors other than colon carcinoma that produce CEA are also detected using 111In anti-CEA.

Prostate imaging with the anti-prostatic acid phosphatase MoAb has been disappointing with slightly over 20% of the lesions being detected. Four patients have been studied with prostate specific MoAb and lesions have been detected; however, the study is too small to be of any significance.

Tumor has been targeted by the human IgM antibodies and in some cases the results are excellent. Unfortunately there is a great deal of liver uptake which has a detrimental effect on the scanning.

Imaging of patients with T-cell lymphoma with the T-101 antibody has shown some spectacular results with uptake in < .5 cm lymph nodes. It is of interest that even though normal T-cells have the antigen on their surface, we did not image lymph nodes in the the one patient we studied who had minimal disease. This suggests that the malignant T-cells, possibly because of their greater numbers (as well as abundance of antigen on their surface), are more likely to be removed by lymph nodes than normal T-cells.

TABLE 1      Percent Dose per Organ
ZME-018 In a Nude Mouse-Melanoma Model

| | 24 hrs | | 72 hrs | | 144 hrs | |
|---|---|---|---|---|---|---|
| | 111 In | 88Y | 111 In | 88Y | 111In | 88Y |
| Blood | 27 | 27 | 13 | 14 | 8 | 7 |
| Bone | 5 | 5 | 4 | 6 | 6 | 4 |
| Kidney | 1 | 1 | 1 | 1 | 0.5 | 0.4 |
| Liver | 6 | 7 | 7 | 10 | 6 | 9 |
| Muscle | 11 | 10 | 6 | 6 | 5 | 5 |
| Skin | 15 | 16 | 12 | 12 | 8 | 8 |
| Tumor | 9 | 9 | 16 | 18 | 14 | 13 |
| Intestine | 6 | 6 | 5 | 5 | 4 | 4 |
| Urine | 1 | 2 | 6 | 6 | 11 | 7 |
| Feces | 7 | 9 | 17 | 14 | 34 | 27 |

Our efforts with 113mIn has shown great promise. Working with a 100 mCi 113Sn-113mIn generator, we have been able to achieve specific activities as high as 40 mCi/mg of IgG. One of the problems with 113mIn labeling has been competing ions. If the generator is old, this becomes a major problem. We have found that the best results are obtained by first eluting a relatively new generator several hours before labeling and discarding the first elution. The elution which takes place after this results in an eluent which gives excellent labeling efficiency, presumably because competing ions were removed during the first elution. Distribution studies in mice indicate the 113mIn MoAb has the same distribution and kinetics as the 111In labeled MoAb. While 113mIn has a short 1/2 life, it can be used simultaneously in the same animal or patient as a 111In labeled moiety. As such, it is a powerful tool for comparing early (0-10 hr) serum kinetics of different immunoreactive molecules.

Finally, Table 1 shows the comparison of the 111In and 88Y anti-melanoma MoAb simultaneously in the same mouse model. The kinetics are almost identical and work in our laboratory shows the radiopharmaceutical to be stable for a minimum of three days. Polyclonal antibodies labeled with 90Y by our technique have been administered to patients with hepatoma at Johns Hopkins University.

DISCUSSION

Our data to date, both in animals and patients indicate that the bifunctional chelation technique has great potential as a way of radiolabeling antibodies. It has the advantage of offering a greater number of radionuclides to be used as well as greater stability of the antibody radionuclide complex. The major problems in this work continue to be the low concentration of radionuclide per gram of lesion (the greatest that we have seen has been approximately .007% of the injected dose per gram) and the background activity. Other major factors are the relatively small amounts of antigen on most tumors, the poor blood flow to the tumor, and the peculiarities of each antibody system. To make this technology work correctly we must find ways to enhance the amount of antigen on the tumor, make the antigen more ubiquitous in each tumor type and decrease the background. Since we can do little about the blood flow to the tumor, we must increase the fraction of the radiopharmaceutical that is removed in each pass through the tumor. Experiments in our laboratory indicate that this may be possible (ref.15). Theoretically a small molecule should pass through a capillary more easily than a large molecule. Thus Fab, at a molecular weight of 50,000 daltons is cleared by the normal glomerulus while intact antibody (150,000 daltons) remains in the vascular compartment. Yet, tumor uptake in a nude mouse model indicates more uptake of the intact MoAb by the tumor than the Fab. When we repeated this study in

200

mice in whom the kidneys had been removed we found nearly twice as much Fab in the tumor by 8 hours as intact MoAb. In short, when excretion of the Fab was blocked by nephrectomy the tumor uptake reflected the fact that the small molecule more easily passed the capillary membrane to enter the tumor. Work should proceed to develop a small immunoreactivemolecule that will remain in the vascular compartment. If we can do this there is an excellent chance of developing not only a diagnostic but a therapeutic modality.

REFERENCES

1 D. Pressman and L. Korngold, Cancer, The in vivo...; 6 (1953) 619-623.
2 T. Ghose, S.T. Norvell, J. Aquino, et al, Can. Res., Localization of...; 40 (1980) 3018-3031.
3 J-P. Mach, S. Carrel, C. Merenda, et al, Nature (Lond), In Vivo Localization...; 248 (1974) 704-706.
4 T. Kogi, N. Ishii, T. Munehisa, et al, Can. Res., Localization of Radioiodinated...; 40 (1980) 3013-3015.
5 D.M. Goldenberg, F.H. DeLand, E.E. Kim, et al, N. Eng. J. Med., The Use of Radiolabeled Antibodies...; 298 (1978) 1384-1388.
6 J-P. Mach, S. Carrel, N. Forni, J. Ritschard, A. Donath, and P. Alberto, N. Eng. J. Med., Tumor Localization....; 303 (1980) 5-10.
7 D.C. Sullivan, J.S. Silva, C.E. Cox, et al, Invest. Radiol. Localization of ...; 17 (1982) 350-355.
8 G, Kohler and C. Milstein, Nature (Lond), Continuous Cultures of...; 256 (1975) 495-497.
9 P. Stern, P. Hagan, S. Halpern, et al, The Effect of Radiolabel on the Kinetics of Monoclonal Anti-CEA in a Nude Mouse-Colon Tumor Model in Hybridomas and Cancer Diagnosis and Treatment; Raven Press, New York, 1982, p. 245.
10 S. Halpern, P. Stern, P. Hagan, et al, The labeling of Monoclonal Antibodies with 111In Techniqueand Advantages Compared to Radioiodine Labeling, In Radioimmunoimaging and Radioimmunotherapy El Sevier, New York, 1983, p. 197.
11 S.E. Halpern, P.L. Hagan, P.R. Garver, Can.Res; Stability, Characterization...; 43 (1983) 5347-5355.
12 S.E.Halpern, R.O.Dillman, P.L. Hagan, Diagnostic Imaging, The Problems and Promise...; (June 1983) 40-47.
13 S.E. Halpern, R.O. Dillman, K.F. Witztum, et al, Radiology, Radioimmunodetection of...; 155(1985) 493-499.
14 P.L. Hagan, S.E. Halpern, A. Chen, Accepted J. Nucl. Med., In Vivo Kinetics...
15 S.E. Halpern, F. Buchegger, M. Schreyer, et al, J. Nucl. Med., Effect of size of radiolabeled antibody...; 24 (1983) 15.

*Synthesis and Applications of Isotopically Labeled Compounds 1985.*
Proceedings of the Second International Symposium, Kansas City, MO, U.S.A.,
3—6 September 1985, R.R. Muccino (Ed.), 201—206
© 1986 Elsevier Science Publishers B.V., Amsterdam — Printed in The Netherlands

NEW APPROACHES TO [15]N-LABELED COMPOUNDS: AMIDOCARBONYLATION

Alfred M. Ajami and Sun-Shine Yuan

Tracer Technologies, Inc., 225 Needham Street, Newton, MA 02164

ABSTRACT

Based on the pioneering work of Wakamatsu, amidocarbonylation involves the high pressure carbonylation of amides in the presence of a co-reactant aldehyde (or aldehyde precursor) to afford N-acylamino acids in one step. Thus, a spectrum of [15]N labeled amino acids may be prepared from readily available alkyl or aryl amides under circumstances which permit concurrent labeling with [13]C (from [13]CO) or any other isotopes previously incorporated into the skeleton of the co-reactant aldehyde. Amidocarbonylation is an industrial scale reaction, similar in many respects to hydrocarbonylation with which it shares cobalt octacarbonyl as catalyst. Kilogram quantities of [15]N and [13]C labeled amino acids now can be prepared at low cost for use in nutritional research.

INTRODUCTION AND BACKGROUND

Because nitrogen turnover and flux are the more commonly studied parameters of protein dynamics, there has been a resurgence of investigations with [15]N-tracers, particularly in clinical nutrition (ref.1,2). Progress in mass spectrometry and optical emission spectroscopy also has militated in favor of stable over radioactive nuclides for in vivo research of essential metabolic process in humans and animals (ref.3).

If one were to identify the family of nitrogen compounds whose role as topics for research must be characterized as primary, it would be the amino acids and their [15]N and [13]C isotomers. Thus, it follows that advances in the synthesis of amino acids should be construed for practical purposes as synonymous with the development of new chemistry for the effective manipulation of [15]N-synthons.

There are many traditional approaches for the incorporation of [15]N into useful end-products. These will be reviewed, in order to identfy their shortcomings vis-a-vis the new process, which our laboratory has introduced to supplant them.

By far the oldest and most obvious method for [15]N incorporation into any target end-product is the nucleophilic displacement of a primary or secondary halogen with ammonia. Chiral amino acids have been prepared in this manner (ref. 4,5) but with an obvious disadvantage in economic terms. Usually, a ten to twenty fold excess of [15]N species is required to afford high yields of product. The same criticism applies to the venerable Strecker reaction, although ammoniation of the cyanohydrin intermediate can be effected with as little as 2 equivalents of [15]N-ammonia (ref.6). Moreover, this synthetic approach fails to incorporate label as the final step, since the 2-amino-nitrile intermediate must be isolated, hydrolyzed to the racemic amino acid and acetylated prior to enzymatic resolution into the desired L-amino acid end-product.

Reductive amination of ketoacids with aqueous ammonia, catalyzed by noble metals or effected by cyanoborohydride (ref.7) is convenient for small scale work, but there are adverse cost factors associated not only with the excess [15]N required but with the ketoacids themselves, since the ketoacids of many essential amino acids, such as isoleucine or methionine, are not readily available.

To the extent that [15]N-labeling with ammonia is not an isotope conserving process, might not this inefficiency be circumvented by resorting to the alkylation of more complex synthons, in which the [15]N-tracers has been pre-incorporated? The alkylation of glycine offers a case in point. The Gabriel synthesis from [15]N-phthalimide affords high yields and the resulting glycine, obviously, need not be resolved. After derivatization into one of many possible ketamines (ref.8), the [15]N-glycine moiety can be alkylated in high yield at the 2-carbon, thus serving as a common precursor for a spectrum of racemic amino acids. Unfortunately, in practice, this approach, together with the congeneric alkylation of [15]N-acetamidomalonates (ref.9) or [15]N-acetamidocyanoacetates, is labor and materials intensive, scarcely characterizeable as a "one-pot" procedure.

From the preceding discussion, the following desiderata should have become evident. Any new route for $^{15}N$ incorporation into amino acids on the reaction scale required by the demand for these nutritional research substrates should a) use $^{15}N$ ammonia or a simple derivative of ammonia conservatively, as well as inexpensive reagents, b) afford an amino acid in one or two steps, c) avoid dependence on complex purification schemes for intermediates, d) permit rapid entry into enzymatic resolution and, e) be amenable to bench scale (100 g to 1 kg) and pilot plant scale up. In short, it should be "industrializeable".

AMIDOCARBONYLATION

Amidocarbonylation, the process by which acetamide, carbon monoxide and an aldehyde are combined under pressure into an acetyl-amino acid fits this description, almost ideally (Figure A). But before discussing its scope and applications, a recounting of its lineage is in order.

In the late sixties, chemists at Ajinomoto, under the direction of Wakamatsu, began exploring extensions of the "oxo" reaction and other reductive hydrocarbonylations catalyzed by cobalt octacarbonyl. The goal was to find a synthesis for amino acids, derived from petrochemical intermediates, and its advent (ref.10) was communicated first in 1970 and thereafter in a grandfather patent (ref.11). Subsequent mechanistic studies on this reaction have been reported from Pino's group (ref.12) and most recently by Ojima and collaborators (ref.13). Because amidocarbonylation is potentially a source for phenylalanine (and therefore, by extension, of aspartame), industrial laboratories (ref.14,15) continue to enhance the corpus of variations on the amidocarbonylation theme.

Also worthy of note were the independent efforts in 1972 of Witte and Seliger (ref.16) and Giordano (ref.17) on the synthesis of glycine via carbonylation of hydroxymethyl phthalamide, an especially useful alternative to the traditional Gabriel approach referred to earlier.

Although a full discussion of the mechanism will be reserved for a later report (ref.18), the first step in this reaction appears to be formation of a Schiff base between the N-donor amide and the aldehyde (or pro-aldehyde) precursor. There follows insertion of $HCo(CO)_4$ forming a carbon (from the aldehyde)-cobalt adduct which is displaced by CO and hydrolyzed by water (from the initial dehydration to form the Schiff base), thereby affording the acylamino acid.

For the purpose of isotopic labeling, the reaction is especially versatile, since it permits the introduction of $^{15}N$ and $^{13}C$, either singly or together, into the same amino acid. Opportunities for remote labeling in the carbon chain, as illustrated in Figure B), are also feasible since the reaction is conservative towards the precursor aldehyde, even if the latter is functionalized with otherwise reactive functional groups.

Representative reaction conditions as applied to the synthesis of $^{15}N$-leucine are as follows:

A mixture of freshly distilled isovaleraldehyde (43 g, 0.5 mole), $^{15}N$-acetamide (30 g, 0.5 mole) and cobalt hydroxide (0.8 g) were dissolved in 300 ml ACS reagent grade ethyl acetate. This solution was placed in the 1000 ml rocking autoclave and charged with approximately 0.75 mole of CO (estimate based on pressure gauge readings) then pressurized with $H_2$ to 1350 psi so as to give a 1:1 $CO/H_2$ gas composition. The autoclave was heated to $110°C$ for 4-6 hours (1750 psi). Upon cooling, the residual gas (at 500 psi) was vented into a recovery cylinder. After an aliquot of reaction mixture was taken for gas chromatographic evaluation, the full contents of the autoclave was extracted into 500 ml of 10% sodium carbonate. The aqueous phase was washed sequentially with ether and methylene chloride then acidified to pH 1. After chilling in the refrigerator overnight, the off-white crystalline dl-$^{15}N$-acetyl leucine was isolated by filtration, affording 45 g (52% yield). A second crop of 10 g was obtained by partitioning the aqueous phase with ethyl acetate and evaporating the extract under reduced pressure. NMR ($CD_3COCD_3$) $\delta$ : 0.9

(d,J5Hz, (C$\underline{H}_3$)$_2$); 1.4-1.8 (m, $-CHCH_2$); 2.1 (s, C$\underline{H}_3$CO), 4.5 (t, J=6 Hz,$\propto$-H); 5.1 (s, COO$\underline{H}$); and 7.4 (bd, J=6H, N$\underline{H}$).

By contrast to the conditions indicated in the original literature, amidocarbonylation can be catalyzed by _in situ_ generated cobalt octacarbonyl. We have found that cobalt hydroxide is an effective precursor, and its use therefore permits the more conservative utilization of $^{13}$CO, especially since the spent autoclave charges can be recycled. Unutilized acetamide also can be recovered and recycled.

Lastly, amidocarbonylation is amenable to linear scale up, permitting the preparation of multi-hundred gram batches of tracer labeled acetylamino acids in 60 to 70 per cent yields. Because these intermediates are crystalline and sufficiently pure without further elaboration, they can be resolved by the same unit processes used industrially. This advantageous feature further confirms the utility and value of amidocarbonylation as an advance in syntheses with stable isotopes. We have used it in our laboratory in the preparation of all branched chain amino acids, alanine, phenylalaniane, methionine, glutamic acid and lysine. The synthesis of proline and hydroxyproline as illustrated in Figure B, is underway. It is accurate to state that large scale synthesis of these compounds by the traditional approach for $^{15}$N labeling would not have been economically or logistically feasible without amidocarbonylation (ref.19).

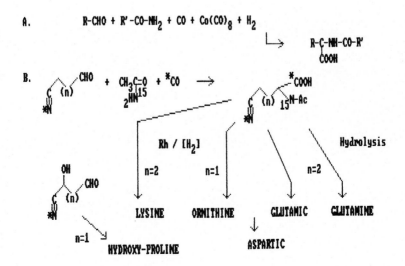

REFERENCES

1 Matthews, D.E. and Bier, D.M., _Ann. Rev. Nutr._ $\underline{3}$:309, 1983.
2 Rennie, M.J. and Halliday, D., _Proc. Nutr. Soc._ $\underline{43}$:189, 1984.
3 Bier, D.M., _J. Trauma_ $\underline{24}$:147, 1984.
4 Neuberger, A. and Sanger, F., _Biochem. J._ $\underline{38}$:125, 1944.
5 Shimohigashi, Y., et al., _Mem. Fac. Sci._ (Kyushu) Ser C, $\underline{11}$:217, 1978.
6 Yuan, S.-S., _J. Lab. Comp. Radiopharm._ $\underline{20}$:173, 1982.
7 Cooper, A.J.L., et al., _Chem. Rev._ $\underline{83}$:321, 1983.
8 Stork, G., et al., _J. Org. Chem._ $\underline{41}$:3493, 1976.
9 Berger, A., et al., _J. Org. Chem._ $\underline{38}$:457, 1973.
10 Wakamatsu, H., et al., _Chem. Comm._, 1540, 1971.
11 Wakamatsu, H., et al., US Patent 3,766,266 (Ajinomoto), 1973.
12 Parnaud, J.-J., et al., _J. Mol. Catal._ $\underline{6}$:341 (1979).
13 Ojima, I., et al., _J. Organomet. Chem._ $\underline{279}$:203 (1985).
14 Getman, D.P., Monsanto Company, St. Louis, MO, personal communication, 1984.
15 Bauer, D.P., US Patent 4,496,756 (Ethyl Corporation), 1985.
16 Witte, H. and Seeliger, W., _Ann. Chem._ $\underline{755}$:163, 1972.
17 Giordano, C., _Gazz. Chim. Ital._ $\underline{102}$:167, 1972.
18 Yuan, S.-S. and Ajami, A.M., _J. Lab. Comp. Radiopharm._, In press, 1985.
19 Supported in part by HHS-NCI grants I-R43-CA36666-01 and I-R43-CA36666-02.

*Synthesis and Applications of Isotopically Labeled Compounds 1985.*
Proceedings of the Second International Symposium, Kansas City, MO, U.S.A.,
3—6 September 1985, R.R. Muccino (Ed.), 207—212
© 1986 Elsevier Science Publishers B.V., Amsterdam — Printed in The Netherlands

A NEW SYNTHESIS OF CHIRAL METHYL GROUPS VIA SUPERTRITIDE REDUCTION. ELUCIDATION
OF THE METHYL-METHYLENE STEREOCHEMISTRY IN KAURENE BIOSYNTHESIS

R. M. COATES, S. HEGDE, S. C. KOCH, and P. K. CHAKRABORTY

Department of Chemistry, University of Illinois, 1209 W. California St.,

Urbana, Illinois 61801 (U.S.A.)

ABSTRACT

Resolution of (E)-phenyl[2-$^2$H$_1$]oxirane via an amino hydrin, reduction with
super-tritide, and oxidative degradation afforded chiral acetate in high
radiochemical yield, albeit with some racemization (67-78% ee). Chiral methyl
mevalonates prepared from phenyl acetate were used as substrate for kaurene
biosynthesis with an enzyme preparation from Marah macrocarpus. Re-creation of
a chiral methyl at C-17, regiospecific degradation to acetate, and enzymatic
analysis revealed overall net retention of configuration. It is concluded that
the CH$_3$ → CH$_2$ elimination forming the exocyclic methylene group of kaurene
occurs with an endo orientation.

INTRODUCTION

The stereochemistry attending methyl → methylene transformations or their

reverse may be elucidated by use of substrates or analysis of products bearing

chiral methyl groups (ref.1). In connection with investigations in our

laboratory on the stereospecificity and mechanism of diterpene biosynthesis

(ref.2), we became interested in determining the stereochemistry of the two

methyl → methylene eliminations that take place in the biosynthesis of

(-)-kaurene (3) from geranylgeranyl pyrophosphate (1) (Scheme 1). Enzyme

extracts from the endosperm of immature seeds of Marah macrocarpus are rich in

kaurene synthetase activity and contain as well the necessary enzymes to

convert mevalonic acid to geranylgeranyl PP (ref.3) (Scheme 1). We therefore

Scheme 1. Enzyme-catalyzed cyclization of geranylgeranyl
pyrophosphate (1) to kaurene (3) via copalyl pyrophosphate (2)

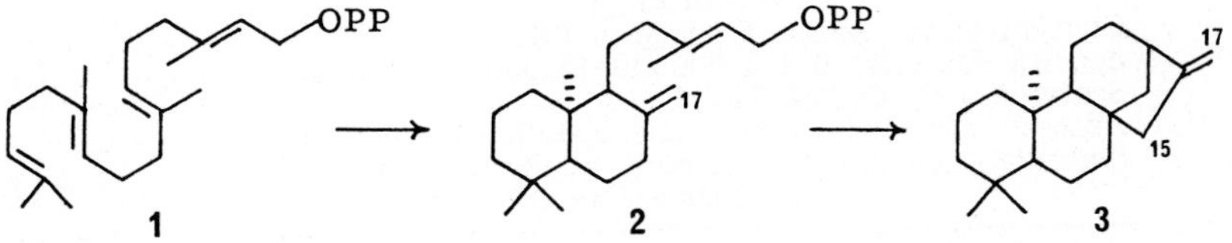

decided to synthesize mevalonic acid bearing a chiral methyl group. The need

for relatively high specific activity prompted us to develop a preparation of

supertritide and to use this new tritium-labelling reagent to create chiral methyl groups. This paper describes a new synthesis of chiral acetic acid and the use of chiral methyl groups to deduce the stereospecificity of exocyclic methylene formation in kaurene biosynthesis.

SYNTHESIS OF CHIRAL METHYL GROUPS VIA SUPER-TRITIDE REDUCTION

The micromolar scale of the biochemical procedures and the need for multi-microcurie quantities of $[^3H]$kaurene for degradations necessitated synthesis of millicurie amounts of mevalonate at the relatively high specific activity of 20 mCi/mmol. Since none of the syntheses of chiral methyl groups known at the time this work was initiated seemed adaptable to these requirements (ref.1), we considered alternative approaches. The major disadvantages of Cornforth's original synthesis of chiral acetate (ref.4) were the early introduction of tritium and an optical resolution of a radioactive intermediate. However, direct reduction of optically active R,R (or S,S) (E)-phenyl[2-$^2H_1$]oxirane with a suitable tritide donor would circumvent these difficulties.

The high cost and moderate specific activities of LiAlT$_4$ and the rather low nucleophilic character of LiBT$_4$ stimulated us in collaboration with Dr. C. J. Pearce to prepare super-tritide (LiBEt$_3$T) for the epoxide reduction (ref.5). The high reactivity of super-hydride in reductive displacement is well established (ref.6). THF solutions of super-tritide were formed by reaction of LiT with commercially available 1 M triethylborane in THF in a glove bag according to literature descriptions for its hydride parent. The procedure and properties are summarized in Table 1. The scale of the laboratory preparations

TABLE 1

Preparation and properties of super-tritide

$$LiT \ + \ (C_2H_5)_3B \ \xrightarrow[\text{THF}]{N_2} \ \left[ C_2H_5 - \overset{\overset{\displaystyle C_2H_5}{|}}{\underset{\underset{\displaystyle C_2H_5}{|}}{B}} \ominus T \qquad Li^{\oplus} \right]$$

Procedure: 1. 3-48 h at 25 °C
2. 2-3 h at 90 °C  } under nitrogen
3. Cool and filter
Concentration: normally ~1 M in THF
Specific Activity: 0.1-3,000 (10-15,000) mCi/mmol
Scale: 0.1-72 Ci in 2-24 ml
Assay: reduction on cinnamaldehyde to cinnamyl alcohol
Stability (3 Ci/mmol): > 2 mos. at -20 °C under N$_2$
(less stable at higher S.A.)

was 100-500 mCi of LiT in 1-5 mL of triethylborane solution resulting in specific activities estimated at 50-75 mCi/mmol.

Large scale preparations carried out by Mr. Joseph Maroun in the Tritium Laboratory at New England Nuclear afforded 24-72 Ci of super-tritide in 8-24 mL of THF with specific activities of about 3 Ci/mmol. CAUTION. The pronounced dispersive tendency of LiT necessitate secure containment procedures and extreme care in the preparation of high specific activity super-tritide. The smooth reductive tritiation of carbonyl compounds, alkyl halides, alkyl tosylates, and epoxides with low specific activity super-tritide served to demonstrate the utility of the reagent (ref.5). The high radiochemical yields (estimated at 61-100% of theoretical) indicate that isotope effects in these tritide transfer reactions are apparently low in accord with competitive reductions with 1:1 mixtures of super hydride and super-deuteride.

Racemic styrene oxide was resolved by formation of diastereomeric amino hydrins with S (or R) α-phenethyl amine. The less soluble S,S (or R,R) isomer was reconverted to the optically pure epoxide by quaternization with $CH_3I$ and subsequent t-butoxide-induced elimination. Reduction of S(-) epoxide derived from (E)[2-$^2H_1$]styrene with super-tritide afforded (R) α-phenethanol bearing a chiral methyl group of S configuration (70 mCi, 64 mCi/mmol) (Scheme 2). Oxidation of the 1R,2S (and 1S,2R) α-phenethanol (5) to phenyl acetate (7) via acetophenone was carried out according to the Cornforth procedures (ref.4) in about 70% radiochemical yield with the theoretical specific activity. An alternative route involved $RuO_4$ oxidation of α-phenethyl acetate to lactic acetate followed by saponification and chromic acid oxidation (60% overall yield) (ref.7).

Scheme 2. Synthesis of (S) chiral acetate and (3'S) chiral methyl mevalonolactone via supertritide reduction of (E, S, S)[2-$^2H_1$]styrene oxide.

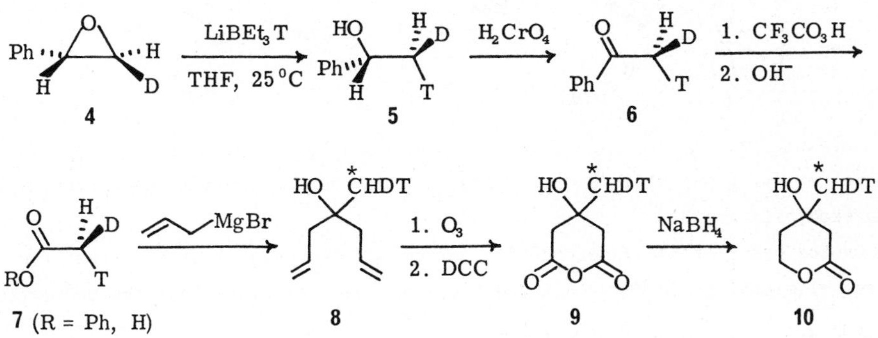

Although the high radiochemical yield (~43-50% based on super-tritide) was gratifying, evidently some racemization of the chiral methyl groups occurred during both oxidation sequences. The enzymatic chirality assay (refs.1,4) gave F values of 72.6 ± 1.4 (78% ee) for (R) acetate and 30.5 ± 1.6 (67% ee) for (S) acetate prepared via acetophenone. The F values for (R) and (S) acetate via the lactate route were 63.0 ± 1.5 (45% ee) and 38.1 ± 1.7 (41% ee), respectively.[*]

Phenyl acetate was converted to chiral methyl mevalonolactone (10) by a modification of the Fetizon synthesis (ref.9). Addition of allyl Grignard reagent (66%) followed by ozonolysis (80%) and carbodiimide-induced dehydration of the diacid in acetone gave cyclic anhydride 9. Partial reduction with $NaBH_4$ in isopropyl alcohol afforded 19 mg (2.8 mCi, 19.2 mCi/mmol) of mevalonolactone bearing an S chiral methyl group and 12 mg (1.8 mCi, 19.9 mCi/mmol) bearing an R chiral methyl group.

STEREOSPECIFICITY OF $CH_3 \rightarrow CH_2$ ELIMINATIONS IN KAURENE BIOSYNTHESIS

The exocyclic methylene groups of copalyl PP and kaurene must arise by regiospecific eliminations induced by the position of the basic proton acceptor within the enzyme active site. There are two stereochemical options for these methyl → methylene eliminations (Scheme 3). Thus proton elimination from a

Scheme 3. Stereochemical options for the methyl/methylene transformation

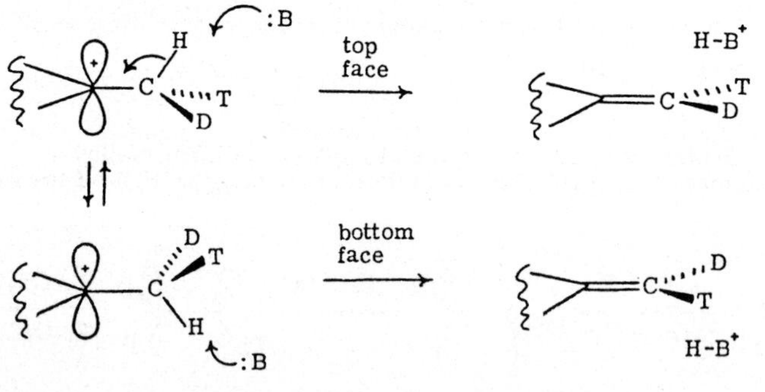

chiral methyl group will lead to opposite positions of tritium and deuterium in the exocyclic group.

On the basis of the independently determined deuterium isotope effect for these eliminations ($k_H/k_D$ = 4.2 and 5.6), one can calculate that the proportion

[*]For an alternative synthesis of enantiomerically pure chiral acetate using a supertritide displacement, see ref. 8.

of deuterium elimination should be only 15-20%. That is, the distribution of
tritium at the two different vinyl positions should be 80-85:20-15. The
stereospecificity of the eliminations can therefore be deduced from the
chirality of the methyl group and the distribution of tritium at the two
prochiral methylene groups. Since the $S_N'$ cyclization of copalyl PP is known
to occur on the si face of the C-17 exocyclic methylene group (ref.2a), the
location of the tritium in the intermediate can be inferred from the exo or
endo stereochemistry of tritium at C-15 in kaurene.

Incubation of chiral methyl mevalonate (10-20 μmol, 0.13 μM), ATP (3-6 mM)
MgCl$_2$ (3-6 mM), and KHPO$_4$ buffer (30-40 mM, pH 7.0) with the S-150 enzyme
extract isolated from M. macrocarpus (ref.3) afforded 68-177 μg (10-14% from
3'S mevalonate) and 14-337 μg (2-33% from 3'R mevalonate) of [$^3$H]kaurene that
was isolated by dilution with (-)-kaurene and purified by crystallization.
Although experimental work to determine the exo/endo distribution of tritium at
C-15 remains incomplete, the chemical methods for the stereoselective
degradation have been developed. Ozonolysis of kaurene to norkauranone
followed by stereospecific exo deprotonation with Ph$_3$CLi and phosphorylation of
the enolate with diethyl chlorophosphate afforded enol phosphate 13 (64%) and
recovered triphenylmethane. This degradation allows independent measurement of
the tritium retained in the enol phosphate (summation of C-15, C-19, and C-20)
and tritium removed (triphenylmethane).

Scheme 4. Incorporation of chiral methyl mevalonic acid into kaurene and stereospecific
degradation of the labelled kaurene.

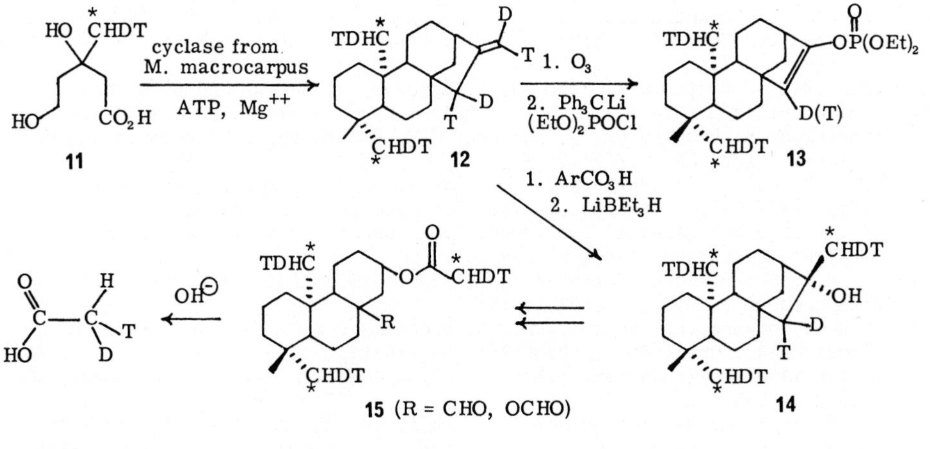

To ascertain the stereochemistry of the tritium in the exocyclic methylene
group of kaurene, we adopted the tactic of re-creating a chiral methyl group at
this position (ref.1). Thus, exo selective epoxidation of the biosynthetic

kaurene followed by superhydride reduction gave kauranol (14) bearing three chiral methyl groups. Dehydration with $SOCl_2$, separation of isokaurene and kaurene by argentic chromatography, and oxidation of isokaurene with $OsO_4$ afforded kauran-15,16-diol. Regiospecific removal of the chiral methyl group at C-17 was achieved by periodate cleavage, Bayer-Villiger oxidation, and saponification of the resulting mixture of formyl acetate and formate acetate (15). The configuration of the acetate derived originally from 3'R mevalonate proved to be R according to the enzymatic chirality assay (F = 66.3 ± 2.9, 54% ee) and that from 3'S mevalonate was S (F = 42.0 ± 2.4, 27% ee). The overall retention of configuration proves that the enzyme-catalyzed formation of the exocyclic methylene group in kaurene occurs with an _endo_ (rather than _exo_) orientation.

## ACKNOWLEDGMENT

The original preparations of super-tritide were carried out by Dr. Cedric Pearce. We thank Mr. Joseph Maroun for information regarding super-tritide, Dr. Charles West for M. macrocarpus seeds, Christine Klodnycky for conducting enzymatic chirality assays, and Dr. Heinz Floss for some chirality assays performed in his laboratory. Financial support from the National Institutes of Health (GM 13956) is gratefully acknowledged.

## REFERENCES

1  (a) H.G. Floss, M.-D. Tsai and R.W. Woodward, Top. Stereochem., 15 (1984) 253-321.   (b) H.G. Floss and M.-D. Tsai, Adv. Enzymol., 50 (1979) 243-302.
2  (a) R.M. Coates and P.L. Cavender, J. Am. Chem. Soc., 102 (1980) 6358-6359. (b) R.M. Coates and W.J. Guilford, Ibid., 104 (1982) 2198-2208.   (c) R.M. Coates and K.A. Drengler, J. Chem. Soc., Chem. Commun., (1980) 856-857. (d) R.M. Coates and P.S. Sherwin, Ibid., (1982) 1013-1014.
3  (a) C.D. Upper and C.A. West, J. Biol. Chem., 242 (1967) 3285-3292. (b) M. O. Oster and C.A. West, Arch. Biochem. Biophys., 127 (1968) 112-123.   (c) I. Shechter and C.A. West, J. Biol. Chem., 244 (1969) 3200-3209.
4  (a) J.W. Cornforth, J.W. Redmond, H. Eggerer, W. Buckel and C. Gutschow, Eur. J. Biochem., 14 (1970) 1-13.   (b) H. Lenz, W. Buckel, P. Wunderwald, G. Biederman, V. Buschmeier, H. Eggerer, J.W. Cornforth, J.W. Redmond and R. Mallaby, Ibid., 24 (1971) 207-215.
5  (a) R.M. Coates, S. Hegde and C.J. Pearce, J. Chem. Soc., Chem. Commun. (1983) 1484-1485.   (b) R.M. Coates, S. Hegde and C.J. Pearce, in Application of Isotopically Labelled Compounds, W.P. Duncan and A.B. Susan (Eds.), Elsevier, Amsterdam, 1983, p. 429.
6  (a) H.C. Brown and S. Krishnamurthy, Aldrichimica Acta, 12 (1979) 3.   (b) S. Krishnamurthy, Ibid., 7 (1974), 55.
7  R. W. Wododward, L. Mascaro, Jr., R. Hörhammer, S Eisenstein, and H. G. Floss, J. Am. Chem. Soc., 102 (1980) 6314-6318.
8  K. Kobayashi, P.K. Jadhav, T.M. Zydowsky and H.G. Floss, J. Org. Chem., 48 (1983) 3510-3512.
9  (a) M. Fetizon, M. Golfier and J.M. Louis, Tetrahedron 31 (1975) 171-176. (b) G.T. Phillips and K.H. Clifford, Eur. J. Biochem., 61 (1976), 271-286. (c) P. Lewer and J. MacMillan, J. Chem. Soc., Perkin Trans 1 (1983) 1417-1420.

*Synthesis and Applications of Isotopically Labeled Compounds 1985.*
Proceedings of the Second International Symposium, Kansas City, MO, U.S.A.,
3—6 September 1985, R.R. Muccino (Ed.), 213—218
© 1986 Elsevier Science Publishers B.V., Amsterdam — Printed in The Netherlands

INCORPORATION OF RADIOHALOGENS VIA VERSATILE ORGANOMETALLIC REACTIONS:
APPLICATIONS IN RADIOPHARMACEUTICAL CHEMISTRY

PREM C. SRIVASTAVA, M. M. GOODMAN, and FURN F. KNAPP, JR.
Nuclear Medicine Group, Oak Ridge National Laboratory, Oak Ridge, Tennessee
37831

ABSTRACT

Factors that must be considered for the design of radiohalogenated radiopharmaceuticals include the stability and availability of the substrate, the
physical half-life of the radiohalogen and the in vivo stability of the radiolabel. Vinyl and phenyl radiohalogen bonds show more in vivo stability than the
alkyl radiohalogen bonds. Consequently, a variety of methods suitable for the
synthesis of tissue specific radiopharmaceuticals bearing a vinyl or phenyl
radiohalogen have been developed involving the synthesis and halogenation of
metallovinyl and phenyl intermediates. The halogens and metallation reactions
include iodine and bromine and alanation, boronation, mercuration, stannylation,
and thallation, respectively.

INTRODUCTION

There are a number of halogen radioisotopes which exhibit a broad spectrum of
radionuclidic properties (Table 1) useful for scanning, tracer techniques and
therapeutic applications. The usefulness of these radioisotopes is further
enhanced if the isotopes can be conveniently incorporated into the organic
molecules (or radiopharmaceuticals) appropriate for use as a vehicle for such
applications. The ease of incorporation of the radiohalogen in the molecule,
stability and availability of the substrate, physical half-life of the
radiohalogen and in vivo stability of the carbon halogen bond are important
factors to be considered in designing the synthesis of a radiopharmaceutical.

Properties and principle mode of decay
of halogen radioisotopes

| Isotope | Half-life | Mode of decay | Principle radiation energy (keV) |
|---|---|---|---|
| $^{18}F$ | 1.83 h | $^+\beta$ | 511 |
| $^{75}Br$ | 1.62 h | $^+\beta$,EC | 511 |
| $^{76}Br$ | 16.2 h | $^+\beta$,EC | 511 |
| $^{77}Br$ | 2.38 d | EC | 239 |
| $^{82}Br$ | 35.3 h | $^-\beta$ | 554 |
| $^{123}I$ | 13.2 h | EC | 159 |
| $^{125}I$ | 60.14 d | EC | Te-X-rays |
| $^{131}I$ | 8.02 d | $^-\beta$ | 364 |

Table 1

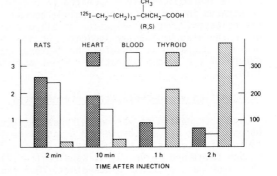

IODOALKYL SUBSTITUTED $\beta$-METHYL BRANCHED FATTY ACIDS EXHIBIT SIGNIFICANT *IN VIVO* DEIODINATION

$$^{125}I-CH_2-(CH_2)_{13}-\underset{\underset{CH_3}{|}}{CH}CH_2-COOH$$
(R,S)

Figure 1

In general, halogens can be attached to a radiopharmaceutical as alkyl, aklenyl and aryl (phenyl) halides. The reactivity of alkyl halides follows the order RI>RBr>RCl>RF. This order is reversed for the stability of these alkyl halides, consequently, RF and RI would be expected to be the most and least in vivo stable of the alkyl halides, respectively. This trend of reactivity and/or stability is obvious from various examples cited in the literature, e.g., the stability of 2-deoxy-2-fluoro-D-glucose as compared to that of 2-deoxy-2-iodo-D-glucose which has eluded synthetic attempts by several investigators (ref.1 and 2). The clinical potential of such radioiodinated agents is often marred due to their in vivo instability or deiodination. For example, 17-[$^{123}$I]iodoheptadecanoic acid, a useful probe of regional fatty acid metabolism, undergoes in vivo deiodination and special correction methods have to be applied to account for the activity in the blood pool (ref.3 and 4). Similarly, 17-[$^{125}$I]iodo-3-(R,S)-methylheptadecanoic acid shows high heart uptake in rats but washes out rapidly from the heart with significant accumulation of the activity in the thyroid (Fig. 1) indicating in vivo carbon-iodide bond cleavage of the radioiodinated fatty acid (ref.5).

A detailed animal tissue distribution study in our laboratory with a variety of functionallized radioiodinated agents indicate the following order of carbon-iodine (C-I) bond stability in vivo: iodoaryl>iodovinyl>iodoalkyl. This order of in vivo stability would indeed be expected for the following reasons. In aryl and vinyl halides the iodine bearing carbon is sp$^2$ hybridized and the C-I bond is resonance stabilized by electron delocalization giving C-I bond a double bond character as compared to pure single bond in alkyl iodides in which carbon bearing iodine is sp$^3$ hybridized.

Methods were subsequently investigated for easy, straight forward and facile incorporation of radiohalogens into the tissue specific radiopharmaceuticals functionallized as vinyl and aryl halides. A comprehensive report on the radiohalogenation subject is beyond the scope of these proceedings and only the incorporation of radiohalogens via organometallic reactions is briefly described here.

## Synthesis of radiohalogenated radiopharmaceuticals via organometallic reactions

The synthetic procedure normally involves the preparation of an appropriately metallated organic intermediate which can be readily radiohalogenated. The metallated intermediates should preferably be stable at room temperature under normal conditions to allow shipment for an offsite radiohalogenation. Metallation methods which appeared to provide appropriate radiohalogenation substrates in our laboratory include boronation, thallation, mercuration and stannylation. Hydroalumination of alkynes gives, in situ, the alkylvinyl alanes which can also be readily iodinated or brominated (ref.6). This method, however, appeared less useful for radiohalogenations due to the highly reactive nature of the hydroaluminating reagent and the alane intermediate formed in situ.

## Halogenation via boronic acid intermediates

Hydroboronation of various alkynes (1) gives the corresponding alkylvinyl boronic acids (2) as stable and crystalline intermediates suitable for radioiodination using sodium iodide and chloramine-T. This radioiodination method developed by Dr. G. W. Kabalka (ref.7) who will discuss this subject in the later part of these proceedings. Our experience with this reaction pertaining to radiopharmaceutical development is described here.

Several radioiodinated iodopentenyl-trisubstituted phosphonium, arsonium and ammonium iodides (5) have been prepared and evaluated in rats to determine the effects of structural variations of the cations on myocardial uptake and retention. The synthesis of (5) involved condensation of (E)-1,5-diiodopentene (3) with trisubstituted phosphine arsine and amine precursors respectively. Alternatively the crystalline vinylboronic acid intermediates (4) were first synthesized and radioiodinated using $Na^{125}I$-sodium iodide and chloramine-T (Scheme 1). The radioiodinated cations showed good heart uptake and retention in rats (ref.8).

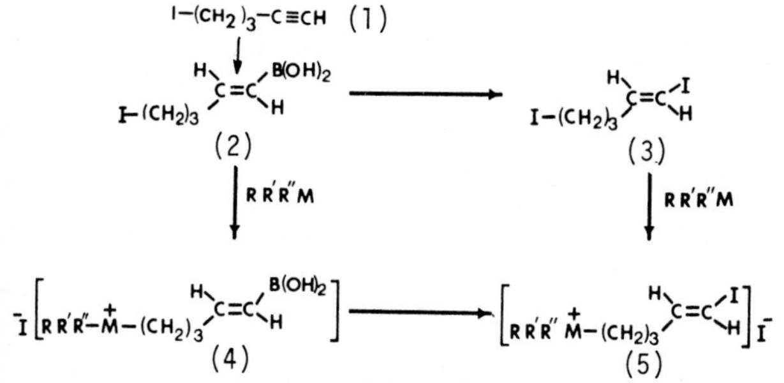

Scheme 1

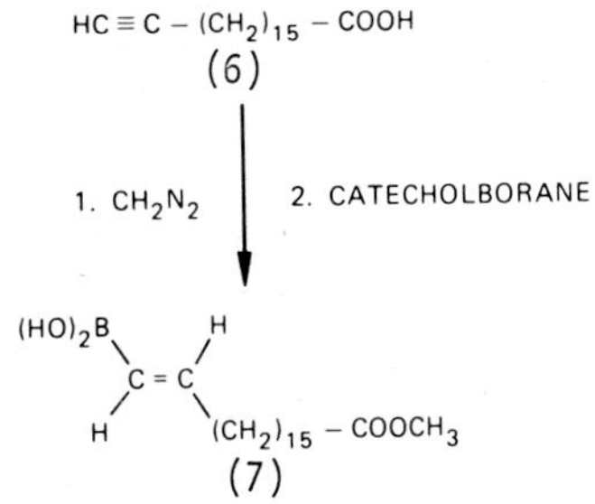

Scheme II

Various radioiodinated fatty acids in which radioiodine is stabilized as a terminal vinyl iodide have been conveniently prepared by this method (ref.9). It is also pertinent to discuss here certain limitations this reaction may have. The hydroboration of alkynes with reducible or carbon-hetero atom multiple bond groups is difficult and often impossible. For example, the hydroboronation of 17-octadecynoic acid (6) with catecholborane (Scheme II) required special conditions (ref.10), where as similar boronation of 5-ethyl-5-(1-pentyn-5-yl)barbituric acid (14) failed to give the corresponding borono intermediate 15, prepared alternatively by a long route (Scheme III), as iodination substrate (ref.11).

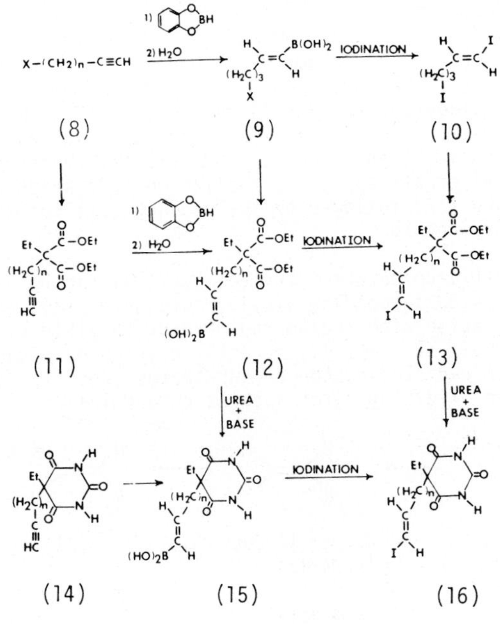

Scheme III

## Halogenation via thallation of vinyl and aryl compounds

Aryl iodination via thallation developed by Taylor et al. (ref.12) has been found satisfactory for the corresponding radioiodination reactions and has been used extensively in our laboratory for aryl radioiodination of phenyl (ref.13) and thienyl (ref.14) fatty acids. Recently a new $\beta,\beta$-dimethyl-branched fatty acid, 15-p-[$^{125}$I]iodophenyl-3,3-dimethylpentadecanoic acid (18) has been prepared by thallation-iodination treatment of the corresponding phenyl fatty acid 17 (Scheme IV). Compound 18 shows excellent myocardial uptake and retention properties (ref.15).

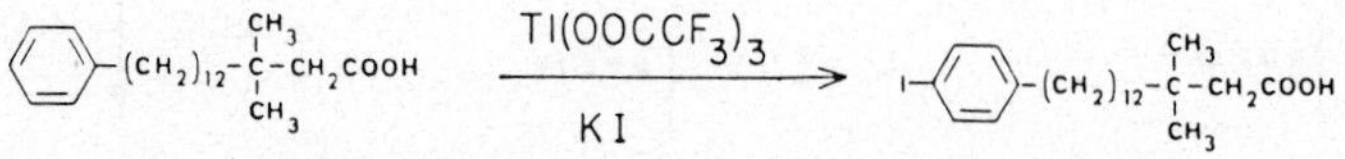

(17)    (18)

Scheme IV

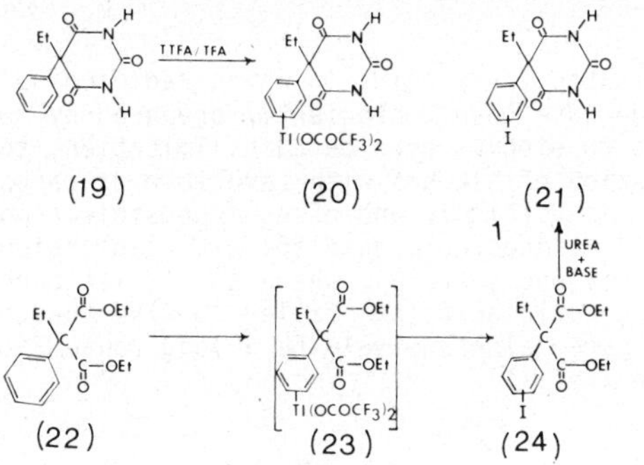

(19)    (20)    (21)

(22)    (23)    (24)

Scheme V

Direct thallium(III)trifluoroacetate/trifluoroacetic acid (TTFA/TFA) thallation of molecules with NH and OH tautomeric groups (such as in 5-ethyl-5-phenylbarbituric acid, 19) has been found to be difficult. Under these conditions, however, an alternate approach, thallation-iodination of a TTFA-insensitive substrate (22) followed by the product (21) formation was found more convenient (Scheme V, ref.16).

Alkylvinylthallium trifluoroacetate intermediates (26) can be easily generated in situ from the corresponding vinylboronic acids (25) and TTFA to undergo facile radioiodination with sodium radioiodide to yield vinyl iodides (27). This reaction (Scheme VI, ref.17), recently developed in our laboratory may find applications for radioiodination of substrates sensitive to an acidic medium such as TFA and an oxidizing agent such as chloramine-T.

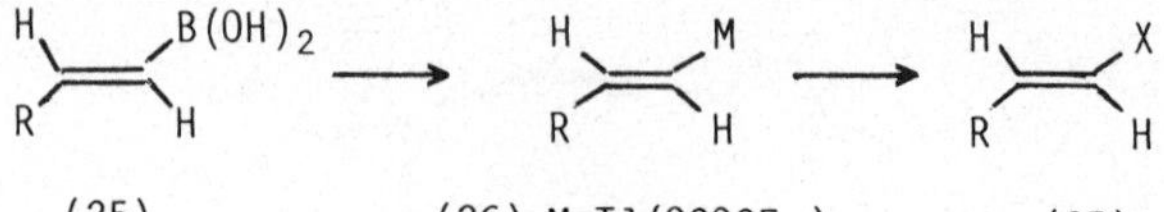

(25)    (26),M=Tl(OCOCF$_3$)$_2$    (27)
        (28),M=HgX

Scheme VI

## Halogenation via mercuration

Treatment of vinylboronic acids (25 or 29) with mercuric acetate in tetrahydrofuran gives the corresponding vinyl mercuric acetates in situ which after treatment with a halide such as sodium iodide or sodium bromide give the corresponding vinylmercuric halides (28 or 30) in the crystalline form. The mercury halide intermediates (28) undergo radioiodination similar to boronic acids when treated with sodium radioiodide and chloramine-T to furnish vinyl radioiodides (27). Iododemercuration of p-aminophenylmercuric acetate with $I_2$-$^{125}I^-$ has proven to be a very convenient and facile method for the synthesis of p-[$^{125}I$]iodoaniline (ref.17). The method could be used for the synthesis of similar aryl iodides.

Treatment of 30 with bromine-radiobromide gives, almost instantaneously the corresponding vinylradiobromide (31) as a mixture of cis and trans isomers. The cis/trans-1-[$^{82}Br$]bromo-5-iodo-1-pentene (31) thus prepared has been used for the synthesis of a potential myocardial perfusion agent, triphenyl-(cis/trans-1-[$^{82}Br$]bromo-1-penten-5-yl)phosphonium iodide (32) (Scheme VII).

## Iodination via stannylation

Hydrostannylation of alkynes with tri-n-butyltin hydride (n-Bu$_3$)SnH is a versatile reaction which gives the corresponding trans-vinyl-tri-n-butyltin compounds as stable substrates for radioiodination. The method has successfully been used for the radioiodination of steriods and fatty acids, functionalized as trans-vinyl-(tri-n-butyl)tin substrates, with $^{125}I^-$-hydrogen peroxide (ref.18) and $^{125}I^-$-N-chlorosuccinimide (ref.5), respectively.

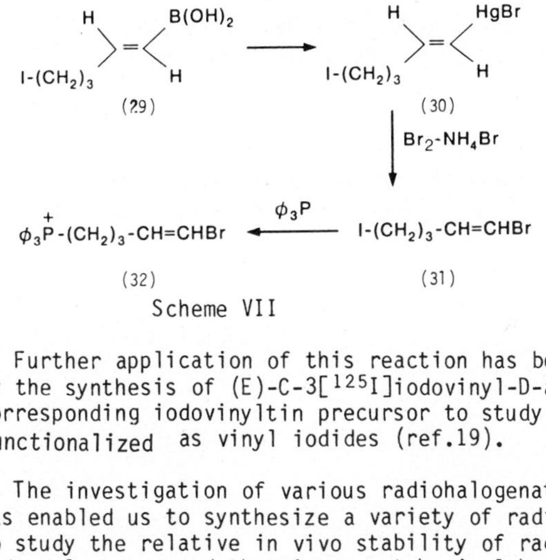

Scheme VII

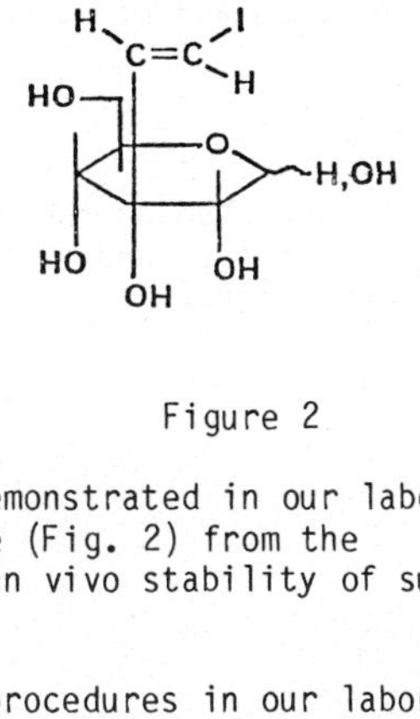

Figure 2

Further application of this reaction has been demonstrated in our laboratory by the synthesis of (E)-C-3[$^{125}I$]iodovinyl-D-allose (Fig. 2) from the corresponding iodovinyltin precursor to study the in vivo stability of sugars functionalized as vinyl iodides (ref.19).

The investigation of various radiohalogenation procedures in our laboratory has enabled us to synthesize a variety of radiohalogenated radiopharmaceuticals to study the relative in vivo stability of radioiodide attached to alkyl, vinyl and aryl groups and the tissue uptake in laboratory animals and human models. With recent advances in imaging techniques, increasing interest in radioiodinated agents and availability of pure iodine-123, undoubtedly, these methods will find useful applications in radiopharmaceutical development.

## REFERENCES

1. G. Kloster, P. Laufer, W. Witz and G. Stocklin, Symposium Abstracts, J. Lab. Comp. Radiopharm., 19 (1982) 1626-1628.
2. J. S. Fowler, R. E. Lade, R. R. Macgregor, C. Shiue, C. N. Wan and A. P. Wolf, J. Lab. Comp. Radiopharm., 16 (1979) 7-9.

218

3. C. H. Freundlieb, A. Hock, K. Vyska, L. F. Feinendegen, H.-J. Machulla and G. Stocklin, Eur. J. Nucl. Med., 21 (1980) 1043-1050.
4. L. F. Feinendegen, K. Vyska, C. H. Freundlieb, A. Hock, H.-J. Machulla, G. Kloster and G. Stocklin, Eur. J. Nucl. Med., 6 (1981) 191-200.
5. M. M. Goodman, A. P. Callahan and F. F. Knapp, Jr., J. Med. Chem., 28 (1985) 807-815.
6. G. Zweifel and C. C. Whitney, J. Amer. Chem. Soc., 86 (1964) 2753-2755.
7. G. W. Kabalka, Acc. Chem. Res., 17 (1984) 215-221.
8. P. C. Srivastava, H. G. Hay and F. F. Knapp, Jr., J. Med. Chem., 28 (1985) 901-904.
9. F. F. Knapp, Jr., P. C. Srivastava, A. P. Callahan, E. B. Cunningham, G. W. Kabalka and K. A. R. Sastry, J. Med. Chem., 27 (1984) 57-63.
10. F. F. Knapp, Jr., M. M. Goodman, G. W. Kabalka and K. A. R. Sastry, J. Med. Chem., 27 (1984) 94-97.
11. P. C. Srivastava, A. P. Callahan, E. B. Cunningham and F. F. Knapp, Jr., J. Med. Chem., 26 (1983) 742-746.
12. E. C. Taylor, F. Kienzle, R. L. Robey, A. McKillop and J. D. Hunt, J. Amer. Chem. Soc., 93 (1971) 4845-4850.
13. M. M. Goodman, G. Kirsch and F. F. Knapp, Jr., J. Med. Chem., 27 (1984) 390-397.
14. M. M. Goodman, G. Kirsch and F. F. Knapp, Jr., J. Heterocycl. Chem., 21 (1984) 1579-1583.
15. F. F. Knapp, Jr., M. M. Goodman, G. Kirsch and A. P. Callahan, J. Nucl. Med., 26 (1985) P 123.
16. P. C. Srivastava, C. E. Guyer and F. F. Knapp, Jr., J. Heterocycl. Chem., 20 (1983) 1081.
17. P. C. Srivastava, F. F. Knapp, Jr., G. W. Kabalka and K. A. R. Sastry, Syn. Commun., 15 (1985) 355-364.
18. L. A. Franke and R. N. Hanson, J. Nucl. Med., 25 (1984) 1116-1121.
19. M. M. Goodman and F. F. Knapp, Jr., J. Nucl. Med., 26 (1985) P 121.

ACKNOWLEDGEMENT

Research supported by the Office of Health and Environmental Research, U.S. Department of Energy, under contract DE-AC05-84OR21400 with Martin Marietta Energy Systems, Inc.

*Synthesis and Applications of Isotopically Labeled Compounds 1985.*
Proceedings of the Second International Symposium, Kansas City, MO, U.S.A.,
3—6 September 1985, R.R. Muccino (Ed.), 219—224
© 1986 Elsevier Science Publishers B.V., Amsterdam — Printed in The Netherlands

# CARBON 14 PHOTOSYNTHESIS LABELING OF NATURAL COMPOUNDS AND DRUGS FROM PLANTS

A. Benakis[1], F.R. Sugnaux[1], G.F. Collet[2], J.P. Kradolfer[2], C. Berney[2], R. Sion[3], J. Necciari[4] and W. Cautreels[4]

[1]*Laboratory Drug Metabolism, Dept Pharmacology, University Geneva, Switzerland,* [2]*Federal Agriculture Research Station, Nyon, Switzerland,* [3]*Labaz-Sanofi Research Lab., Bruxelles, Belgium,* [4]*Clin-Midy Research Center (SANOFI), Montpellier, France*

A widely used method for obtaining metabolic and pharmacokinetic data is that of labeling the compound to be studied with either radioactive or stable isotopes. However, although such labeling is perfectly feasible for synthetic compounds, it is quite impractical for compounds extracted from plants.

In the present study therefore, an attempt was made to label the natural plant extracted compound Endotelon with carbon 14 by photosynthetic route. Endotelon, which is extracted from grape seeds, is a drug used for the treatment of peripheral vein insufficiency [refs 1,2].

Labeling by photosynthesis is one of the earliest applications of the $^{14}C$ isotope. This method has been used to investigate fundamental mechanisms related to biochemical and biological processes.

A survey of the literature has revealed more than a hundred references of studies made over the last thirty years in which $^{14}C$ labeled precursors such as [1-$^{14}C$]- or [2-$^{14}C$]-acetate, [U-$^{14}C$]-glucose, [U-$^{14}C$]-sucrose, [$^{14}C$]-phenylalanine, [$^{14}C$]-tyrosine, as well as some with a more complicated structure have been used in order to investigate the natural route of synthesis of plant compounds. Almost all of these studies were done *in vitro* while a few of them were performed in greenhouses.

In the present study, however, in view of the possible effects of different growing conditions (geographical, climatic and seasonal) on the chemical structure and ratio of the extractable products synthesized by the plant, it was decided to conduct the photosynthetic labeling procedure under natural growing conditions in the field (Experimental Vinyard, Pully near Lausanne, Switzerland).

---

*A review paper of these studies is currently under preparation

Preliminary data indicated that at least 10 kg of grapes were necessary to obtain the desired amount of labeled Endotelon. Three plants of the UNIBLANC strain were used. Each plant was enclosed in a 300 liter airtight polyethylene chamber (Fig. 1) equipped with a vacuum pump for evacuation of air in order to reduce the dilution of the $^{14}CO_2$ which was obtained in a generator from $Ba^{14}CO_3$ (56.6 mCi/mM) and 60 % $H_3PO_4$. An air balloon was used for rinsing the generator. The $^{14}CO_2$ permeability of the chamber was about 15 nCi/h/cm$^2$.

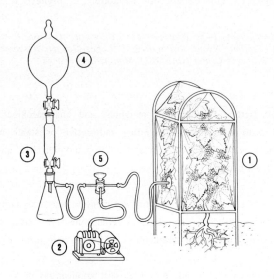

① Plastic Chamber
② Vacuum pump for evacuation of air from plastic chamber
③ $^{14}CO_2$ generator flask (60 % $H_3PO_4$ on $Ba^{14}CO_3$)
④ Air balloon for rinsing $^{14}CO_2$ generator flask
⑤ 3 - way cockstop

Figure 1

An air conditioning system was used to maintain stable climatic conditions in the labeling chamber (Fig. 2). Illumination was regulated and on cloudy days it was supplemented by mirrors. Precautions were taken to avoid a "greenhouse effect" in the chamber and it was assured that no leaves adhered to the plastic foil. The air was sampled for radioactivity measurement every hour of the first day and once at the beginning and at the end of the night (Fig. 3).

The labeling conditions are given in Table I. The labeling procedure was terminated when the $^{14}CO_2$ in the atmosphere of the chamber was found to be less than 50 $\mu$Ci/m$^3$. For safety, all air was evacuated through a KOH trap which also allowed for determination of $^{14}CO_2$ consumption. Less than one thousanth of the radioactivity used in the labeling was recovered in the trap. The plant was then liberated from the chamber. The grapes were picked about six weeks after the labeling procedure, refrigerated at liquid nitrogen temperature and stored at -30°C until processing. It should be noted that the choice of time for picking the grapes is based on the maturity of the seeds rather than the grapes which only mature several weeks later.

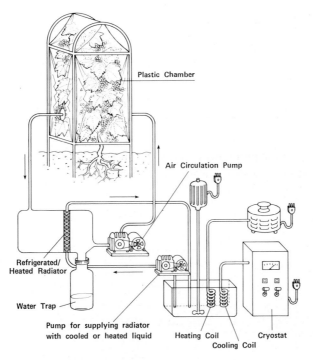

Figure 2

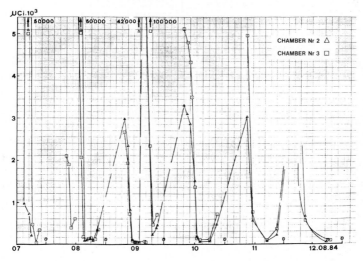

Figure 3

Table I

**LABELING CONDITIONS**

| Bunch No | Number of grapes | Dose Administered : mCi Day | | | | Duration of Procedure |
|----------|------------------|-----|-----|-----|-----|-----------|
|          |                  | 1st | 2nd | 3rd | 4th |           |
| 1 | 12 | 50 | – | – | – | 4 days |
| 2 | 15 | – | 50 | 50 | 50 | 5 days |
| 3 | 20 | – | 50 | 50 | 100 | 8 days |

The flavonolic oligomers (OFT) which constitute the active principle of Endotelon were extracted from the fresh seeds according to the following procedure :

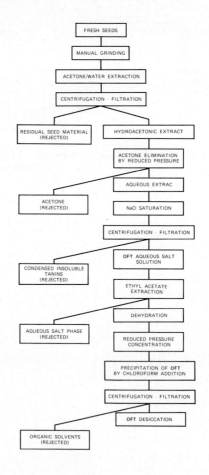

Table II shows the results obtained from one series of experiments. It should be noted that when the epidermis and subepidermis layers of the stem were removed, there was a substantial increase in specific activity of the obtained compound possibly due to blockage of sap in this level.

## Table II

RESULTS OBTAINED FROM ONE SERIES OF EXPERIMENTS

| Bunch No | Position on Plant | Bunch weight g | Seed weight g | Yield % | Endotelon Yield g | obtained μCi | specific activity μCi/mg |
|---|---|---|---|---|---|---|---|
| 31/32 | Bottom* | 553.5 | 22.0 | 3.9 | 0.3489 | 156.6 | 0.45 |
| 81/82 | Middle | 711.6 | 37.6 | 5.2 | 0.5489 | 126.3 | 0.23 |
| 111/112 | Top | 846.9 | 38.8 | 4.5 | 0.7377 | 213.7 | 0.29 |
| | | 2112.0 | 98.4 | 4.5 | 1.6355 | 496.6 | 0.32 |

* outer layer of the stem removed.

HPLC [$C_{18}$ Bondapak (Waters) 10m; acetonitril/formic acid 10/90 %; 1 ml/min; UV : 280 nm] data (Fig. 4) indicated that the labeled compound was practically identical with the compound used for therapeutics.

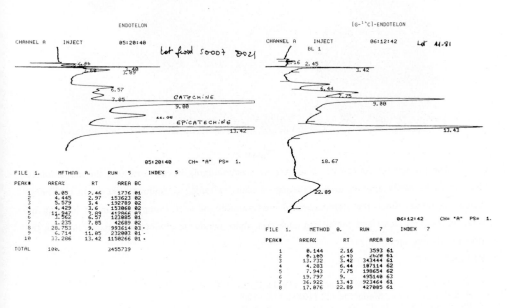

Figure 4

The separation revealed that the compound consisted of catechine, epicatechine and their corresponding dimers. Radioactivty measurements of the dimer eluates showed a higher specific activity than that attributed to the monomers. Although there have been some studies dealing with the formation of flavonoids in plants [refs 3,4,5,6], the present data do not allow for a determination of possible differences in specific activity between the two catechine cycles.

It should be noted that the procedure used in the present study results in labeling of all biological material that responds to photosynthetic mechanisms. An example of the plant material used is given in Fig. 5 which shows an autoradiogram of grape leaves with the dark areas indicating the presence of radioactive compounds. The light area on the larger leaf is due to lesser photosynthetic labeling because of shade.

Figure 5

The present results can be considered very encouraging in the sense that the methodology used could be easily applied to the labeling of plant extracted compounds known to traditional herbal medicine. Since the stereochemical configuration of such compounds make labeling by total synthesis difficult and sometimes uncertain, there would be obvious advantages in using the present labeling method.

REFERENCES

1  M. Massin, Gaz. Méd. de France, 89 (1981) 3272-3274.
2  P. Delacroix, Rev. Médecine, 22 (1981) 1793-1802.
3  Ph. Comte, A. Ville, G. Zwingelstein, J. Favre-Bonvin and C. Mentzer, Bull. Soc. Chim. Biol., 42 (1960) 1079
4  M.N. Zaprometov and H. Grisebach, Fiziol. Rast. (English translation), 19 (1972) 1034-1040.
5  A.C. Neish, in Biochemistry of phenolic compounds, Academic Press, London, 1964, pp. 295-359.
6  P. Courbat, Angiologica, 9 (1972) 135-161.

*Synthesis and Applications of Isotopically Labeled Compounds 1985.*
Proceedings of the Second International Symposium, Kansas City, MO, U.S.A.,
3—6 September 1985, R.R. Muccino (Ed.), 225—230

ISOTOPE INCORPORATION VIA ORGANOBORANE CHEMISTRY

GEORGE W. KABALKA

Chemistry Department, University of Tennessee, Knoxville, Tennessee 37996-1600

U.S.A.

ABSTRACT

Isotopically labeled compounds play an important role in chemistry,
biology, and medicine. In recent years, organometallic chemistry has been
utilized extensively in the development of labeled compounds. Syntheses
involving the use of organoboranes have proven to be among the most versatile
and effective of the new labeling methodologies (ref.1).

INTRODUCTION

Isotopically labeled compounds have played an important role in chemistry, biology, and medicine since Hevesey pioneered their use as tracers. Both
stable and radioactive isotopes were used in early investigations but, in
recent years, radioisotopes have been used more extensively due to advances in
radiation detection techniques (ref.2). Currently, the need for materials
labeled with stable isotopes is increasing dramatically due to instrumentation
advances in mass spectrometry and nuclear magnetic resonance spectrometry
(ref.3).

Organometallic reagents have been used extensively in the syntheses of
isotopically labeled compounds. The classic example involves the preparation
of labeled fatty acids via the reaction of isotopically labeled carbon dioxide
with Grignard reagents. Unfortunately, the reactivity of many organometallic
reagents precludes their use in the syntheses of molecules containing acidic
or other sensitive functional groups.

BACKGROUND

We have had a long term interest in the chemistry of organoboranes because of their proven utility in organic syntheses and the fact that they
tolerate a variety of useful functional groups (ref.4). Under the proper

conditions, functionally substituted organoboranes are obtained via the simple addition of a suitable boron hydride reagent (ref.5) to an appropriately substituted alkene:

$$R'CH_2CH=CH_2 \xrightarrow{R_2BH} R'CH_2CH_2CH_2BR_2$$

(where R' can contain: $-NO_2$, $-CN$, $-CO_2H$, $-CO_2R$, $-X$, etc.)

We initiated a program focused on the use of these reactive intermediates for the incorporation of a number of isotopes of interest in medicine, chemistry, and biology (ref.6). Interestingly, at the time we began our investigation, in 1975, boron chemistry had only been used to incorporate hydrogen isotopes. Tritium was introduced into hydrocarbons via a reaction sequence involving the addition of tritiated $BH_3$ to alkenes followed by the subsequent removal of isotopically normal $BH_3$. Deuterium was introduced, stereospecifically via the solvolysis of organoboranes with deuterated acetic acid.

The extensive investigations by H. C. Brown and others suggested that organoboranes would be useful for isotope incorporation reactions. However, the reactions described in the literature utilized reagents which were not readily obtainable in isotopically labeled forms or involved reaction conditions which were often not amenable to syntheses involving radioisotopes (this was especially true for the syntheses involving short-lived isotopes.)

DISCUSSION

Radioiodination methodology was examined early in our investigations because of the obvious utility of the numerous iodine isotopes. We developed a new route to radioiodinated reagents via the reaction of appropriate organoboranes with sodium iodide in the presence of mild oxidizing agents such as chloramine-T (ref.7), N-chlorosuccinimide (ref.8), and air (ref.9).

$$R_3B \xrightarrow[\text{[0]}]{Na^{123}I} R-^{123}I$$

The iodination reaction was utilized to synthesize a number of radio-iodinated agents for the first time. These agents include the 17-iodovinyl-estradiols (ref.10) [receptor-site agents (ref.11)] and iodovinyl tellurium substituted fatty acids [myocardial agents (ref.12)].

$$^{125}ICH=CH(CH_2)_{11}Te(CH_2)_3CO_2H$$

We are currently synthesizing a series of cholesterol ethers (ref.13) labeled with iodovinyl groups for the construction of modified liposomes. We are also designing a series of iodovinyl unnatural amino acids for potential use in tumor imaging.

$$^{123}ICH_2(CH_2)_5 \quad \text{(cyclobutane)} \quad CO_2H, NH_2$$

Organoboranes can also be used to incorporate chlorine (ref.14) and bromine (ref.15) isotopes. The yields are good but not as high as those realized

$$ClCH_8=CH(CH_2)_8CO_2CH_3 \qquad ^{82}BrCH=CH(CH_2)_{11}Te(CH_2)_3CO_2H$$

in the iodination reactions. Incorporation of fluorine has been achieved but the yields are not particularly good and traditional substitution reactions are currently more effective.

Carbon isotopes are of obvious utility. We have been particularly interested in the short-lived, carbon-11 isotope because of its potential utility in positron tomography, a rapidly growing area in nuclear medicine. The short half-life ($t_{1/2}$ = 20.4 min.) of this isotope offers a significant challenge to the synthetic chemist. The reaction of carbon monoxide with organoboranes provided a direct entry into carbon labeled aldehydes and alcohols (ref.16).

$$R_3B \xrightarrow[\text{2. [O]}]{\text{1. }^{14}CO/H^-} R\text{-}^{14}CHO$$

Dr. Wolf's group at Brookhaven National Laboratory independently developed a synthesis of carbon-11 labeled aldehydes (ref.17).

In collaboration with Dr. Ronald D. Finn's group at the National Institute of Health and the Mount Sinai Medical Center, Miami Beach, Florida, we have been investigating the incorporation of carbon-11 into alcohols such as 1-butanol (ref.18) for use in cerebral blood flow measurements. We have also investigated the reaction of organoboranes with carbon-11 labeled cyanide (ref.19) to generate carbon-11 labeled steroids for potential use in in vivo steroid receptor-site measurements.

$CH_3CH_2CH_2\text{-}^{11}CH_2OH$

A particularly challenging area of research has been the development of methods to introduce very short-lived isotopes such as oxygen-15 ($t_{1/2}$ = 2.04 min.) and nitrogen-13 ($t_{1/2}$ = 9.96 min.). Not surprisingly, the research has resulted in methodology which has proven useful for the synthesis of materials labeled with stable isotopes of oxygen and nitrogen.

The new synthesis of compounds labeled with nitrogen isotopes involves the reaction of simple, appropriately labeled, ammonium salts with organoboranes in the presence of a simple oxidant, bleach (ref.20).

$$R_3B \xrightarrow[\text{NaOCl}]{^{15}NH_4Cl} R\text{-}^{15}NH_2$$

The reaction has proven effective for a variety of functionally substituted organic molecules of varying structural types.

$$CH_3OCCH_2(CH_2)_8CH_2-{}^{15}NH_2$$

The nitrogen incorporation reaction is rapid and has been used to incorporate nitrogen-13 into simple amines which hold promise for use in nuclear medicine (ref.21).

$$CH_3(CH_2)_9CH_2-{}^{13}NH_2$$

The reaction of oxygen with organoboranes has been known for over a hundred years. However, the use of the reaction for the preparation of oxygenated organic molecules was uncommon, until recently (ref.22), because of the concomitant formation of a variety of side products. It was then discovered that the reaction could be used to synthesize oxygen-17 labeled alcohols under appropriate conditions (ref.23).

$$CH_3OCCH_2(CH_2)_8CH_2-{}^{17}OH$$

We recently utilized the reaction to prepare oxygen-15 labeled butanol for potential use in blood flow measurements (ref.24). The reaction is rapid

$$CH_3CH_2CH_2CH_2-{}^{15}OH$$

(ref.25) and is currently being developed for preclinical tests (ref.26). We feel that the reaction is suitable for the synthesis of wide variety of oxygenated materials of use in nuclear medicine.

ACKNOWLEDGEMENT

We thank the Department of Energy (DE-AS05-80EV10363) for support of this research.

REFERENCES

1   G. W. Kabalka, Acc. Chem. Res., 17 (1984) 215-221.
2   M. E. Phelps and J. C. Mazziotta, Science, 228 (1985) 799-809.
3   D. G. Ott, Synthesis with Stable Isotopes, Wiley Interscience, New York, 1981.
4   H. C. Brown, Organic Synthesis Via Boranes, Wiley, New York, 1975.
5   H. C. Brown, M. Zaidlewicz and E. Negishi, in G. Wilkinson and F. G. A. Stone (Eds.), Comprehensive Organometallic Chemistry, Vol. 7, Pergamon Press, Oxford, 1982
6   G. W. Kabalka, in J. H. Brewster (Ed.), Aspects of Mechanism and Organometallic Chemistry, Marcel Dekker, New York, 1978.
7   G. W. Kabalka and E. E. Gooch, J. Chem. Soc., Chem. Commun., (1981) 1011-1012.
8   G. W. Kabalka, in Developing Role of Short-Lived Radionuclides in Nuclear Medical Practice, DOE Symposium Series, 56 (1985) 377-383.
9   T. E. Boothe, R. D. Finn, M. M. Vora, A. Emran, P. Kothari and G. W. Kabalka, J. Labelled Compd. Radiopharm., in press.
10  G. W. Kabalka, E. E. Gooch and K. A. Sastry, J. Nucl. Med., 26 (1981) 908-912.
11  E. M. Jagoda, R. E. Gibson, H. Goodgold, N. Ferreira, B. E. Francis, R. C. Reba, W. J. Rzeszotarski and W. C. Eckelman, J. Nucl. Med., 25 (1984) 472-476.
12  F. F. Knapp, M. M. Goodman, A. P. Callahan, L. A. Ferren, G. W. Kabalka and K. A. Sastry, J. Med. Chem., 26 (1983) 1293-1300.
13  G. W. Kabalka, R. S. Varma, V. Jinaraj, L. Huang, S. K. Painter, J. Labelled Compd. Radiopharm., 22 (1985) 333-338.
14  S. A. Kunda, T. L. Smith, M. D. Hylarides and G. W. Kabalka, Tetrahedron Lett., 26 (1985) 279-280.
15  P. C. Srivastava, F. F. Knapp, A. P. Callahan, B. A. Owen, G. W. Kabalka and K. A. Sastry, S. Med. Chem., 28 (1985) 408-413).
16  G. W. Kabalka, E. E. Gooch, C. J. Collins and V. F. Raaen, J. Chem. Soc., Chem. Commun., (1979) 607-608.
17  D. Y. Tang, A. Lipman, G.-J. Meyer, C.-N. Wan and A. P. Wolf, J. Labelled Compd. Radiopharm., 16 (1979) 435-440.
18  P. J. Kothari, R. D. Finn, M. M. Vora, T. E. Boothe, A. M. Emran and G. W. Kabalka, Int. J. Appl. Rad. Isotopes, 36 (1985) 412-413.
19  P. J. Kothari, R. D. Finn, G. W. Kabalka, M. Mohammadi, A. M. Emran, T. E. Bothe and M. M. Vora, Abstracts, 1985 American Chemical Society National Meeting, Miami Beach, Nucl 134.
20  G. W. Kabalka, K. A. Sastry, G. W. McCollum and C. A. Lane, J. Chem. Soc., Chem. Commun., (1982) 62-63.
21  P. J. Kothari, R. D. Finn, G. W. Kabalka, M. M. Vora, S. T. Carrol, T. E., Boothe and A. M. Emran, Abstracts, 1985 American Chemical Society National Meeting, Chicago, Nucl 135.
22  H. C. Brown, M. M. Midland and G. W. Kabalka, J. Am. Chem. Soc., 93 (1971) 1024-1027.
23  G. W. Kabalka, T. J. Reed and K. A. Sastry, Synth. Commun., 13 (1983) 737-740.
24  G. W. Kabalka, G. W. McCollum, A. S. Fabirkiewicz, R. M. Lambrecht, J. S. Fowler, M. Sajjad and A. P. Wolf, J. Labelled Comp. Radiopharm., 21 (1984) 1247.
25  G. W. Kabalka, R. M. Lambrecht, M. Sajjad, J. S. Fowler, S. A. Kunda, G. W. McCollum, and R. MacGregor, Int. J. Appl. Radat. Isot., in press.
26  M. S. Berridge and M. P. Franceschini, Abstracts, 1985 Society of Nuclear Medicine Annual Meeting, Houston.

*Synthesis and Applications of Isotopically Labeled Compounds 1985.*
Proceedings of the Second International Symposium, Kansas City, MO, U.S.A.,
3—6 September 1985, R.R. Muccino (Ed.), 231—238
© 1986 Elsevier Science Publishers B.V., Amsterdam — Printed in The Netherlands

# SURVEY OF THE APPLICATION OF ²H NMR TO BIOLOGICAL SYSTEMS

J.H. Davis, Physics Department, University of Guelph, Guelph, Ontario, Canada N1G 2W1

## ABSTRACT

The most useful applications of $^2$H nuclear magnetic resonance are in the study of systems with some degree of local orientational order. Due to the incomplete motional averaging of the electric quadrupole interaction in these systems, this interaction dominates the NMR spectrum of $^2$H. For $^2$H in C-$^2$H bonds, the electric field gradient tensor is very nearly axially symmetric, with its principle component along the C-$^2$H bond. This simplifies the interpretation of the spectrum considerably. In comparison the orientation of the chemical shift tensors of carbon, nitrogen and phosphorus must be determined in each individual case. $^2$H NMR has been successfully applied to the study of labelled proteins and lipids in biological and model membrane systems. A brief review of results obtained on these systems is presented.

For molecules in solution, the $^2$H NMR spectrum is essentially equivalent to the $^1$H spectrum, however, the spin interactions will all have been scaled by ratio of the $^1$H to $^2$H magnetic moments. For this reason, the most significant contribution of deuterium labelling to high resolution NMR has been to simplify the interpretation of $^1$H NMR spectra, i.e., the labelled group is easily identified by its absence from the proton spectrum.

A valuable application of this method is the measurement of the rate of exchange of a labile solute proton with $^2$H in the solvent. In the case of the amide protons of proteins, comparison of the exchange rates observed for different amino acid residues can provide qualitative evidence on the nature of the protein's secondary and tertiary structure. The ease with which these protons exchange depends on their accessibility to the solvent. Residues in tightly wound hydrophobic sections of the protein will exchange more slowly than those in random coil segments in direct contact with the solvent. A beautiful example will be presented by Prof. Dahlquist later in this session (ref.1).

Small molecules in solution undergo rapid isotropic reorientation. This motion effectively averages away the orientation dependent interactions leaving the isotropic part of the chemical shift and the indirect spin-spin couplings to dominate the high resolution spectrum. Even in cases of rapid isotropic reorientation, the tensor interactions can dominate the nuclear relaxation processes. When the motion slows down, or becomes anisotropic, the orientation dependent interactions can also dominate the spectrum. These interactions include the dipole-dipole and quadrupolar interactions as well as the anisotropic part of the chemical shift.

In the case of deuterium in C-$^2$H bonds, the quadrupolar interaction is predominant. Only non-spherical nuclei, those with spin I greater than or equal to 1, possess a quadrupolar moment. This quadrupolar moment is affected by any non-zero electric field gradient at the nucleus, resulting in a slightly preferential nuclear orientation, i.e., the 2I+1 nuclear spin energy levels are shifted. In the presence of an external magnetic field, these quadrupolar shifts are superimposed on the Zeeman splittings so that, for spin 1, two separate NMR transitions are observed, separated by an amount called the quadrupolar splitting. The value of the splitting depends on the strengths of the quadrupolar moment and the electric field gradient and on the relative orientation, ß, of the principal axis of the electric field gradient tensor and the magnetic field, varying as 3cos²ß-1 (ref. 2).

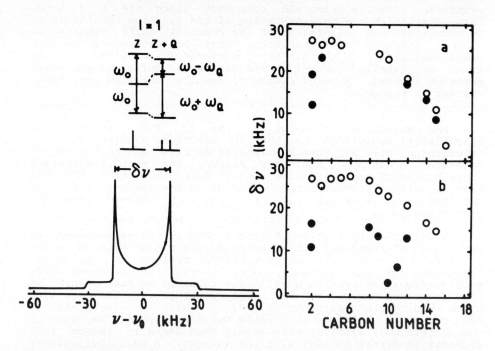

Fig.1. The spin 1 nuclear energy levels and the $^2$H NMR powder pattern spectrum characteristic of axial symmetry.

Fig.2. $^2$H quadrupolar splittings vs labelled position for (a) DPPC and (b) POPC. O , sn-1 ; ●, sn-2 chain.

Unless we are fortunate enough to have a single crystal or can otherwise orient all of the molecules in the same way, we need to work with powder samples. In this case, since the value of the quadrupolar splitting depends on orientation, and since all orientations are simultaneously present, we observe powder pattern spectra, Figure 1. The characteristic lineshape for a spin 1 powder pattern is easy to understand when you consider that, on the surface of a sphere, there is much more room near

the equator than near the poles. Thus, more molecules have
orientations perpendicular to any given direction, say along the
magnetic field, than parallel to that direction. The 90°
orientation gives the largest signal intensity and the 0°
orientation the smallest.

Because of its relative strength, 250 kHz compared to about
4 kHz for the $^2H$-$^2H$ dipole-dipole interaction, the quadrupolar
interaction dominates not only the $^2H$ spectrum but also $^2H$
relaxation. Fluctuations in the quadrupolar interaction strength
due to molecular reorientation can lead to spin lattice
relaxation times, Tl, as short as 2 ms, and to transverse
relaxation times in the millisecond to microsecond range. While
these relatively short time scales can lead to some special
problems in extreme cases, the short Tl's permit short recycle
delays (recovery times between pulse sequences) allowing rapid
data acquisition. Thus, while $^2H$ NMR is inherently relatively
insensitive due to the small nuclear magnetic moment, rapid
signal averaging and a good high field spectrometer allow us to
work routinely with ordered samples containing as few as $10^{18}$ $^2H$
nuclei.

Molecular motion can influence the $^2H$ NMR lineshape in a
number of ways. Rapid axially symmetric motion reduces the
quadrupolar splitting. In the limit of rapid isotropic motion,
the splitting goes to zero and the high resolution spectrum is
observed. When the motions are not axially symmetric, or are
slow (of the order of l/width of the spectrum) the effect on the
spectral lineshape is more complex and a more detailed knowledge
of the time scales and amplitudes of the motions is required to
describe the spectrum. In the application of $^2H$ NMR to biology,
and especially to membrane systems, the molecular motions often
fall in the intermediate to slow motion regime. Numerous
attempts have been made to simulate lineshapes from models for
molecular motion. A typical model might consider molecules
hopping between inequivalent sites so that the lineshape depends
on the relative populations of the sites as well as the hopping
rate and of course on the orientation of the C-$^2H$ bonds within
each site.

Biological membranes are composed of two kinds of molecule:
lipids, whose amphiphilic nature results in the formation, in
water, of structures whose surfaces are in contact with the water
but whose interiors are hydrophobic; and proteins, which also
have an amphiphilic character, matching them to the lipid bilayer
structure. Membrane lipids perform a largely structural role
while membrane proteins perform a wide range of important
physiological functions. Considerable interest in the
relationship between lipid and protein has arisen.

Because of the relative ease in synthesizing phospholipids,
most of the $^2H$ NMR work on membrane systems has used deuterium
labelled lipids. A typical phospholipid has two hydrocarbon
chains which may be of different length or have different degrees
of unsaturation. Early $^2H$ NMR studies examined di-saturated
phosphatidylcholines where one or more of the chain positions
were $^2H$ labelled. 1,2-dipalmitoyl-sn-glycero-3-phosphocholine
(DPPC) in water is undoubtedly the most extensively studied model
membrane. With a series of specifically $^2H$ labelled DPPC/water
samples, Seelig, et al.(ref. 3) found a gradient of hydrocarbon
chain flexibility, as shown in Figure la. As the position of the

²H label is moved closer to the center of the bilayer, i.e., nearer the terminal methyl group, the degree of motional averaging increases leading to a decrease in the size of the quadrupolar splitting.

While changes in the amplitudes and rates of local reorientation can alter the quadrupolar splitting, the average orientation of a C-²H bond relative to a local motional symmetry axis also plays an important role. An excellent example of this effect is illustrated in Figure 2a where it is shown that, for ²H at the second carbon position there are three very different quadrupolar splittings. The largest of these comes from the ²H nuclei on the sn-1 chain, while the other two are from the two inequivalent nuclei on the sn-2 chain. These two nuclei are different because there is a twist in the sn-2 chain such that the two C-²H bonds have slightly different orientations relative to the local bilayer normal.

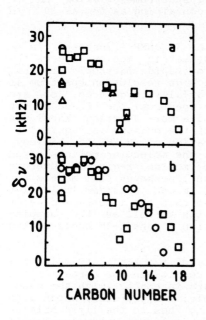

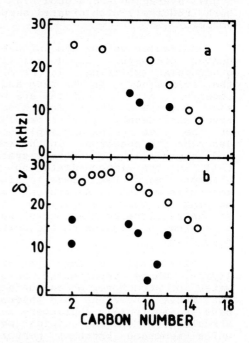

Fig.3. ²H quadrupolar splittings for A.laidlawii grown on ²H labelled oleic acid, □, compared to (a) POPC, O for palmitoyl and Δ for oleoyl chains, at 27 °C; and (b) palmitate labelled A. laidlawii,

Fig.4. Comparison of quadrupolar splitting profiles of (a) E. coli at 40 °C; ●, oleoyl; O, palmitoyl; (b) POPC at 22 °C, O, sn-1 and ●, sn-2 chain.

Another example of the influence of average orientation on the size of the quadrupolar splitting is shown in Figure 2b. Here the variation of quadrupolar splitting with position in 1-palmitoyl,2-oleoyl-sn-glycero-3-phosphocholine (POPC) (ref. 4) has a sharp minimum at the double-bond position for the oleoyl chain. This is due not to increased motional averaging at that position, but to an average orientation of the C-$^2$H bond which is close to the "magic angle" where $3\cos^2\beta-1 = 0$. Aside from this effect, the comparison of the results for DPPC and POPC shows that the chain dynamics of these two model membrane systems are similar.

The variation in quadrupolar splitting with chain position has also been measured for the membranes of Acholeplasma laidlawii, Figure 3 (ref. 5). In this case, the $^2$H labelled fatty acids were biosynthetically incorporated into the membrane lipids. This and similar work on Escherichia coli membranes, Figure 4 (ref. 6) clearly established the similarity among the different membrane systems, both model and biological. Subsequent work has suggested, however, that this quadrupolar splitting profile may reflect more the effect of a unixial environment on hydrocarbon chain order than the effect of a bilayer structure.

The lipid head-group, in contrast to the hydrocarbon chains, is polar and therefore lies at the lipid/ water interface. It's strategic position suggests that it may play a useful role in reporting events occurring at the cell surface. Through the use of $^2$H labelled head groups it is possible to monitor head-group orientation and mobility.

In the case of phosphatidylcholine (PC), the number of degrees of freedom the head-group possesses makes it difficult to determine unambiguously the head-group conformation. Using the quadrupolar splittings of selectively $^2$H labelled PC it has been possible to place limits on the range of conformations (ref. 7). The orientation of lipid head groups with fewer orientational degrees of freedom, e.g., N-palmitoyl-glucosyl-ceramide (ref. 8) can be determined, in some cases.

Below the hydrocarbon chain melting transition, lipid mobility is highly restricted. The lateral diffusion rate decreases by two orders of magnitude and the hydrocarbon chain packing becomes much closer. The decrease in the degree of motional averaging and the increase in the time scales of the motions result in much broader $^2$H NMR spectra (ref. 9). The shapes of these spectra, Figure 5, are due to the intermediate rates of molecular motion. Griffin, et al. (ref. 10) have developed a model for simulating these types of spectra. In their model, the molecules undergo axial diffusion about the long molecular axis by hopping among three different sites. In addition, a given C-C bond can be either trans of gauche (effectively two sites). Adjusting the populations and hopping rates permits them to simulate these types of spectra quite successfully. An important effect which their simulations reproduce is the loss of echo intensity due to the slow motions. The use of echo spectroscopy has introduced an extra time dimension, providing valuable information on these slow molecular motions.

Kothe, et al. (ref. 11) have developed another model for phospholipid chain motion. They are able to describe the motions, and simulate the spectra, in terms of correlation times for trans-gauche isomerization, chain reorientation and chain fluctuations, together with trans populations and quadrupolar splittings characteristic of the different sites.

236

The large changes in the $^2$H NMR spectrum that occur at the lipid chain melting transition have made it possible to map out phase boundaries in temperature/composition plots. Even the changes in the $^2$H2O spectrum in DPPC/$^2$H2O mixtures can be used to identify the phase boundaries. In mixtures of two phospholipids, DPPC/DPPE (1,2-dipalmitoyl-sn-glycero-3-phosphoethanolamine) in excess water, $^2$H and $^{13}$C NMR have been coupled with calorimetry experiments to map the interesting phase behaviour of this simple two component membrane system (ref. 10).

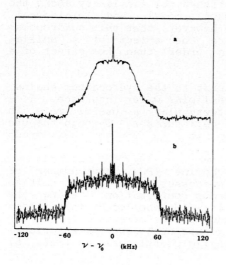

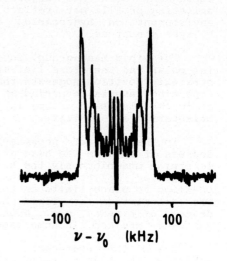

Fig.5. $^2$H NMR spectra of 1,2-[8,8-$^2$H]DPPC in excess water at (a) 37 °C and (b) 0 °C.

Fig.6. $^2$H spectrum of amide-exchanged gramicidin A in an oriented potassium laurate/decanol/water micellar phase

Phospholipid/cholesterol mixtures have been extensively studied, firstly, because of the important role cholesterol plays in higher organisms, secondly, because of the large effect it has on phospholipid bilayer properties and, thirdly, because of many apparently conflicting results. While there have been differing interpretations of many results, there are some interesting agreements. Coupling $^2$H spectroscopy and calorimetry with earlier work, a coherent picture of the DPPC/cholesterol system should soon emerge.

In natural membranes, proteins and lipids coexist. The significance of protein/lipid interactions, i.e., the role of lipids in protein function and the influence of protein on lipid bilayer structural properties, is being studied by $^2$H NMR and many other techniques.

A simple model system consisting of a synthetic amphiphilic peptide in DPPC bilayers forms a good physical model of a biological membrane. The peptide has been designed to mimic the hydrophobic segments of natural membrane proteins. It has two polar ends, each containing two lysine residues, and a hydrophobic core of either 16 or 24 leucines. The length of this hydrophobic core was designed to test the importance of matching with the hydrophobic thickness of the phospholipid bilayer. $^2H$ NMR studies of the phase equilibria of this peptide/DPPC system, and calorimetric data on the same samples, have been interpreted in terms of a simple application of non-ideal solution theory (ref. 12). The observed phase boundaries are well described by the theoretical model as is the dependence of the calorimetric transition enthalpy on peptide concentration. The similarity between the results observed in the peptide model system and those seen in a variety of reconstituted protein/lipid systems suggests that this simple model for protein/lipid interaction is applicable to the natural membrane.

Studies of reconstitutions of purified membrane protein in lipid bilayers by $^2H$ NMR have shown that the presence of physiological concentrations of protein has little effect on the molecular order and dynamics of the lipid. Work on rhodopsin (from bovine rod outer segments) in 1,2-dimyristoyl-sn-glycero-3-phosphocholine (DMPC) (ref. 13) and cytochrome c oxidase (from beef heart mytochondria) in 1-palmitoyl,2-palmitoleoyl-sn-glycero-3-phosphocholine (PPOPC) (ref. 14) has shown that these proteins partition preferentially into the fluid lipid phase, as does the synthetic amphiphilic peptide, and the phase behaviour can be interpreted in the same manner as the model system.

While the isotopic labelling of lipid molecules is relatively straightforward, the labelling of membrane proteins presents a formidable problem. Even if specific isotopic labelling of proteins was easily accomplished, the amount of $^2H$ would usually not be sufficient for NMR. With lipids, a few micromoles of $^2H$ has proven sufficient, however, at one $^2H$ label per protein of 40,000 daltons, this would require of the order of 100 mgs of protein. Furthermore, since a protein with 400 amino acid residues has at least 2000 hydrogen nuclei, the $^2H$ label will occur in the NMR spectrum at the same level as the natural abundance deuterium.

Often bacteria can be grown on $^2H$ labelled amino acids which it incorporates into its proteins. If upon extraction of the membrane, a single type of protein is predominant, as in the case of bacteriorhodopsin in the purple membrane of halobacterium halobium, then it is fairly easy to obtain large quantities of labelled protein. However, the label is not site specific since it has been inserted wherever the particular amino acid is required. If the local environments of the different labelled sites are different the NMR spectrum will consist of overlapping resonances.

Another method of unspecific labelling of proteins is through $^1H$-$^2H$ exchange. This procedure has been used in a study of our synthetic amphiphilic peptide. Under appropriate conditions it is possible to exchange the peptide backbone's amide protons. Analysis of the quadrupolar echo relaxation times for this system yields a value of about $2 \times 10^{-7}$ s for the

238

correlation time for axial diffusion of the peptide within the liquid crystalline phase of DPPC (ref. 15).

A similar experiment on the natural peptide, gramicidin A, from _bacillus_ _brevis_, in an oriented lyotropic nematic liquid crystalline phase, gives the spectrum shown in Figure 6. Most of the intensity in this spectrum is in the peak with the largest splitting. There are two other groups of peaks with smaller splittings. These smaller splittings may be due to differing average orientations or to increased mobility in certain regions of the peptide.

REFERENCES

1 R. H. Griffey, A. G. Redfield, R. E. Loomis and F. W. Dahlquist, Biochemistry, 24 (1985) 817-822.
2 J. H. Davis, Biochim. Biophys. Acta, 737 (1983) 117-171.
3 A. Seelig and J. Seelig, Biochemistry, 13 (1974) 4839-4845 and A. Seelig and J. Seelig, Biochim. Biophys. Acta, 406 (1975) 1-5.
4 J. Seelig and N. Waespe-Sarcevic, Biochemistry, 17 (1978) 3310-3315 and A. Seelig and J. Seelig, Biochemistry, 16 (1977) 45-50.
5 G. W. Stockton, K. G. Johnson, K. W. Butler, A. P. Tulloch, Y. Boulanger, I. C. P. Smith, J. H. Davis and M. Bloom, Nature, 269 (1977) 267-268; J. H. Davis, M. Bloom, K. W. Butler and I. C. P. Smith, Biochim. Biophys. Acta, 597 (1980) 477-491; and M. A. Rance, K. R. Jeffrey, A. P. Tulloch, K. W. Butler and I. C. P. Smith, Biochim. Biophys. Acta, 600 (1980) 245-262.
6 J. H. Davis, C. P. Nichol, G. Weeks and M. Bloom, Biochemistry 18 (1979) 2103-2112; C. P. Nichol, J. H. Davis, G. Weeks and M. Bloom, Biochemistry, 19 (1980) 451-457; and H. -U. Gally, G. Pluschke, P. Overath and J. Seelig, Biochemistry 18 (1979) 5605-5610.
7 H. -U. Gally, W. Niederberger and J. Seelig, Biochemistry 16 (1975) 3647-3652; J. Seelig, H. -U. Gally and R. Wohlgemuth, Biochim. Biophys. Acta, 467 (1977) 109-119; and R. Skarjune and E. Oldfield, Biochemistry 18 (1979) 5903-5909.
8 R. Skarjune and E. Oldfield, Biochemistry 21 (1982) 3154-3160.
9 J.H. Davis, Biophys. J., 27 (1979) 339-358.
10 R. G. Griffin, Methods Enzymol., 72 (1981) 108-174; A. Blume, R. J. Wittebort, S. K. Das Gupta and R. G. Griffin, Biochemistry, 24 (1982) 6243-6253; and A. Blume and R. G. Griffin, Biochemistry 24 (1982) 6230-6242.
11 P. Meier, E. Ohmes, G. Kothe, A. Blume, J. Weldner and H. -J. Eibl, J. Phys. Chem., 87 (1983) 4904-4912.
12 J. C. Huschilt, R. S. Hodges and J. H. Davis, Biochemistry, 24 (1985) 1377-1386 and M. R. Morrow, J. C. Huschilt and J. H. Davis, Biochemistry, 24 (1985), Sept.
13 A. Bienvenue, M. Bloom, J. H. Davis and P. F. Devaux, J. Biol. Chem., 257 (1982) 3032-3038.
14 M. R. Paddy, F. W. Dahlquist, J. H. Davis and M. Bloom, Biochemistry, 20 (1981) 3152-3162.
15 K. P. Pauls, A. L. MacKay, O. Soderman, M. Bloom, A. K. Tanjea and R. S. Hodges, Eur. Biophys. J., 3 (1985) 1-11.

*Synthesis and Applications of Isotopically Labeled Compounds 1985.*
Proceedings of the Second International Symposium, Kansas City, MO, U.S.A.,
3—6 September 1985, R.R. Muccino (Ed.), 239—246
© 1986 Elsevier Science Publishers B.V., Amsterdam — Printed in The Netherlands

SOLID-STATE $^{13}$C- and $^{15}$N-NMR STUDIES OF INTRINSIC MEMBRANE PROTEINS:
BACTERIORHODOPSIN

S.O. SMITH[1], G.S. HARBISON[2], D.P. RALEIGH[1], J.E. ROBERTS[1], J.A. PARDOEN[3], S.K.
DAS GUPTA[1], R.A. MATHIES[4], J. LUGTENBURG[3], J. HERZFELD[2] AND R.G. GRIFFIN[1]

[1]Francis Bitter National Magnet Laboratory, Massachusetts Institute of
Technology, Cambridge, MA   02139

[2]Department of Physiology and Biophysics, Harvard Medical School, Boston,
MA  02115

[3]Department of Chemistry, University of Leiden, 2300 RA Leiden (The Netherlands)

[4]Department of Chemistry, University of California, Berkeley, CA   94720

ABSTRACT

   Solid-state NMR techniques are used to probe the structure and protein
environment of the retinal chromophore and the protonation state of tyrosine in
bacteriorhodopsin (bR).  Spectra were obtained of bR selectively labeled with
$^{13}$C at fourteen positions on the retinal prosthetic group, with $^{15}$N at the
retinal Schiff base nitrogen, and with $^{13}$C at the 4'-position of tyrosine.  The
$^{13}$C-retinal spectra indicate that dark-adapted bR contains a mixture of all-
*trans* and 13,15-di*cis* protonated Schiff base chromophores.  The $C_6$-$C_7$ single
bond is shown to be *trans* and there is evidence for a negative bacterio-opsin
charge near $C_5$ of the retinal.  The $^{15}$N spectra demonstrate that the  Schiff
base is protonated and weakly hydrogen-bonded.  Finally, the $^{13}$C-tyrosine
spectra indicate that the observed tyrosine residues in dark-adapted bR are
protonated.

INTRODUCTION

   Determining the structure and chemical environment of prosthetic groups or

catalytic residues in proteins is often crucial for unraveling the molecular

mechanism of protein function.  In the case of noncrystalline intrinsic membrane

proteins, the recent emergence of solid-state NMR spectroscopy using selective

isotopic enrichment provides a powerful method for probing specific protein

sites.

   Bacteriorhodopsin (bR) (MW = 26000) is an intrinsic membrane protein in the

"purple membrane" of *Halobacterium halobium* (ref.1) whose structure and function

can be examined using solid-state $^{13}$C- and $^{15}$N-NMR (ref.2-5).  As in the visual

pigment rhodopsin, the light-sensitive prosthetic group in bR is the protonated

Schiff base (PSB) of retinal (Figure 1).  Absorption of light by bR initiates a

cyclic photochemical reaction ($bR_{568}$ → $K_{625}$ → $L_{550}$ → $M_{412}$ → $O_{640}$ → $bR_{568}$) which

drives the transport of protons across the bacterial cell membrane (ref.6).  The initial step in this reaction involves photochemical 13-*trans* → 13-*cis* isomerization of the retinal which serves to translate the Schiff base proton across the retinal binding site (ref.7). After isomerization, the Schiff base transfers its proton to a nearby protein residue, and subsequently reprotonates and reisomerizes during the thermal steps of the cycle. In this way, the retinal chromophore functions both as a "gate" to insure the flow of protons in only one direction across the membrane, and also as an "impeller", providing the driving force for proton transport. However, the pathway for protons through the protein has not been established. Fourier transform infrared (FTIR) difference spectroscopy (ref.8,9) and kinetic UV absorption studies (ref.10) have indicated that changes in protonation of aspartate, glutamate and tyrosine residues occur during the proton-pumping photocycle. These studies are consistent with the proposal that protons are transported along a "proton wire" connecting the cytoplasmic and exterior surfaces of the protein through

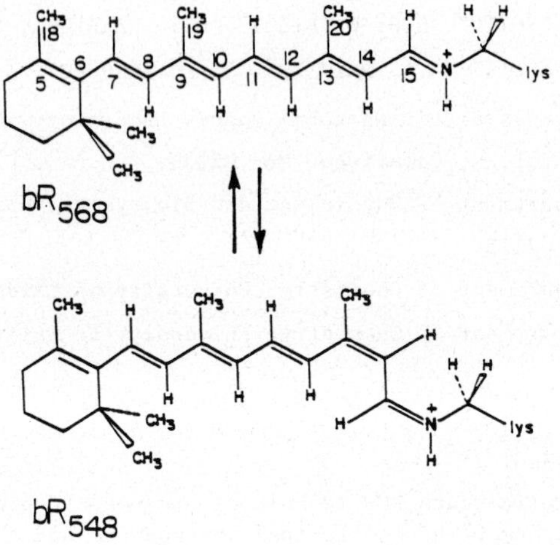

Fig. 1. Light-adapted bacteriorhodopsin ($bR_{568}$) contains an all-*trans* retinal protonated Schiff base chromophore. In the dark, bacteriorhodopsin converts to dark-adapted bR which contains a 40:60 mixture of $bR_{568}$ and $bR_{548}$. The retinal chromophore in $bR_{548}$ has a 13,15-di*cis* structure. $^{13}$C and $^{15}$N MASS NMR spectra were obtained of the dark-adapted pigment. Note the retinal in both $bR_{568}$ and $bR_{548}$ is shown in the 6-s-*trans* conformation.

a chain of hydrogen-bonded amino acids (ref.11). In this paper we discuss recent $^{13}$C and $^{15}$N solid-state NMR studies on two important aspects of the proton-pumping mechanism of bR. First, the structure and chemical environment of the retinal chromophore is investigated using bR containing $^{13}$C- and $^{15}$N-retinal. Second, the protonation state of tyrosine, one of the amino acids thought to be involved in proton translocation, is probed using bR containing 4'-$^{13}$C-labeled tyrosine.

High-resolution $^{13}$C- and $^{15}$N-NMR spectra of bR can be obtained using magic angle sample spinning (MASS) and cross-polarization (CP) techniques. MASS increases spectral resolution by resolving shift anisotropy powder patterns of the $^{13}$C and $^{15}$N resonances into a centerband and sets of rotational sidebands. The former provides the isotropic chemical shift and the latter the anisotropic shift. Typically, a single chromophore or amino acid position is isotopically labeled to permit observation of the resonance over natural-abundance levels. An additional increase in sensitivity is attained by transfer of magnetization between $^1H$ and $^{13}C$ or $^{15}N$ spins by cross-polarization. In contrast, in "solution-state" NMR the low rotational correlation time of the large purple membrane fragments produces incomplete averaging of the dipolar interactions and broad NMR resonances. Further, the dilute solutions required to prevent aggregation of the protein in these experiments result in a reduction in signal-to-noise ratios.

Since molecular orientation is "frozen" in the solid, the anisotropic components of the chemical shift are retained in the MASS NMR experiment. This information can be "extracted" from the relative intensities of the rotational sidebands which are observed in spectra of slow-spinning samples using the methods of Herzfeld and Berger (ref.12). The principal values of the chemical shift tensor are invaluable in determining the *origin* of the differences in isotropic chemical shift observed in the protein. For instance, *trans* → *cis* isomerization of a C=C bond in the retinal chain causes an upfield shift of the $^{13}C$ resonance one bond away. This shift, termed the γ-effect, results from steric interaction between the hydrogen atoms across the *cis* bond. Comparison of the shielding tensors of $^{13}C$-12 all-*trans* and $^{13}C$-12 13-*cis* retinal show that the γ-effect is localized in the $\sigma_{11}$ element (ref.13).

## RESULTS AND DISCUSSION
### $^{15}N$-Labeling of the Retinal Schiff Base in bR

The first solid-state NMR spectra of isotopically-labeled bR were obtained of purple membrane containing ε-$^{15}N$-labeled lysine (ref.1). Figure 2C presents the $^{15}N$ spectrum of bR. The six free lysine residues of the protein give rise to the intense resonance on the right of the spectrum. The strong line downfield from the lysine resonance is due to the natural-abundance amide backbone and the small doublet to the left of the amide line arises from the retinal-lysine Schiff base introgen. The splitting in the Schiff base resonance is due to the presence of the two isomers (bR$_{568}$ and bR$_{548}$) in dark-adapted bR. The spectrum illustrates that high-resolution spectra can be obtained of an intrinsic membrane protein isotopically enriched *at a single site*.

The $^{15}N$ chemical shift of Schiff bases is extremely sensitive to protonation. In the retinal N-butylamine Schiff base (Figure 2A), the $^{15}N$ isotropic chemical shift is at 317 ppm and shifts ~150 ppm to 172 ppm upon protonation (Figure 2B). Further, the shift anisotropy changes from an η ≃ 1 powder pattern with a breadth of 600 ppm to an η ≃ 0.5 pattern with a breadth of 270 ppm. Thus, a simple measurement of the isotropic or anisotropic shift is sufficient to distinguish between protonated and nonprotonated Schiff bases. The average

242

chemical shift shown in Figure 2C is 148 ppm and is clearly much closer to protonated ($\sigma_I$ = 172 ppm) that to non-protonated ($\sigma_I$ = 317 ppm) Schiff bases.

The $^{15}$N chemical shift in protonated Schiff bases is also sensitive to the strength of hydrogen bonding between the Schiff base proton and its counterion. Using two-dimensional dipolar/chemical shift experiments, we have measured bond distances in protonated Schiff bases where the $^{15}$N chemical shift spans a range of 150-170 ppm (ref.14). These data show a clear linear correlation between $^{15}$N chemical shift, shift anisotropies, and NH bond distance. Thus, the isotropic chemical shift in bR can be directly related to the presence of a weak hydrogen-

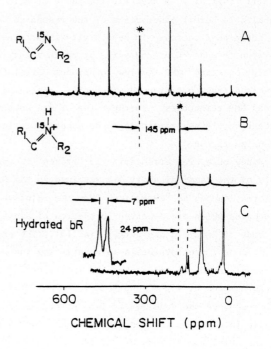

Fig. 2. $^{15}$N-MASS NMR spectra of the unprotonated (A) and protonated (B) retinal $^{15}$N-butylamine Schiff bases, and $\epsilon$-$^{15}$N-lysine bR (C). $\nu_R$ (spectrum C) = 2 kHz. $\nu 15_N$ = 32.2 MHz. Note the large differences between the isotropic and anisotropic chemical shifts of the protonated and unprotonated Schiff bases.

bond between the Schiff base proton and its protein counterion.

$^{13}$C-Labeling of the Retinal Chromophore in bR

MASS NMR spectra of bR have been obtained using bacteriorhodopsin regenerated with $^{13}$C-retinal labeled at the 5, 6, 7, 8, 9, 10, 11, 12, 13, 14 and 15 positions as well as on the C-18, C-19 and C-20 methyl groups. These spectra, with the exception of $^{13}$C-5 and $^{13}$C-methyl bR, all exhibit a splitting of the $^{13}$C resonance due to the bR$_{568}$ and bR$_{548}$ components of the dark-adapted protein. Interestingly, this splitting is less than 4 ppm *except* in the $^{13}$C-12- and $^{13}$C-14-bR derivatives where the $^{13}$C resonance assigned to bR$_{548}$ has shifted upfield by 10.1 and 11.5 ppm, respectively. The upfield shift of the $^{13}$C-12 line is localized in the $\sigma_{11}$ element of the shift tensor and is attributed to a $\gamma$-effect between the C-12 and C-14 protons in agreement with previous chemical extraction (ref.15) and resonance Raman (ref.16) experiments demonstrating a 13-*cis* chromophore in bR$_{548}$. The upfield shift of the $^{13}$C-14 line, also localized in the $\sigma_{11}$ tensor element, was unexpected and attributed to a $\gamma$-effect between the C-14 proton and the ε-CH$_2$ protons of lysine, indicating that the C=N bond is *syn* (or *cis*) in bR$_{548}$.

Figure 3 presents the spectrum of hydrated purple membrane containing retinal labeled with $^{13}$C at C-5. The lines on the right of the spectrum are due to the aliphatic and methyl carbons which have small chemical shift tensors and therefore no prominent rotational sidebands. The broad band at ~175 ppm is the C=O centerband from the 248 backbone carbonyls in bR, and is flanked by rotational sidebands spaced at the spinning frequency. The sharp line at 145 ppm (asterisked) is the centerband of the $^{13}$C-5 label which is also flanked by intense sidebands, and is unusual in two respects. First, as mentioned above, it shows no splitting from the two components, bR$_{568}$ and bR$_{548}$, present in the sample. The differences between bR$_{568}$ and bR$_{548}$ involve

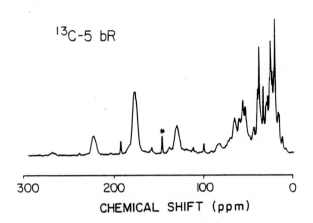

$^{13}$C-5 bR

CHEMICAL SHIFT (ppm)

Fig. 3. $^{13}$C MASS NMR spectrum of hydrated bR containing $^{13}$C-5 retinal. $\nu_R$ = 3.7 kHz. $\nu^{13}$C = 79.9 MHz. The centerband due to the $^{13}$C-5 label is marked with an asterisk. The strong sideband intensities permit a determination of the shift anisotropy of $^{13}$C-5.

isomerization about the C$_{13}$=C$_{14}$ and C=N bonds which are localized near the Schiff base end of the retinal (Figure 1) and apparently must not generate significant displacement of the $^{13}$C-5 position of the ionone ring. Second, the isotropic $^{13}$C chemical shift of C-5 is ~16 ppm downfield from the $^{13}$C-5 chemical shift of the all-*trans* PSB model compound. This large shift in σ$_I$ can be attributed to two independent effects, isomerization about the C$_6$-C$_7$ single bond of the retinal and a negative bacterio-opsin charge localized near C-5 of the chromophore.

The effects of C$_6$-C$_7$ isomerization can be gauged by comparing the chemical shifts between the 6-s-*cis* and 6-s-*trans* forms of retinoic acid (ref.13). The most pronounced differences are observed at C-5 (7.1 ppm), C-8 (8.0 ppm), and C-9 (6.7 ppm). An analysis of the shift ansotropies from the sideband patterns shows that the shift of C-5 is localized in the σ$_{33}$ element which moves 20 ppm, with essentially no change occurring in the σ$_{11}$ and σ$_{22}$ elements. In bR, a similar shift of the σ$_{33}$ element is observed in comparison with the 6-s-*cis* protonated Schiff base, arguing that the $C_6-C_7$ bond is *trans* in the pigment, a conclusion which is supported by measuring the $T_1$ of the [13]C-18 methyl group. Specifically, in 6-s-*cis* retinal model compounds, $T_1$'s for the [13]C-18 methyl groups are relatively short (0.4 - 4.0 sec), while for the 6-s-*trans* retinals and bR, the $T_1$'s are much longer, ~25 sec and 17 sec, respectively.

In contrast to the model compounds, we observe an additional 27 ppm downfield shift in the $\sigma_{22}$ element which is due to the presence of a negative bacterio-opsin charge close to the C-5 position of the ionone ring. The 16 ppm chemical shift difference between bR and the all-*trans* PSB can therefore be decomposed into an ~7 ppm shift due to $C_6-C_7$ isomerization and an ~9 ppm shift due to protein charge perturbation.

## [13]C-Labeling of Tyrosine in bR

In order to study the protonation state of the tyrosine sidechains in dark-adapted bR we have prepared samples of purple membrane containing tyrosine labeled at the 4'-position (proximal to the hydroxyl group) with [13]C. The [13]C chemical shift of this position is very sensitive to the state of protonation. In particular, a downfield shift of 12 ppm is observed in simple phenols upon deprotonation (ref.17). A similar 10 to 14 ppm shift has been observed for tyrosyl residues in simple peptides and proteins on going from the protonated to the ionized state.

Studies with simple phenols in this laboratory have shown that the same effect occurs in the solid-state and, in addition, the asymmetry parameter of the [13]C shift tensor changes from 0.9 to 0.4 upon deprotonation.

Figure 4 shows the solid-state [13]C CP-MASS spectrum of *fully hydrated* [13]C-4'-tyrosine-labeled, dark-adapted bR obtained at pH 7.2. The strong line present at 157 ppm is due to the 4' resonance of the tyrosine sidechain; two strong rotational sidebands are also present. The isotropic chemical shift is similar to those measured for protonated tyrosines in other peptides and proteins (ref.18). The asymmetry parameter, calculated by analyzing the sideband intensities is $0.9 \pm 0.1$, the expected value for a protonated tyrosine.

Previous studies have examined the titration behavior of tyrosyl residues in proteins by [13]C-NMR. In particular, Wilbur and Allerhand (ref.18) showed that residues accessible to the solvent had $pK_a$'s close to those of free tyro-sine, while residues known from the crystal structure to be "buried" were essentially untitratable ($pK_a > 12.5$). These studies were carried out using solution [13]C-NMR methods which have invariably failed when applied to bacteriorhodopsin. However, using solid-state spectroscopy we have examined the titration behavior of tyrosine resonance from pH 2.0 to pH 11.5. The chemical shifts of all tyrosines in fully-hydrated, dark-adapted bR are essentially invariant between pH 2.0 and pH 10 and at most, only small changes

occur at a pH of
11.5. Thus, all
tyrosines in dark-
adapted bR appear to
have a high pK
(> 11).

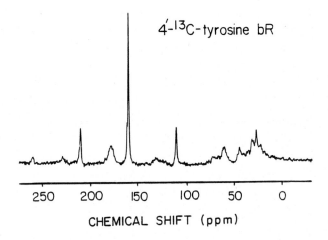

Fig. 4. $^{13}$C MASS NMR spectrum of $^{13}$C-4'-tyrosyl-labeled dark-adapted bR obtained with $\nu_R$ = 4.1 kHz. The spectrum was obtained on a home-built instrument operating at 7.4 T ($\nu_1$ $^{13}$C = 79.9 MHz). The $^1$H decoupling field was equivalent to 100 kHz. 26,000 transients were accumulated with a recycle delay of 3 seconds. Chemical shifts are referenced to external TMS.

ACKNOWLEDGEMENTS

This research was supported by the U.S. National Institutes of Health (GM-23316, GM-23289, EY-02051, and RR-00995), the U.S. National Science Foundation (CHE-8116042 and DMR-8211416), the Netherlands Foundation for Chemical Research (SON) and the Netherlands Organization for the Advancement of Pure Research (ZWO). R.A.M. is a recipient of an NIH Research Career Development Award. D.P.R. is an NSF Predoctoral Fellow and S.O.S. is an NIH Postdoctoral Fellow.

REFERENCES

1   W. Stoeckenius and R.A. Bogomolni, Ann. Rev. Biochem., 51 (1982) 587-616.
2   G.S. Harbison, J. Herzfeld and R.G. Griffin, Biochemistry, 22 (1983) 1-5.
3   G.S. Harbison, S.O. Smith, J.A. Pardoen, C. Winkel, J. Lugtenburg, J. Herzfeld, R. Mathies and R.G. Griffin, Proc. Natl. Acad. Sci. USA, 81 (1984) 1706-1709.
4   G.S. Harbison, S.O. Smith, J.A. Pardoen, P.P.J. Mulder, J. Lugtenburg, J. Herzfeld, R. Mathies and R.G. Griffin, Biochemistry, 23 (1984) 2662-2667.
5   G.S. Harbison, S.O. Smith, J.A. Pardoen, J.M.L. Courtin, J. Lugtenburg, J. Herzfeld, R.A. Mathies and R.G. Griffin, Biochemistry (1985), in the press.
6   R.H. Lozier, R.A. Bogomolni and W. Stoeckenius, Biophys. J., 15 (1975) 955-962.
7   S.O. Smith, A.B. Myers, J.A. Pardoen, C. Winkel, P.P.J. Mulder, J. Lugtenburg and R. Mathies, Proc. Natl. Acad. Sci. USA, 81 (1984) 2055-2059.
8   K. Rothschild and H. Marrero, Proc. Natl. Acad. Sci. USA, 79 (1982) 4045-4049.

246

9   M. Engelhard, K. Gerwert, B. Hess and F. Siebert, Biochemistry, 24 (1985) 400-407.
10  R.A. Bogomolni, L. Stubbs and J.K. Lanyi, Biochemistry, 17 (1978) 1037-1041.
11  W. Stoeckenius, Acct. Chem. Res., 13 (1980) 337-344.
12  J. Herzfeld and A.G. Berger, J. Chem. Phys., 73 (1980) 6021-6030.
13. G.S. Harbison, P.P.J. Mulder, J.A. Pardoen, J. Lugtenburg, J. Herzfeld and R.G. Griffin, J. Am. Chem. Soc. (1985), submitted.
14. J.E. Roberts, G.S. Harbison, J. Herzfeld and R.G. Griffin, Biochemistry (1986), to be submitted.
15  M.J. Pettei, A.P. Yudd, K. Nakanishi, R. Helselman and W. Stoeckenius, Biochemistry, 16 (1977)1955-1959.
16  S.O. Smith, J. Lugtenburg and R. Mathies, J. Memb. Biol., 85 (1985) 95-109.
17  G.C. Levy, R.C. Lichter and G.L. Nelson , in, Carbon-13 Nuclear Magnetic Resonance Spectroscopy, John Wiley and Sons, New York, New York, 1982.
18  D.J. Wilbur and S. Allerhand, J. Biol. Chem., 251 (1976) 5187-5194.

*Synthesis and Applications of Isotopically Labeled Compounds 1985.*
Proceedings of the Second International Symposium, Kansas City, MO, U.S.A.,
3—6 September 1985, R.R. Muccino (Ed.), 247—252

DYNAMIC AND STRUCTURAL ELUCIDATION OF BIOMOLECULES BY SOLID STATE NMR

T. A. Cross

Dept. of Chemistry, Florida State University, Tallahassee, Fl. 32306-3006.

ABSTRACT
    A new method for determining the structure and dynamics of proteins by solid
state NMR is described. The method is not dependent upon the crystallization of
proteins, but rather on an ability to align the molecules uniformly in a
magnetic field. Predicted spectra for Gramicidin A which forms a transmembrane
cation selective channel are presented. The spectra show dramatic differences
depending on whether the cation binding sites in the channel are occupied with
cations or not.

INTRODUCTION
    The dynamic and structural elucidation of certain classes of biomolecules
has proven to be exceptionally difficult. Large macromolecular complexes such
as viruses can rarely be crystallized, particularly if the dimensions of the
particle are characterized by a large axial ratio. Presently, the structural
analysis of Tobacco Mosaic virus is at a resolution of 4Å which has permitted
the tracing of the polypeptide backbone of the coat protein, but has not
resolved the protein-nucleic acid contacts (ref. 1). This structural refinement
is the result of four decades of effort from several laboratories. Similarly,
transmembrane proteins have proven to be exceptionally difficult to crystallize
resulting in only a very limited knowledge of their structures (ref. 2-3).
Clearly there is a need for a new method to determine the structures of proteins
with atomic resolution that is not dependent upon crystallization. Such a
method, referred to as DASEL for Dynamic And Structural ELucidation will be
discussed in this paper.
    The solid state NMR method is dependent upon isotopic enrichment of the
protein and aligning the protein in the magnetic field of the NMR spectrometer.
The isotopic labeling of the protein is necessary to reduce the number of sites
observed in the NMR spectra thereby facilitating the identification of the
resonances. Isotopic labeling also provides increased sensitivity which permits
the recording of **inherently** insensitive spectra. The alignment of the protein
molecules in the magnetic field permits the observation of the angular
dependence of the nuclear spin interactions for the specifically labeled atomic
sites. It is the interpretation of this angular dependence for each of the
labeled sites that provides the data for the structural solution (ref. 4-5).

Data can also be obtained for a dynamic characterization of the molecule with the same resolution as that for the structure determination using the same labeled samples. Through the analysis of the magnitude of the nuclear spin interactions determined from unoriented samples and through the determination of relaxation parameters a dynamic characterization from the msec to the psec time scale can be achieved (ref. 6-7).

## METHODS

Labeling of the naturally abundant [14]N site in the peptide linkages of the protein backbone with [15]N is very advantageous. This site is protonated and consequently subject to a large heteronuclear dipolar interaction. From this dipolar interaction the orientation of the N-H bond can be determined with respect to the magnetic field and the alignment axis of the protein (ref. 5). The dominance of this dipolar interaction provides a unique relaxation mechanism for this site and therefore, justifies a detailed analysis of the relaxation parameters (ref. 7). In unoriented samples the lineshape of the chemical shift anisotropy and the magnitude of the dipolar interaction provides dynamic information. Another advantage to this site is that during protein synthesis it becomes bonded to the carboxyl carbon of the previous amino acid. If the carboxyl carbon has been labeled with [13]C then a second heteronuclear dipolar interaction can be observed resulting in another bond orientation and dynamic information (ref. 5). This double labeling approach can also help with making resonance assignments. If a number of amino acids have been labeled with [15]N, by labeling a different kind of amino acid with [13]C only the specific amino acid pairs will show the C-N dipolar interaction.

The orientations of two bonds within the planar peptide linkage (see Fig.1) results in the determination of the orientation of this plane with respect to the magnetic field. Similarly, bond orientations and the peptide linkage orientation can be achieved for the neighboring linkage. From the orientations of these planes and a knowledge of the tetrahedral geometry of the alpha carbon which joins adjacent planes, the value of the torsion angles can be calculated (ref. 8). This is all achieved with just the [15]N and [13]C labels mentioned above, however, the orientations are ambiguous, because the sign of many of the direction cosines is not defined. These ambiguities can be eliminated with both more NMR experiments and with further isotopic labeling. Interpretations of the chemical shifts of the [15]N and [13]C sites in the oriented samples will provide information on the orientation of the axis normal to the plane of the peptide linkage with respect to the field. Usually these chemical shifts are not easily interpreted because of the incomplete knowledge of the orientation of the chemical shift tensor with respect to the molecular frame (ref. 5 & 9).

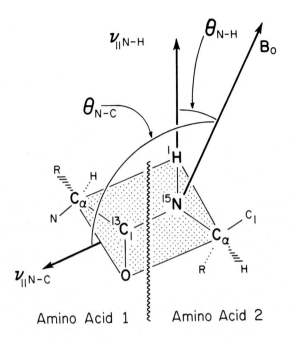

Fig. 1. The peptide linkage formed by two amino acid residues. Six atoms form the plane as indicated by the stippled region. The $\nu_{\parallel}$ components of the dipolar interactions are shown as vectors and the angles, $\Theta_{N-H}$ and $\Theta_{N-C}$ formed with respect to the magnetic field, $B_0$ are also shown. It is these angles that are determined by the NMR experiments.

However, since only the sign of the direction cosine needs to be determined, a qualitative interpretation of the chemical shift needs to be made rather than a detailed quantitative interpretation. Furthermore, labeling of the alpha carbon proton with $^2H$ will provide a quadrupolar interaction which is approximately symmetric about the C-H bond and can therefore, provide the same information that the dipolar interactions provided as described above. Another labeling possibility would be to label both the alpha carbon with $^{13}C$ and the amide nitrogen with $^{15}N$ in a single amino acid residue. The orientation of the $C_\alpha$-N bond could then be determined directly, thereby eliminating another sign ambiguity.

Microbiological methods for the incorporation of labeled amino acids appears to be the most generally useful and efficient way to isotopically label proteins in their backbone. Particularly, with the nearly routine application of genetic engineering techniques it can be hoped that a great many proteins can be labeled in this way. Not only can advantage be taken of the protein synthesizing apparatus of bacteria, but also the specific polypeptide synthesizing enzymes of some bacteria, such as enzymes that produce Gramicidin and other polypeptides in *Bacillus* (ref. 10). In this particular instance the protein synthesizing enzymes can be shut down when Gramicidin is being produced so that the labeled amino acids can be most efficiently incorporated into Gramicidin.

A number of possibilities exist for aligning the proteins in the magnetic field of the NMR spectometer. An approach that has received considerable attention has been to take advantage of the anisotropic nature of the diamagnetic susceptibility of the proteins in a liquid crystalline solution. Several filamentous and rod-shaped viruses have been shown to form such solutions and when positioned in a high magnetic field the long axis of the virus aligns with the field (ref. 11-12). A number of biological complexes such as chloroplasts (ref. 13), retinal rod outer segments (ref. 14), purple membrane preparations (ref. 15) and muscle fibers (ref. 16) have been oriented by the presence of a strong magnetic field. Even for highly anisotropic molecules the interaction with very strong magnets is large enough to only result in a minute degree of orientation. However, because the interaction is additive, when arrays of parallel molecules form, near perfect alignment of various systems can be achieved. As with some of the biological complexes mentioned above it is not necessary for the pure proteins to form a liquid crystalline array, but rather the proteins can be embedded in an orientable matrix. For the purpose of orienting transmembrane proteins, pure phospholipid bilayers have been prepared which have shown a high degree of orientation in the magnetic field without the usual aid of stacked glass plates (ref. 17).

RESULTS AND DISCUSSION

As a demonstration of the usefulness of this approach calculated spectra are presented in Fig. 2 based on a structural model of the polypeptide, Gramicidin A, which as a dimer forms a monovalent cation selective transmembrane channel. The spectra are calculated based on the known orientation of the channel axis parallel with the field (ref. 18). The primary sequence of the polypeptide is given below showing the alternation of L and D amino acids.

HCO - L Val - GLY - L Ala - D Leu - L Ala - D Val - L Val - D Val - L Trp - 
D Leu - L Trp - D Leu - L Trp - D Leu - L Trp - NHCH$_2$CH$_2$OH

In the structural model proposed by Urry in 1971 (ref. 19) the orientations of the peptide linkages relative to the channel axis alternate with every other linkage having the same orientation. This implies that the polypeptide backbone of Gramicidin A forms a very uniform structure. This regular structure does not account for the specific location of the two cation binding sites in the

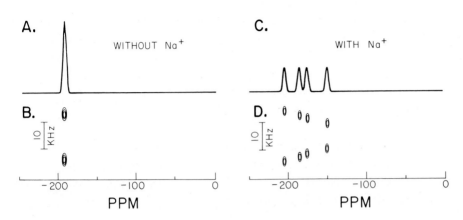

## ¹⁵N LEUCINE GRAMICIDIN A

Fig. 2. Calculated NMR spectra for ¹⁵N Leucine labeled Gramicidin A. Chemical shift spectra are shown in A and C while contour plots of the ¹⁵N-¹H dipolar spectra are displayed in a two dimensional format with chemical shift on the horizontal axis and dipolar coupling on the vertical axis in B and D. Spectra A and B are calculated based on the model of Urry (ref. 19) with no cation in the channel and spectra C and D are calculated based on the calculated deformations of the carbonyl groups caused by Na⁺ in the Gramicidin channel (ref. 21).

Gramicidin dimer that forms the transmembrane channel (ref. 20).

From the peptide linkage orientations and the calculated or observed static values of the nuclear spin interactions the dipolar and chemical shift spectra can be predicted. For these predictions it is assumed that the nuclear spin interactions are not averaged by large amplitude molecular motions. The predicted spectra for ¹⁵N leucine labeled Gramicidin A (see Fig. 2A) is neither remarkable nor difficult to interpret. The lack of resolution for the four isotopically labeled sites very simply implies that the orientations of the sites are identical. However, from molecular dynamics calculations and other physical data it is known that the carbonyl groups of the peptide linkages are involved in coordinating the monovalent cations in the Gramicidin channel. Estimates of the orientational change of the carbonyl bonds with respect to the helical axis of the channel have been published (ref. 21). The change in the orientation of the carbonyl bond is reflected in a change in the orientation of the amide N-H bond. Therefore, it is possible to predict the ¹⁵N spectra of ¹⁵N leucine labeled Gramicidin A not only when it is devoid of Na⁺ (Fig. 2A), but also in its presence (Fig. 2C). Because there is a unique location for the cation binding site the different carbonyls (and consequently amide protons) will be affected to a greater or lesser degree.

This prediction of the NMR spectra together with the previously published NMR data on other oriented systems demonstrates the usefulness of this approach for determining structures and for providing data that will allow correlations between structure and function. While the dynamics of this molecule are equally interesting the spectral results are more difficult to predict, because less is known about both the amplitude and frequency of the motions associated with specific molecular sites. Consequently, the dynamic information may prove to be even more useful than the structural data in gaining a more complete understanding of how the channel functions.

The author thanks Prof. Dan Urry for providing the coordinates of the Gramicidin model structure. This research is being supported by grants from that National Science Foundation, DMB - 8451876, and Procter and Gamble through a Presidential Young Investigator Award.

REFERENCES

1    G. Stubbs, S. Warren and K. Holmes, Nature, 267 (1977) 216-221.
2    R. Henderson and P.M.T. Unwin, Nature, 257 (1975) 28-32.
3    B.A. Wallace, Biopolymers, 22 (1983) 397-402.
4    T.A. Cross and S.J. Opella, J. Am. Chem. Soc., 105 (1983) 306-308.
5    T.A. Cross and S.J. Opella, J. Mol. Biol., 1982 (1985) 367-381.
6    C.M. Gall, J.A. DiVerdi and S.J. Opella, J. Am. Chem. Soc., 103 (1981) 5039-5043.
7    T.A. Cross and S.J. Opella, J. Mol. Biol., 159 (1982) 543-549.
8    T.A. Cross, Biophys. J., (1986) in press.
9    G.S. Harbison, L.W. Jelinski, R.E. Stark, D.A. Torchia, J. Herzfeld and R.G. Griffin, J. Mag. Res., 60 (1984) 79-82.
10   F. Lipmann, Science, 173 (1971) 875-884.
11   G. Maret and K. Dransfeld, Physica, 86-88B (1977) 1077-1083.
12   T.A. Cross, S.J. Opella, G. Stubbs and D.L.D. Caspar, J. Mol. Biol., 170 (1983) 1037-1043.
13   N.E. Geacintov, F. van Nostrand, J.F. Becker and J.B. Tinkel, Biochim. Biophys. Acta, 79 (1982) 101-105.
14   Chalazonitis, R. Changeux and A. Arvanitaki, C.R. Acad. Sci. Paris, ser. D271 (1970) 130-133.
15   D.-Ch. Neugebauer, A.E. Blaurock and D.L. Worcester, FEBS Lett., 78 (1977) 31-35.
16   W. Arnold, R. Steele and H. Mueller, Proc. Natl. Acad. Sci. USA, 44, (1958) 1-4.
17   J. Seelig, F. Borle and T.A. Cross, Biochim. Biophys. Acta, 814 (1985) 195-198.
18   C.J.A. van Echteld, B. de Kruijff, A.J. Verkleij, J. Leunissen-Bijvelt and J. de Gier, Biochim. Biophys. Acta, 692 (1981) 287-291.
19   D.W. Urry, Proc. Natl. Acad. Sci. USA, 68 (1971) 672-676.
20   D.W. Urry, K.U. Prasad and T.L. Trapane, Proc. Natl. Acad. Sci. USA, 79 (1982) 390-394.
21   D.H.J. MacKay, P.H. Berens, K.R. Wilson and A.T. Hagler, Biophys. J., 46 (1984) 229-248.

*Synthesis and Applications of Isotopically Labeled Compounds 1985.*   253
Proceedings of the Second International Symposium, Kansas City, MO, U.S.A.,
3—6 September 1985, R.R. Muccino (Ed.), 253—255
© 1986 Elsevier Science Publishers B.V., Amsterdam — Printed in The Netherlands

THE USE OF ISOTOPES IN NMR STUDIES OF BIOLOGICAL SYSTEMS

D. L. FOXALL
Varian Associates, 1120 Auburn Street, Fremont, California  94538

INTRODUCTION

Isotopes have been used extensively in biochemistry for studying the kinetics of individual enzymes and suites of enzymes that make up metabolic pathways (1,2).  NMR is able to add a new dimension to such studies by introducing parameters such as chemical shift, spin coupling and multiple quantum frequencies.  These pure NMR parameters, while of no direct biological relevance, allow new types of experiments which can separate the information from chemically different labeled species and isotopomers of a single chemical species (3,4,5).  These features combined with the ability of NMR to examine complex mixtures, crude biological preparations and tissue make it a powerful tool for the biologist.

METHODS

The methods employed in all the studies described here are variations upon the Carr-Purcell spin echo sequence (eq 1), however, the development of the variant sequences and the applications for them has been carried out in a number of laboratories (3,4,5,6,7).

Carr-Purcell Spin Echo (CP) Method:

H-1    :--D1--90(x)--D2--180(y)--D2--ACQUISITION--:                    (1)

Heteronuclear Spin Echo (HCP) Method:

H-1    :--D1--90(x)--D2--180(y)--D2--ACQUISITION--:                    (2)
C-13   :--D1---------D2--180(x)--D2---------------:

Heteronuclear Multiple Quantum (HMQ) Method:

H-1    :--D1--90(x)--D2--:---180---:--D2--ACQUISITION--:               (3)
N-15   :--D1-----------90(p)-----90(x)---------------:

In equations (1) to (3) the delay D1 is to allow T1 relaxation, the delay D2 is normally set to 1/2*J the spin coupling constant. The phase cycle "p" in the HMQ method is chosen to select either heteronuclear zero or double quantum signals.

DISCUSSION

The CP method is one of the oldest pulse sequences in the NMR literature and its application to biochemistry was essentially discovered by accident when applied as a method for simplifying the proton spectra from intact red blood cells in deuterated media (8). A natural exchange process, which is part of the glycolytic pathway in these cells converts lactate into (2-H2) lactate. The transformation, which manifests itself as a phase change in the lactate C-3 proton resonance in CP spectra, is caused because proton-proton spin coupling is converted to proton-deuterium spin coupling. The exchange has been studied extensively (9,10,11) and has revealed a great deal about the glycolytic enzymes involved, in particular about glyceraldehyde 3-phosphate dehydrogenase (GAPDH). The inhibition of this enzyme with iodoacetate terminates the lactate exchange. The kinetics of the uninhibited and inhibited lactate exchange can be analyzed with the aid of model enzyme systems, hemolysates and equilibrium isotope exchange theory. The conclusions that can be drawn suggest that GAPDH is not associated with the red cell membrane as had been originally thought.

The method of following deuteration through the disappearance of proton-proton spin coupling by the CP method seems generally applicable as dehydrogenase enzymes, transaminases and ketolases which cause hydrogen substitution are common enzymes present in a wide diversity of species.

The HCP method is a natural extension of the CP method allowing the biochemist to track carbon-13 through a metabolic process. The method can be extended to the study of nitrogen-15 and phosphorus-31 (7,6). The value of the method lies in the increase in sensitivity that can be obtained by observing the spin coupling of insensitive nuclei such as carbon-13 to protons. The method has only been applied to biochemical problems recently and the scope of its application is not yet fully clear. An early experiment to demonstrate the feasibility of the HCP method involved the study of glucose uptake by yeast suspensions. This topic had previously been studied by direct observation of carbon-13. The results were consistent with the original findings that glucose uptake in yeast exhibits an anomeric specificity.

The HMQ method is even newer than the HCP method, but has already found application in the study of large biopolymers such as tRNAs, proteins and DNA. The method shares the sensitivity advantages of the HCP technique when protons or another sensitive nucleus is observed. The method produces a two dimensional correlation map of proton chemical shift vs heteronuclear multiple quantum frequency. The experiment is available in both zero and double quantum versions, which allows the reconstruction of true two dimensional chemical shift correlation maps. Examples will be shown of the results obtainable from tRNAs and small molecules.

## CONCLUSIONS

A range of powerful NMR techniques exist that significantly extend the ability of the biochemist to perform isotope experiments.

## REFERENCES

1. D.B. Northrup "Isotope effects on Enzyme Catalysed Reactions" (edited by W.W. Cleland, M.H. O'Leary and D.B. Northrup) p 122. University Park Press, London (1977).

2. I.A. Rose & J.V.B. Warms (1969) J. Biol. Chem: 257,1438-1442.

3. D.L. Foxall, J.S. Cohen, R.G. Tschudin (1983) J. Mag. Reson: 51,330.

4. A.D. Bax, R.H. Griffey & B.L. Hawkins (1983) J. Mag. Reson: 55, 301-315.

5. D. Neuhaus, G. Wider, G. Wagner & K. Wuthrich (1984) J. Mag. Reson: 57, 164-168.

6. J.S. Cohen, C. Chen & A.D. Bax (1984) J. Mag. Reson: 59, 181-187.

7. K.M. Brindle, R. Porteus & I.D. Campbell (1984) J. Mag. Reson: 56, 543-547.

8. F.F. Brown, I.D. Campbell, P.W. Kuchel & D.C. Rabenstein (1977) FEBS Lett: 82, 12-16.

9. K.M. Brindle, F.F. Brown, I.D. Campbell, D.L. Foxall & R.J. Simpson (1982) Biochem. J: 202, 589-602.

10. D.L. Foxall, K.M. Brindle, I.D. Campbell & R.J. Simpson (1983) Tetrahedron: 39, 3443-3448.

11. D.L. Foxall, K.M. Brindle, I.D. Campbell & R.J. Simpson (1984) Biochem et Biophys Acta: 804, 209-215.

*Synthesis and Applications of Isotopically Labeled Compounds 1985.*
Proceedings of the Second International Symposium, Kansas City, MO, U.S.A.,
3—6 September 1985, R.R. Muccino (Ed.), 257—262
© 1986 Elsevier Science Publishers B.V., Amsterdam — Printed in The Netherlands

APPLICATIONS OF THE $^{18}$O-ISOTOPE SHIFT ON $^{13}$C and $^{15}$N NUCLEAR MAGNETIC
RESONANCE SPECTROSCOPY TO THE STUDY OF BIOORGANIC REACTION MECHANISMS*

ROBERT L. VAN ETTEN

Department of Chemistry, Purdue University, West Lafayette, IN  47907 (U.S.A.)

ABSTRACT

The study of reactions involving the formation and cleavage of carbon-oxygen or nitrogen-oxygen bonds has been significantly aided by recent demonstrations of the generality and characteristics of the $^{18}$O-isotope shift in $^{13}$C and $^{15}$N nuclear magnetic resonance spectroscopy.  In many instances, the magnitudes of the $^{18}$O-induced isotopic shifts are sufficiently large as to permit the use of even modest NMR instrumentation and natural abundance $^{13}$C. Studies involving less soluble compounds, higher molecular weight materials or relatively rapid reactions may often be carried out using $^{13}$C enrichment. Because NMR spectroscopy is non-destructive, it has proven to be extremely useful in the study of natural product biosynthetic pathways.  Another area where important applications are being made is in the study of enzymatic and non-enzymatic reaction mechanisms.  The characteristics of the $^{18}$O isotope shift in $^{13}$C NMR spectroscopy are reviewed.  Several examples from the work of other groups in the area of natural product biosynthesis are briefly mentioned.  This is followed by a number of illustrative applications in the area of bioorganic and enzymatic reaction mechanism that have been examined in our laboratory.  The enzymatic examples include acid phosphatases, epoxide hydratase, acetylcholinesterase and asparaginase.

INTRODUCTION

Although the first experimental demonstrations of $^{18}$O-induced isotope

shifts on $^{13}$C and $^{15}$N nuclear magnetic resonance (NMR) spectral signals have

appeared only relatively recently (refs. 1,2), these isotopic shifts have

already found a surprisingly wide range and number of applications in chemistry

and biochemistry.  Many of these applications, together with much background

material and related references, are presented in two excellent review articles

that have recently been published (refs. 3,4).  Consequently, the present

brief treatment does not attempt to review this already extensive area.

CHARACTERISTICS OF THE $^{18}$O ISOTOPE SHIFT ON $^{13}$C NMR

When the $^{13}$C NMR spectrum of $^{18}$O-labeled $t$-butyl alcohol was closely

examined and compared with mixtures containing various amounts of normal

$^{16}$O-containing $t$-butyl alcohol, it was found that the resonance position of the

*Research support was provided by DHHS NIH Grants GM 27003 and GM 22933.
Instrumentation support was from NIH Grant RR 01077

hydroxyl-bonded carbon was shifted upfield by 0.035 ppm in the $^{18}O$ labeled alcohol (ref. 1). This shift may be regarded as a prototypical $^{18}O$ isotope shift in $^{13}C$ NMR spectroscopy, in that the presence of the heavy oxygen isotope causes an upfield shift of the $^{13}C$ resonance. In an analogous way, replacement of $^{16}O$ by $^{18}O$ results in upfield shifts of 0.138 and 0.056 ppm (per $^{18}O$) on the $^{15}N$ NMR spectra of nitrite and nitrate, respectively (refs. 3 and 5).

Such isotope shifts are quite dependent on the structural nature of the compound, reflecting the fact that the nuclear shielding factors controlling NMR resonance positions are affected by changes in bond hybridization and average internuclear distances. Although the complete calculation of nuclear shielding factors for polyatomic molecules continues to be difficult, a theoretical prediction of an $^{18}O$ isotope effect on $^{13}C$ NMR was made some years ago for the case of carbon monoxide (ref. 6). Related theoretical considerations are discussed in recent reviews (refs. 3,4). For our purposes, however, it will be sufficient to examine the $^{18}O$-induced isotope shifts on $^{13}C$ and $^{15}N$ NMR spectroscopy from a phenomenological point-of-view. That is, how large are typical shifts, how sensitive are they to structural and experimental variables, and how can they be useful in experimental investigations in chemistry and biochemistry?

### Dependence on structure

Some $^{18}O$ isotope shifts of $^{13}C$ NMR spectral positions are given in Table 1. In each case, the cited value is the shift of the $^{13}C$ resonance towards higher applied magnetic field when $^{18}O$ rather than $^{16}O$ is directly bonded to the carbon. In many cases, such as aldehydes, ketones, pyrylium cations and $t$-alcohols, the shifts are large enough to be observed even using low field spectrometers such as a Varian CFT-20 (equivalent to an 80 MHz proton instrument). Indeed, the first published report documenting the $^{18}O$-isotope shift in $^{13}C$ NMR spectroscopy and its use in following the oxygen exchange of $t$-butyl alcohol were examined using just such an instrument (ref. 1). Convenient examination of the three possible $^{13}C$ NMR signals of $^{18}O$-labeled carboxyl groups ($^{16}O_2, ^{16}O^{18}O, ^{18}O_2$) generally requires a higher field instrument, but a 200 MHz instrument (operating at 50 MHz for $^{13}C$) is more than sufficient. Oxygen exchange at the anomeric carbons of various sugars can be followed by $^{13}C$ NMR using the $^{18}O$-induced isotope shift (ref. 9; S. Cortes and R. L. Van Etten, unpublished results). Because these reactions are followed by observing the appearance or disappearance of $^{18}O$-labeled acetals or hydrated carbonyl derivatives that possess isotope shifts similar to those of $sec$-alcohols, high field instruments, possibly even in conjunction with $^{13}C$ enrichment, are necessary in order to provide a satisfactory signal-to-noise

TABLE 1

$^{18}O$-Induced isotope shifts on $^{13}C$ NMR spectra

| Compound | $^{18}O$-Induced shift (ppm) | Reference |
|---|---|---|
| phenol | 0.016 | 7 |
| benzyl alcohol | 0.019 | 7 |
| $n$-butyl alcohol | 0.020 | 8 |
| erythrose (C-1 carbon; β anomer) | 0.019 | 9 |
| isopropyl alcohol | 0.023 | 7 |
| $t$-butyl alcohol | 0.035 | 1 |
| benzophenone | 0.045 | 7 |
| acetone | 0.050 | 7 |
| benzaldehyde | 0.043 | 7 |
| 1-butanal | 0.047 | 7 |
| $m$-bromoacetophenone | 0.047 | 10 |
| benzoic acid | 0.031 (per $^{18}O$) | 7 |
| acetic acid | 0.026 (per $^{18}O$) | 11 |
| 2,2-dimethyloxirane | 0.031 (C-3) | 12 |
| | 0.042 (C-2) | 12 |
| 2,4,6-trimethylpyrylium ion | 0.038 | 13 |
| benzamide | 0.030 | 14 |
| benzyl phosphate | 0.024 | 15 |

ratio and to make it convenient to follow relatively rapid reactions. Where reactions are slow and instrument time is readily available, then $^{13}C$ enrichment may be unnecessary except when solutes are relatively insoluble or have high molecular weights.

Electronic effects

When the size of the $^{18}O$ isotope-induced shift of the $^{13}C$ NMR signal of benzamide is compared with a typical ketone such as $m$-bromoacetophenone (Table 1), it may be seen that the shift of the amide is significantly less than for the ketone (0.030 vs. 0.047 ppm, respectively). In amides, a major contributor to the resonance hybrid is the form $C_6H_5C\overset{O^-}{\underset{NH_2^+}{}}$ , in which there is substantial C-O single bond character. This provides an exaggerated example of a factor that is seen in a careful study of electronic effects in substituted acetophenones (ref. 10). A small but experimentally significant increase in the magnitude of the $^{18}O$-induced isotope shift of the carbonyl $^{13}C$ resonance occurs in going from electron-donating to electron withdrawing phenyl substitutents. The increase can be correlated using Hammett sigma constants but a much more detailed analysis is available (ref. 10). Although electron withdrawing groups enhance the carbonyl oxygen double bond character and result in slightly larger $^{18}O$ isotope shifts, the effects are small relative to the changes that result when the functional group is changed (cf. Fig. 6 in ref. 7).

## Additivity effects

In contrast to ketones or alcohols, for example, compounds such as carboxylic acids, aldehyde hydrates, esters, carbonates, etc., may have several oxygen atoms bound to a given carbon. When these are chemically equivalent oxygens, they cause additive $^{18}O$ isotope shifts in $^{13}C$ NMR. This has been explored in some detail (ref. 8), with carboxylic acids and orthocarbonates providing particularly clear illustrations. Experiments on the acetylcholinesterase-catalyzed exchange of the oxygens of acetate may also be used to illustrate the additivity effect. It is evident that the three peaks corresponding to 0,1 or 2 $^{18}O$-atoms bound to the carboxyl group occur at equally spaced intervals (Fig. 1).

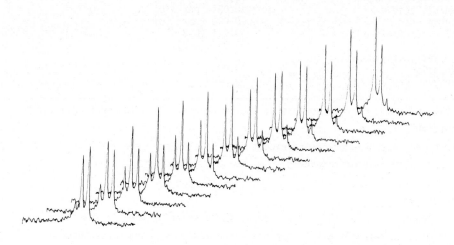

Fig. 1. $^{13}C$ NMR spectra illustrating the $^{18}O$ isotope shift additivity effect as well as the time-dependent exchange of oxygen between 1-$^{13}C$, $^{18}O_2$-acetate and water as catalyzed by acetylcholinesterase. The X and Z axes are magnetic field strength $H_0$ and time, respectively. With time, $^{18}O_2$-acetate disappears and is replaced by $^{18}O^{16}O$- and, finally, $^{16}O_2$-acetate.

## Steric effects

By comparing the $^{18}O$-induced shifts of several unhindered and highly hindered alcohols and ketones (ref. 8), it has been clearly demonstrated that steric effects are not important in affecting the magnitude of the $^{18}O$ shifts. Only in cases where substantial steric inhibition of resonance would lead to changes in hybridization might we expect to see alterations in the magnitude of the $^{18}O$ shift. Generally, steric effects will be unimportant, as would be expected for a parameter that is critically related to nuclear shielding.

APPLICATIONS OF THE $^{18}$O ISOTOPE SHIFT ON $^{13}$C NMR SPECTRA

The $^{18}$O isotope effect on $^{13}$C NMR has proved to be exceedingly useful for studying biosynthetic pathways involving oxygen-containing natural products. For example, the use of $^{13}$C-enriched acetate or propionate, either in conjunction with prior $^{18}$O-labeling or using $^{18}$O-water or $^{18}$O-oxygen gas, can provide detailed information about the origin of oxygenated metabolites. The groups of J. Vederas, D. Cane and C. Hutchinson have been particularly active in this area. Examination of $^{13}$C NMR spectra of the antibiotic averufin obtained after biosynthesis by an *Aspergillus* species starting from $^{13}$C,$^{18}$O-labeled acetate and from $^{18}$O-oxygen permitted the clear elucidation of the overall biosynthetic pathway in a way that would have been extraordinarily difficult using mass spectrometry (ref. 16). The use of $^{13}$C-labeled propionate and succinate permitted similarly elegant studies of erythromycin biosyntheses (ref. 17).

In our laboratory, recent work has centered on the use of the $^{18}$O-isotope shift on $^{13}$C NMR in bioorganic chemistry and enzymology. For example, the synthesis of $C_6H_5{}^{13}CH_2{}^{18}OPO_3H_2$ permitted extensive studies of the enzymatic and non-enzymatic position of bond cleavage during hydrolysis reactions (refs. 15,18). The ease of obtaining regiospecificity data and kinetic data simultaneously and without additional experimental manipulations made it possible to demonstrate the region of mechanistic transition from P-O to C-O bond scission as the pH was decreased. Similarly, the synthesis of $^{13}$C,$^{18}$O-labeled 2,2-dimethyloxirane enabled us to easily demonstrate the regio-specificity involved in hydrolysis of this epoxide using the enzyme epoxide hydratase, and to contrast it with the known course of the acid-catalyzed hydrolysis reaction (ref. 12).

Besides the additivity effect, the spectra shown in Fig. 1 also illustrate the time-dependent changes in the $^{13}$C NMR spectrum of $1$-$^{13}$C,$^{18}$O$_2$-acetate in water in the presence of the enzyme acetylcholinesterase (B. Dayton and R. L. Van Etten, unpublished observations). The enzyme catalyzes a reversible acylation-deacylation of an active site serine and this results in an exchange of acetate oxygens with those of the aqueous medium. The kinetics and particularly the pH dependence of the reaction provide information about other groups involved in the catalysis, as well as the kinetics of the (partial) reverse reaction. Similar experiments have been conducted with the enzyme asparaginase, using L-[1,4-$^{13}$C$_2$]-aspartic acid and related compounds (refs. 19,20).

In such mechanistic and biosynthetic studies NMR spectroscopy possesses several advantages over commonly used mass spectral techniques. One of the latter approaches requires combustion of the compound to $CO_2$, followed by

262

measurement of the $^{18}O$ content of the $CO_2$. Besides the requirement for derivatization or combustion, such an approach loses the positional information that would be revealed by $^{13}C$ NMR studies of the initial product. (Is $^{18}O$ present in C-1 or C-4 of aspartic acid? In which oxygen of the sugar?) Moreover, $^{13}C$ NMR is non-destructive. Finally, the ability to distinguish between single and multiple substitution patterns ($^{18}O_2$, $^{18}O^{16}O$ and $^{16}O_2$ in a carboxyl group, for example) makes it possible to distinguish between exchange mechanisms involving single versus multiple (coupled) exchange events (see Fig. 2 in ref. 11). This type of information may be particularly important in biological and inorganic chemistry.

ACKNOWLEDGMENTS

The author is indebted to his collaborators in this area, and particularly to Brian Dayton, John Risley and Klaus Röhm for discussions of research in progress.

REFERENCES

1  J. M. Risley and R. L. Van Etten, *J. Amer. Chem. Soc.*, 101 (1979) 252-253.
2  R. L. Van Etten and J. M. Risley, *J. Amer. Chem. Soc.*, 103 (1981) 5633-5636.
3  P. E. Hansen, *Ann. Repts. NMR Spectroscopy*, 6 (1983) 105-234.
4  D. A. Forsyth, in E. Buncel and C. C. Lee (Eds.), Isotopes in Organic Chemistry, Vol. 6, Elsevier, Amsterdam, 1984, pp. 1-66.
5  R. L. Van Etten and J. M. Risley, in W. P. Duncan and A. B. Susan (Eds.), Synthesis and Applications of Isotopically Labeled Compounds, Elsevier, Amsterdam, 1983, pp. 477-482.
6  W. T. Raynes and G. Stanney, *J. Magn. Reson.*, 14 (1974) 378-380.
7  J. M. Risley and R. L. Van Etten, *J. Amer. Chem. Soc.*, 102 (1980) 4609-4614.
8  J. M. Risley and R. L. Van Etten, *J. Amer. Chem. Soc.*, 102 (1980) 6699-6702.
9  J. M. Risley and R. L. Van Etten, *Biochemistry*, 21 (1982) 6360-6365.
10 J. M. Risley, S. A. DeFrees and R. L. Van Etten, *Org. Magn. Reson.*, 21 (1983) 28-35.
11 J. M. Risley and R. L. Van Etten, *J. Amer. Chem. Soc.*, 103 (1981) 4389-4392.
12 J. M. Risley, F. Kuo and R. L. Van Etten, *J. Amer. Chem. Soc.*, 105 (1983) 1647-1652.
13 J. M. Risley, R. L. Van Etten, C. Uncuta and A. T. Balaban, *J. Amer. Chem. Soc.*, 106 (1984) 7836-7840.
14 J. C. Vederas, *J. Amer. Chem. Soc.*, 102 (1980) 374-376.
15 J. E. Parente, J. M. Risley and R. L. Van Etten, *J. Amer. Chem. Soc.*, 106 (1984) 8156-8160.
16 J. C. Vederas and T. Nakashima, *Chem. Commun.*, (1980) 183-185.
17 D. E. Cane, H. Hasler, P. B. Taylor and T.-C. Liang, *Tetrahedron*, 39 (1983) 3449-3455.
18 R. L. Van Etten, *Ann. N.Y. Acad. Sci.*, 390 (1982) 26-53.
19 K. H. Röhm and R. L. Van Etten, *J. Labeled Compds. Radiopharm.*, in press.
20 K. H. Röhm and R. L. Van Etten, *Arch. Biochem. Biophys.*, in press.

*Synthesis and Applications of Isotopically Labeled Compounds 1985.*
Proceedings of the Second International Symposium, Kansas City, MO, U.S.A.,
3—6 September 1985, R.R. Muccino (Ed.), 263—266

THE EFFECTS OF DEUTERATION ON THE METABOLISM OF HALOGENATED ANESTHETICS
IN THE RAT


Leslie P. McCarty
U.S. Area Medical, The Dow Chemical Company, Midland, MI 48674


ABSTRACT

The toxicity of inhalation anesthetics is not due to the agents themselves
but, rather, to the products of their metabolism. Any mechanism which decreases their metabolism should decrease their toxicity. A key step in the
metabolism is the loss of a proton; thus, replacement of hydrogen by deuterium
alters the rate of metabolism.
Several deuterated anesthetics were synthesized and the metabolism compared with their non-deuterated analogs. The metabolism of those agents containing more than one hydrogen changed, depending on which hydrogens were replaced by deuterium. The results also indicate that carbanion formation may
be an important factor in the metabolism. In some cases, metabolism was decreased while, in others, the pathways were altered.


INTRODUCTION

The toxicity of inhalation anesthetics is not due to the agents themselves
but rather to products of their metabolism. Any mechanism which decreases
their metabolism should decrease their toxicity. A key step in metabolism is
the loss of a proton and replacement of hydrogen by deuterium alters the rate
of metabolism.


METHODS

Seven deuterated analogs of halogenated anesthetics were synthesized.
Groups of 4 to 8 rats were anesthetized in small glass chambers with these
agents and their non-deuterated analogs. The concentration of the anesthetic
in the inspired air and the length of exposure for each agent are indicated
in Table 1.

The rats were removed from the exposure chamber and placed in stainless
steel metabolism cages with food and water ad lib. The urine was collected
at 24 and 48 hours, the volume measured and fluoride ion was measured in each
sample with an Orion fluoride electrode.

RESULTS

If methoxyflurane is deuterated in the ethyl portion of the molecule, compound #1, there is a 19% increase in urinary fluoride compared to the non-deuterated compound. If, however, the methyl portion of the molecule is deuterated, compound #2, there is a 33% decrease in urinary fluoride. If the compound is fully deuterated, all four protons replaced as in compound #3, there is a 29% decrease in urinary fluoride.

These observations can be explained by the deuterium in the ethyl portion blocking the metabolism via Path A (Figure 1) and forcing metabolism via Path B, increasing the production of fluoride ion. If the methyl portion is deuterated, then path B is blocked and metabolism proceeds via path A. The metabolism of the fully deuterated compound is not much different from the methyl deuterated compound, but probably prolongs the life of the material in the body and may produce more urinary fluoride, although the differences are not significantly different.

$$CH_3OCF_2CCl_2H \xrightarrow{\quad A \quad} CH_3OCF_2COOH + 2Cl^-$$

$$\xrightarrow{\quad B \quad} CH_2O + HOCF_2CCl_2H \longrightarrow CHCl_2COOH + 2F^-$$

FIGURE 1

Introduction of deuterium into the ethyl portion of enflurane decreases urinary fluoride by 65% by blocking the metabolism as proposed in Figure 2. The difluoromethyl group essentially blocks metabolic attack on that portion of the molecule, thus most of the metabolism takes place on the ethyl portion.

$$CF_2HOCF_2CFClH \longrightarrow CF_2OCF_2COOH + F^- + Cl^-$$

FIGURE 2

The most striking effect of deuteration is seen with compound 5. Deuteration in this case produces a 76% reduction in urinary fluoride. Bromide is also liberated by the metabolism of this compound and deuteration reduces the levels of serum bromide almost to control levels. The metabolic scheme is proposed in Figure 3.

$$CF_2HOCF_2CBrFH \longrightarrow CF_2HOCF_2COOH + Br^- + F^-$$

FIGURE 3

The metabolic pathways which are usually postulated cannot explain the effect of deuteration on compound 6. If metabolism were to proceed by the oxidation of the ethyl portion, Path A, then the fluorinated acetic acid would be produced with chloride ion but no inorganic fluoride. This is shown in Figure 4.

Another mechanism has been proposed for the metabolism of anesthetics which invokes the removal of a proton and the production of a carbanion, Path B. This could result in the alpha-beta unsaturated ether which would be unstable and result in the disintegration of the molecule, Path B, Figure 4. The results of our experiments indicate that Path B is more probable.

$$CF_2OCF_2CCl_2H \xrightarrow{A} CF_2HOCF_2COOH + 2Cl^-$$
$$\xrightarrow{B} CF_2HOCF_2CCl_2^- \longrightarrow CF_2HOCF=CCl_2 + F^-$$

FIGURE 4

The deuteration of isoflurane, compound 7, also has an effect on its metabolism which results in a 57% reduction of urinary fluoride. The metabolic pathway for this material has been proposed to be that shown in Figure 5. Deuteration should produce a decrease in trifluoroacetic acid as well as inorganic fluoride but trifluoroacetic acid was not measured in our studies.

$$CF_2HOCHClCF_3 \longrightarrow CF_3COOH + 2F^- + Cl^- + CO_2$$

FIGURE 5

DISCUSSION

Extensive studies have been carried out with deuterated enflurane and the results of these studies indicate that deuteration has no effect on the anesthetic properties of the material when compared with the non-deuterated compound. The minimal anesthetic concentration and the cardiovascular effects are the same. In addition, the $LC_{50}$ is the same for the two compounds. Thus, deuteration changes only the degree of metabolism but not the anesthetic properties of these compounds.

If one were to consider which compounds were good candidates for a clinical anesthetic, then compounds 6 and 7 would appear to be good choices because they produce the smallest amount of total urinary fluoride of those studied as shown in Table 1. Compound 7 is already in clinical use in the non-deuterated form as isoflurane or Forane. Compound 6 has not been used clinically but is a very interesting material in that it is approximately three times more potent than isoflurane and thus would require much less for anesthesia. Induction of anesthesia and recovery are very rapid, which probably indicates that the material has a low solubility in fat.

TABLE 1

| Compound | Structure | %Change $F^-$* | Conc./Hrs.** | Total $F^-$ nmol x $10^{-1}$*** |
|----------|-----------|-----------|-----------|-----------|
| #1 | $CH_3OCF_2CCl_2D$ | +19 | .5/2 | 221 |
| #2 | $CD_3OCF_2CCl_2H$ | -33 | .5/2 | 134 |
| #3 | $CD_3OCF_2CCl_2D$ | -29 | .5/2 | 149 |
| #4 | $CF_2HOCF_2CFClD$ | -65 | 2.5/3 | 29 |
| #5 | $CF_2HOCF_2CFBrD$ | -76 | 1.5/3 | 38 |
| #6 | $CF_2HOCF_2CCl_2D$ | -29 | .5/2 | 22 |
| #7 | $CF_2HOCDClF_3$ | -56 | 2.5/2 | 12 |

\* %Change $F^-$ = % change in urinary fluoride compared to the non-deuterated compound.
\*\* Conc./Hrs. = The concentration of the anesthetic in %v/v and the number of hours the anesthetic was administered.
\*\*\* Total $F^-$ = The total amount of inorganic fluoride in the urine during the 48 hour collection period expressed in nanomoles x $10^{-1}$.

*Synthesis and Applications of Isotopically Labeled Compounds 1985.*
Proceedings of the Second International Symposium, Kansas City, MO, U.S.A.,
3—6 September 1985, R.R. Muccino (Ed.), 267—270
© 1986 Elsevier Science Publishers B.V., Amsterdam — Printed in The Netherlands

SYNTHETIC AND MANUFACTURING CONSIDERATIONS FOR DEUTERATED INHALATION
ANESTHETICS

Eric R. Larsen, Ph.D.
The Dow Chemical Company, Midland, Michigan

ABSTRACT

A series of eight deuterated analogs of inhalation general
anesthetics (methoxyflurane, isoflurane, enflurane, roflurane, and
halothane) were prepared for metabolic and anesthetic screening.
One of the deuterated analogs of enflurane, $CHF_2OCF_2CDClF$, was
selected for scale-up to mini-plant size in order to obtain process
development and large scale screening data.
Process considerations that led to the development of a multistage,
two phase process that produced > 90% enflurane and $D_2O$ will be
discussed, as well as product and $D_2O$ cleanup procedures.

Inhalation general anesthetics, especially halogenated ones,
represent a class of drugs that are ideally suited for deriving the
maximum benefit from the replacement of selected hydrogen atoms by
deuterium.  The primary reason for this is that anesthetic agents, in
general, function through a purely physical mechanism and any
metabolism is undesirable.  The commonly used fluorinated agents, when
metabolized, release varying amounts of fluoride ion, which in
sufficient quantity exhibit toxic properties.  Metabolism of these
materials appear to result, in most cases, from an initial attack on
one of the several hydrogen atoms in the compound, followed by the
loss of one or more fluoride ions.  An exception to this rule is
halothane, in which the bromine atom as well as the hydrogen appear to
represent metabolic weak points.

To explore deuterium as a means of blocking metabolism, a series
of eight deuterated analogs of various known fluorinated anesthetics
(methoxyflurane, isoflurane, enflurane, and halothane) were
synthesized.  The metabolic properties of these compounds were
discussed in the preceding paper by Dr. L. McCarty (ref. 1).  From
these studies it was decided that the best candidates for development
as clinically useful agents were 2-deuteroenflurane (ref. 2) and
1-deuteroisoflurane (ref. 3); i.e., $CHF_2OCF_2CDClF$ and $CHF_2OCDClCF_3$,
respectively.

For several reasons, 2-deuteroenflurane was selected for scale-up studies. Firstly, enflurane is commercially available and thus a plentiful supply of raw material existed for process studies. Secondly, any process data obtained should be equally applicable to the deuteration of isoflurane, if and when this compound becomes commercially available. Both of these materials will probably become generic drugs when their composition-of-matter patents expire in 1987 (ref. 4,5).

Ideally, the deuteration of either agent should be carried out in the manufacturing process prior to the finishing end of the process so as to avoid redundant equipment and operations.

The availability of deuterium was not of great concern since it is produced as a commodity chemical for the nuclear power industry and because the deuterium content of these agents represent only about 1% of the compound's molecular weight. The cost of deuterium was, however, a prime concern; at \$500/lb for the deuterium atom (based on \$100/lb for liter quantities of 99.9% $D_2O$ in 1981) this would add about \$5-6/lb to the raw material cost. Whether or not $D_2O$ could be obtained for less in bulk purchase has not been fully explored, but it would seem reasonable that purchases of 20-40 M lbs/year would result is lower costs. The recycle value of the reaction water which may contain up to 15% $D_2O$ also needs to be explored.

The cost of $D_2O$ is prohibitive for procedures used for making the agents by the processes described in the 2-deuteroenflurane and 1-deuteroisoflurane patents, especially if > 90% of the hydrogen on the -CHClF or -CHCl groups are to be replaced. In these processes, a ratio of 20/1 $D_2O$/RH was employed.

In developing a viable process, it was necessary to consider both the physical and chemical properties of the compound to be developed, i.e., 2-deuteroenflurane. Enflurane is a dense (1.517 g/cc), low boiling (56.5°C) liquid that has limited water solubility (0.027 mole %) and a limited ability to dissolve water (1.32 mole %). It was anticipated that the deuterated analog would have very similar properties. Any system using a co-solvent for the enflurane and $D_2O$, in order to give a homogeneous reaction, was rejected since the most one could obtain would be an equilibrium mixture having about a 60/40 mixture of deuterated and protonated compounds and a large $D_2O$ loss.

A two phase system using a phase transfer catalyst, such as tetrabutylammonium hydroxide, was felt to be nearly ideal since it would allow for a staged reaction and a means of driving the reaction to completion while using a minimum amount of $D_2O$.

The deuterium exchange reaction can be represented superficially by the equation

$$2CHF_2OCF_2CHClF + D_2O \overset{OH^-}{\rightleftharpoons} CHF_2OCF_2CDClF + H_2O \qquad \text{Equation 1}$$

I                    II

A simple base catalyzed exchange of ethyl hydrogen with deuterium oxide would give an equilibrium mixture.

In reality, each proton in I can exchange independently, albeit at different rates, so the actual process is more realistically viewed as

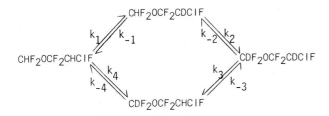

It involves eight reactions and four equilibria; not counting the $D_2O/H_2O$ equilibria, the various mass transfer rates and equilibria, nor the minor side reactions.

Computer simulation of the process shown in Equation I, using the equilibrium constants,

$$EK_1 = \frac{[RD]^2[H_2O]}{[RH]^2[D_2O]} = 1.9 \quad ; \quad EK_2 = \frac{[HOD]^2}{[H_2O][D_2O]} = 3.12$$

indicated that six stages should yield a product containing > 90% -CDClF and should have about 85% D efficiency. The lower D efficiency is unavoidable since some D is lost due to the deuteration of the $CF_2HO$ group.

The process was set up as a series of six staged reactors; compound I was introduced into reactor 1 and forwarded through the series to emerge from reactor six as compound II. $D_2O$ moved through the series in a countercurrent manner and emerged from reactor 1 as $H_2O$.

Agitation studies in the baffled reactors, carried out at ambient room temperatures and employing 0.001 mole % PTC, showed that the system was mass transfer controlled at low agitator speeds but readily became controlled by chemical kinetics at higher agitator speeds. Reaction rates were determined in each stage and reaction times of less than three hours for each stage were found to be useable. Conversion at each stage was monitored by NMR or IR analysis and the reactor composition was frozen at the optimum conversion by stopping the agitator.

Minor side reactions were identified which lead to the liberation of fluoride ions and the formation of $CHF_2OCF = CFCl$. Previous work on the stabilization of methoxyflurane suggested that such impurities could be readily converted to stable, high boiling compounds by bromination; thus, readily removed during distillation.

The crude product was washed with dilute bicarbonate, freeze dried, and distilled using a 50 theoretical plate column, to yield a product meeting the present enflurane assay specifications.

Recovered aqueous $D_2O$ solutions were treated with $CaCO_3$ in order to reduce the fluoride level from a concentration of 4500 ppm to a level acceptable to a $D_2O$ plant. An alternative procedure would involve simple stripping of the water from the fluoride containing salt after steam stripping the organic materials.

Using the above process, a total of ~ 38 kgs of 2-deuteroenflurane was prepared that had an average composition of $CHF_2OCF_2CHClF$ (< 10%), $C_3HDClF_5O$ (> 85%), and $CDF_2OCF_2CDClF$ (5%) and had an assay of > 99.9%.

While the work reported here clearly demonstrates that the deuteration of anesthetics (enflurane and isoflurane) can be readily scaled to commercial size, a number of questions remain unanswered. Among these is the degree of deuteration required to give the optimum cost-benefit performance from a metabolic viewpoint; i.e., one reaction step could be dropped from the series if the level of deuteration of the -CHClF group could be reduced to 80% rather than the > 85% targeted for in this work.

The size and number of reactors and intermediate storage tanks also need further study, since reactors are considerably more expensive than intermediate storage tanks. On an annual basis, a 300,000 lb/year plant would have an output of only 65 gallons/day; one large reactor (750-1000 gallons) and a number of intermediate tanks could be programmed to turn out the needed material.

Additional studies need to be done in order to optimize the product composition at each stage since $t_{1/2}$ for the reaction was found to vary by an order of magnitude from reactor 1 (RH + $H_2O$ + $D_2O$) to reactor 6 (RD(H) + $D_2O$). Any unnecessary residence time in any given stage will result in the formation of $CDF_2O$ groups that will in turn lower $D_2O$ efficiency.

REFERENCES

1. L. P. McCarty, "Deuterated Inhalation Anesthetics", Second International Symposium On Synthesis And Applications Of Isotopically Labeled Compounds, Kansas City, Missouri, September 3-6, 1985.
2. E. R. Larsen et al, U.S. Patent 4,154,971 (1979).
3. L. P. McCarty and E. R. Larsen, U.S. Patent 4,262,144 (1981).
4. R. C. Terrell, U.S. Patent 3,469,011 (1969).
5. R. C. Terrell, U.S. Patent 3,535,388 (1970).

*Synthesis and Applications of Isotopically Labeled Compounds 1985.*
Proceedings of the Second International Symposium, Kansas City, MO, U.S.A.,
3—6 September 1985, R.R. Muccino (Ed.), 271—276
1986 Elsevier Science Publishers B.V., Amsterdam — Printed in The Netherlands

# THE METABOLISM IN MICE OF TWO DEUTERATED ANALOGS OF DIAZEPAM

W.A. GARLAND[1], B.J. MIWA[1], C. ELIAHOU[2] and W. DAIRMAN[2]

[1]Department of Drug Metabolism, Hoffmann-La Roche, Nutley, New Jersey 07110

[2]Department of Toxicology, Hoffmann-La Roche, Nutley, New Jersey 07110

## ABSTRACT

Diazepam, diazepam dideuterated at the C-3 carbon (DZ-$d_2$) and diazepam trideuterated at the N-methyl carbon (DZ-$d_3$) were separately administered i.v., 4 mg kg$^{-1}$, in parallel experiments to mice. Blood samples from the animals were analyzed by GC/NCIMS (SIM) for DZ and three metabolties of DZ, nordiazepam (NDZ), oxazepam (OX) and temazepam (TMZ). The blood concentration-time profile, AUC and $t_{1/2}$ for intact drug were similar for all three parent compounds. NDZ in plasma after administration of DZ-$d_2$ (62 μg) was slightly greater than that after administration of DZ (50 μg), while that after administration of DZ-$d_3$ was slightly less (46 μg). OX in plasma after administration of DZ-$d_2$ (9 μg) was much less than that after administration of either DZ (44 μg) or DZ-$d_3$ (46 μg). TMZ in plasma after administration of DZ-$d_2$ (0.4 μg) was also much less than that after DZ administration (1.4 μg), while TMZ after DZ-$d_3$ administration was much greater (3-5 μg). Thus, the deuterium labeling caused "metabolic switching" with no effect on the disposition of the parent compound.

## INTRODUCTION

Deuterium kinetic isotope effects have often been used to study the mechanism of the in-vitro metabolism of drugs (ref. 1,2). Theoretically, this effect can also be used in-vivo to either increase the bioavailability of intact drugs (by slowing metabolism), or to modify the pharmacology or toxicology of a drug by redirecting metabolism. This latter effect, i.e., "metabolic switching" (ref. 3), is based on a shift of metabolic pathways (for a drug with alternate metabolic pathways) when deuterium is placed at a site of metabolism.

This paper compares the blood concentrations and resulting pharmacokinetics after administration to mice of DZ and two deuterated analogs of DZ that are labeled at positions known to be the principle sites of metabolism of DZ in mice and man (ref. 4,5).

DZ          DZ-$d_2$          DZ-$d_3$

METHODS

Chemicals. DZ, NDZ, TMZ and OX were obtained from Dr. W.E. Scott, Chemical Research Department, Hoffmann-La Roche, Nutley, NJ 07110. DZ-d$_3$, NDZ-d$_5$, OX-d$_5$ and TMZ-d$_8$ were obtained from Dr. A. Liebman, Isotope Synthesis Group, Hoffmann-La Roche, Nutley, New Jersey, 07110 (ref. 6). DZ-d$_2$ was prepared by heating 500 mg of DZ in 3 ml of $^2$H$_2$O (>99% $^2$H) and 7 ml of DMF in a sealed tube in a 100°C oven. After 24 hr, the solvents were removed at 60°C under a stream of N$_2$, fresh solvents were added, and the solution was heated for another 24 hr. The solvents were removed, and the residue was recrystallized from hexane-acetone. The resulting crystals (320 mg) were dried in a vacuum desiccator containing H$_2$SO$_4$. All deuterated analogs were more than 95% labeled as described when analyzed by isobutane positive chemical ionization mass spectrometry (probe inlet).

Mouse Experiments. Fifty three day old male CF-1 mice from Charles River Inc. were given 4 mg kg$^{-1}$ of either DZ, DZ-d$_2$ or DZ-d$_3$ by i.v. injection into the tail vein. Prior to dosing, the mice fasted for 24 hr. Mice scheduled for sacrifice at 2 and 10 min. post-dose were given no food. All other animals were allowed to eat post-dose. Mice scheduled for sacrifice 2 to 24 hr post-dose were given water. All other mice were not given water.

The injection solution was prepared as follows. A weighed amount of either DZ, DZ-d$_2$ or DZ-d$_3$ was added to an appropriate volume of an aqueous solution containing 40% propylene glycol, 10% ethanol, 5% sodium benzoate (by weight), 5% benzoic acid (by weight) and 1.5% benzyl alcohol. The resulting suspension was ground with a mortar and pestle until the solution was clear. This solution was diluted with sufficient distilled water to give the final solution a concentration of 30% water by volume.

The mean weights ± SD of the mice were 24.0 ± 1.3 g (DZ administration), 23.9 ± 1.3 g (DZ-d$_2$ administration) and 23.9 ± 1.5 g (DZ-d$_3$ administration). The injection volume was 0.2 ml per 20 g of body weight.

Mice were killed by decapitation, and the blood drained into a pre-weighed BD Vacutainer 6481 fortified with 0.5 ml of heparin (1000 USP units ml$^{-1}$). After collection, the vacutainer was re-weighed to measure the weight of heparin-diluted blood.

GC/MS Assay for DZ, NDZ, OX and TMX. A 0.55 ml aliquot from each heparin-diluted blood sample was added to a 15-ml culture tube equipped with a Teflon-lined screw cap. The tubes were fortified (0.1 ml methanol solution) with 100 ng of DZ-d$_8$, 50 ng of both OX-d$_5$ and NDZ-d$_5$, and 25 ng of TMZ-d$_8$. The tubes were stirred and 2 ml of 1.0 M pH 9 borate buffer and 6 ml of toluene (80)/heptane (20) were added. The tubes were shaken on a horizontal shaker for 30 min and centrifuged at 5°C and 1000 xg for 10 minutes. The organic layers were transferred to 8-ml culture tubes equipped with Teflon-lined screw caps, and were evaporated to dryness under a stream of N$_2$. Methanol (0.1 ml) and trimethylamine (0.05 ml of a 25% methanol solution) were added to each tube. The tubes were capped and placed in a 100°C oven for 24 hr to exchange all the deuteriums at C-3. The solvents were removed under a stream of N$_2$, 5 ml of a toluene (80)/heptane (20) solution and 1 ml of pH 9, 1.0 M borate buffer were added, and the tubes were shaken for 20 min. The tubes were centrifuged at 5°C and 1000 xg for 5 min. The organic layers were transferred to 5-ml conical centrifuge tubes, and removed under a stream N$_2$. The tubes were placed in a vacuum desiccator, the desiccator was evacuated, and the tubes were allowed to stand for 12 hr.

The extracts were reconstituted in 40 μl of ethyl acetate and 1-4 μl of this solution was injected into a 4 ft x 2 mm (i.d.) glass GC column packed with 3% OV-17 on 100-120 mesh GCQ (column temperature = 260°C). The effluent from the GC was analyzed by negative chemical ionization mass spectrometry.

Ions at m/z 268, the $M^{\pm}$ ion of the thermal rearrangement product of OX (ref. 7), m/z 270, $M^{\pm}$ ion of NDZ, m/z 273, $M^{\pm}$ ion of the thermal rearrangement product of OX-d5, and m/z 275, $M^{\pm}$ ion of NDZ-d5, were monitored. Following injection, the samples were returned to the vacuum desiccator, the desiccator was evacuated, and the samples were allowed to stand for another 12 hr. The samples were reconstituted in 40 μl of a 15% Regisil in hexane solution, and were allowed to stand for 30 min. Two μl of this solution was injected, and the ions at m/z 284, $M^{\pm}$ of both DZ and DZ-d2; m/z 292, $M^{\pm}$ of DZ-d8; m/z 372, $M^{\pm}$ of silylated TMZ and m/z 380, $M^{\pm}$ of silylated TMZ-d8, were monitored. The ion ratio of analyte response to the response from the internal standard was calculated, and the ion ratios converted to amounts of analytes using the slope and intercept values from a linear regression analysis of the ion ratio versus amount added data from the assay of drug-free mouse plasma containing known amounts of DZ, NDZ, OX and TMZ. Following DZ-d3 administration, appropriate $M^{\pm}$ ions were monitored instead of those stated above.

Pharmacokinetic Analysis. Using NONLIN (ref. 8), the mean DZ, DZ-d2 and DZ-d3 blood concentration-time data were fitted to the following equation for a two-compartment pharmacokinetic model: $C = Ae^{-\alpha t} + Be^{-\beta t}$, where A and B are coefficients and α and β are hybrid rate constants (ref. 9). For the metabolites, the terminal slopes ($\lambda_z$) were estimated by unweighted linear regression of the linear segment of the log concentration-time curve data. The AUC (0-∞) was calculated by summing values for AUC (0-t) determined by the trapezoidal rule and $C_z$ ($\lambda_z)^{-1}$ where $C_z$ is the last quantifiable blood concentration. The AUMC (0-t) was calculated using the following equation: AUMC (0-t) = $(t_1C_1 + t_2C_2)$ ($\Delta t$) $(2)^{-1}$ (ref. 10). The AUMC (0-∞) was calculated by summing the values for AUMC (0-t) and the calculated value for $[t_z C_z (\lambda_z)^{-1} + C_z (\lambda_z)^{-2}]$ (ref. 10). The equivalent dose in the plasma was calculated using the following equation: Dose = $(AUC)^2 (AUMC)^{-1}$ VD (ref. 11). The VD's for NDZ, OX and TMZ were obtained by recalculating the data in ref. 12.

RESULTS

Analytical. Correlation coefficients were >0.99 for all calibration curves. Interassay precision from a consideration of the calibration curve data is as follows (RSD = Relative Standard Deviation):

| ADDED | FOUND (DZ) | FOUND (NDZ) | FOUND (OX) | FOUND (TMZ) |
|---|---|---|---|---|
| ng ml$^{-1}$ | ng ml$^{-1}$±SD (RSD) | ng ml$^{-1}$±SD (RSD) | ng ml$^{-1}$±SD (RSD) | ng ml$^{-1}$±SD (RSD) |
| 2 | 2.7 ± 0.4 (15%) | - | - | 2.3 ± 0.7 (30%) |
| 5 | - | 5.9 ± 0.6 (10%) | 6.0 ± 0.6 (10%) | - |
| 10 | 11.3 ± 1.2 (11%) | - | - | 10.7 ± 0.6 (6%) |
| 25 | - | 28.5 ± 3.4 (12%) | 27.2 ± 1.7 (6%) | 25.6 ± 1.4 (6%) |
| 50 | 52.5 ± 2.4 (5%) | - | 52.7 ± 1.6 (3%) | 52.1 ± 3.5 (7%) |
| 100 | 104 ± 3.9 (4%) | 106 ± 10 (9%) | 104 ± 3.6 (4%) | 97.1 ± 3.7 (4%) |
| 200 | - | 208 ± 18 (9%) | 192 ± 8.1 (4%) | - |
| 400 | 392 ± 11 (3%) | 388 ± 16 (4%) | - | - |
| Mean RSD = 8% | | 11% | 5% | 11% |

Dose Proportionality. A preliminary experiment was performed to determine dose proportionality. The ratio of values for the 5 mg kg$^{-1}$ and 1 mg kg$^{-1}$ doses were as follows (values in parentheses are those for the 1 mg kg$^{-1}$ dose).

| ITEM | DZ | NDZ | OX | TMZ |
|------|-----|-----|-----|-----|
| AUC | 5.4 $(4.3 \frac{\mu g \cdot min.}{ml})$[a] | 6.3 $(8.8 \frac{\mu g \cdot min.}{ml})$ | 4.0 $(65.9 \frac{\mu g \cdot min.}{ml})$ | 7.1 $(0.2 \frac{\mu g \cdot min.}{ml})$ |
| $C_{MAX}$ | 4.5 $(320 \text{ ng ml}^{-1})$ | 6.3 $(122 \text{ ng ml}^{-1})$ | 4.9 $(110 \text{ ng ml}^{-1})$ | 7.5 $(4 \text{ ng ml}^{-1})$ |
| TIME OF $C_{MAX}$ | 1.0 (2 min.) | 1.0 (30 min.) | 1.0 (90 min.) | 1.0 (10 min.) |

Concentrations of DZ, NDZ, OX and TMZ. Mean concentrations $(\text{ng ml}^{-1})$ ± SD in blood samples from mice at various times after i.v. administration of 4 mg kg$^{-1}$ of either DZ, DZ-d$_2$ or DZ-d$_3$ are as follows (six mice were sacrificed at each time point, NM = nonmeasurable):

|  | TIME (MIN) | DZ NM | DZ-d$_2$ NM | DZ-d$_3$ NM |
|------|-----------|-----|-----|-----|
|      | 0         | NM | NM | NM |
|      | 2         | 1052 ± 118 | 1050 ± 65 | 1022 ± 83 |
|      | 10        | 480 ± 126 | 497 ± 96 | 569 ± 119 |
| DZ   | 30        | 138 ± 23 | 115 ± 19 | 181 ± 44 |
|      | 60        | 56 ± 33 | 55 ± 11 | 72 ± 20 |
|      | 120       | 12 ± 2.9 | 14 ± 5.5 | 22 ± 5.5[a] |
|      | 360       | NM | NM | NM |
|      | 0         | NM | NM | NM |
|      | 2         | 123 ± 84 | 136 ± 37 | 59 ± 9[b] |
|      | 10        | 365 ± 84 | 497 ± 96[a] | 321 ± 64 |
|      | 30        | 486 ± 77 | 670 ± 112[b] | 555 ± 58 |
| NDZ  | 60        | 401 ± 68 | 601 ± 91[b] | 433 ± 106 |
|      | 120       | 429 ± 89 | 685 ± 133[b] | 427 ± 30 |
|      | 360       | 58 ± 24 | 336 ± 144[c] | 258 ± 203[a] |
|      | 720       | 3.0 ± 0.5[f] | 74 ± 33[b] | 10 ± 1[c,g] |
|      | 1440      | NM | 3.4 ± 1.1[h] | 3 ± 0.7 |
|      | 0         | NM | NM | NM |
|      | 2         | 10 ± 1.5 | NM | 7 ± 2[a] |
|      | 10        | 75 ± 41 | 20 ± 3[b] | 58 ± 18 |
|      | 30        | 241 ± 44 | 33 ± 7[c] | 209 ± 51 |
| OX   | 60        | 425 ± 65 | 65 ± 11[c] | 409 ± 51 |
|      | 120       | 409 ± 76 | 69 ± 14[c] | 413 ± 55 |
|      | 360       | 335 ± 43 | 87 ± 11[c] | 330 ± 84 |
|      | 720       | 230 ± 42 | 73 ± 7.8[c] | 254 ± 47 |
|      | 1440      | 68 ± 23[e] | 35 ± 11[a] | 70 ± 18[e] |
|      | 0         | NM | NM | NM |
|      | 2         | 22 ± 11 | 8 ± 2[a] | 17 ± 3 |
|      | 10        | 28 ± 15 | 7 ± 0.8[b] | 59 ± 7[b] |
| TMZ  | 30        | 16 ± 3 | 4 ± 0.8[c] | 78 ± 19[c] |
|      | 60        | 11 ± 3 | 2 ± 0.6[c] | 45 ± 11[c] |
|      | 120       | 3.7 ± 0.5 | NM | 19 ± 7[c] |
|      | 360       | NM | NM | 5 ± 2[e] |

SUPERSCRIPTS: mean different from mean for DZ administration at $p < 0.05$ (a), $p < 0.01$ (b), $p < 0.001$ (c). One sample lost (e). Disregarding one value of either 38 ng ml$^{-1}$ (f), 70 ng ml$^{-1}$ (g), 41 ng ml$^{-1}$ (h) or 18 ng ml$^{-1}$.

Diazepam Kinetics. Parameters from the pharmacokinetic analysis (two compartment model) of the blood concentration-time data for DZ are as follows (TBC = Total Body Clearance):

| PARAMETERS | UNITS | DZ | DZ-$d_2$ | DZ-$d_3$ |
|---|---|---|---|---|
| Correlation Coefficient | dimensionless | 1.00 | 1.00 | 1.00 |
| A | ng ml$^{-1}$ | 1057 | 1144 | 989 |
| B | ng ml$^{-1}$ | 252 | 153 | 206 |
| $t_{1/2}$ (alpha) | min | 5.3 | 6.0 | 7.6 |
| $t_{1/2}$ (beta) | min | 27.4 | 36.1 | 37.2 |
| $VD_{ss}$ | ml | 130 | 150 | 140 |
| $AUC_{theoretical}$ | $\mu g \cdot min \cdot ml^{-1}$ | 18.0 | 17.9 | 21.9 |
| $AUC_{trapezoidal}$ | $\mu g \cdot min \cdot ml^{-1}$ | 17.7 | 17.5 | 21.4 |
| $TBC_{theoretical}$ | $ml \cdot min^{-1}$ | 5.3 | 5.4 | 4.4 |
| $TBC_{trapezoidal}$ | $ml \cdot min^{-1}$ | 5.4 | 5.4 | 4.4 |
| AUMC | $\mu g \cdot min^2 \cdot ml^{-1}$ | 451 | 491 | 705 |

Metabolite Formation. Parameters from the pharmacokinetic analysis (model independent) of the blood concentration-time data for the metabolites are as follows (VD for NDZ, OX and TMZ were 58,77 and 49 ml, respectively):

| | ITEM | UNITS | NDZ | OX | TMZ |
|---|---|---|---|---|---|
| DZ | AUC | $\mu g \cdot min \cdot ml^{-1}$ | 119 | 377 | 1.6 |
| | AUMC | $\mu g \cdot min^2 \cdot ml^{-1}$ | 16,277 | 250,685 | 83.9 |
| | AMOUNT | $\mu g$ | 50 | 44 | 1.4 |
| DZ-$d_2$ | AUC | $\mu g \cdot min \cdot ml^{-1}$ | 297 | 122 | 0.34 |
| | AUMC | $\mu g \cdot min^2 \cdot ml^{-1}$ | 82,670 | 123,672 | 13.9 |
| | AMOUNT | $\mu g$ | 62 | 9 | 0.4 |
| DZ-$d_2$ | AUC | $\mu g \cdot min \cdot ml^{-1}$ | 187 | 381 | 9.0 |
| | AUMC | $\mu g \cdot min^2 \cdot ml^{-1}$ | 44,154 | 243,259 | 1,119 |
| | AMOUNT | $\mu g$ | 46 | 46 | 3.5 |

DISCUSSION

In mice, DZ is metabolized as follows:

TMZ          DZ          NDZ

OX

Replacement of hydrogens by deuteriums on the N-methyl group of DZ caused no apparent change in the blood concentration-time profile (or kinetics) of DZ. However, the substitution did cause a slight decrease in the amount of NDZ in the blood (isotope effect on N-demethylation) and a substantial increase in the amount of TMZ formed (metabolic switching).

Replacement of hydrogens by deuteriums at C-3 also did not cause any apparent change in the blood concentration-time profile (or kinetics) of DZ. However, the substitution did cause an increase in the amount of NDZ formed (metabolic switching) and a substantial decrease in the amount of OX and TMZ formed (isotope efect on hydroxylation). In addition, a lower recovery of drug (in terms of NDZ, OX and TMZ plasma concentrations) was observed following the DZ-$d_2$ administration than following DZ or DZ-$d_3$ administrations, suggesting the possible formation of an additional metabolite following DZ-$d_2$ administration.

## REFERENCES

1 T.A. Baille, The Use of Stable Isotopes in Pharmacological Research, Pharmacol. Rev., 33 (1981) 81-132.
2 D.B. Northrop, Deuterium and Tritium Kinetic Isotope Effects on Initial Rates, in S. Coldwick and N.O. Kaplan (Eds), Methods Enzymology, 87 (1982) 607-641.
3 M.G. Horning, K.D. Haegele, K.R. Sommer, J. Nowlin, M. Stafford, J.P. Thenot, Metabolic Switching of Drug Pathways as a Consequence of Deuterium Substitution, in E.R. Klein and P.D. Klein (Eds.), Proceedings of the Second International Conference on Stable Isotopes NTIS, Springfield, Virginia , 1976, pp 41-54.
4 S. Garattini, E. Mussini and L. Randall (Eds.), The Benzodiazepines, Raven Press, New York, 1973, pp 75-97.
5 S.A. Kaplan and M. Jack, Metabolism of the Benzodiazepines: Pharmacokinetic and Pharmacodynamic Considerations, in E. Costa (Eds.), The Benzodiazepines: From Molecular Biology to Clinical Practice, Raven Press, New York, 1983, pp 173-199.
6 A. Liebman, G.J. Bader, W. Burger, J. Cupano, C.M. Delaney, Y-Y. Liu, R.R. Muccino, C.W. Perry and E. Thom, Specific Deuterium Labelling of 1,4 Benzodiazepines, in H.L. Schmidt, H. Forstel and K. Heinzinger (Eds.), Stable Isotopes, Elsevier, Amsterdam, 1982, pp 735-741.
7 J. Vessman, M. Johansson, P. Magnusson and S. Stromberg, Determination of Intact Oxazepam by Electron Capture Gas Chromatography After an Extractive Alkylation Reaction, Anal. Chem., 49 (1977), 1545-1549.
8 C.M. Metzler, G.L. Elfring and A.J. McEwen, A Package of Programs for Pharmacokinetic Modeling, Biometrics, 30 (1974) 562-563.
9 M. Gibaldi and D. Perrier, Pharmacokinetics, Marcel Dekker, New York, 1975, pp 49-55.
10 K.K. Chan, A Simple Integrated Method for Drug and Derived Metabolite Kinetics: An Application of the Statistical Moment Theory, Drug Metab. Dispos., 10 (1982) 474-479.
11 L.Z. Benet and R.L. Galeazzi, Noncompartmental Determination of the Steady-State Volume of Distribution, J. Pharm. Sci., 68 (1979) 1071-1074.
12 F. Marcucci, E. Mussini, R. Fanelli and S. Garattini, Species Differences in Diazepam Metabolites, Biochem. Pharmacol., 19 (1970), 1847-1851.

*Synthesis and Applications of Isotopically Labeled Compounds 1985.*
Proceedings of the Second International Symposium, Kansas City, MO, U.S.A.,
3—6 September 1985, R.R. Muccino (Ed.), 277—281
© 1986 Elsevier Science Publishers B.V., Amsterdam — Printed in The Netherlands

The Metabolism of 2-Deutero-3-Fluoro-D-Alanine (DFA). G. Darland, H. Kropp,
F. M. Kahan, R. Hajdu, R. Walker and W. J. A. VandenHeuvel. Merck Institute,
Rahway, NJ.

ABSTRACT

The rate of metabolism of 3-fluoro- D-alanine is controlled by the enzyme D-
amino acid oxidase. Substitution of deuterium for hydrogen at C-2 reduces the
rate of oxidation to fluoropyruvate 2-3 fold. The major organofluorine metabolite is 3- fluoro-L- lactate which is in dynamic equilibrium with fluoropyruvate. Pyruvate dehydrogenase catalyzes the defluorination of FP yielding equimolar quantities of $F^-$, $CO_2$ and acetate.

INTRODUCTION

The search for fluorinated analogues of bacterial cell wall components resulted
in the discovery of 3- F- D- alanine (FA) (1). FA was deuterated at C-2 to
give fludalanine (DFA). Both compounds are potent inhibitors of alanine race-
mase the enzyme required for the synthesis of D-alanine, an essential component
of the bacterial cell wall. A combination drug with broad spectrum antibacterial activity results when DFA and pentizidone, a prodrug of cycloserine, are
used together (2).

FA is extensively metabolized by several mammalian species. The sequence of
biochemical reactions is illustrated below:

$$F-CH_2-CH(NH_2)-COOH \xrightarrow{DAO} F-CH_2-CO-COOH \underset{LDH}{\rightleftharpoons} F-CH_2-CH(OH)-COOH$$
$$\downarrow PDC$$
$$CH_3COOH + CO_2 + F^-$$

Primary metabolism results in the loss of biological activity while maintaining
the integrity of the C-F bond. The only enzyme involved in primary metabolism
is D- amino acid oxidase (DAO), which catalyzes the oxidation of FA to 3-
fluoropyruvate (FP). The two enzymes involved in secondary metabolism are
lactate dehydrogenase (LDH) and pyruvate dehydrogenase. The terminal metabolite
of secondary metabolism is inorganic fluoride. The liberation of $F^-$ from FP is
catalyzed by the pyruvate dehydrogenase complex (PDC). The products of the
defluorinative pathway are equimolar amounts of inorganic fluoride ($F^-$), $CO_2$ and
acetate. The reaction does not require the addition of an external electron
acceptor but is obligately dependent on thiamin pyrophosphate. The steady state
relationship that exists between FP and FL is maintained by LDH.

The present paper discusses the experimental data that has led to our current
understanding of the biochemical reactions involved in the metabolism of FA.

D-AMINO ACID OXIDASE CONTROLS THE RATE OF METABOLISM

A reduction in the rate of primary metabolism was desirable to increase bioavailability and to reduce the risk due to exposure to inorganic fluoride. The
knowledge that DAO catalyzed the first metabolic step offered an attractive way
of reducing the metabolic flux. Since the oxidation of FA to FP by DAO requires
the scission of a C-H bond, it was predicted that the α-deutero analog of FA,
3- F- 2- ²H- D- alanine (DFA), would be oxidized at a substantially slower rate
than FA by virtue of a kinetic isotope effect. This hypothesis was tested <u>in</u>

vitro with purified hog kidney DAO and in vivo in several species of laboratory animal.

The existance of an in vitro kinetic isotope effect was confirmed using purified hog kidney DAO. The reaction conditions were chosen to mimic the physiological state as closely as practicable. Over the 10 fold concentration range of 0.1-1 mM (selected to reflect the average and peak serum levels, respectively) the rate of FA oxidation is three times that of DFA at pH 7.4. There is no detectable difference in the affinity of the substrates for DAO (Km= 1.7mM), so the effect of deuterium substitution at C-2 is exclusively on Vmax.

Since the renal clearance rates of FA and DFA are identical (equal to the glomerular filtration rate) it is possible to estimate the relative rates of oxidation in vivo from the following equation:

$$Kox= (1-Urec)/Urec$$

where Kox is the relative rate of oxidation and Urec represents the fraction of unmetabolized drug recovered in the urine. Analysis of urinary recovery data from laboratory animals using the above equation demonstrated that the relative rate of metabolism of FA was 2-3 times that of DFA (Table 1).

TABLE 1. The effect of substituting deuterium for the α-protium on the rate of oxidative metabolism estimated by the urinary recovery of intact drug.

| Species | Drug | Urec | Kox | Ratio (FA/DFA) |
|---------|------|------|------|----------------|
| Mouse | FA | 0.60 | 0.7 | 1.7 |
|  | DFA | 0.72 | 0.4 |  |
| Rat | FA | 0.16 | 5.3 | 3.2 |
|  | DFA | 0.38 | 1.6 |  |
| Rhesus monkey | FA | 0.76 | 0.32 | 2.1 |
|  | DFA | 0.87 | 0.15 |  |

A second method of demonstrating that DFA is metabolized more slowly than FA is to determine the ratio of bioactive drug in the serum to circulating $F^-$. The results in Table 2 were obtained from cross over studies in Rhesus monkeys.

TABLE 2. Effect in Rhesus monkeys of deuteration on the bioavailability of drug (FA or DFA) vs. inorganic fluoride.

AUC (mcg hr/ml)

| Subject | Drug | Drug | $F^-$ | Ratio |
|---------|------|------|-------|-------|
| RH-I | DFA | 149 | 1.8 | 82.4 |
|  | FA | 145 | 3.2 | 40.3 |
| RH-X | DFA | 146 | 0.9 | 162.4 |
|  | FA | 180 | 1.9 | 94.9 |

The ratio of drug to $F^-$ is increased two-fold for DFA relative to FA. Since the substitution of deuterium for hydrogen at C-2 has no effect on antibacterial activity, this ratio is a valid estimate of the relative therapeutic index of the two compounds.

THE BIOCHEMICAL PATHWAY OF DFA METABOLISM

As the α-hydrogen is lost at the first step of metabolism, substitution of deuterium for hydrogen at C-2 has no effect on metabolism subsequent to oxidation. Studies of the metabolic fate of drug were all done with DFA.

In order to define the details of DFA metabolism, we developed sensitive GC/MS assays for both FP and FL. In spite of the sensitivity of the assay ($\leq$0.5nmoles/ml), no FP could be detected in the serum of laboratory animals treated with DFA. This indicates that the ratio of FL/FP in serum is greater than 1000/1. Even in blood samples from rats treated with 40 mg/kg sodium fluoropyruvate, no FP could be detected. Rather, FL was present at concentrations suggesting FP had been quantitatively reduced within 15 minutes. FP was detectable in the urine of rats and mice shortly after treatment with DFA although total recovery never represented more than 0.5% of the administered drug.

In contrast, FL was readily quantified in the serum, and its recovery in the urine was at least an order of magnitude greater than observed for FP. In rats, orally administered DFA is rapidly and completely absorbed; peak concentrations in the serum is achieved within 15-20 minutes. The serum concentration of FL lags behind DFA and reaches a maximum at about 30 minutes and is relatively constant for 90 minutes. The peak FL concentration is proportional to dose up to 200 mg/kg DFA, at this dose the maximum concentration in the serum was approximately 1 mM. Repeated daily doses of DFA do not alter the nature of the dose response curve, suggesting that metabolism is neither inducible nor saturable.

Prior to the development of the GC/MS assay for FL, blood samples from rats and mice were analyzed for or organic fluoride by a wet ashing technique (3). Comparison of organic fluoride with subsequent GC/MS indicate that FL is the only significant organic fluoride metabolite of DFA.

The reduction of FP to FL is stereospecific, i.e., only the L-isomer is produced (4). Since the GC/MS assay does not distinguish between the two isomers of FL, a method of resolving the two isomers was sought. We took advantage of the fact that yeast lactate dehydrogenase (YLDH) catalyzes a stereospecific oxidation of L-FL to FP (5) to develop an assay specific for the L-isomer of FL. Application of the assay to serum samples from several species of laboratory animal demonstrated that only the L-isomer of FL was formed (Table 3), consistent with the hypothesis that FP reduction is catalyzed by LDH.

TABLE 3. Concentration of total FL and L-FL in the serum of Rhesus monkeys dosed with DFA.

| Dose (mg/kg) | N | nmoles/ml$\pm$sd total FL (GC/MS) | L-FL (YLDH) |
|---|---|---|---|
| 125 | 5 | 9.5$\pm$4.3 | 10.7$\pm$3.3 |
| 250 | 6 | 32.1$\pm$16.0 | 26.6$\pm$12.6 |
| 750 | 6 | 35.5$\pm$11.5 | 33.9$\pm$12.7 |

Since FL was the only demonstrable organic fluoride metabolite in the serum of laboratory animals, initial efforts to identify the immediate precursor of F$^-$ focused on FL. Repeated attempts to identify an enzymatic mechanism for FL defluorination met with failure. A potential pathway was provided with the discovery by Leung and Frey (6) that E. coli pyruvate dehydrogenase catalyzed a defluorinative decarboxylation of FP producing equimolar amounts of F$^-$, acetate and $CO_2$. We partially purified a pyruvate dehydrogenase complex from beef heart mitochondria and showed that it performed the same reaction (Table 4).

TABLE 4. Stoichiometry of defluorination of $1,2-^{14}C$-FP by mammalian pyruvate dehydrogenase.

| Time (min) | Expt 1 | | Expt 2 | |
|---|---|---|---|---|
| | Acetate | Fluoride | $CO_2$ | Fluoride |
| 0 | nd | <0.1 | nd | <0.1 |
| 1 | | | 5 | 3 |
| 3 | | | 15 | 13 |
| 5 | 29 | 31 | 24 | 23 |
| 30 | 58 | 57 | | |

This biochemical reaction explained early animal experiments which had shown that fluoroacetate was not a product of DFA metabolism and that $F^-$ and $CO_2$ were produced in equimolar quantities.

There remained, however, the paradox that FP could not be detected in the serum of animals treated with DFA. Although it was thought that the reduction of FP to FL was irreversible (7), there was the possibility that the reaction was in fact reversible but that the equilibrium greatly favored FL. Evidence for the existence of a small pool of FP in dynamic equilibrium with FL was obtained by following the fate of the L- and D- isomers of α-deutero-FL (Fig. 1). The exchange of the α-deuteron in rats treated with $2-^2H-$ L- FL was several times more rapid than the plasma clearance rate of FL. Since renal clearance of FL

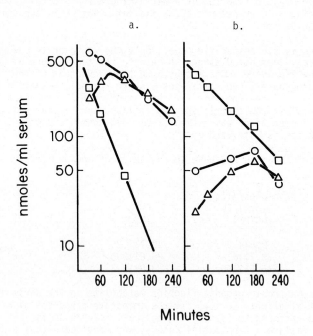

Minutes

Fig. 1. In vivo exchange of the α-hydrogen in rats treated with: a. $2-^2H$-L-FL. b. $2-^2$-H-D-FL.□ $2-^2H$-FL; △ $2-^1H$-FL; O ,L-FL.

in the rat is negligible, the plasma clearance rate is identical to the rate of defluorinative metabolism. Exchange of the $\alpha$-deuteron was not accompanied by racemization. This is consistent with a steady state relationship between FP and L-FL.

In the case of the D-isomer, exchange of the $\alpha$-deuteron was only marginally faster than FL clearance and was accompanied by racemization suggesting that FP is an intermediate in this exchange reaction as well. The mechanism of D- FL oxidation is unknown but may be due to the mitochondrial D- $\alpha$- OH- acid oxidase.

The existence of a small pool of FP in equilibrium with FL and the demonstration of the PDC catalyzed defluorination of FP provides a plausible explanation for the source of inorganic fluoride.

REFERENCES

1. Kollonitsch, J., L. Barash, F. M. Kahan and H. Kropp. Nature 243:346-347 (1973).
2. Kahan, F. M. and H. Kropp. Abstracts of 15th Inter-Science Conference on Antimicrobial Agents and Chemotherapy. Abstract #100 (1975).
3. Taves, D. R. Nature 217:1050-1051 (1968).
4. Craig, J. C., R. J. Dummel, E. Kun and S. K. Roy. Biochemistry 4:2547-2549 (1965).
5. Dikstein, S. Biochem. Biophys. Acta 36:397-401 (1959).
6. Leung, L. S. and P. A. Frey. Biochem. Biophys. Res. Commun. 8:274-279 (1978).
7. Ayling, J. E. and E. Kun. Mol. Pharmacol. 2:255-265 (1965).

*Synthesis and Applications of Isotopically Labeled Compounds 1985.*
Proceedings of the Second International Symposium, Kansas City, MO, U.S.A.,
3—6 September 1985, R.R. Muccino (Ed.), 283—284
© 1986 Elsevier Science Publishers B.V., Amsterdam — Printed in The Netherlands

THE USE OF DEUTERATED ANALOGS OF DRUGS AS MEDICINAL AGENTS: INTRODUCTION
AND REPORT OF DISCUSSION

W.A. Garland (Session Chairman)
Department of Drug Metabolism, Hoffmann-La Roche, Nutley, New Jersey 07110.

The purpose of this session was to evaluate why no deuterated drugs are
marketed in spite of several literature reports suggesting that such
compounds may be either more active (e.g., ref. 1-3) or less toxic (e.g.,
ref. 4-6) than the corresponding protio analogs. [Several literature
reports suggest that deuteration has no effect on pharmacological activity
(e.g., ref. 7-8).] Recently, Foster (ref. 9) made the following comment
on this situation: "For drugs not intended for use in humans or for
products such as insecticides, the advantages to be gained by specific or
general deuteration in modifying biological activity and/or duration of
action must significantly outweigh the additional cost associated with the
synthesis of deuterated analogues. For drugs intended for use in humans
there will be a substantial additional cost, namely, that associated with
preclinical toxicology and clinical trials. It seems very unlikely that
the regulatory authorities associated with the pharmaceutical industry
would regard a deuterated drug designed to have a biological activity
significantly different from that of the parent protium form as other than
a new drug."
During the discussions which followed each speaker's talk, and during a
panel discussion which followed the talks, the following points were made:

I. Dr. Leslie McCarty
   A. Certain deuterated anesthesia agents would probably be useful with
surgical patients having impaired renal function.
   B. The potency of anesthesia agents is a function of the water-octanol
partition function which is determined by the halogens on the molecule,
not by the hydrogens (or deuteriums).
   C. Other metabolites beside fluoride ion may be responsible for the
toxicity of many anesthesia agents. To date, these biotransformations
have not been addressed in deuterium-labelling experiments.
   D. FDA concerns focused on establishing that the deuterated anesthesia
agents were not more toxic than the protio compounds, and that the potency
and cardiovascular effects of protio and deuterio compounds were equivalent.

II. Dr. Eric Larsen
   A. To supply the US population with one typical commmonly-used anesthesia
agent requires the manufacturing of about 65 gallons of agent per day.
   B. A typical anesthesia agents sells for approximately $100 per pound
with a manufacturing cost of $ 10- 15 per pound. A deuterated analog of
the same agent would cost approximately 50% more to manufacture.
   C. The decisions not to market the deuterated anesthesia agent were
based on business, and not technical concerns.

III. Dr. Gary Darland
   A. Deuterated fluoroalanine failed as a product because it (as well as
its protio analog) lacked potency relative to other antibacterial agents,
and because its manufacturing cost were twice that expected of a typical
agent of this type.

284

B. The relative toxicities of deuterio and protio fluoroalanine were never compared in long term studies because the decision was made to market only the deuterated compound. In short term testing, the deuterated compound was 50-75% times less toxic than the protio compound.

C. The FDA requested data showing that deuterated fluoroalanine was not more toxic than protio fluoroalanine, i.e., FDA concerns were not a major problem.

IV. Dr. Bill Garland

A. Conclusions based solely on urinary concentration measurements are invalid, except when studying the modification of the renal pharmacology or toxicology of a drug by deuterium labeling, because differences in urinary product formation may not establish differences in blood concentrations.

B. Experiments with the deuterated diazepam analogs were directed towards establishing metabolic switching in plasma concentrations, not to changing the pharmacological effect of diazepam (in this regard, all the metabolites showed a similar pharmacological profile).

C. The occasional loss of deuterium in DZ-$d_2$ occurs on the GC column, not in sample work-up.

D. The use of a deuteration to increase bioavailability is probably a waste of effort since simpler procedures such as increasing the dose are available to accomplish the same goal. In addition, the magnitude of the in-vivo deuterium isotope effects is too small to completely overcome a drug's toxicity, if the drug itself is toxic. The technique might be successful, however, in eliminating toxicity by "metabolic switching" if toxicity is related to formation of a minor metabolite.

E. In a competitive market for a generic product, a deuterium labeled compound might provide a strong marketing advantage in spite of a marginal therapeutic advantage.

F. A difference in activity between protio and deuterio analogs of a drug could be caused by either a deuterium isotope effect or by a unique effect of deuterium at the site of action of the drug.

1  M. Tanabe, D. Yasuda, S. LeValley and C. Mitoma, The Pharmacologic Effect of Deuterium Substitution on 5-n-Butyl-5-ethylbarbituric Acid, Life Sci., 8 (1969), 1123-1128.

2  S.E. Najjar, M.I. Blake, P.A. Benoit and M.C. Lu, Effect of Deuteration on Locomotor Activity of Amphetamine, J. Med. Chem., 21 (1978), 555-558.

3. L. Dyck, D.A. Durden, P.H. Yu, B.A. Davis and A. Boulton, Potentiation of the Biochemical Effects of ß-Phenylethylhydrazine by Deuterium Substitution, Biochem. Pharmacol., 32 (1983), 1519-1522.

4. S.D. Nelson, W.A. Garland, J.R. Mitchell, Y. Vaishnav, C.N. Stratham and A.R. Buckpitt, Drug Metab. Dispos., 6 (1978), 363-367.

5. T. Mizutani, K. Yamamoto and K. Tajima, Isotope Effects on the Metabolism and Pulmonary Toxicity of Buthylated Hydroxytoluene in Mice by Deuteration of the 4-Methyl Group. Toxicol. Appl. Pharmacol., 69 (1983), 283-290.

6  L. McCarty, R. Malek, E.R. Larsen, The Effect of Deuteration on the Metabolism of Halogenated Anesthetics in the Rat, Anesthesiology, 51 (1979), 106-110.

7  J. Perel, P. Dayton, C. Tauriello, L. Brand and L. Mark, Metabolic Studies with Deuterated Phenobarbital, J. Med. Chem., 10 (1967), 371-374.

8  M. Tanabe, J. Tagg, D. Yasuda, S. LeValley and C. Mitoma, Pharmacologic and Metabolic Studies with Deuterated Zoxazolamine, J. Med. Chem., 13 (1969), 374-374.

9  A. Foster, Deuterium Isotope Effects in Studies of Drug Metabolism, Trends in Pharmacological Sciences, 5 (1984), 524-527.

*Synthesis and Applications of Isotopically Labeled Compounds 1985.*
Proceedings of the Second International Symposium, Kansas City, MO, U.S.A.,
3—6 September 1985, R.R. Muccino (Ed.), 285—286
© 1986 Elsevier Science Publishers B.V., Amsterdam — Printed in The Netherlands

SYNTHESIS AND USE OF ISOTOPICALLY LABELED PEPTIDES

JOHN M. STEWART

Department of Biochemistry, University of Colorado School of Medicine,

Denver, Colorado 80262

ABSTRACT

Peptides labeled with heavy or radioactive isotopes are useful for metabolic studies, for ligands for receptor and antibody binding and for assignment of resonances in NMR. Methods for synthesis of these peptides are discussed.

METHODS OF SYNTHESIS

Isotopically labeled peptides may be synthesized directly from labeled amino acids. This is the usual procedure when stable isotopes are to be incorporated, but is less common with radioactive isotopes due to the hazards involved in handling such materials. If the use intended for the peptide will allow the choice, one should label simple amino acids, and not those with side-chain functional groups. The additional losses involved in derivatization of the latter will greatly increase the cost of the synthesis. Greater efficiency of label incorporation will also be achieved if the label is introduced late in the synthetic scheme and in high-yield steps. If the peptide will be used for metabolic studies, the label must be placed at an appropriate location in the peptide chain so that useful information will be obtained. Solid-phase peptide synthesis (SPPS) (ref.1) has been widely used for synthesis of labeled peptides. SPPS can be efficiently carried out on a very small scale for incorporation of highly radioactive amino acids. Purification schemes should be carefully designed so as not to contaminate equipment with radioactivity; simple, disposable chromatographic equipment is recommended.

Iodination of Tyr or His residues in peptides is useful for introduction of radioactivity for radioimmunoassay (RIA) or for receptor radioligand production. Moreover, these residues can be iodinated with "cold" iodine, which is then replaced by tritium or deuterium by catalytic "hydrogenation." For metabolic studies, one should be aware that an isotopic hydrogen ortho to the hydroxyl of Tyr is not metabolically stable, and may be enzymatically removed. If the peptide contains Tyr, these procedures are straightforward. If it does not contain Tyr, often a Phe residue can be replaced by Tyr in synthesis. The peptide can be synthesized using dehydroPro, which can be saturated catalytically using $D_2$ or $T_2$. Incorporation of label may damage the peptide, since the oxidation usually used in radioiodination (chloramine T, peroxidase) may harm Met, Cys and Trp, and catalytic hydrogenation can destroy Met and Cys residues.

If the structure of the peptide does not allow use of Tyr or Pro labels, free amino groups in the peptide can be derivatized with the Bolton-Hunter reagent, which is commercially available and adds the equivalent of a tyrosine to the peptide. This group can then be iodinated, or the Bolton-Hunter reagent can be purchased already labeled with radioactive iodine.

## SOME EXAMPLES OF USE OF LABELED PEPTIDES

To produce radioiodinated ligands of bradykinin (BK) (Arg-Pro-Pro-Gly-Phe-Ser-Pro-Phe-Arg) for RIA (ref.2) and receptor binding (ref.3), each Phe residue was replaced by Tyr, and also a Tyr residue was added to the amino end of the chain. In RIA, different tyrosine analogs were found to combine differently with antibodies raised with different immunogens, while for receptor binding, Tyr-BK was found to be the best ligand. For a receptor ligand, BK was also synthesized with dehydroproline in positions 2 and 3 and subjected to catalytic tritiation. Similar tritiated BK and BK labeled with $^{14}$C in Phe-8 were used for studies of pulmonary metabolism.

Substance P (SP, Arg-Pro-Lys-Pro-Gln-Gln-Phe-Phe-Gly-Leu-Met-amide) was originally labeled by use of an 8-Tyr analog, but iodination caused significant oxidation of the methionine residue. Chromatographic purification of the product was particularly important. For a receptor ligand, Arg was replaced by Tyr and Met by norleucine (ref.4). Bolton-Hunter-SP has also been used successfully. For metabolism, the two prolines were tritiated, using a dehydroPro analog.

For assignment of alanine NMR resonances in a peptide containing 3 Ala residues, one Ala was fully deuterated, the second 50% deuterated and the third was normal. This allowed complete assignment with one synthesis.

## REFERENCES

1 J.M. Stewart and J.D. Young, Solid-Phase Peptide Synthesis, Pierce Chemical Co., Rockford, IL, 1985, 176 pp.
2 C.E. Odya, T.L. Goodfriend, J.M. Stewart and C. Peña, J. Immunol. Meth. 19 (1978) 243-257.
3 M.J. Fredrick, R.J. Vavrek, J.M. Stewart and C.E. Odya, Biochem. Pharmacol. 33 (1984) 2887-2892.
4 S.W. Bahouth, J.M. Stewart and J.M. Musacchio, J. Pharmacol. Exp. Therap. 230 (1984) 116-123.

*Synthesis and Applications of Isotopically Labeled Compounds 1985.*
Proceedings of the Second International Symposium, Kansas City, MO, U.S.A.,
3—6 September 1985, R.R. Muccino (Ed.), 287—292
© 1986 Elsevier Science Publishers B.V., Amsterdam — Printed in The Netherlands

SYNTHESIS AND USE OF SPECIFIC ISOTOPICALLY LABELED PEPTIDE HORMONES FOR STUDIES
OF CONFORMATION, DYNAMICS, AND HORMONE-PROTEIN INTERACTIONS

VICTOR J. HRUBY

Department of Chemistry, University of Arizona, Tucson, Arizona 85721 (USA)

ABSTRACT

The synthesis of amino acids specifically labeled with deuterium at the $C_\alpha$ and $C_\beta$ positions, with carbon-13 at the $C'$, $C_\alpha$, and $C_\beta$ carbon atoms of most amino acids, with deuterium and/or carbon-13 at the 3' and 5' positions of tyrosine, phenylalanine, and related amino acids can be readily accomplished. These compounds can be resolved into their purified enantiomers if desired, and the pure enantiomers (or enantiomeric mixture) can be suitably protected for incorporation into peptide hormones or neurotransmitters by total synthesis. The diastereoisomeric peptides can be purified by partition chromatography or preparative reversed phase high pressure liquid chromatography. These peptide hormone derivatives and their analogues can be used for a wide variety of biochemical and biophysical studies including: a) the unambiguous assignment of $^1H$ and $^{13}C$ NMR spectra for conformational studies; b) careful examination of the chemical and dynamic properties of individual amino acid residues or of individual atoms in specific amino acid residues of these peptides; c) simplification of complex spectral regions with overlapping signals for assignments of other non-labeled amino acid residues; d) examination of conformational and dynamic properties of peptide hormones and neurotransmitters as they interact with receptors and other macromolecules important to their biological activity.

INTRODUCTION

Since the pioneering work on the total synthesis of deuterated amino acid derivatives by Blomquist and co-workers (1,2) and of Katz and Crespie (3,4) on the synthesis of perdeuterated amino acids and proteins by microbiological methods, the uses of uniformly labeled amino acids and proteins have greatly increased. For many applications, however, uniformly labeled amino acid derivatives are not appropriate, and specifically labeled amino acid derivatives are needed. This brief review we will concentrate on the latter group of compounds, and illustrate the use of these compounds in structural, biochemical, and biophysical applications with examples primarily from our laboratory.

SYNTHESIS OF $^2H$ AND $^{13}C$ SPECIFICALLY LABELED AMINO ACID DERIVATIVES

With the exception of α-deuterated and to a lesser extent β-deuterated amino acids and 3',5'-deuterated tyrosine, most specifically labeled amino acids must be prepared by total synthesis. The preparation of $[3',5'-^2H_2]$tyrosine is accomplished (4) by chemical exchange in strong acid (electrophilic aromatic substitution). α-Deuteration can be accomplished by treatment of most amino acids or acetyl amino acids with a solution containing $D_2O$, acetic anhydride, and deuterated acetic acid (5,6). This leads to α-deuterated N-acetyl-DL-amino acid derivatives which require resolution. Wong and Whitesides have reported an enzyme-catalyzed synthesis of L-[α-$^2$H]glutamic acid (7). The method should be applicable to many other amino acids.

The synthesis of β-deuterated amino acids often requires total synthesis (e.g. 8) though in some cases metal catalyzed exchange reactions can be used (9). Other specifically deuterated amino acid derivatives generally can be prepared from available deuterated alkyl and aryl derivatives. (See for example the synthesis of 2S,5R-[5-$^2$H]proline (10) and S-benzyl-DL-[3-$^2$H$_2$]-cysteine (7)). A general approach may be possible with use of pyridoxal phosphate dependent enzymes to give specific α-, β-, or γ-substituted derivatives (e.g. 11).

Most $^{13}$C amino acids specifically enriched in the C'-position are commercially available at a moderate price because most of these amino acids can be readily prepared from the relatively cheap [$^{13}$C]CN$^-$ (e.g. 12). Many $^{13}$C-amino acids specifically enriched at the $C_\alpha$-carbon atom also can be obtained commercially, though they are quite expensive. However, most of the normal α-amino acids can be prepared from $C_\alpha$-labeled diethyl acetamidomalonate or the corresponding ethyl acetamidocyanoacetate via condensation with the appropriate electrophile followed by acid hydrolysis.

Amino acids specifically $^{13}$C-labeled in β or γ or other carbon atoms are less readily available. In most cases the synthesis can be done from available $^{13}$C-labeled compounds, though multistep syntheses generally will be required. We reported at the first International Symposium on the Synthesis of Isotopically Labeled Compounds on the synthesis of [3-$^{13}$C]cysteine derivatives suitable for peptide synthesis (13). [3',5'-$^{13}$C$_2$]Tyrosine can be prepared in 20% overall yield in 10 steps from [1,3-$^{13}$C$_2$]acetone (14), and a high yield 2 or 3 step process can be used to convert the labeled tyrosine derivative directly to L-[3',5'-$^{13}$C]phenylalanine with retention of configuration (15).

## SYNTHESIS AND PURIFICATION OF $^2$H AND $^{13}$C SPECIFICALLY LABELED PEPTIDE HORMONE AND NEUROTRANSMITTER ANALOGUES

In general, preparation of peptide hormones, neurotransmitters, and other peptide compounds specifically labeled at a particular site of interest requires total synthesis utilizing the specifically labeled amino acid derivative. This can be accomplished using standard solution or solid phase methods of peptide synthesis, and usually it is possible to minimize the amount of excess of precious labeled amino acid derivative by a suitable choice of reaction conditions. Though the pure L(or D) labeled amino acid derivative can be used, we often have found it desirable to utilize the DL-amino acid derivative in the synthesis and

then separate the diastereoisomeric peptides. This has the advantage of mini-
mizing losses of precious amino acid derivative resulting from the resolution
steps. Furthermore, it provides both of the diastereoisomeric peptides in one
synthesis, which is often desirable since the diastereoisomeric peptide analogues usually have unique biological and chemical properties (vide infra).
Recent developments in partition chromatography and reverse phase high pressure
liquid chromatography (RP-HPLC) have greatly aided this approach, and we have
made considerable effort to render these methods routine (see for example
5,8,12,16-20).

## APPLICATIONS OF $^2$H AND $^{13}$C SPECIFICALLY LABELED PEPTIDE HORMONE AND NEUROTRANS-MITTER ANALOGUES

### Uses in Conformational Studies

Analysis of peptide conformation and dynamics requires as a first step the
unambiguous assignment of all proton and carbon resonances in the NMR spectra.
Despite the numerous advances in NMR spectroscopy including 2-dimensional and
double quantum techniques (for reviews see 21), there are still many circumstances in which a specific $^2$H or $^{13}$C label is needed to <u>unambiguously</u> make assignments. Either deuterium or carbon-13 labeled derivatives can be used to make
both assignments. However, since deuterium-labeled amino acids are generally
much less expensive and more readily available, deuterium-labeled compounds are
more commonly used. For example, specifically-labeled oxytocin derivatives containing deuterium labels in several specific positions led to complete assignments of the proton (22) <u>and</u> carbon-13 (23,24) NMR spectra. Similar labeled
derivatives of vasopressin, which has a considerably more complex proton NMR
spectra in the β-proton region, led to sufficent spectra simplification so that
the assignments could be made unambiguously (25). Similar kinds of studies have
been made on numerous peptides by many investigators. We are still finding it
necessary to utilize this methodology (26), and it is our opinion that this
approach is still the one for making unambiguous assignments.

### For Studies of Dynamics and Chemical Properties of Individual Atoms or Groups in Peptides

The use of $^3$H- and $^{14}$C-labeled peptides specifically labeled at a specific
amino acid residue for biochemical studies of metabolism, enzymatic stability,
receptor binding, etc. is well established and will not be discussed here.
Rather we will briefly outline the use of peptides specifically labeled with $^2$H
or $^{13}$C nuclei to examine their chemical and dynamic properties.

The application of $^2$H NMR as a "clean" way to examine the motional characteristics of organic compounds in general (27) and amino acids and peptides in

particular (28,29) has long been recognized. Despite its potential, few comprehensive studies have been made using this method. One important exception has been studies on the microdynamics of oxytocin (H-Cys-Tyr-Ile-Glu-Asn-Cys-Pro-Leu-Gly-NH$_2$) in solution (29,30), where it was first shown that the cyclic 20-membered disulfide-containing ring in this peptide has uniform motional properties, but the tripeptide side chain has much more extensive motion relative to the ring. It also was shown that the Tyr$^2$ aromatic group was rapidly in motion relative to the backbone of the 20-membered ring. These studies demonstrated the ability of deuterium to unambiguously evaluate segmental motion in peptides without the ambiguities of interpretation inherent in $^{13}$C NMR relaxation studies. More recently, $^2$H NMR methods have proven to be useful for examining the dynamic properties of aromatic moieties and other side chain groups of proteins in solution and in the solid state (e.g. 31-33).

$^{13}$C NMR has been widely used to study the dynamic behavior of peptide hormones and neurotransmitters since the mid-1970's (e.g. 34). However, these studies generally have been done at natural abundance. In view of the high concentrations, many of these results may be questionable since association of peptides at these concentrations is common (e.g. 35). Extensive $T_1$ studies using specifically labeled peptide analogues at high dilution are needed. Finally, it is possible to obtain $pK_a$ values and to examine other chemical properties of groups in peptides using specifically $^{13}$C-labeled compounds (37), and much more could be done in this area.

## For Examination of Peptide-Macromolecular Receptor (Acceptor) Interactions

$^2$H and $^{13}$C NMR studies with specifically labeled peptides has been widely used to study peptide-macromolecular interactions. This research has been reviewed recently (37) and will not be discussed here. Rather we will outline the basic approach and indicate the kinds of results which can be obtained using our own work to illustrate a few of the points.

$^2$D NMR using specific deuterium labeled peptides is a sensitive method for examining peptide hormone or neurotransmitter interactions with macromolecules including receptors, acceptors, membranes, etc. due to the significant line broadening of deuterium which generally occurs on interaction. This can be used to monitor the interaction, obtain quantitative information about the interaction, and examine on and off rates. Such studies have been made on the interactions of oxytocin and vasopressin with their neurosecretory carrier proteins, the neurophysins, and have demonstrated that such interactions occur in different time domains for the residues in the 20-membered ring of the hormones and those in the tripeptide side chain (30). In a different approach, small perdeuterated peptides have been used to examine the effect of peptide-neurophysin interactions on the protein proton NMR parameters (38).

By systematically replacing C', $C_\alpha$, $C_\beta$ or other carbon atoms with $^{13}C$, and examining the changes in chemical shifts, relaxation times, and other NMR parameters of the labeled atoms it has been possible to obtain a detailed picture of the dynamics of neurohypophyseal hormone-neurophysin interactions, of changes in $pK_A$ and other chemical properties which accompany the hormone-protein interaction, and of the changes in the conformation which accompany formation of the peptide-protein complex (38,39). Particularly interesting were the observations made with oxytocin containing a 3',5'-[$^{13}C_2$]tyrosine-2 residue (40). On interaction of the hormone with neurophysin, the sharp single resonance for the 3' and 5' carbon-13 atoms became nonequivalent with a chemical shift difference of 3.3 ppm. Moreover, whereas the $C^\alpha$ carbon of Tyr$^2$ is in slow exchange (less that 5 sec$^{-1}$), the aromatic ring is in intermediate exchange with a rotation rate of ~ 300 sec$^{-1}$ at 20° and 1000 sec$^{-1}$ at 40° in the hormone-protein complex. Interestingly, the rotation rate is increased to $10^4$-$10^8$ sec$^{-1}$ when a 3',5'-[$^{13}C_2$]phenylalanine-2 residue replaced Tyr$^2$, demonstrating the importance of the hydroxyl group on the tyrosine ring in the dynamic behavior of the ring in the bound state. These and many other such studies (37) suggest that specifically $^2H$ and $^{13}C$ labeled peptide hormones and neurotransmitters will be powerful tools for examining the details of hormone-receptor interactions.

## ACKNOWLEDGEMENTS

This work was supported by grants from the National Science Foundation and U.S. Public Health Service. I am particularly indebted to my co-workers, especially M. Blumenstein, D.A. Upson, V. Viswanatha, and D. Chaturvedi without whom the work from my laboratory could not have been done.

## REFERENCES

1. A.T. Blomquist, B.F. Hiscock and D.N. Harpp, J. Org. Chem., 31 (1966) 338-339, and references therein.
2. A.F. Spatola, D.A. Cornelius, V.J. Hruby and A.T. Blomquist, J. Org. Chem., 39 (1974) 2207-2212, and references therein.
3. J.J. Katz and H.L. Crespie, in J. Collins and H. Bauman (Eds.), Isotope Effects in Chemical Reactions, Reinhold, New York, 1971, 286-363 pp.
4. J.S. Cohen, M. Feil and I.M. Chaiken, Biochim. Biophys. Acta, 236 (1971) 468-478.
5. D.A. Upson and V.J. Hruby, J. Org. Chem., 42 (1977) 2329-2330.
6. H. Fujihara and R.L. Schowen, J. Org. Chem., 49 (1984) 2819-2820.
7. C.H. Wong and G.N. Whitesides, J. Am. Chem. Soc., 105 (1983) 3012-3014.
8. D.A. Upson and V.J. Hruby, J. Org. Chem., 41 (1976) 1353-1358.
9. E.H. Abbott and A.E. Martell, J. Am. Chem. Soc., 91 (1969) 6931-6939.
10. P. Gamatica and P. Manitto, J. Lab. Comps. Radiopharm., 18 (1980) 955-962.
11. M.N.T. Chang and C. Walsh, J. Am. Chem. Soc, 102 (1980) 7368-7370.
12. V.J. Hruby, V. Viswanatha and Y.C.S. Yang, J. Lab. Comps. Radiopharm., 17 (1980) 801-812.
13. D.N. Chaturvedi and V.J. Hruby, in J.F. Engel (Ed.) Procedures for the Synthesis of Isotopically Labeled Compounds, Midwest Research Institute, Kansas City, 1982, 56-58; 59-61 pp.

292

14. V. Viswanatha and V.J. Hruby, J. Org. Chem., 44 (1979) 2892-2896.
15. V. Viswanatha and V.J. Hruby, ibid., 45 (1980) 2010-2012.
16. B. Larsen, R.L. Fox, M.F. Burke and V.J. Hruby, Int. J. Peptide Protein Res., 13 (1979) 12-21.
17. V. Viswanatha, B. Larsen and V.J. Hruby, Tetrahedron, 35 (1979) 1575-1580.
18. D.D. Blevins, M.F. Burke and V.J. Hruby, in W.S. Hancock (Ed.), Handbook of the Use of HPLC for the Separation of Amino Acids, Peptides and Proteins, Vol. II, CRC Press, Boca Raton, 1984, 137-143 pp.
19. W.L. Cody, B.C. Wilkes and V.J. Hruby, J. Chromatogr., 314 (1984) 313-321.
20. D.M. Yamamoto, D.A. Upson, D.K. Linn and V.J. Hruby, J. Am. Chem. Soc., 99 (1977) 1564-1570.
21. V.J. Hruby (Ed.), The Peptides:  Analysis, Synthesis, Biology, Vol. 7, Academic Press, San Diego, 1985, in press.
22. A.I.R. Brewster and V.J. Hruby, Proc. Natl. Acad. Sci. U.S.A., 70 (1973) 3806-3809.
23. A.I.R. Brewster, V.J. Hruby, A.F. Spatola and F.A. Bovey, Biochemistry, 12 (1973) 1643-1649.
24. V.J. Hruby, K.K. Deb, A.F. Spatola, D.A. Upson and D.M. Yamamoto, J. Am. Chem. Soc., 101 (1979) 202-212.
25. H.R. Wyssbrod, A.J. Fischman, D.H. Live, V.J. Hruby, N.S. Agarwal and D.A. Upson, J. Am. Chem. Soc., 101 (1979) 4037-4043.
26. W.L. Cody, Ph.D. Dissertation, University of Arizona, 1985.
27. H.H. Mantsch, H. Saito, L.C. Leitch and I.C.P. Smith, J. Am. Chem. Soc., 96 (1974) 256-258.
28. J.D. Cutnell, J.A. Glasel and V.J. Hruby, Ann. N.Y. Acad. Sci., 248 (1975) 458-462.
29. J.A. Glasel, J.F. McKelvy, V.J. Hruby and A.F. Spatola, ibid., 222 (1973) 778-788.
30. J.A. Glasel, V.J. Hruby, J.F. McKelvy and A.F. Spatola, J. Mol. Biol., 79 (1973) 555-575.
31. J.B. Wooten and J.S. Cohen, Biochemistry, 18 (1979) 4188-4191.
32. R.A. Kinsey, A. Kintanar and E. Oldfield, J. Biol. Chem., 256 (1981) 9028-9036.
33. G.M. Gall, J.A. DiVerdi and S.J. Opella, J. Am. Chem. Soc., 103 (1981) 5039-5043.
34. I.C.P. Smith, R. Deslauriers, H. Saito, R. Walter, C. Garrigou-Lagrange, H. McGregor and D. Sarantakis, Ann. N.Y. Acad. Sci., 222 (1973) 597-627.
35. J.P. Meraldi and V.J. Hruby, J. Am. Chem. Soc., 98 (1976) 6408-6410.
36. M. Blumenstein, V.J. Hruby, D.M. Yamamoto and Y.C.S. Yang, FEBS Letters, 81 (1977) 347-356.
37. M. Blumenstein, in V.J. Hruby (Ed.), The Peptides:  Analysis, Synthesis, Biology, Vol. 7, Academic Press, San Diego, 1985, in press.
38. D. Peyton and E. Breslow, Biochem. Biophys. Res. Commun., 128 (1985) 1211-1218.
39. M. Blumenstein, V.J. Hruby, V. Viswanatha and D. Chaturvedi, Biochemistry, 23 (1984) 2153-2161.
40. M. Blumenstein, V.J. Hruby and V. Viswanatha, Biochem. Biophys. Res. Commun., 94 (1980) 431-437.

*Synthesis and Applications of Isotopically Labeled Compounds 1985.*
Proceedings of the Second International Symposium, Kansas City, MO, U.S.A.,
3—6 September 1985, R.R. Muccino (Ed.), 293—298

SPECIFIC RADIOACTIVITY DETERMINATIONS OF AMINO ACIDS AND PEPTIDES OF HIGH SPECIFIC ACTIVITY BY FAST ATOM BOMBARDMENT MASS SPECTROMETRY

W.D.Lehmann

Abteilung Medizinische Biochemie, Instiut für Physiologische Chemie,

Universitäts-Krankenhaus-Eppendorf, Martinistr. 52, D-2000 Hamburg 20,

(Fed.Rep.Germany)

ABSTRACT
    Amino acids and oligopeptides highly labelled with carbon-14 or hydrogen-3 have been analyzed for their specific radioactivity and for their label distribution by fast atom bombardment mass spectrometry. A sample amount in the order of one nanomole is required for a single analysis and the precision of the specific radioactivity determined in general is between 1 % and 5 %.

INTRODUCTION
    Specific radioactivity determination of biochemicals highly labelled with carbon-14 and hydrogen-3, respectively, has been performed by field desorption mass spectrometry for steroids (ref. 1), carbohydrates (ref. 2), amino acids (ref. 3), and for lipids (ref. 4). These determinations are characterized by a relatively moderate time consumption and a high precision, essentially identical to that obtained in mass spectrometric stable isotope dilution experiments. Compared to conventional specific activity determinations based on the combination of chromatography and radioactivity counting, the mass spectrometric results often show an increased precision and accuracy, as with this technique both labelled and nonlabelled species are detected by the same technique in a single analytical run. As an additional information besides the specific activity mass spectrometry also provides the label distribution.
    Being a soft ionization technique, field desorption (ref. 5) is particularly suited for these direct isotope determinations of biochemicals, as in general a substantial portion of the total ion current produced is carried by species containing the intact molecule, being either molecular ions or cationated molecules generated by attachment of protons or metal ions. In principle, the same arguments are in favour of fast atom bombardment (FAB) ionization (ref. 6), which has extended the mass spectrometric capabilities to extremely polar compounds and to compounds of several thousand mass units molecular weight. Specific radioactivity determinations of drugs and oligopeptides wih FAB mass spectrometry (MS) have been reported (ref. 7), and it has been demonstrated that quantitative field desorption and FAB determinations yield results identical within the error of the measurements (refs. 7,8). In the following, quantitative fast atom bombardment analyses of

radiolabelled amino acids and oligopeptides are presented aiming at a fast and accurate determination of their specific radioactivity.

## METHODS
### Radiochemicals

L-(u-$^{14}$C)Phenylalanine CFB.70 batch 107 was obtained from Amersham Int. (Buckinghamshire, UK), specific activity 18.65 GBq/mmol (= 504 mCi/mmol).

($^3$H)-Org 2766 (H-Met(O$_2$)-Glu-His-Phe-D-Lys-Phe-OH) was prepared by reaction of tritium gas with (Phe(I))$^4$-Org 2766 in the presence of Pd/C plus Pd/CaCO$_3$.

(Acetyl-$^3$H)-Org 30276, acetyl-D-Phe(4-Cl)D-Phe(4-Cl)-D-Trp-L-Ser-L-Tyr-D-Arg-L-Leu-L-Arg-L-Pro-D-Ala-NH$_2$, was prepared by reaction of the corresponding non-acetylated peptide with $^3$H-acetic anhydride of a specific activity of 262 GBq/mmol (= 7.1 Ci/mmol).

### Mass Spectrometry

Mass spectrometric measurements were performed with a double focusing instrument type VG ZAB-1F (VG Analytical, UK) equipped with a FAB source and saddle field atom gun (Ion Tech, UK) producing a xenon beam. The mass spectra were accumulated in a multichannel analyzer type Canberra series 80 and evaluated using a microcomputer type CBM 8032 interfaced to the multichannel analyzer. The spectra were documented via a graphic plotter type Hewlett Packard 7225A.

### RESULTS AND DISCUSSION

Ion production by fast atom bombardment has considerably expanded the mass range of compounds accessible by mass spectrometry. This ionization technique also produces relatively intense ion currents of polar compounds with molecular weights in the low mass range, however, at low masses interference with FAB matrix ions is much more pronounced than it is at m/z values around 1000 or higher. Using a double focusing instrument, in the low mass range this difficulty often can be overcome by a separation of analyte and matrix ions on the basis of their different accurate mass. Figure 1 gives such an example for the FAB analysis of L-Phe uniformally labelled with carbon-14 using thioglycerol as matrix. The mass spectrum in Figure 1a shows a strong overlap with respect to nominal masses of the protonated molecules of radiolabelled L-Phe and of thioglycerol matrix ions centered around m/z 181. Due to the incorporation of sulfur, the thioglycerol matrix ion species all are mass deficient relative to the phenylalanine ions, thus allowing their separate detection at moderate high resolution. After subtraction of the FAB matrix ions, a clear mass spectrum is obtained as given in Figure 1b, showing the

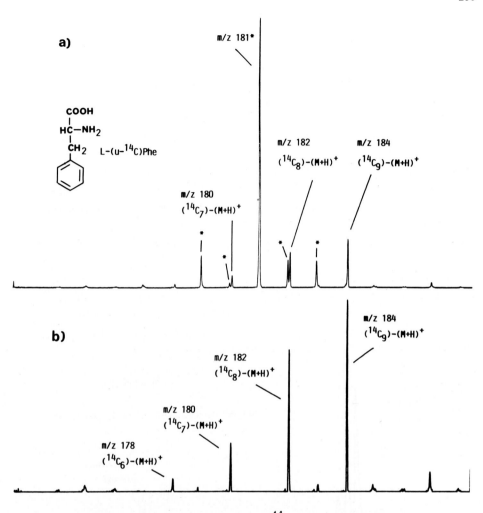

Fig. 1. Partial FAB mass spectrum of L-(u-$^{14}$C)Phe; matrix thioglycerol, sample amount ca. 700 ng corresponding to 80 kBq
( = ca. 2 uCi).
a) original spectrum, * thioglycerol matrix ion signals;
b) matrix ions subtracted from original spectrum.

TABLE 1
Calculation of specific activity of L-(u-$^{14}$C)Phe from the FAB mass
spectrum given in Figure 1.

| species | rel.abundance (%) | rel.specific activity (GBq/mmol) |
|---------|------------------|-----------------------------------|
| 14-C-6 | 3.4 | 0.471 |
| 14-C-7 | 12.0 | 1.939 |
| 14-C-8 | 36.1 | 6.666 |
| 14-C-9 | 48.5 | 10.074 |

specific activity (FAB MS)  = 19.150 (GBq/mmol) (= 517.6 mCi/mmol)
specific activity (specified) = 18.65  (GBq/mmol) (= 504  mCi/mmol)

presence of 6 to 9 carbon-14 atoms in the labelled L-Phe, the completely labelled species occurring with the highest relative abundance. The quantitative evaluation of this spectrum is given in Table 1, resulting in a specific activity of 19.15 GBq/mmol, a value being in good agreement to the specified value of 18.65 GBq/mmol.

The principle of direct isotope determination is also applicable for the analysis of labelled oligopeptides, as FAB MS in general produces abundant protonated molecules for this class of compounds. Figure 2 exemplifies such a determination for a tritiated hexapeptide, comparing the molecular isotopic patterns of the nonlabelled and of the labelled material. The FAB spectrum clearly shows, that the radiolabelled hexapeptide analyzed is a mixture of non-, mono-, and ditritiated material. The quantitative evaluation of this pattern results in an abundance of 39.1 % for the nonlabelled, of 58.1 % for the monotritiated, and of 2.8 % for the ditritiated species. From these abundances, a specific activity of 0.6778 TBq/mmol (= 18.32 Ci/mmol) is calculated. The additional signals in Figure 2b at m/z 882 and 884 indicate a reaction of the peptide with formaldehyde produced in the glycerol matrix during the FAB process (ref. 8), and the ion group from m/z 892-898 represents the overlap of $(M+Na)^+$ ions with other FAB reaction products.

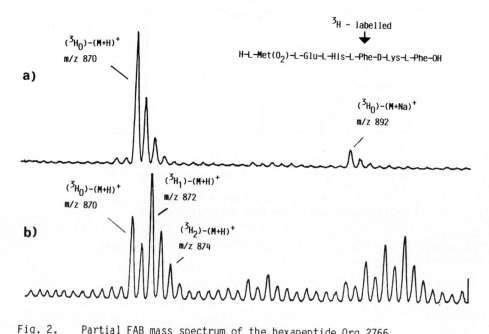

Fig. 2.    Partial FAB mass spectrum of the hexapeptide Org 2766,
           matrix thioglycerol/glycerol (ca. 1:1),
           a) nonlabelled Org 2766, sample amount ca. 5 ug,
           b) 3-H labelled Org 2766, sample amount ca. 1.5 ug corresponding
              to about 1.15 MBq (= ca. 30 uCi).

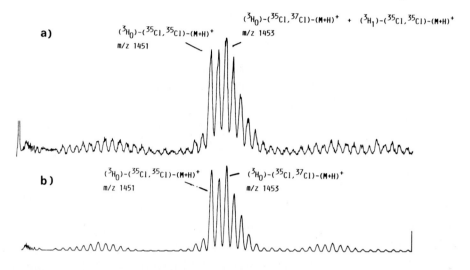

Fig. 3.  Partial FAB mass spectrum of the acetylated decapeptide Org 30276,
nominal monoisotopic molecular weight 1450, matrix glycerol.
a)  acetyl-(3-H)-Org 303276, sample amount ca. 1.5 ug corresponding
to about 170 kBq (= 4.6 uCi).
b)  nonlabelled acetyl-Org 30276, sample amount ca. 5 ug,

TABLE 2
Specific radioactivity determination of (acetyl-3-H)-Org 30276, evaluation of
three spectra.

| m/z | calc.ab. nonlabelled (%) | expt.ab. nonlabelled (%) | expt.ab. labelled pattern I | expt.ab. labelled pattern II | expt.ab. labelled pattern III |
|------|------|------|------|------|------|
| 1449 | - | 8.66 | 12.2 | 10.7 | 8.7 |
| 1450 | - | 14.72 | 18.0 | 13.4 | 15.2 |
| 1451 | 95.79 | 95.73 | 85.8 | 94.6 | 89.9 |
| 1452 | 82.26 | 86.07 | 81.0 | 80.4 | 89.9 |
| 1453 | 100 | 100 | 100 | 100 | 100 |
| 1454 | 65.57 | 66.99 | 72.6 | 71.4 | 82.6 |
| 1455 | 37.57 | 41.69 | 52.2 | 48.7 | 49.3 |
| 1456 | 17.13 | 19.83 | 30.0 | 30.4 | 28.3 |
| 1457 | 6.02 | 8.41 | 19.5 | 14.7 | 18.8 |
| 1458 | 1.68 | 3.60 | 12.4 | 7.1 | 7.3 |
| 1459 | 0.39 | 3.97 | - | - | - |

| species | rel.ab. I (%) | spec.act. (TBq/mmol) | rel.ab. II (%) | spec.act. (TBq/mmol) | rel.ab. III (%) | spec.act. (TBq/mmol) |
|------|------|------|------|------|------|------|
| 3-H-0 | 84.7 | 0 | 89.3 | 0 | 89.6 | 0 |
| 3-H-1 | 9.9 | 0.1053 | 4.2 | 0.0447 | 10.4 | 0.1107 |
| 3-H-2 | 5.2 | 0.1107 | 6.5 | 0.1383 | - | - |

| specific activity | 0.2160 | | 0.1830 | | 0.1107 |

The isotopic molecular pattern of a Cl-substituted decapeptide with nominal molecular weight of 1450 also produced by FAB MS is given in Figure 3, which compares the spectrum of the unlabelled peptide in Figure 3b with that of the tritiated peptide in Figure 3a. Due to the relatively low specific activity in this case, both spectra look very similar at the first glance, however, quantitative analysis of three different spectra as outlined in Table 2 reveals characteristic differences which allow an estimation of the specific activity. The average value obtained from three measuremts is 0.170 +- 0.05 TBq/mmol (= 4.6 +- 1.5 Ci/mmol). This is in reasonable agreemnent with the value of 0.131 TBq/mmol, as expected from the reaction of the peptide with ($^3$H)acetic anhydride with a specific activity of 0.262 TBq/mmol.

CONCLUSION

The accuracy of fast atom bombardment mass spectrometry for quantitative determinations may be influenced by the generally present "chemical noise" background ions or by specific FAB induced reactions between matrix and analyte. However, in many cases it is a powerful technique for a fast and accurate determination of the specific radioactivity of amino acids and oligopeptides highly labelled with hydrogen-3 or carbon-14.

ACKNOWLEDGEMENT

The two labelled oligopeptides presented were provided by Dr.F.Kaspersen, Organon, Oss, The Netherlands, which is gratefully acknowledged.

REFERENCES

1  H.R. Schulten, R. Müller, R.E. O'Brien, and N. Tzodikov, Fresenius Z. Anal. Chem., 302 (1980) 387-392.
2  L.J. Altman, R.E. O'Brien, S.K. Gupta, and H.R. Schulten, Carbohydr. Res., 87 (1980) 189-199.
3  H.R. Schulten and W.D. Lehmann, Biomed. Mass Spectrom., 7 (1980) 468-472.
4  W.D. Lehmann and M. Kessler. Fresenius Z. Anal. Chem., 312 (1982) 311-316.
5  H.R. Schulten, Int. J. Mass Spectrom. Ion Phys., 32 (1979) 97-283.
6  M. Barber, R.S.Bordoli, R.D. Sedgwick, and A.N. Tyler, J. Chem. Soc. Chem. Commun., 7 (1981) 325-327.
7  W.D. Lehmann and F.M. Kaspersen, J. Label. Comp. Radiopharm., 21 (1984) 455-469.
8  W.D. Lehmann, M. Kessler, and W.A. König, Biomed. Mass Spectrom., 11 (1984) 217-222.

*Synthesis and Applications of Isotopically Labeled Compounds 1985.*
Proceedings of the Second International Symposium, Kansas City, MO, U.S.A.,
3—6 September 1985, R.R. Muccino (Ed.), 299—304
© 1986 Elsevier Science Publishers B.V., Amsterdam — Printed in The Netherlands

# MEASUREMENT OF ENDOGENOUS PEPTIDES WITH MASS SPECTROMETRY AND $^{18}$O-LABELED PEPTIDES

D.M. DESIDERIO

Department of Neurology and The Charles B. Stout Neuroscience
Mass Spectrometry Laboratory, University of Tennessee Center for the Health
Sciences, 800 Madison Avenue, Memphis, Tennessee   38163

ABSTRACT

Endogenous biologically important neuropeptides have been measured in tissue extracts by utilizing mass spectrometry techniques. Internal standards used for this research include stable isotope-incorporated neuropeptides methionine enkephalin and leucine enkephalin. $^{18}$O is the stable isotope utilized and derives from $^{18}$O-labeled water. RP-HPLC is used to separate a peptide-rich fraction into its constituents; fast atom bombardment mass spectrometry produces a protonated molecular ion of the peptide; and linked-field methods select a structurally unique fragment ion for quantitation. Use of these methods provides the maximum level of molecular specificity for measuring peptides.

INTRODUCTION

The purpose of this paper is to describe a fast and facile preparation of stable isotope-incorporated peptide internal standards that have been used for quantification of endogenous HPLC-purified peptides by means of fast atom bombardment mass spectrometry (FAB-MS) (1). Chemical- and enzymatic-catalyzedsteps (2) are used for preparation of $^{18}$O-incorporated peptides where the stable isotope is exchanged for $^{16}$O atoms in the peptide carboxyl group. The stable isotope-incorporated peptides are used as internal standards for measurement of endogenous neuropeptides in biologic tissue extracts employing off-line combination of reversed phase high performance liquid chromatography (RP-HPLC) and FAB-MS (3). To avoid any isotope cross-contamination in the (M+H)$^{+}$ region of the mass spectrum, these internal standards are required to have a mass at least four mass units higher than that of the endogenous peptide. The overall objective of using these peptide internal standards is to measure endogenous peptides with the maximum level of molecular specificity. A comprehensive analytical scheme of measuring opioid peptides that uses a combination of four analytical techniques has been designed: (1) FAB-MS to produce a protonated molecular ion $(M+H)^+$ that can be measured directly, or that molecular ion can be studied in a linked-field scanning mode to provide amino acid sequence-determining information; (2) radioimmunoassay (RIA), which is based upon the specificity of an antibody for an antigen; (3) radioreceptor assay (RRA), which is based upon the affinity of a receptor for its ligand; (4) gradient RP-HPLC, which attaches a UV absorption to a retention time. It is the thesis of this laboratory that the latter three methods are highly sensitive and easy to use, but do not provide a sufficient level of structural ambiguity, whereas MS does.

The analytical methodologies described in the previous paragraph are being utilized in our research program that focuses on several peptidergic pathways including the enkephalinergic, endorphinergic, dynorphinergic, and substance P-ergic pathways. Each one of these peptide pathways consists of a larger precursor, intermediate precursors, the working peptide, and inactive metabolites. We study the metabolic relationships amongst the individual pathways as well as individual peptides in both the normal and stressed situation. Tissues studied include brain, tooth pulp, and cerebrospinal fluid.

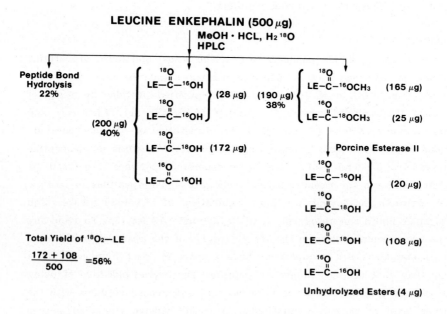

Fig. 1. Scheme for acid- and enzymatic-catalyzed incorporation of $^{18}O$ into leucine enkephalin.

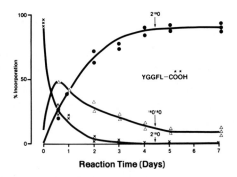

Fig. 2. Kinetic study of acid-catalyzed incorporation of two 18O atoms into leucine enkephalin free acid.

## METHODS

### $^{18}O$-incorporation

The pentapeptides methionine enkephalin and leucine enkephalin were esterified with methanolic HCl and $H_2^{18}O$ (Fig. 1). Solution equivalent to 6.7 μg enkephalin was removed at various incubation times (15 h, 1, 2, 3, 4, 5, and 7 days), and analyzed for the kinetics of stable isotope-incorporation by an off-line combination of RP-HPLC separation and MS. Leucine enkephalin kinetic data are given in Fig. 2.

Data for acid- and enzymatic-catalyzed $^{18}O$ incorporation into methionine enkephalin indicated that more peptide bond hydrolysis (35%), less acid-catalysis (32%), and much less enzyme-catalyzed $^{18}O_2$-incorporation (10%) occurs compared to leucine enkephalin.

### Reversed phase-high performance liquid chromatography

The HPLC system was from Waters Associates (two Model 6000A pumps, Model 660 solvent programmer, model U6K injector, and Model 450 variable wavelength detector). A microBondapack C-18 column (ten micron sphere) followed a guard column (Corasil, 37-50 microns). Typical chromatography conditions were: UV detector, 200 nm; flow rate, 1.5 ml min$^{-1}$; triethylamine-formic acid buffer (0.04 M, pH 3.15); organic modifier, acetonitrile. The volatile triethylamine-formic acid buffer was used in RP-HPLC when sample collection was required for subsequent MS, RRA, or RIA.

## Tissue acquisition

In our laboratory, canine brain tissue is procured rapidly. Temperature is lowered to avoid metabolic and/or chemical interconversions of precursors, neuropeptides of interest, and metabolites. Following exsanguination via a femoral artery, brain and other tissues (tooth pulp, pituitary) are removed. Various neuroanatomical regions are identified, excised, and placed in liquid nitrogen. The entire post-exsanguination procedures takes approximately 4 min.

## Mass spectrometry

Either a Varian MAT 731 or a VG 7070E-HF/11-250 MS is utilized in these studies. FAB uses xenon atoms (8kV). Either pure peptide standards, the 18O-incorporated peptide internal standard, or an HPLC-purified fraction is deposited in a methanol solution onto the FAB tip, and the methanol is evaporated. Several hundred nanoliters of glycerol are applied to the probe tip to redissolve the sample and prevent analyte damage.

## RESULTS AND DISCUSSION

MS clearly illustrates the incorporation of two $^{18}$O atoms into the pentapeptides methionine enkephalin and leucine enkephalin (1). FAB-collision activation-linked field (B/E) MS analysis of the enkephalin and the $^{18}O_2$-enkephalin unambiguously demonstrates that the two carboxy terminus oxygen atoms are the only two atoms which exchange the $^{18}$O atoms; no exchange occurs in the amide bonds or the N-terminal tyrosine hydroxy group. Figure 2 shows the kinetics of the incorporation of the two $^{18}$O atoms into the pentapeptide and indicate a leveling-off in $^{18}$O-incorporation following four days. Similar results were found for methionine enkephalin.

A microcomputer data acquisition useful for MS was developed, where a commercial microcomputer was interfaced to the 731 MS to facilitate the analytical measurement of these HPLC-purified endogenous brain peptides (4). This microcomputer increase the number of accumulated data points, which is an important factor to increase the accuracy and precision of the measurement of the endogenous peptide and also to eliminate operator error and fatigue.

Table 1 contains the analytical measurements of endogenous methionine enkephalin and leucine enkephalin in several biologic tissues by means of FAB-MS, and indicate a sensitivity at the part per billion level.

TABLE 1

Measurement of endogenous enkephalins by mass spectrometry
(ng enkephalin $g^{-1}$ or ng $ml^{-1}$)

| Method | Source | Peptide | Amount |
|---|---|---|---|
| FDMS-SIM | Hypothalamus | LE | 170 |
| | CSF | LE | 44 |
| FAB-CAD-(B/E, B'/E')- COM | Pituitary anterior | LE | 70 |
| | | ME | 2,970 |
| | posterior | LE | 2 |
| | | ME | 3,970 |
| | Caudate nucleus | LE | 50 |
| | Tooth pulp* | LE | 30 |
| | | ME | 170 |
| | Tooth pulp control | LE | 20 |
| | | ME | 487 |
| | electrostimulated | LE | 45 |
| | | ME | 390 |

*Unstimulated pooled tooth pulp tissue from five dogs.

CONCLUSIONS

Several conclusions drive from the use of this type of stable isotope-labeled peptide internal standard in a laboratory setting, where the concept of one laboratory performing several comprehensive analytical methodologies is undertaken.

Molecular specificities

The authors feel that FAB-CAD-B/E,B'/E'-SIM-COM methodology produces the optimum molecular specificity that can be obtained to date. This statement is the basic premise of this paper.

Sensitivity

Currently, the MS procedures described can be used to quantify endogenous peptides at the nanogram (generally the picomole) level, a sensitivity level not directly competitive with RIA. However, the MS procedures offer an incomparably higher level of molecular specificity (3). Nonetheless, for many biologic tissue extracts such as several brain regions and tooth pulp (Table 1), the level of the MS detection sensitivity is quite adequate for quantification of endogenous peptides. Furthermore computer techniques and negative ion MS techniques are currently under investigation and may offer higher levels of detection sensitivity to the femtomole level.

## MS versus RIA cost analysis

Up to now, many authors have stated the opinion that RIA is relatively cheap to perform compared to MS. However, if one considers the fact that one could purchase a $500,000 MS instrument, then one could obtain state-of-the-art molecular specificity and detection sensitivity and readily measure an endogenous peptide every ten minutes. Therefore, 48 analyses can be done in an eight-hour work-day; 96 in two shifts; and 144 in three shifts. An estimate for an RIA analysis is approximately $50.00 (a wide range exists here); thus one can then readily calculate that, in a few months, an entire mass spectrometer system is amortized.

## ACKNOWLEDGEMENTS

The authors gratefully acknowledge the financial assistance from NIH (GM 26666, GM 28611, RR 01651) and the typing assistance of Dianne Cubbins.

## REFERENCES

1    D.M. Desiderio and M. Kai, Biomed. Mass Spectrom. 10 (1983) 471-479.
2    W.C.  Pickett and R.C. Murphy, Anal. Biochem. 111 (1981) 115-121.
3    D.M. Desiderio, Analysis of Neuropeptides by Liquid Chromatography and Mass Spectrometry, Elsevier, Amsterdam, 1984, 235 pp.
4    D.M. Desiderio, J.S. Laughter, I. Katakuse, M. Kai, and J. Trimble, Comp. Enhanced Spectros. 2 (1984) 21-31.

*Synthesis and Applications of Isotopically Labeled Compounds 1985.*
Proceedings of the Second International Symposium, Kansas City, MO, U.S.A.,
3—6 September 1985, R.R. Muccino (Ed.), 305—306
© 1986 Elsevier Science Publishers B.V., Amsterdam — Printed in The Netherlands

# SYNTHESIS OF DOUBLE CARBON-14 LABELED CI-937, A POTENTIAL NEW ANTICANCER DRUG

JAMES L. HICKS, C. C. HUANG, and H. D. HOLLIS SHOWALTER

Chemistry Department, Warner-Lambert/Parke-Davis Pharmaceutical Research, Ann
Arbor, MI 48105

## ABSTRACT

CI-937, a potent anticancer agent, was synthesized with double labeled high
specific activity $^{14}$C.

## INTRODUCTION

The current strategy in our chemotherapy program is the search for a potent
broad spectrum anticancer compound with lower toxicity, especially cardio-
toxicity. CI-937 (7,10-Dihydroxy-2-[2-[(2-hydroxyethyl)amino]ethyl]-5-[[2-
(methylamino)ethyl]amino]anthra[1,9-cd]pyrazol-6(2H)-one) has shown such a
promise. It exhibits potent broad spectrum activity against a panel of
murine tumors. Because of the potency of this material it was desirable to
provide double labeled CI-937 with high specific activity $^{14}$C in a metabolically
stable position for pharmacokinetics and metabolism studies. The compound was
labeled with two $^{14}$C atoms as outlined in the following scheme:

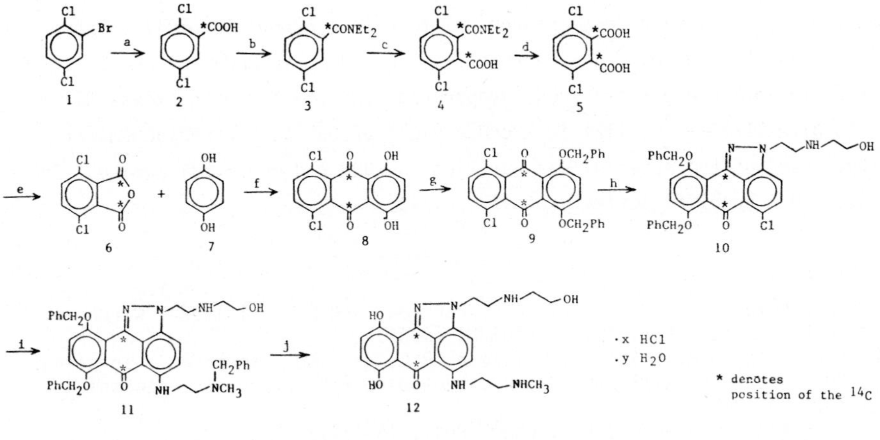

a) 1. n-BuLi, 2. $^{14}CO_2$, 3. H$^+$.   b) 1. SOCl$_2$, 2. HNEt$_2$.   c) 1. s-BuLi, TMEDA,
2. $^{14}CO_2$, 3. H$^+$.   d) 10% HClO$_4$.   e) AcCl, heat.   f) AlCl$_3$, NaCl.   g) PhCH$_2$Br,
Cs$_2$CO$_3$.   h) NH$_2$NH(CH$_2$)$_2$NH(CH$_2$)$_2$OH, ((CH$_3$)$_2$CH)$_2$NEt, DMA, THF.
i) NH$_2$CH$_2$CH$_2$N(CH$_2$Ph)CH$_3$.   j) 1. H$_2$, 20% Pd/C, AcOH, MeOH, 2. HCl/MeOH.

The original synthesis of unlabeled CI-937 begins with 1,4-dichloro-5,8-dihydroxy-9,10-anthracenedione and proceeds similarly as in the labeled synthesis. [1-$^{14}$C]1,3-Isobenzofurandione, an intermediate in the synthesis of 1,4-dihydroxy-5,8-dichloro-9,10-anthracenedione, was reported, but not applicable in our double labeled synthesis. We thus devised a synthetic route which allowed the sequential introduction of two $^{14}$C labels into CI-937. The first $^{14}$C was introduced by lithium-halogen exchange on 1 followed by carboxylation. The second label was incorporated by the use of amide-directed ortho lithiation and subsequent carboxylation. The following is a description of the synthesis:

To 1 in ether at -78°C was added 1 eq. of n-BuLi. The anion was treated with $^{14}$CO$_2$ (from 399 mCi of Ba$^{14}$CO$_3$ @ 58.3 mCi/mmol) at -78°C to give 2 (84%). The acid (2) was heated with SOCl$_2$ and DMF at 55°C for 3 h. The solution was concentrated and the residue was mixed with toluene and excess diethylamine at room temperature for 2.5 h. After chromatography, 3 (90%) was isolated. The amide (3) and TMEDA in ether was treated with s-BuLi below -75°C followed by addition of $^{14}$CO$_2$ (from 271 mCi of Ba$^{14}$CO$_3$ @ 52.2 mCi/mmol). After workup and crystallization from ether, 4 (72%) was obtained. A mixture of 4 and 10% HClO$_4$ was heated to reflux for 3 h. The diacid (5) was isolated and heated with excess AcCl. The resulting crude anhydride was sublimed to give 6 (81%). This was mixed with 7 in a NaCl-AlCl$_3$ melt at 180°-230°C for 90 min to produce 8 (55%). (Bromomethyl)benzene, Cs$_2$CO$_3$, and 8 in refluxing acetone gave 9 (91%). 9 was heated with 2-[(2-hydrazinoethyl)amino]ethanol, N,N-diisopropylethane-amine, KF, DMA, and THF at 90°C for 6 h to yield 10 (58%). A portion of 10 was treated with N-methyl-N-(phenylmethyl)-1,2-ethanediamine at 150°C for 3 h. The product was crystallized from isopropanol to give a 52% yield of 11. The material was deprotected under hydrogen with 20% Pd/C in MeOH and AcOH for 2 h. The reaction mixture was filtered, evaporated, and treated with excess HCl in MeOH to give CI-937-$^{14}$C$_2$ (12) in a crude yield of 69% at 93% radiochemical purity. Part of the material was purified to >98% radiochemical purity. The product had a specific activity of 172 uCi/mg.

## REFERENCES

1 H.D.H. Showalter, L.M. Werbel, J.L. Johnson, and E.F. Elslager, Warner-Lambert Co., Eur. Pat. Appl. EP103381, 1984.
2 W.R. Leopold, J.M. Nelson, J. Plowman, R.C. Jackson, Cancer Res. in press.
3 A. Murry and D.L. Williams, Organic Synthesis with Isotopes, Interscience, (1958) 439, 898.
4 P. Beak and V. Snieckus, Acc. Chem. Res., 15 (1982) 306-312.
5 K. Zahn, Methoden Der Organischen Chemie, 3, Georg Thieme Verlag, Stuttgart (1979) 97.

*Synthesis and Applications of Isotopically Labeled Compounds 1985.*
Proceedings of the Second International Symposium, Kansas City, MO, U.S.A.,
3—6 September 1985, R.R. Muccino (Ed.), 307—308
© 1986 Elsevier Science Publishers B.V., Amsterdam — Printed in The Netherlands

SELECTIVE REAGENTS FOR CARBON-14 RADIOSYNTHESIS OF ADVANCED CHEMICAL

INTERMEDIATES

David J Lester - Labelled Compounds, ICI Physics and Radioisotope

Services, PO Box 1, Billingham, Cleveland, ENGLAND

ABSTRACT

Reagents suitable for small scale organic synthesis are often suitable for
radiochemical synthesis. Reagents reacting via radical pathways are less
predictable than electronic reagents. Two useful reagents routinely used in
our radiochemical syntheses are benzeneseleninic anhydride and
trifluoromethyl iodide. Their successful radiochemical reactions are
described.

Benzeneseleninic anhydride (ref.1)

$$Ph - Se - O - Se - Ph$$

This reagent is available commercially and used for a variety of oxidation

reactions. Of particular interest is the oxidation of aromatic alcohols to

aldehydes, where treatment of the alcohol in THF at 20-80°C with the anhydride

affords the aldehyde in quantitative yield. In the absence of oxygen, no

further oxidation to the corresponding acid is observed. The reaction has been

successfully applied to a large variety of aromatic substrates.

Benzeneseleninic anhydride is an extremely versatile oxidant. Two other areas

of important radiochemical application have been in the regeneration of

ketones from their hydrazones and oximes, and in the oxidation of ketones to

enones. The results are summarised in table 1.

TABLE 1

Reactions of benzeneseleninic anhydride applied to radiochemical synthesis

| SUBSTRATE | PRODUCT | MOLE ANHYDRIDE | SOLVENT | TIME H | YIELD % |
|---|---|---|---|---|---|
| $PhCH_2OH$ | PhCHO | 2 | PhH | 0.3 | 99.5 |
| $p-NO_2C_6H_4CH_2OH$ | $p-NO_2C_6H_4CHO$ | 0.5 | PhH | 0.12 | 97 |
| $p-MeOC_6H_4CH_2OH$ | $p-MeOC_6H_4CHO$ | 0.5 | PhH | 0.25 | 99 |
| PhCHOHPh | PhCOPh | 1 | THF | 3 | 85 |
| Lanostanone | 1-enone | 1 | PhCl | 0.75 | 67 |
| Cholest-4-en-3-one | 1, 4-dienone | 1 | PhCl | 0.7 | 92 |
| Hecogenin Acetate | 9 (11)-enone | 2 | PhCl | 0.9 | 91 |
| Benzophenone phenylhydrazone | Benzophenone | 1 | THF | 3 | 90 |
| Benzophenone tosylhydrazone | Benzophenone | 1 | THF | 0.3 | 95 |
| Benzophenone oxime | Benzophenone | 1 | THF | 3 | 89 |

## Methods of Introducing the Trifluoromethyl Group

The most obvious method for preparing the trifluoromethyl derivatives is from the corresponding acid by treatment with $SF_4$ and HF (ref.2). We have successfully used this route to prepare [3-14C] 3-trifluoromethyl pyridine in 85% yield. The reagents necessitate using high pressure and corrosion resistant apparatus and are not generally applicable to small scale work.

We investigated the copper catalysed introduction of trifluoromethyl groups from trifluoromethyl iodide (ref.3). After a series of mechanistic studies in a similar system, we believe this reaction to be ionic in nature. Our first target molecule was [U-14C] p-aminobenzotrifluoride which we obtained in 60% yield from p-iodoacetanilide by treatment with a four fold excess of trifluoromethyl iodide, at 120°C for 16h in pyridine/acetonitrile 1:4, in the presence of an excess of finely divided copper. The reaction has been applied to a variety of aromatic substrates, the solvent being the most critical parameter in ensuring high yields. A summary is given in Scheme 1.

Scheme 1

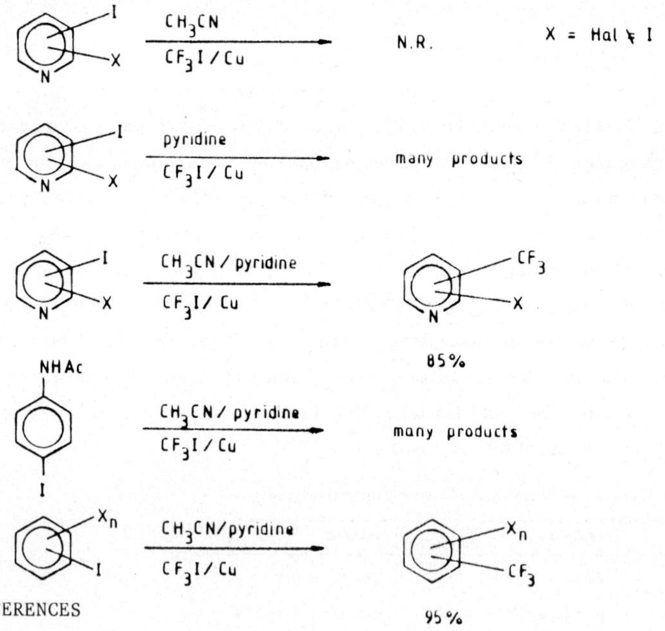

REFERENCES

1. S.V. Ley, "Seleninic Anhydrides and Acids in Organic Synthesis". In Press.
2. G.A. Boswell, Jr., W.C. Ripka, R.M. Scribner, and C.W. Tullock, Organic Reactions 21, 1, (1974).
3. J Lindley, Tetrahedron, 40, 1433, (1984).

*Synthesis and Applications of Isotopically Labeled Compounds 1985.*
Proceedings of the Second International Symposium, Kansas City, MO, U.S.A.,
3—6 September 1985, R.R. Muccino (Ed.), 309—310
© 1986 Elsevier Science Publishers B.V., Amsterdam — Printed in The Netherlands

STRATEGIC CONSIDERATIONS IN THE RADIOSYNTHESIS OF SUBSTITUTED 1-PHENYL-2,3,4,5-TETRAHYDRO-1H-3-BENZAZEPINE-7,8-DIOLS

Dale Blackburn, Anthony Villani, Steve Senderoff, Scott Landvatter and Keith Garnes, Smith Kline and French Laboratories, 1500 Spring Garden Street, Philadelphia, PA 19101

ABSTRACT

We initiated the labeling of substituted 1-phenyl-2,3,4,5-tetrahydro-1H-3-benzazepine-7,8-diols for the further development of the dopaminergic agents SK&F 38393 (1), SK&F 82526 (2) and SK&F 85174 (4). The compounds (1-2, D-3 and 4) were tagged with carbon-14 and tritium for the determination of metabolic profiles, pharmacokinetic studies and receptor binding studies.

SK&F 38393 (1), 1-Phenyl-2,3,4,5-tetrahydro-1H-3-benzazepine-7,8-diol, was identified as a lead compound of a series of 3-benzazepines having dopamine (DA) agonist activity with selectivity for the adenylate cyclase modulated D-1 subtypes of DA receptors.

1, R=R'=X=H; Ar=$C_6H_5$

2, R=R'=H; X=Cl; Ar=4-$HOC_6H_5$

3, R=R'=$CH_3$; X=H; Ar=$C_6H_5$

4, R=H; R'= $CH_2CH=CH_2$; X=Cl; Ar=4-$HOC_6H_5$

The most desirable tagging location from a metabolic standpoint was carbon-1 between the two benzene rings. Labeling of the styrene oxide radiochemical intermediate was precluded because of the low variable yields experienced in the preparation of cold amino alcohol 8a. It was decided that 2-bromo-1-phenyl-ethanol-1-$^{14}$C (7a) was capable of giving better yields and could be prepared from the relatively cheap sodium acetate-1-$^{14}$C in 3 steps. The labeled bromohydrin 7a was condensed with N-benzylhomoveratrylamine (5a) and the N-benzyl protective group was removed by catalytic hydrogenation to give 8a. Cyclization and demethylation were carried out in refluxing hydrogen bromide to give SK&F [$^{14}$C] 38393 (1) in 43% overall yield from 7a. Carbon-14 labeling of 6-chloro-1-(4'-hydroxyphenyl)-2,3,4,5-1H-3-benzazepine-7,8-diols. In an intense effort to develop an economic synthesis of Fenoldopam (SK&F 82526), a number of alternate routes became accessible. Ultimately a route similar to that applied to SK&F [$^{14}$C] 38393 was chosen. The hydroxy group of 2-bromo-1-(4'-methoxyphenyl)-ethanol-1-$^{14}$C was protected with the tetrahydropyranyl group (7b) for the following coupling step with chlorohomoveratrylamine (5c). The protective group was removed with dilute acid and the resulting uncyclized amino alcohol 8b (SK&F [$^{14}$C] 87179) was readily purified by crystallization. This intermediate was

(* Denotes position of C-14 label)

a. H⁺; b. H₂; c. NaBH₄; d. 48% HBr; e. CH₃SO₃H;
f. TFA/H₂SO₄; g. Allyl Bromide/Et₃N; h. BBr₃; i. (+)DBTA

REACTION SCHEME

also used to prepare the N-allylbenzazepine 4 (SK&F [$^{14}$C] 85174). Cyclization of SK&F [$^{14}$C] 87179 was effected with methanesulfonic acid or trifluoroacetic acid (TFA) in sulfuric acid. The resulting trimethyl ether was demethylated with boron tribromide to give [$^{14}$C] Fenoldopam (2) or alkylated with allyl bromide followed by demethylation to give SK&F [$^{14}$C] 85174 (4). The major metabolites of Fenoldopam in dog and rat were the 7,8-phenolic sulfates, 7-glucouronide and the 7 & 8 methyl ethers.  D-1-Phenyl-7,8-dimethoxy-3-methyl-2,3,4,5-tetrahydro-1H-3-benzazepine. In order to compare the absorption characteristics and pharmacokinetics of Fenoldopam with the trimethyl D-3, the labeled compound was prepared by the reaction of α-bromoacetophenone-1-$^{14}$C(6) with N-methylveratrylamine (5b). The ketone group was reduced with sodium borohydride to give 8c followed by cyclization to give D-3 after resolution with D(+) dibenzoyltartaric acid.  Tritium Labeling of SK&F 38393 and Fenoldopam. In order to characterize the dopamine D1 receptors in a saturation and competitive binding assay, a HSA tritium label was required for SK&F 38393 and the racemic and R-enantiomer of Fenoldopam. The SK&F [$^3$H] 38393 was prepared by the dehalogenative tritiation of 1-(4'-chlorophenyl)-2,3,4,5-tetrahydro-1H-3-benzazepine-7,8-diol. The [$^3$H] rac-Fenoldopam was prepared by the dehalogenative tritiation of the 3'-bromo analog and the SK&F R-[$^3$H] 82526 was prepared from the 3',5'-diiodo analog. The highest specific activity achieved was 23 Ci/mmol. A five-fold excess of tritium (50 Ci) was necessary to remove starting haloprecursors. Preliminary cold studies with selective dehalogenation showing insignificant removal of the 6-chloro group were confirmed in the tritiation reactions.

*Synthesis and Applications of Isotopically Labeled Compounds 1985.*
Proceedings of the Second International Symposium, Kansas City, MO, U.S.A.,
3—6 September 1985, R.R. Muccino (Ed.), 311—312

# RADIOCHEMICAL AND ENZYMATIC SYNTHESES OF THE COENZYME A ESTER OF 2-TETRADECYLGLYCIDIC ACID

L.E. WEANER and D.C. HOERR

Department of Chemical Development, McNeil Pharmaceutical, Spring House,
Pennsylvania  19477 (USA)

## ABSTRACT

The synthesis of the coenzyme A (CoA) ester of carbon-14-labeled
R,S-2-tetradecylglycidic acid (TDGA-$^{14}$C) was investigated using chemical
and enzymatic methods. TDGA-$^{14}$C, labeled in the tetradecyl hydrocarbon
chain, was converted to TDGA-$^{14}$C-CoA by formation of the acid chloride with
oxalyl chloride followed by reaction with CoA. Enzymatic synthesis in a rat
hepatic microsomal mixture provided TDGA-CoA with an enantiomeric composition
of 16:1, R:S, (88% ee) and demonstrates a previously unreported stereoselectivity of the coenzyme A synthetase for chiral fatty acids. Stability of the
TDGA-$^{14}$C-CoA and the relationship between _in vitro_ biological activity and
chemical purity are reported.

## INTRODUCTION

Fatty acid analog sodium 2-tetradecylglycidate (TDGA) is a potent hypo-
glycemic agent in animals and man (ref.1a). Previous research has shown TDGA
to be a specific inhibitor of long chain fatty acid oxidation. In order to
study the mechanism of action, a sample of carbon-14-labeled TDGA-CoA was
prepared.

## RESULTS AND DISCUSSION

The synthesis of racemic TDGA-$^{14}$C-CoA was investigated using both
enzymatic and chemical procedures. Enzymatic synthesis employing an isolated
rat hepatic microsomal mixture was examined using tracer amounts of
TDGA-$^{14}$C. A decrease in reaction rate after 50% reaction was determined to
be due to selectivity of the CoA synthetase for the R enantiomer. Kinetic
studies utilizing the resolved enantiomers* showed that the R enantiomer
reacted at a rate approximately ten times faster than the S enantiomer.
TDGA-CoA isolated from an enzymatic reaction mixture was shown to have an
enantiomeric composition of 16:1, R:S (88% ee) by hydrolysis, derivatization

and HPLC analysis (ref.1a). Experimental conditions for the reactions were: 3μmol TDGA, 1.0 eq. CoA, magnesium adenosine triphosphate, tris(hydroxymethyl)aminomethane adjusted to pH 7.4, Triton X-100$^{TM}$, 37°C, 2 h.

Pilot reactions with CoA and TDGA-acid chloride (prepared by the reaction of dry sodium TDGA with oxalyl chloride, ref.2) showed that the optimum reactant ratio is a 15 fold excess of TDGA-acid chloride. This result is in contrast to the literature which utilized 0.33 equivalents of labeled acid chloride to synthesize palmitoyl-$^{14}$C-CoA (ref.2a). Excess TDGA was also required to obtain acceptable yields when TDGA-CoA was prepared via the N-hydroxysuccinimide ester.

Racemic TDGA-$^{14}$C-CoA was synthesized from TDGA-$^{14}$C-acid chloride (54 mCi/mmol) labeled in the tetradecyl hydrocarbon chain (ref.2). The labeled TDGA-acid chloride was prepared from 1-bromotetradecane-1-$^{14}$C. Excess TDGA-$^{14}$C (15X) used in the reaction was recovered by extraction during workup.

Radiochemical purity of the labeled CoA ester decreased at a rate of 3-5% per month when stored as a dry crystalline solid at -20°C. In vitro biological activity (ref.1) of the TDGA-CoA ester decreased exponentially as chemical purity decreased.* Samples with purities of less than 85-90% showed significantly reduced biological activity.

REFERENCES

1 T.C. Kiorpes, D.C. Hoerr, W. Ho, L.E. Weaner, M.G. Inman, and G.F. Tutwiler, J. of Biol. Chem., 259(15) (1984) 9750-9755. a. See references in ref.1.
2 L.E. Weaner and D.C. Hoerr, J. Labeled Compd. Radiopharm., In press. a. See references in ref.2.

---

*The authors thank Dr. W. Ho for providing samples of the resolved TDGA enantiomers and Dr T.C. Kiorpes for performing the biological assays.

*Synthesis and Applications of Isotopically Labeled Compounds 1985.*
Proceedings of the Second International Symposium, Kansas City, MO, U.S.A.,
3—6 September 1985, R.R. Muccino (Ed.), 313—314
© 1986 Elsevier Science Publishers B.V., Amsterdam — Printed in The Netherlands

SYNTHESIS OF CARBON-14 LABELED CI-930, A POTENTIAL NEW CARDIOTONIC AGENT

SHERYL J. HAYS and JAMES L. HICKS

Chemistry Department, Warner-Lambert/Parke-Davis Pharmaceutical Research, Ann Arbor, MI   48105

ABSTRACT

CI-930, a potent new cardiotonic agent, was $^{14}C$ labeled in nine steps at a specific activity of 106.8 mCi/mmol starting from $[^{14}C]BaCO_3$.

INTRODUCTION

CI-930, 4,5-dihydro-6-[4-(1H-imidazol-1-yl)phenyl]-5-methyl-3(2H)-pyridazin-one hydrochloride, is a nonsympathomimetic cardiotonic agent, which is presently in clinical trials.  An $ED_{50}$ value was calculated for CI-930 from the linear portion of its dose-response curve and found to be 0.013 mg/kg in the dog.[1]  Due to this high potency, double-labeled carbon-14 material of specific activity greater than 100 mCi/mmol was required for pharmacokinetic and drug metabolism studies.  Previous synthetic routes to unlabeled CI-930 and the need for a metabolically-stable label suggested that the two labeled carbons be placed in the pyridazinone ring.

RESULTS AND DISCUSSION

The synthesis of $[^{14}C]CI-930$ was completed in nine steps as shown below.

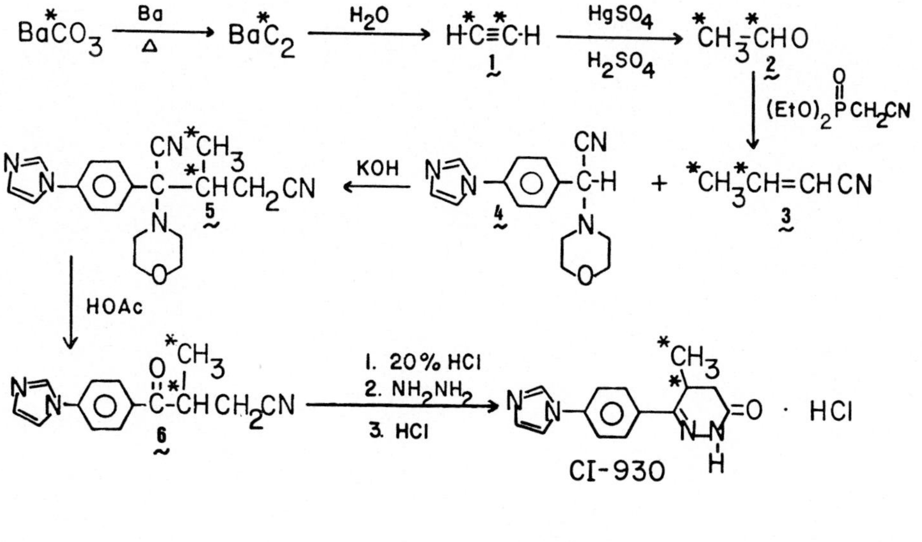

Carbon-14 labeled barium carbonate was mixed with barium filings and fused at high temperature to form barium carbide. Treatment of the carbide with water according to the method of Cox and Warne[2] produced a 92% yield of [1,2-$^{14}$C] acetylene (1). Mercuric sulfate in aqueous sulfuric acid was added to the labeled acetylene (1) and heated to 100°C for 25 minutes. Aqueous [1,2-$^{14}$C] acetaldehyde (2) was isolated by distillation in a 92% radiochemical yield.[3] In a modified Wittig-Horner reaction employing phase transfer conditions,[4] the labeled acetaldehyde (2) and diethylcyanomethyl phosphonate were combined to produce [3,4-$^{14}$C]2-butenenitrile (3) in 72% yield. Addition of the alkene 3 to 2-[4-(1H-imidazol-1-yl)-phenyl]-4-morpholineacetonitrile (4) in the presence of a catalytic amount of potassium hydroxide resulted in an 87% yield of Michael product 5. Aqueous acetic acid hydrolysis produced the ketone 6 in 95% yield. The cyano compound 6 was further hydrolyzed in 20% hydrochloric acid to yield the carboxylic acid, which was treated directly with hydrazine at pH 5 to form the pyridazinone ring. After silica gel chromatography, the free base of CI-930 was isolated in a combined 42% yield for the two steps. Conversion to the hydrochloride salt proceeded quantitatively. [$^{14}$C]CI-930 was greater than 98% radiochemically pure and had a specific activity of 106.8 mCi/mmol.

REFERENCES

1  J.A. Bristol, Ila Sircar, W.H. Moos, D.B. Evans, and R.E. Weishaar, J. Med. Chem., 27 (1984) 1101.
2  J.D. Cox and R.J. Warne, J. Chem. Soc., (1951) 1893.
3  R.D. Cramer and G.B. Kistiakowsky, J. Biol. Chem., 137 (1951) 549.
4  C. Piechucki, Synthesis, 12 (1974) 869.

*Synthesis and Applications of Isotopically Labeled Compounds 1985.*
Proceedings of the Second International Symposium, Kansas City, MO, U.S.A.,
3—6 September 1985, R.R. Muccino (Ed.), 315
© 1986 Elsevier Science Publishers B.V., Amsterdam — Printed in The Netherlands

SYNTHESIS OF ALL-TRANS-RETINOIC-[10,11-$^{14}$C$_2$]-ACID

S. W. RHEE and H. H. KAEGI

Bio-Organic Chemistry Laboratory, SRI International, 333 Ravenswood Avenue,

Menlo Park, CA 94025 (USA)

The synthetic path used for the labeling of all-trans-retinoic acid with carbon-14 is shown in Scheme 1. Carbon-14 was placed into positions 10 and 11 of the side chain by a combination of well-known reaction steps. The procedure is partly an adaptation of the commercial manufacturing method developed by Pommer (Angew. Chem. 72, 811-819, 1960). From 250 mCi of barium carbonate-$^{14}$C, acetylene-$^{14}$C was prepared and then transformed into the monobromomagnesium acetylide-$^{14}$C$_2$ (1) with the aid of magnesium ethylbromide. Treatment of β-ionone (2) with the acetylide 1 gave ethynyl-$^{14}$C$_2$-β-ionol (3). Even though yields as high as 60-70% were obtained in cold runs the reaction using labeled material yielded 3 only in 29% overall yield. The ethynyl-$^{14}$C$_2$-β-ionol (3) was diluted with some inactive material and then partially reduced to vinyl-$^{14}$C$_2$-β-ionol (4). Treatment of (4) with triphenylphosphine-hydrobromide in methanol gave the phosphonium salt (5). Reaction with sodium methoxide in methanol furnished the intermediate β-C$_{15}$-phosphorane, which in the presence of trans-β-formyl-crotonic acid (6) and excess base, gave a mixture of labeled 11-cis- and all-trans-retinoic acid. Isomerization with the aid of iodine then gave the all-trans-retinoic-[10,11-$^{14}$C$_2$]-acid (7), which was purified by recrystallization from ethanol. A total of 31.8 mg (6.3 mCi) of 7, with a specific activity of 59.8 mCi/mmol (199 μCi/mg) and a radiopurity of 94%, was obtained. The acid portion contained 2.7% of 13-cis-retinoic-[10,11-$^{14}$C$_2$]-acid (for a total retinoic acid content of 96.7%).

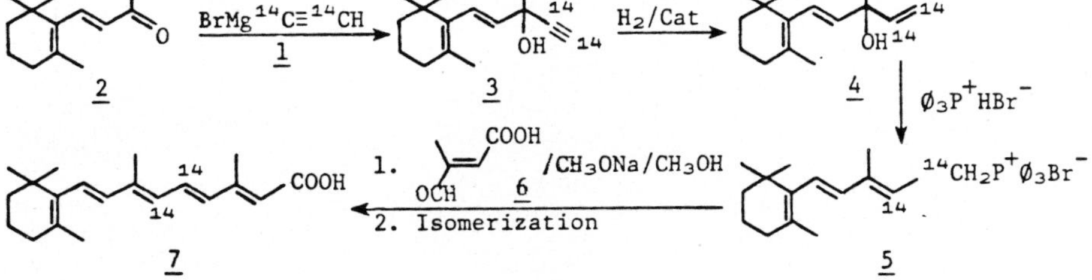

Scheme 1

*Synthesis and Applications of Isotopically Labeled Compounds 1985.*
Proceedings of the Second International Symposium, Kansas City, MO, U.S.A.,
3—6 September 1985, R.R. Muccino (Ed.), 317—318
© 1986 Elsevier Science Publishers B.V., Amsterdam — Printed in The Netherlands

SYNTHESIS OF RADIOLABELED HERBICIDES FOR ENVIRONMENTAL FATE STUDIES

W. B. BURTON, T. D. HOEWING and M. V. NAIDU

Shell Development Co., BSRC, P. O. Box 4248, Modesto, California 95352 (USA)

ABSTRACT

Cinmethylin, (+)-exo-1-methyl-4-(1-methylethyl)-2-(2-methylphenylmethoxy)-
-7-oxabicyclo(2.2.1)heptane, is a new soil applied herbicide which provides
excellent control of grassy weeds in soybeans and other crops. To facilitate
the development and evaluation, carbon-14 labeled cinmethylin and two of its
analogues were prepared for use in tracer studies. The methods of purification
and characterization are given.

INTRODUCTION

The use of radiolabeled compounds to study the environmental fate of
agricultural chemicals has found widespread acceptance. Radiochemicals provide
required sensitivity to detect the residues of very low concentration (parts
per billion). Such sensitivity demands that the radiochemical substrate must
meet high standards of chemical and radiochemical purity.

Cinmethylin, (+)-exo-1-methyl-4-(1-methylethyl)-2-(2-methylphenylmethoxy)-
-7-oxabicyclo(2.2.1)heptane (IIIa) is a new soil applied herbicide discovered
by Shell Development Company which provides excellent control of grassy weeds
in soybeans and other crops. This product is registered under the trademark
CINCH® Herbicide. Radiolabeled samples of this herbicide and two analogues
(IIIb and IIIc) were needed to study degradation, metabolism, comparative
evaluation and the mode of biological action. This report describes the
radiosynthesis and purification of IIIa, IIIb and IIIc labeled with carbon-14
in the phenyl ring.

SCHEME 1

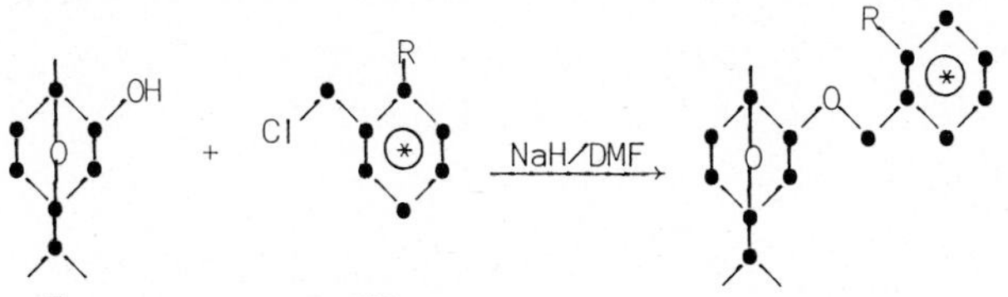

| | II | | III | |
|---|---|---|---|---|
| I | a) R = CH₃ | | a) R = CH₃ | |
| | b) R = F | | b) R = F | |
| | c) R = H | | c) R = H | |

MATERIALS AND METHODS

2-Substituted benzyl chlorides (ring-U-$^{14}$C) were purchased from New England Nuclear Corporation, Boston, MA. The exo-2-hydroxy-1,4-cineole was prepared according to the procedure described by G. B. Payne (ref.1).

## Synthesis of $^{14}$C-Cinmethylin (IIIa) and its Analogues (IIIb an IIIc)

Alkylation of exo-2-hydroxy-1,4-cineole with ring labeled 2-substituted benzyl chlorides (Scheme 1) provided radiolabeled IIIa, IIIb and IIIc. The following is the typical experimental procedure of alkylation. Into a dry 10 ml pear shaped flask fitted with a cold finger and drying tube was placed 86 mg sodium hydride (50% suspension in mineral oil). The sodium hydride suspension was washed two times with dry hexane followed by dry DMF. (The washings were removed by means of a filter stick.) 292.4 mg of I and 500 ul of dry DMF were added to the reaction flask. The reaction mixture was stirred for one hour at room temperature, then 30 minutes at 80°C. After cooling, 243 mg of $^{14}$C-2-methylbenzyl chloride (15.8 mCi, specific activity 9.1 mCi/mmol) in 500 ul of DMF was added in portions. The reaction was stirred for one hour at 20°C and 30 min at 50°C. 3 ml of water was added and pH was adjusted to 7.0 with 5N HCl. Extraction with hexane (3 ml x 7) yielded IIIa with radiochemical purity of about 80%. The crude compound was purified by preparative thin-layer chromatography (TLC) using solvent system toluene:ethyl acetate (4:1). The second TLC purification of this material in heptane: dioxane (4:1) afforded 6 mCi with a radiochemical purity of 98.5%. The structure of IIIa was further confirmed by GC/MS.

A similar alkylation of I with 16 mCi of 2-fluorobenzyl chloride (IIb) provided 12.5 mCi of IIIb in a yield of 78%. Purification by TLC in methylene chloride:hexane:ethyl acetate (3:6:1) yielded 9.2 mCi with 98.7% radiochemical purity. The product was rechromatographed, developing twice in heptane:dioxane (4:1) to yield 7.9 mCi of IIIb with a purity of >99%.

5 mCi of $^{14}$C-benzyl chloride (IIc) was used to obtain 4.3 mCi of desmethyl analogue IIIc. TLC purification of the compound in toluene:ethyl acetate (4:1) solvent system provided 1.6 mCi with a radiochemical purity of 98.9%. The second purification in hexane:CH$_2$Cl$_2$:ether (6:3:1) yielded 1 mCi of 99.7% purity.

REFERENCES

1 (a) G. B. Payne, U.S.A. Patent 4,487,945 (to Shell Development Company, 12/11/84).

*Synthesis and Applications of Isotopically Labeled Compounds 1985.*
Proceedings of the Second International Symposium, Kansas City, MO, U.S.A.,
3—6 September 1985, R.R. Muccino (Ed.), 319—324
© 1986 Elsevier Science Publishers B.V., Amsterdam — Printed in The Netherlands

# A CONVENIENT SYNTHESIS AND ANALYSIS OF ISOTOPICALLY LABELED ALKALI METAL CYANIDES

Bánfi D. and Mlinkó S.

Central Research Institute for Chemistry, Hungarian Academy

of Sciences, Budapest H-1525 POB 17

The production of $^{14}CO_2$ in nuclear reactors and the laboratory conversion of $^{14}CO_2$ and its $Ba^{14}CO_3$ salt to alkali metal
cyanides constitutes a significant and exciting part of the
history of radio-carbon chemistry. From the earliest time up
to now a great number of papers have been published (1-12)
clearly indicating the importance of these investigations.
Recent papers also point to the significance and necessity of
a reliable and convenient synthesis of alkali cyanides labeled
with $^{11}C$-, $^{13}C$, and $^{15}N$-isotopes (21-25).

At the end of the fifties a practical gas-catalytic one-line
synthesis for preparing $^{14}C$-labeled alkali metal cyanides was
developed by us. The method is based on the consecutive reac-
tion $^{14}CO_2 \longrightarrow {}^{14}CH_4 \longrightarrow H^{14}CN$. On the occasion of the 25th
anniversary of introducing this process now we report on
some details and the most important parameters of the improved method and equipment, which have not been published yet.
The improved method is based on the following reaction scheme:

1. $3Ba^{14}CO_3 + 3FeCl_3 + H_2O \xrightarrow{20-80°C} 2BaCl_2 + Fe(OH)_3 + 3{}^{14}CO_2$

$FeCl_3 + H_2O \longrightarrow 3HCl + Fe(OH)_3$ primer step

2. $^{14}CO_2 + 4H_2 \xrightarrow[350°C]{Ni} {}^{14}CH_4 + 2H_2O$

3. $^{14}CH_4 + NH_3 \xrightarrow[1150°C]{Pt} H^{14}CN/NH_4{}^{14}CN + 3H_2$

4. $H^{14}CN/NH_4{}^{14}CN + KOH \longrightarrow K^{14}CN + NH_3 + H_2O$

Figure 1

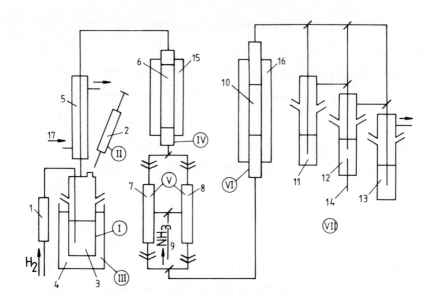

Fig. 1 System for the synthesis of high purity alkali cyanides labeled with $^{14}C$-isotope (laboratory equipment).
1, hydrogen flow-meter (350 mL/min.); 2, hypodermic syringe,
3, reaction vessel; 4, temperature regulated water bath, 5,
condenser; 6, Ni catalyst; 7, 8, drying towers packed with
KOH pellets; 9, ammonia inlet (150 mL/min); 10, quartz reactor tube containing 6.5 g (8.0x0.6 cm) rolled platinum gauze;

11, 12, 13, absorption train containing 3x5 mL of 0.4 M
ethanolic alkali hydroxide; 14, sensor electrode or GM-tube
in the indicator vessel; 15, resistance heater; 16, infra
heater; 17, cooling water.

Procedure:

I.   $Ba^{14}CO_3$ samples are weighed into the reaction vessel
     suspended in 0.5 ml of water.

II.  $FeCl_3$ solution (7 ml of 0.5 M $FeCl_3$, 2.5-fold excess)
     is added to the carbonate (see reaction 1).

III. The mixture is gradually heated. Temperature programming:
     20-60-80$^{o}$C for 3x5 minutes. Longer heating favours the
     formation of $Fe(OH)_3$ precipitate. The $CO_2$ concentration
     of the gas stream must be controlled in order to drive
     the $CO_2/CH_4$ conversion toward completion.

IV.  Conversion of carbon oxides to methane and water with
     hydrogen over a nickel catalyst (see reaction 2).

V.   The gases are dried over potassium hydroxide pellets and
     ammonia is introduced into the drying tower.

VI.  Conversion of methane to hydrogen/ammonium cyanides over
     a platinum catalyst (see reaction 3).

VII. The ammonium cyanide is trapped in the absorption
     vessels containing known quantities of a standard alkali
     hydroxide solution. The ethanol and the water produced
     by the reaction in the first absorber are removed and
     the remaining product is evaporated to dryness for use
     in the next synthesis. The ammonium cyanide dissolved
     in the ethanol is swept into the third trap with hydro-
     gen.

     The synthesis is completed within 15-20 minutes. An over-
all chemical yield of 98-100% can be attained.

The analysis of high specific activity cyanide proceeds as follows:

1. A few crystals (about 2-3 mg, without weighing) of the $K^{14}CN$ preparate are placed into a titration vessel

2. containing 15 ml of 5% of ammonium hydroxide and 1-2 mg of potassium iodide.

3. The solution is titrated by injecting 0.05 M silver nitrate by means of a micro burette or micro doser according to Deniges' method.

4. The slight turbidity should disappear on adding a crystal of inactive potassium cyanide into the solution.

5. The titrated solution is carefully rinsed with distilled water into a 1000-ml volumetric flask.

6. The solution in the volumetric flask is filled up to mark with distilled water.

7. After thorough mixing of the contents of the flask 100-1000 $\mu$l aliquots of the standard solution

8. are pipetted into vials containing liquid scintillation coctail.

9. The radioactivity measurement of the aliquots is carried out by a liquid scintillation spectrometer.

The analysis of the $K^{14}CN$ preparates is based on the following equation:

$$2\ K^{14}CN + AgNO_3 = K/Ag(CN)_2/ + KNO_3$$

where 1 mL of 0.05 M $AgNO_3$ is equivalent to 6.71 mg of $K^{14}CN$. From the radioactivity measurement data of the aliquots of the standard solution containing the $K/Ag(CN)_2/$ complex the specific activity of the $K^{14}CN$ sample can be calculated in

Bequerels. Based on the net weight of the preparate in ampoule 1 and the specific activity of the sample, the chemical purity of the crude preparate can be determined. The accuracy of the measurement is dependent on the accuracy of the radioactivity measurement ($\pm 3\%$).

## Acknowledgements

The authors thank the Organizing Committee, first of all Professor Dr. R. MUCCINO, for the possibility taking part in the Symposium and thanks are due to the Central Research Institute for Chemistry, Hungarian Academy of Sciences, for supporting this work.

## References

1. LOTFIELD, R. B. - Nucleonics, 1 : 54 (1947).
2. ADAMSON, A. W. - J. Am. Chem. Soc., 69 : 2564 (1947).
3. CALVIN, M., HEIDELBERGER, C., REID, J. C., TOLBERT, B. M. and JANKWICH, P. F. - "Isotopic Carbon", Wiley, New York (1949).
4. ZBARSKY, S. H. and FISCHER, I. - Can. J. Research, 27 B : 81 (1949).
5. MAIMID, V. I., TOKAREV, B. V. and SHEMYAKIN, M. M. - Doklady Akad. Nauk. S.S.S.R., 81 : 195 (1951).
6. BOS, J. A. - Experientia, 7 : 258 (1951).
7. Mc CARTER, J. A. - J. Am. Chem. Soc., 73 : 483 (1951).
8. JEANES, K. J. - Science, 118 : 719 (1953).
9. SIXMA, F. L. J., HENDRIKS, H., HELLE, K., HOLISTEIN, U. and VAN LING, R. - Rec. trav, chim., 73 : 161 (1954).
10. MURRAY, A. and WILLIAMS, L. - "Organic Syntheses with Isotopes", Interscience Publishers, INC., N. Y. (1958).

11. ANDREEVA, O. J. and KOSTIKOVA, G. J. - Proceedings of the I.A.E.A. Conference on the Uses of Radioisotopes, Copenhague, 1960. Vol. 3, p. 111.

12. VERCIER, P., - J. Labeled Compds., 4 91 (1968).

13. BÁNFI, D., MLINKÓ, S. and PALÁGYI, T. - Hung. Pat., 152 035 (1963), Belgian Pat., 687 350 (1966), French Pat. 1 500 300 (1967), B. P. 1 141 483 (1969), German Pat. 1 227 225 (1969), U. S. Pat. 3 499 727 (1969).

14. BÁNFI, D., MLINKÓ, S. and PALÁGYI, T. - J. Labeled Compds. - 7 221 (1971).

15. MLINKÓ, S. and SZARVAS, T. - Acta Chim. Hung. 33 107 (1962).

16. MLINKÓ, S. - Microchimica Acta, - 1963 456.

17. MLINKÓ, S. - Microchimica Acta, - 1963 699.

18. MLINKÓ, S., BÁNFI, D., GÁCS, I. - Hung. Pat., 163 107 (1970).

19. MLINKÓ, S., BÁNFI, D. at al, - Hung. Pat., 162 608 (1971).

20. MLINKÓ, S., BÁNFI, D. at al, - Hung. Pat. MA. 2317 (1972).

21. WHALEY, T. W. and OTT, D. G. - J. Labeled Compds., 11 307 (1974).

22. CHRITMAN, D. R., FINN, R. D., KARLSTROM, K. J. and WOLF, A. P. - Int. J. Appl. Rad. - 26 435 (1975).

23. OTT, D. G., KERR, V. N., SANHEZ, T. G. and WHALEY, T. W. J. Labeled Compds. 17 255 (1981).

24. SAMBRE, J., LANDECASTEELE, C., GOETHALS, P., RABI,N. A., VANHAUER, D. and SLEGER, G. - Int. J. Appl. Rad. 36 275 (1985).

25. OTT, D. G. - "Syntheses with Stable Isotopes" Wiley, N.Y. (1980).

*Synthesis and Applications of Isotopically Labeled Compounds 1985.*
Proceedings of the Second International Symposium, Kansas City, MO, U.S.A.,
3—6 September 1985, R.R. Muccino (Ed.), 325—330
© 1986 Elsevier Science Publishers B.V., Amsterdam — Printed in The Netherlands

ENERGY EXPENDITURE BY DOUBLY LABELED WATER: VALIDATION AND CLINICAL APPLICATION

D. A. SCHOELLER[1], C.R. FJELD[1,2], and K.H. BROWN[2,3]

[1]Department of Medicine, University of Chicago, Chicago, IL   60637.

[2]The Instituto de Investigacion Nutricional, Lima, Peru.

[3]Division of Human Nutrition, Department of International Health,

Johns Hopkins University, Baltimore, MD 21205.

ABSTRACT

The doubly labeled water method measures energy expenditure in free-living subjects from the difference between the elimination rates of deuterium and $^{18}O$ labeled waters. The method has been validated in humans with an accuracy of 1%. Precisions of 2 to 8% have been achieved depending on isotope dose and length of the metabolic period. We have applied the method to measure energy balance and composition of weight gained in infants recovering from severe malnutrition.

INTRODUCTION

Energy expenditure of free-living subjects is difficult to measure. Laboratory methods such as direct calorimetry or continuous respiratory gas analysis are accurate and precise, but restrictive and thus do not represent real living conditions. Because of this, investigators have turned to activity monitoring, heart rate monitoring, and measured or recalled dietary intake to estimate energy expenditure, but these methods require extensive subject cooperation and are subject to large errors (ref. 1).

Doubly labeled water method has the potential to fill this gap in energy expenditure methodologies. It is nonrestrictive and requires only minimal subject cooperation, and thus it is ideally suited for use in free-living subjects. The method is based on the observation that oxygen in water is in rapid isotopic equilibrium with oxygen from carbon dioxide (ref. 2). After a loading dose of water labeled with deuterium and $^{18}O$, deuterium is eliminated from the body as water, while $^{18}O$ is eliminated as water and carbon dioxide. Because body water behaves as a single compartment, the rate of carbon dioxide production ($r_{CO2}$) can be calculated from the difference between the two isotope elimination rates ($k_O$ and $k_H$) and the total body water pool size (N) (ref. 3):

$$r_{CO2}=(N/2)(k_O-k_H) \tag{1}$$

In practice, neither deuterium nor $^{18}O$ are perfect tracers for water.Equation 1 should therefore be modified to account for the difference between the two isotope dilution spaces and isotope fractionation (ref. 3.4):

$$r_{CO2} = 0.46N \ (1.01 \ k_O - 1.04 \ k_H).$$ (2)

## VALIDATIONS

The doubly labeled water method has been extensively validated in small animals by a number of independent investigators. As recently summarized (ref. 5), these studies demonstrate that the method is accurate and that precisions of 5 % are attainable in species other than arthropods.

Despite the successful use of doubly labeled water in small animals, it was nearly 30 years before the method was applied to human studies. The long delay was probably due to the cost of $^{18}O$, which exceeds $25/gram. Deuterium is much less expensive. The cost of isotope needed to enrich body fluids to 0.5 atom % excess $^{18}O$, the enrichment used in most animal studies, would therefore have exceeded $5,000 for a single human study. Fortunately,advances in isotope ratio mass spectrometry have greatly increased precision, so that we were able to reduce the dose to a twentieth of that used in animal studies. The smaller doses, however, produce smaller increments of enrichment above natural abundance.

Because of possible interference from natural isotopic variation, we determined the accuracy and precision of the method in humans at these lower doses. Table 1 summarizes our validations and those of three other investigators. In studies 1,2, and 3, we administered sufficient isotope to produce initial enrichments of $5 \times 10^{-3}$ atom % excess deuterium and $2.5 \times 10^{-2}$ atom % excess $^{18}O$ body water. Using either the intake/balance method, which calculates energy expenditure from dietary intake minus the change in body energy stores, or near-continuous respiratory gas analysis, we demonstrated that the method was accurate and that the precision was between 6 and 9 % (ref. 4,6, 7). A propagation of error analysis indicated that the precision was limited by the random error of our deuterium enrichment assay (ref. 8). We therefore doubled the dose of deuterium in studies 4 and 5 and demonstrated a precision of 4 to 6 % (ref. 4, 9).

Similar results have been reported by three other groups of investigators (ref. 10-12). Direct comparisons of the accuracies of studies 6, 7, and 8 with ours is difficult, however, because each of these three groups used slightly different modifications of equation 1 to calculate carbon dioxide production from the isotope data. These modifications, may have introduced systematic differences in calculated energy expenditure of 2 to 8 % (ref. 4). In addition, multiple samples were collected throughout the metabolic period and isotope

Table 1.  Summary of validations of the doubly labeled water method for measurement of energy expenditure in humans.

| Study | Subjects | Days | Reference method | (DLW-R/R)x 100 ±SD | Reference |
|-------|----------|------|------------------|--------------------|-----------|
| 1 | 4 | 14 | intake/balance | $-0.5 \pm 5.6$ % | 6 |
| 2 | 5 | 5 | resp. gas exchange | $1.0 \pm 7.5$ % | 7 |
| 3 | 6 | 4 | resp. gas exchange | $2.0 \pm 9.2$ % | 4 |
| 4 | 3 | 4 | resp. gas exchange | $-1.2 \pm 4.2$ % | 4 |
| 5 | 5 | 14 | intake/balance | $2.7 \pm 5.7$ % | 9 |
| 6 | 2 | 3 | resp. gas exchange | $-2.5 \pm 4.9$ % | 10 |
| 7 | 1 | 5 | resp. gas exchange | 1.8 % | 11 |
| 8 | 4 | 12 | resp. gas exchange | $2 \pm 2$ % | 12 |

DLW = value from doubly labeled water, R = value from reference method.

elimination rates were determined from isotopic analyses of each of these samples rather than from the enrichments of the initial and final samples which was the method used in our validations.  In at least two of the studies (ref. 11, 12), multiple sampling was used because it improved the accuracy and precision of the method.  It has been suggested that the improvement resulted from averaging of urine-to-urine isotopic variations that were attributed to in vivo isotopic movement (ref. 11).  We have not observed sporatic variations in the successive urine samples (ref. 4) and have demonstrated excellent accuracy and good precision for the two-point method.  It therefore seems likely that these isotopic variations reported by others are artifacts of sample handling or analysis rather than isotopic movement or natural variations.

Despite the minor controversy over the number of samples required to measure the isotope elimination rates, the accuracy of the method in human studies is excellent and the precision is two to three times better than the other methods that have been used to measure energy expenditure in free-living subjects (ref. 1).  The doubly labeled water method thus fills the gap between the accurate and precise laboratory methods of measuring  energy expenditure under artificial conditions and the less precise methods currently used in free-living subjects.

APPLICATIONS

We have used the doubly labeled water method in a wide range of investigations, including: measurement of energy requirements of mentally handicapped children, and of healthy, but marginally malnourished adults in developing countries; investigations into the role of energy expenditure in the etiology of obesity; and measurement of energy balance and composition of weight gain in infants recovering from severe malnutrition.

The latter study is an interesting example in that it combines the strengths of the doubly labeled water method with more traditional nutrition methodologies in order to study the efficacy of various diets in the treatment of malnourished infants.

Deficits in both height and weight may be severe in malnourished children, and treatment often requires long periods of hospitalization with dietary repletion to recoup these deficits. Currently, the efficacy of treatment is evaluated in terms of weight gain and other indicators of clinical progress. More specific biological criteria have been difficult to define because of a shortage of sophisticated instrumentation in developing countries. We have proposed to evaluate treatments on the basis of the composition of the weight gain to determine if the treatment fosters accretion of a body similar to that of that of a well-fed reference child. The aim of our pilot study was to evaluate the quality of the weight gained during convalescence by determining the percentage of protein, fat and water in the weight gained during dietary treatment of malnutrition. Ultimately, our aim is to compare dietary treatments differing in protein and energy content to determine which results in a body composition most similar to that of well-fed reference infant.

Methods

Five male infants, $16 \pm 5$ months of age with body weights of $7.7 \pm 0.6$ kg, were studied late in their recovery from severe marasmus. Infants were fed one of two fortified cows milk formulas with either 7 % of energy as protein, 44 % as carbohydrate, and 49 % as fat; or 6 % as protein, 63 % as carbohydrate, and 31 % as fat. Infants were placed on measured dietary intake for ten days. Energy intake and fecal energy loss were measured by bomb calorimetry. Nitrogen intake and nitrogen output in feces and urine were measured by Kjeldahl analysis for two 72 hour periods during the ten day study. Total body water was measured by isotope dilution on the first and last days of the ten day study. On the first day, labeled water was given by mouth at doses of 0.1 and 0.3 g/kg of $^2H_2O$ and $H_2^{18}O$ respectively. The respective doses were 0.03 and 0.06 g/kg on the final day of the ten day study. Urines were collected for the next six hours and the total body water was calculated from the enrichment at plateau as described elsewhere (ref. 6). Urines were collected on the morning of the first day after the dose and the last day of the study. Isotope elimination rates were calculated from the enrichments above predose urine for these two urines. Energy expenditure was calculated from carbon dioxide production assuming a respiratory ratio of 0.88 as estimated from the dietary intake and apparent storage of protein and fat as estimated from the change in total body water (ref. 6).

Enrichments were measured by isotope ratio mass spectrometry. Briefly, 1.5 ml of urine was equilibrated with 1 ml STP of carbon dioxide for 72 h at 25 $^\circ$C.

The carbon dioxide was isolated by cryogenic vacuum distillation and the $^{18}O/^{16}O$ isotope ratio measured on a dual inlet/dual collector isotope ratio mass spectrometer (Nuclide Corp., State College, PA). The standard deviation of this analysis is $1 \times 10^{-4}$ atom % excess. A 1 ul urine sample was vacuum distilled and the resulting water reduced to $H_2$ over uranium at 700 $^{\circ}C$. The D/H ratio was measured on a triple inlet/dual collector isotope ratio mass spectrometer (Nuclide Corp.). The standard deviation of this analysis is $1 \times 10^{-5}$ atom % excess.

Results

Energy intake less energy lost in feces averaged $109\pm6$ (SD) kcal/kg/d. Daily energy expenditure from doubly labeled water averaged $78\pm4$ kcal/kg/d, and energy storage by difference was $31\pm2$ kcal/kg/d. From nitrogen balance and an estimated 7.5 mg/kg/d unmeasured nitrogen loss (FAO, 1973), we calculated that 110 mg of nitrogen/kg/d was retained. This was equivalent to $0.70\pm0.15$ g/kg/d of protein accretion or a protein energy storage of $3.1\pm0.7$ kcal/kg/d. Assuming that no energy was stored as additional carbohydrate during the ten day metabolic period, the energy stored as fat was calculated from the difference between total and protein energy storage and was 27 kca/kg/d. This was equivalent to an accretion of $2.8\pm0.3$ g/kg/d of fat. The measured increase in total body water was $2.1\pm0.9$ g/kg/d.

Figure 1 summarizes the composition of the weight gain and compares the average calculated weight gain (5.58 g/kg/d) with the average observed weight gain (5.62 g/kg/d). Agreement was excellent for the group data, although

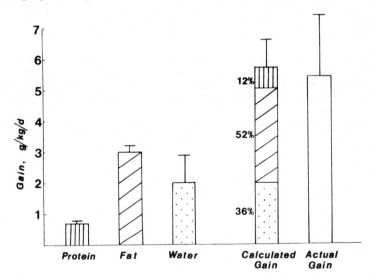

Figure 1. Composition of weighted gained in five infants recovering from marasmus during a period late in recovery.

individual variations were much larger.  The value of 52 % of weight gained as fat is slightly higher than that estimated for the reference infant (ref. 13), however, considering the small number of infants studied to date, it is not possible to tell whether this is a function of treatment , recovery from mal-nutrition| or experimental error.  We are currently extending these studies to a larger number of infants.

We could not have done this study in Peru without use of doubly labeled water because equipment for respiratory gas analysis is not available in Peru. Beyond this clinical application, however, the noninvasive, nonrestrictive character of the doubly labeled water method potentiates numerous field studies of energy metabolism in malnurished children in developing countries.

ACKNOWLEDGEMENTS

This work was supported by grants from NIH (AM 26678 and AM 30031) and from the Thrasher Research Fund.

REFERENCES

1  K.J. Acheson, I.T. Campbell, O.G. Edholm, D.S. Miller and M.J. Stock, Am. J. Clin. Nutr. 33 (1980) 1155-1164.
2  N. Lifson, G.B. Gordon, M.B. Visscher and A.O.C. Nier, J. Biol. Chem. 180 (1949) 803-881.
3  N. Lifson and R. McClintock, J. Theoret. Biol. 12 (1966) 46-74.
4  D.A. Schoeller, E. Ravussin, Y. Schutz, K.J. Acheson, P. Baertschi and E. Jequier. submitted Am. J. Physiol. (1985).
5  D.A. Schoeller, Human Nutr.:  Clin. Nutr. (letter) 38C (1984) 477-480.
6  D.A. Schoeller and E. van Santen, J. Appl. Physiol. 53 (1982) 955-959.
7  D.A. Schoeller and P. Webb, Am. J. Clin. Nutr. 40 (1984) 153-158.
8  D.A. Schoeller, Am. J. Clin. Nutr. 38 (1983) 999-1005.
9  D.A. Schoeller, R. Kushner, P.J.H. Jones, submitted Am. J. Clin. Nutr. (1985)
10  K.R. Westerterp, J.O. de Boer, W.H.M. Sais,P.F.M. Schoffelen and F. ten Hoor, Int. J. Sports Med. 5 (1984) 74-75.
11  P.D. Klein, W.P.T. James, W.W. Wong, C.S. Irving, P.R. Murgatroyd,M. Cabrera, H.M. Dallosso, E.R. Klein and B.L. Nichols, Human Nutr.: Clin. Nutr. 38C (1984) 95-106.
12  W.A. Coward and A.M. Prentice, Am. J. Clin. Nutr. 41 (1985) 659-660.
13  A.J. Fomon, E.E. Ziegler, S.E. Nelson and B.B. Edwards, Am. J. Clin. Nutr.35 (1982) 1169-1179.

*Synthesis and Applications of Isotopically Labeled Compounds 1985.*
Proceedings of the Second International Symposium, Kansas City, MO, U.S.A.,
3—6 September 1985, R.R. Muccino (Ed.), 331—336
© 1986 Elsevier Science Publishers B.V., Amsterdam — Printed in The Netherlands

# METABOLIC TURNOVER STUDIES WITH STABLE ISOTOPES: GLUCOSE PRODUCTION AND GLUCONEOGENESIS IN MAN

Kou-Yi Tserng

Clinical Pharmacology, VA Medical Center, 10701 East Boulevard, Cleveland, Ohio 44106

Department of Pharmacology, Case Western Reserve University, Cleveland, Ohio 44106.

ABSTRACT
    Glucose production and gluconeogenesis are the most studied parameters in assessing fuel metabolism. Stable isotope tracing experiemnts to obtain these parameters are carried out essentially the same as their radioactive counterparts, e.g. using primed-constant infusion or single bolus injection. However, due to the difference in conventional expression of mass spectrometric and radioactivity data, the translation of these data into production rate calculation is different. The easily available tracers used for glucose production rate measurements are $[6,6-^2H_2]$glucose, $[1-^{13}C]$glucose, and $[U-^{13}C]$glucose. Depending on the mass spectrometric method of enrichment measurement, the treatment of the samples, and the caluclation, these can act as reversible or irreversible tracers. Our data indicate that the assumption of $[6,6-^2H_2]$glucose as "true" irreversible tracer has to be reevaluated.
    Gluconeogenesis can be studied with labeled alanine, lactate, or glycerol. We have assessed this capacity with stable isotope labelled alanine. Both $[2,3-^{13}C_2]$alanine and $[^{15}N]$alanine are used. The incorporation of labeled carbon into glucose can be measured when $[2,3-^{13}C]$alanine is used as tracer. The use of deuterium labeled alanine as tracer would produce non-physiological value as a result of non-specific exchange of deuterium with body water.

INTRODUCTION

    The homeostatic mechanism that maintain a constant level of circulating glucose

and the pathophysiology of its disorders in man have been areas where isotopic tracers

play a major contributing role. With the use of radioactive labeled tracers of glucose, the

parameters such as pool size, turnover rate, recycling, and the contribution of carbon

precursors in gluconeogenesis have been determined in normal man and in some

pathophysiological states. However, the corresponding data were unavailable from infants

and pregnant women before the application of stable isotope labeled tracers due to the

potential harmful effects of radioactivity to these populations. Besides the often stated

advantage of safety in human investigation, stable isotope labeled tracers offer more flexibility toward study design. In the studies with radioactive tracers, total radioactivity was generally measured. As a result, valuable information about the distribution of label within the molecule is lost. In certain cases, this disadvantage was overcame by elaborate chemical degradation of the molecule. Unfortunately, the amount of samples that is available generally make this approach unpractical. In contrast, stable isotope study and detection of enrichment with mass spectrometry offer virtually unlimited opportunity of determining specific labeling pattern by the proper choice of derivatization, mode of ionization, and the type of mass spectrometers. Our experience in the use of stable isotopes in the determination of glucose turnover rates and gluconeogenesis will be presented.

## METHODS

### Clinical stable isotope tracer methodology

In planning a stable isotope tracer experiment, the areas that have to be considered are (a) selection of tracers, (b) development of methodology, (c) clinical studies, and (d) data calculation. Considerable effort will be spent in the discussion of tracer selection and methodology development since these are the most time consuming part of developing a new study. Often, these are also very critical in the interpretation of data and the type of information that one is looking for.

### Tracer selection

Tracers suitable for in vivo metabolic study should meet the following criteria: (a) the label on the tracer should be metabolically and chemically stable, (b) no isotopic effect should be resulted from labeling, (c) the label should be located on mass fragment with high intensity, (d) the tracer should have high isotopic purity and specific labeling. In addition, the derivative that is to be made and cost consideration are also factors that affect the choice of tracers.

There are a number of commerically available stable isotope labeled glucose. A number of these compounds have been used by various investigators for the measuring of glucose turnover rates in human (Table 1). Apparently, the cost of labeled compound played a major role in the selection of labeled species, especially in the early studies. $[1,2,3,4,5,6,6-^7H_2]$glucose should not be used in the in vivo metabolic turnover studies of glucose at all. The data obtained would not be interpretable as a combination of various futile cycles (tend to overestimate) and biological isotope effects (tend to underestimate) operate on this labeled compound. Since futile cycle effect would be expected to be predominate, an overestimate of glucose turnover rate was expected. In contrast, an underestimate was reported (1). I believe the discrepancy could be the result of mis-

TABLE 1.

Stable isotope labeled glucose for the study of glucose metabolism.

D-glucose

| Labels | Technique | Oxid.[a] | Type[b] | P.I.[c] |
|---|---|---|---|---|
| [1,2,3,4,5,6,6-$^7$H$_2$]- | EI/GC/MS[d] | No | ? | ? |
| [6,6-$^2$H$_2$]- | EI/GC/MS | No | irrev. | 1 |
| [1-$^{13}$C]- | Enzyme, RMS[e] | Yes | rev. | 6 |
| [U-$^{13}$C]- | CI/GC/MS[f] | Yes | irrev. | 9 |
| [U-$^{13}$C]- | Enzyme, RMS | Yes | rev. | 9 |
| [U-$^{13}$C]- | Combustion, RMS[g] | Yes | rev. | 9 |

[a]oxidation study for the measurement of label incorporation into expired $CO_2$
[b]Type of tracer, whether reversible or irreversible
[c]P.I. = price index, the relative cost of labeled compounds with [6,6-$^2$H$_2$]glucose as 1, which is currently priced at $130/g.
[d]EI/GC/MS: electron impact gas chromatography-mass spectrometry.
[e]Enzyme, RMS = enzymatic decarboxylation of carbon-1 of glucose molecule and measuring the isotopic enrichment of evolved $CO_2$ with isotope ratio mass spectrometry.
[f]CI/GC/MS: chemical ionization gas chromatography-mass spectrometry.
[g]combustion, RMS = combustion of glucose to $CO_2$ and measuring the isotopic enrichment of evolved $CO_2$ with isotope ratio mass spectrometry.

calculation by using enrichment factor in conventional standard curve (2), instead of isotope effect as advanced by the authors. [6,6-$^2$H$_2$]glucose probably is the most poupular tracer employed in the determination of glucose turnover rate. Relatively low price and ease determination with EI/GC/MS are some factors to its advantage. In addition, this tracer has been an "irreversible tracer" for the determination of "true" glucose turnover rate based on the theoretical assumption that the deuterium label would be lost to body water and not recycle back to glucose in glycolytic pathway. Using a more sensitive technique (3), we determined an enrichment of lactate in the magnitude of 0.16 ± 0.03% when premature infants (n=4) were infused with [6,6-$^2$H$_2$]glucose at a steady state enrichment of 1.38 ± 0.13%. If we assume that 50% of lactate is derived from glucose, then more than 20% of the glucose deuterium label on carbon 6 is retained, a figure that is not negligible. As we do not know the extent of deuterium loss from [3,3-$^2$H$_2$]lactate to glucose to assess the possibility that these deuterium label will be completely lost in gluconeogenetic pathway, the interpretation of data by assuming [6,6-$^2$H$_2$]glucose as irreversible tracer should be evaluated carefully. Like its radioactive counterpart (C-14 labeled glucose), carbon-13 labeled glucose is generally termed "reversible" tracer and is less favored as a tracer for glucose turnover study. However, we found that C-13 labeled glucose, especially [U-$^{13}$C]glucose, is a much more versatile choice than the deuterium labeled one. In addition to the advantage of being able to determine the oxidation rate of glucose by measuring $^{13}CO_2$ in expired air, [U-$^{13}$C]glucose can also be used to determine "true" glucose turnover rate and glucose recycling in the same study (4). Because the opportunity for the uniformly labeled glucose, [$^{13}C_6$]glucose, to recycle back as [$^{13}C_6$]glucose is negligible, the true glucose production rate was obtained by measuring the plasma isotope enrichment of [$^{13}C_6$]glucose with chemical ionization mass spectrometry. In contrast, when the isotopic enrichment of C-1 of glucose was measured by enzymatic decarboxylation and ratio mass spectrometry, the "apparent" glucose production including carbon recycling was obtained. The difference between the two rates was the extent of glucose carbon recycling. Indeed, when [6,6-$^2$H$_2$]glucose and [U-$^{13}$C]glucose were infused simultaneoulsy in the same subjects, comparable glucose turnover rates were obtained. Our data indicated that the turnover rates determined by using various tracers and techniques are in the order of [6,6-$^2$H$_2$]- [U-$^{13}$C]-(CI/GC/MS) [1-$^{13}$C]- [U-$^{13}$C]-(enzyme, RMS) [U-$^{13}$C]- (combustion, RMS). The turnover rate determined by using [1-$^{13}$C]glucose and enzymatic decarboxylation of C-1 tend to be higher than the use of [U-$^{13}$C]glucose due to the fact that 75% of the original label on C-1 tends to recycle away from C-1.

By definition, gluconeogenesis is the production of glucose from sources other than glycogen. Out of numerous carbon precursors for gluconeogenesis, alanine is the major contributor. It is logical that this process is mostly studied with labeled alanine. A summary is listed in Table 2. Besides the disadvantage of incapable of measuring gluconeogenesis directly, deuterium labeled alanine yielded data with doubtful physiological meaning. the immediate fate of alanine in the gluconeogenetic pathway is the conversion to pyruvate. As a consequence the deuterium labels next to the carbonyl group are subjected to non-specific label exchange with other active hydrogen in the physiological fluid to yield overestimated alanine turnover rate. The wide-spreaded and inflated alanine turnover rates (1) obtained using this tracer can be easily attributed to this effect. [$^{15}$N]alanine can be used to quantitate the irreversible turnover rate of alanine and the transfer of nitrogen to other amino acids and to urea (5). Due to rapid equilibrium between alanine and pyruvate, it is anticipated that [$^{15}$N]alanine should yield higher turnover rate than carbon labeled alanine tracers. In fact, we found that the turnover rate of alanine in dogs is twice as high when [$^{15}$N]alanine was used instead of [U-$^{14}$C]alanine. A recent report has a reversed order of turnover rates. I do not have ready explanation for this discrepancy. Among carbon-13 labeled alanine tracers, [2,3-$^{13}C_2$]alanine offers the advantage of more precise determination at low enrichment.

## Method development

By chosing the proper derivative, ionization mode, and type of mass spectrometric detection, virtually unlimited combination of methods can be developed. Glucose can be derivatized as pentaacetate, acetonide, aldononitrile pentaacetate, alditol acetate,

TABLE 2.

Stable isotope labeled alanaine for the study of alanine metabolism

$$\overset{NH_2}{\underset{|}{CH_3-CH-COOH}}$$
$$\begin{array}{ccc} 3 & 2 & 1 \end{array}$$

| Labels | Technique | Gluconeog.[a] | Type[b] | P.I.[c] |
|---|---|---|---|---|
| $[2,3,3,3\text{-}{}^2H_4]\text{-}$ | EI/GC/MS | No | ? | 1 |
| $[3,3,3\text{-}{}^2H_3]$ | EI/GC/MS | No | ? | 1 |
| $[{}^{15}N]\text{-}$ | EI/GC/MS | No | irrev. | 1.5 |
| $[1\text{-}{}^{13}C]\text{-}$ | CI/GC/MS | ? | rev. | 1.5 |
| $[3\text{-}{}^{13}C]\text{-}$ | EI/GC/Ms | Yes | rev. | 2 |
| $[2,3\text{-}{}^{13}C_2]$ | EI/GC/MS | Yes | rev. | 6 |

[a]capability of direct quantitation of gluconeogenesis using precursor-product relationship.
[b]type of tracer, whether reversible or irreversible.
[c]P.I.'= price index, the relative cost of labeled alanine, with deuterated alanine as 1, which is currently priced at $230/g.

butaneboronate, or other derivatives. Alanine can be derivatized as propyl ester acetate, propyl ester trifluoroacetate, or others. Proper combination of derivatives and detection mode offer the opportunity of determining specific labeling at the sites of interest without resorting to elaborating chemical degradation.

Clinical studies (6)
Either single bolus injection or primed-constant infusion techniques can be used. The former has the advantage of being used to calculate the flux between different compartments, while the latter has the advantage of model independent, hence less assumption is required. We used primed-constant infusion study in most of our studies. For the determination of gluconeogenesis using double isotope technique. Both $[6,6\text{-}{}^2H_2]$glucose and $[2,3\text{-}{}^{13}C_2]$alanine were infused simultaneous after a priming dose into a superficial vein of the forearm for a period of 5 hours. Heparinized blood samples were obtained at 30-min intervals from an indwelling needle placed in a superficial vein of the opposite forearm. The glucose turnover rate was obtained by measuring the enrichment of $[6,6\text{-}{}^2H_2]$glucose. The incorportaion of $^{13}C$ from $[2,3\text{-}{}^{13}C_2]$alanine was obtained by enzymatic decarboxylation of glucose carbon-1 to carbon dioxide. The $^{13}C$ enrichment in $CO_2$ was then determined with an isotope ratio mass spectrometry. For the measurement of glucose turnover rate alone without simultaneous infusion of labeled gluconeogenic precursor, $[U\text{-}{}^{13}C]$glucose infusion was preferred over $[6,6\text{-}{}^2H_2]$glucose since other information such as glucose carbon recycling and incorporation of glucose carbons into its glycolytic intermediates can also be measured.

## Data calculation

In stable isotope tracer studies, the translation of mass spectrometric data to the calculation of substrate turnover rates has to be carefully manipulated. The conventional practice in presenting isotope enrichments is as isotope ratio (not enrichment) obtained from standard curve constructed from weighed ratios of labeled and unlabeled compounds versus the peak ratios determined. The use of the popular equation, $P = [(E_i/E) - 1]I$ (where $P$ is the turnover rate, $E_i$ is the enrichment of the tracer, $E$ is the enrichment of plasma compartment, and $I$ is the infusion rate of isotope) with $E$ obtained from conventional mass spectrometric determination would produce underestimated turnover rates. Either equations, $p = [(1/E) - 1]I$ or $P = I(y/x)$, (where $y/x$ is the reciprocal of the mole ratio of labeled and unlabeled compounds), should be used. This type of error is most apparent in the cases of multiple labeled or low enriched tracers, such as $[1,2,3,4,5,6,6-^7H_2]$glucose mentioned in previous section.

## References

1.   D.M. Bier, K.J. Arnold, W.R. sherman, et al. Diabetes, 26 (1977) 1005-15.
2.   K-Y. Tserng and S.C. Kalhan, Am. J. Phsyiol. 245 (1983) E308-E311.
3.   K-Y. Tserng, C.A. Gilfillan, and S.C. Kalhan, Anal. Chem. 5-16 (1984) 517-523.
4.   K-Y. Tserng and S.C. Kalhan, Am. J. Phsyiol. 245 (1983) E476-E482.
5.   K-Y. Tserng and S.C. Kalhan, Anal. Chem. 54 (1982) 489-491.
6.   E.S. Ricanati, K-Y. Tserng and S.C. Kalhan, Kidney Intern. 24 (1983) 5121-5127.
7.   S.C. Kalhan, E.S. Ricanati, K-Y. Tserng, et al., Metabolism 32 (1983) 1155-1162.
8.   K.C. King, K-Y. Tserng, and S.C. Kalhan. Pediatr. Res., 16 (1982) 824-833.
9.   S.C. Kalhan, K-Y. Tserng, C.A. Gilfillan, et al., Metabolism, 31 (1982) 824-833.
10.   C.A. Gilfillam, K-Y. Tserng, and S.C. Kalhan, Biol Neonat. 47 (1985) 141-147.

*Synthesis and Applications of Isotopically Labeled Compounds 1985.*
Proceedings of the Second International Symposium, Kansas City, MO, U.S.A.,
3—6 September 1985, R.R. Muccino (Ed.), 337—342
1986 Elsevier Science Publishers B.V., Amsterdam — Printed in The Netherlands

DEVELOPMENT OF RADIOISOTOPICALLY LABELED COMPOUNDS FOR CLINICAL POSITRON
EMISSION TOMOGRAPHY

R.M. COHEN

Section on Clinical Brain Imaging, Laboratory of Cerebral Metabolism, National
Institute of Mental Health, 10/4N317, 9000 Rockville Pike, Bethesda, MD 20205

ABSTRACT

It is its quantitative imaging capacity with high spatial resolution that
makes positron emission tomography a unique tool for the development of quantitative tracer kinetic studies for the measurement of physiological processes
in man. Research success in this area will depend on the ingenuity of biomedical scientists in prioritizing the development of tracers. Choices must
be made based on the importance of different physiological measurements, the
capacity to synthesize an appropriate radioisotopically labeled compound for
this measurement and the ability to determine an adequate kinetic model for
its interpretation. Examples are given of these steps in the development of
PET tracers at the NIMH.

INTRODUCTION

Positron emission tomography (PET) is a method that allows for the precise
quantitation and localization in space of positron-emitting radioactive isotopes. Its uniqueness as a scanning methodology derives from its capacity to
maximize the spatial and quantitative information that is available from the
simultaneous detection of the two 511 kiloelectron-volt photons, angled $180°$
from each other, that are produced in the annihilation event of a positron and
its antiparticle, the electron. Whereas, in general, the clinical researcher
has had to depend on indirect measurements for assessing the function of the
intact human brain, PET, in principle, presents a substantial departure. How
successfully PET will be able to provide answers to questions concerning brain
function, however, will depend on the ingenuity of biomedical scientists. A
major part of this ingenuity will lie in the choice of isotopically labeled
tracers to be developed. Preplanning, in this regard, is very important as
PET is an expensive and labor intensive method. Choices must be based on two
major considerations: First, prioritizing the most relevant and important
physiological measurements that if accomplished would substantially increase
our understanding of scientific and medically relevant issues and second,
assessing whether one can develop an appropriate PET tracer for that particular measurement. As PET measures total radioactivity in a given region at a
specific time, regardless of the chemical form from which that radioactivity
derives, so long as it derives from positron emission, an appropriate kinetic
model for the physiological interpretation of PET data is essential and must
be part of this development. Ideally, the model is based on in vivo experimental determinations for the assessment of the specific chemical forms of the
isotope that are present in the various metabolic compartments over time
following introduction of isotope. In most instances this step follows the
successful synthesis of a compound of high specific activity and purity that
demonstrates the appropriate biological properties in in vitro studies and
incorporates a positron-emitting radionuclide. Phelps, et al. (ref.1) have

published a list of desireable characteristics for potential PET tracers which will not be duplicated here. The core of the matter is that a tracer must ideally undergo one or more relatively (compared to delivery to and exit from a reversible tissue compartment) irreversible steps, i.e. be "trapped", in the tissue region of interest in a way that reflects (depends upon) the physiological process to be examined. In toto, the development of a tracer for PET is an arduous and complex task that has only been achieved with respect to a few tracers. This paper will concentrate on illustration of this process.

STEPS IN DEVELOPMENT

FDG: Both for historical reasons, and because most studies of psychiatric illness, our primary focus at NIMH, have measured localized glucose metabolism, it is useful to recapitulate some of the steps in the development of $^{18}F$-2-fluoro-2-deoxy-D-glucose (FDG) as a PET tracer. Its use in man derives from the pioneering development of the 2-deoxyglucose model for measurement of glucose metabolic rate (GMR) as formulated through the animal experimentation of Dr. Louis Sokoloff and his colleagues (ref.2) at NIMH using $^{14}C$ as the radioactive label for the sugar tracer. Dr. Reivich and coworkers, working closely with Dr. Sokoloff, then adapted the method for PET use (ref.3).

What is important to emphasize is that the development of this tracer, although aided by the availability of a specific compound deoxyglucose with some very fortuitous properties, was primarily driven by the initial scentific questions that were raised by Dr. Kety and his colleagues (ref.4,5 and ref. therein) and pursued by Dr. Sokoloff and his coworkers (ref.5). The one basic concept characterizing this work is the expectation that brain function is closely linked to metabolism and blood flow. Indeed, this concept 30 years later still appears fundamentally sound. This laboratory's pioneering efforts with the nitrous oxide technique confirmed the usefulness of looking at brain function as revealed by metabolism in man particularly in the diffuse alterations of brain function as observed in seizure disorders, dementia and anesthesia, but were disappointing with respect to the study of psychiatric illness where differences from normality were not revealed. However, as only global measurements of metabolism were being made, it seemed plausible that if one could measure localized or regional brain metabolism, a reflection of regional brain function, substantial contributions could be made to the study of psychiatric illness and indeed neurological illness as well. The brain, perhaps unique, in the extent of its heterogenity as an organ or tissue, would be expected to require appropriate relationships among all of the various functional brain regions or units (e.g. neuron networks and/or pathways) to function properly. Nor did it seem sufficient to study these integrated relationships at rest, as it would be equally or more important to examine these with respect to the various task requirements of the brain. It was quickly recognized that despite impressive developments in electrophysiology and histochemistry that a method that could simultaneously examine an entire set of brain regions could make unique contributions toward the understanding of brain function (ref.5).

What made this important with respect to tracer studies in man, was the usefulness of deoxyglucose for the measurement of GMR and the ability to tag deoxyglucose with the positron emitting radionuclide $^{18}F$. FDG is a unique tracer for GMR measurement in that it is treated quite similarly to glucose with respect to its transport into cells and its subsequent phosphorylation, but unlike glucose it is a poor substrate for further metabolism. Since, in normal tissue, under steady state conditions, the rate of phosphorylation is equal to the glycolytic rate, the amount of trapped FDG-PO$_4$ is proportional to the rate of cerebral metabolism. The exact relationship is derived from kinetic constants that adjust for the differences between glucose and FDG transport and phosphorylation, the levels of deoxyglucose and glucose in the plasma, and the slow rate of FDG-PO$_4$ dephosphorylation within the tissue.

It is the rapid decline to a relatively constant level of deoxyglucose in brain tissue that allows for the steady state approximation. With knowledge then of the concentrations of glucose and FDG in the plasma and the amount of isotope accumulated at steady state in any given brain region, the GMR of that same region is rapidly calculable. As steady state is reached by about 30 min in man and $^{18}$F has a half life of 110 min, this is readily achievable.

Where do we stand with respect to other tracers  It is clear that FDG even in conjunction with other PET tracers that measure oxygen metabolism and blood flow, is not sufficient to yield a full understanding of brain function.  The ability to measure physiological processes relevant to specific neurotransmitter pathways appears to be the most important next step to be made in the use of PET in endeavors to understand the brain.  Two fundamentally, but perhaps complementary approaches are being taken to this question. The first, the pharmacologic challenge approach, is to use the available tracers, e.g. FDG, to look at the effects of various neurotransmitter selective drugs on different patient populations implying differences in neurotransmitter pathway function indirectly.  The second, which is our primary interest in this paper is the development of new tracers that will provide information about physiological processes that are directly translatable into an understanding of the functioning of a specific neurotransmitter pathway. Again, this approach is divisible into two ongoing complementary approaches, the presynaptic approach of looking at the uptake, synthesis and turnover of tracers related to specific neurotransmitters and the postsynaptic approach that to date has concentrated on studying the state of the receptors (located on neurons receiving transmitter input) whose occupancy results in the translation of the information provided by the neurotransmitter.

Dopamine Dependent PET Tracers:  Only with respect to the dopamine neurotransmitter pathway have all of these approaches converged.  As a result, it will be examined in some detail.  First, there have been studies of the effects of drugs that are believed to act through dopamine pathways on the FDG PET pattern (e.g., see ref.6).  These will not be discussed further.  Second, attempts have been made to measure dopamine receptor binding with at least three different tracers and to evaluate presynaptic dopamine function also with a variety of tracers, although these efforts now appear to be focussed on $6-^{18}$F-L-dihydroxyphenylalanine (6-F-L-DOPA).  An attempt will be made to briefly evaluate the progress of these two approaches in terms of the evaluation criteria that were set above.

First, the decision to study the dopamine neurotransmitter system as opposed to other pathways appears to be fundamentally sound.  Dopamine function appears relevant to the understanding of fundamental brain activities, e.g., reinforcement and motor behaviors.  The modulation of its activity appears to be of fundamental importance in the molecular processes through which a number of very scientifically important and clinically relevant drugs act, e.g. amphetamine and neuroleptics.  It plays a major role in the pathophysiology of a number of motor system diseases, most notably Parkinson's Disease, and abnormalities in its function have been implicated in the pathophysiology of a number of other disorders including manic-depressive illness and schizophrenia.

The Johns Hopkins group under the leadership of Dr. Henry Wagner have scanned the largest number of individuals with a dopamine pathway dependent ligand, namely $^{11}$C labeled 3-N-methylspiperone (NMSP) (ref.7).  The choice of NMSP was no doubt, in part, encouraged by the high binding affinity of this drug in in vitro and in vivo studies of dopamine receptors which led to higher specific to nonspecific binding ratios than those observed with some other neuroleptics, e.g. haloperidol, but was also driven by the ease of producing this particular tracer for clinical uses compared to $^{18}$F labeled neuroleptics.  NMSP is "trapped" by its binding to receptor.  Interpretation of PET data following NMSP injection utilizes the cerebellum, an area of sufficient sparcity of dopamine receptors to allow it to be of potential use as a measure of the tracer input function (ref.8).  This very interesting approach based primarily on the earlier theoretical modeling efforts of Patlak, et al. (ref.9) and Gjedde (ref.10), in principle, would obviate the need for plasma level tracer measurements in each subject, should the model be verified. Several major issues still need to be addressed, however, before this isotope can be placed in the FDG category. Although the presence of tracer in brain regions appears to be dependent on the presence of dopamine receptors, can the method be expected to be sensitive to the small quantitative changes that are usually associated with disease and/or functional adaptation? For example, catecholamine receptor alterations are generally on the order of 30 percent in response to changes in catecholamine occupancy. In this respect, it is necessary, but not sufficient to show that a ligand is accumulated in a region, such as the striatum, a region of high dopamine receptor density, and not present in the cerebellum, a region which has a dopamine receptor density approximately an order of magnitude less that that of the striatum, and conclude that you have a ligand that can be used to study the subtler changes that are argueably the most medically relevant. On the same theme, it needs to be demonstrated that these types of changes, that can be induced, for example, through 6-hydroxydopamine lesions or withdrawal from neuroleptic treatment are well quantified by in vivo NMSP studies in animals. These experiments are analogous to the initial deoxyglucose studies in animals where the methodology was verified through physiological studies in which the method yielded predictable regional involvement in response to specific environmental stimuli. These studies were extended to the FDG PET experiment confirming the applicability of the extended method to man (ref.1). One problematic part of the NMSP studies are that kinetic models are difficult to evaluate as dissociation of the ligand is extremely slow (high affinity) compared to the half life of the isotope chosen for labeling (half-life of $^{11}$C is 20 min.).

An alternative approach to the use of NMSP has been developed by Farde et al. (ref.11) who have been working with a sulpiride deriviative which demonstrates greater selectivity for the dopamine-2 receptor than NMSP and an order of magnitude lower affinity. Although initial theoretical considerations had prompted some investigators to suggest that a $K_D$ of at least 1 nM was a prerequisite for studying receptor binding with PET, $^{11}$C-raclopride appears to offer some major advantages with respect to PET work. Uptake occurs more rapidly than with NMSP and raclopride appears to reach steady state within about 45 min. Another virtue is its higher dissociation constant which allows for tracer displacement in the time frame permitted by the isotope. Thus, analogous methods to those used in in vitro receptor studies for the verification of specific and non-specific binding can be applied to the PET work with this tracer. However, more data is required, in part, as outlined above for NMSP, before we will know how useful a ligand $^{11}$C-raclopride will prove. Our own group at NIH has taken a third approach to the problem of labeling dopamine receptors which is to try to synthesize an $^{18}$F dopamine ligand in quantities sufficient for clinical studies. The initial step in this regard was to establish the biological appropriateness of compounds that should present fewer production difficulties. Although this work has only progressed to the point of knowing that the 3-N-haloethyl deriviatives display high affinity for the dopamine receptor in vitro (ref.12), it is mentioned here to illustrate the necessary teamwork that must take place between the radiochemist and biologist to select the compounds that are worthy of synthesis with a positron emitting radionuclide label, the requisite for in vivo PET study (ref.12). The latter studies are probably more useful for initial tracer screening than other more labor intensive in vivo experimentation.

With regard to the presynaptic approach, Garnett et al. (ref.13) have visualized dopamine containing regions in the monkey and human brain with 6-$^{18}$F-L-DOPA. Prior attempts with 2- and 5-F-L-DOPA were not successful as these tracers are subject to rapid methylation in the periphery, thus leading to greater nonspecific uptake into brain regions not containing dopamine. 6-F-L-DOPA like L-DOPA passes through the blood brain barrier and is preferentially taken up by the high affinity uptake system of dopamine neurons and subsequently decarboxylated to form 6-F-Dopamine (trapping steps). The latter compound appears to behave as a false transmitter (ref.14). Early studies of hemiparkinsonism and parkinsonism have been able to demonstrate striatal differences in 6-[18]F-L-DOPA uptake compared to controls (ref.15 and personal communication). In very recent studies of MPTP (1-methyl-4-phenyl-1,2,3, 6-tetrahydropyridine), an agent that causes a selective and irreversible lesion of nigostriatal dopaminergic neurons in rhesus monkeys, the degree of 6-[18]F-L-DOPA uptake corresponds to the degree of clinically and neurochemically determined deficits in the same animals (ref.16). In this case the presynaptic ligand offers a distinct advantage as the severely effected animals may have more than a 95 percent loss of dopamine and subclinical cases as high as 50-80 percent alterations in dopamine content. Ideally the turnover of total isotope in these studies would parallel the turnover in dopamine, so that PET studies with 6-[18]F-L-DOPA could be used to evaluate functional dopamine activity in man. Although this may not prove to be a viable alternative, it is possible that the rate of uptake may still show a correspondence to functional activity. In this respect, it will be important to work out standardized conditions for these PET studies. For example, L-DOPA competes with other aromatic amino acids for transport through the blood brain barrier. A continuing problem with respect to the broad utilization of 6-[18]F-L-DOPA as a PET tracer is its relatively low synthetic yield and the time required for the liquid chromatographic procedure necessary for the isolation of the 6-F from the 2- and 5-F-L-DOPA deriviates, produced in the electrophilic substitution reaction with L-DOPA (ref.17).

A final, very significant point for PET isotope development, that is perhaps best illustrated here, is the necessity of toxicology studies for those tracers where there is not already clinical experience. It is essential, for example, to establish tha 6-F-L-DOPA is not converted to appreciable quantities of 6-hydroxydopamine, a highly toxic drug. In general, it may be reasonable to conduct toxicology studies at 100 fold the maximimum dose contemplated for use in man, both for acute and subacute regimens, in one rodent and in one non-rodent species. In this regard, whenever it proves feasible, it is useful to establish in advance of the formal toxicology evaluation, those organs worthy of special attention by studies of toxic doses. Finally, PET itself might prove a uniquely sensitive tool for the evaluation of toxicity with respect to specific pathways of the brain particularly when used in combination with neurotransmitter selective tracers.

TABLE 1

Table 1 is an outline of the steps that need to be considered before deciding to embark on the development of a specific PET tracer.

PREPLANNING CRITERIA

I.   Importance to Biomedical Research

II.  Ability to Devise Appropirate Measurement

       A.   Capacity to synthesize a positron emitting radionuclide of high specific activity and purity

       B.   Appropirate biological properties (e.g., "trapped")

       C.   Potential kinetic model for data interpretation

       D.   Verification

       E.   Toxicology

342

REFERENCES

1   M.E. Phelps, J.C. Mazziotta and S-C. Huang, J. Cerebral Blood Flow and
    Metab., 2 (1982) 113-162.
2   L. Sokoloff, M. Reivich, C. Kennedy, et al., J. Neurochem., 28 (1977)
    897-916.
3   M. Reivich, D. Kuhl, A. Wolf, et al., Circ. Res. 44 (1979) 127-137.
4   S.S. Kety, Am. J. Med., 8 (1950) 205-217.
5   L. Sokoloff, J. Cerebral Blood Flow and Metab., 1 (1981) 7-36.
6   M.E. Phelps, J.C. Mazziotta, L. Baxter and R. Gerner, Ann. of Neurology
    S15 (1984) S149-156.
7   H.N. Wagner, Jr., H.D. Burns, R.F. Dannals, et al., Science, 221 (1983)
    1264-1266.
8   D.F. Wong, H.N. Wagner, Jr, R.F. Dannals, et al., Science, 226 (1983)
    1393-1396.
9   C.S. Patlak, R.G. Blasberg and J.D. Fenstermacher, J. of Cerebral Blood
    Flow and Metab., 3 (1983) 1-7.
10  A. Gjedde, Brain Res. Rev., 4 (1982) 237-274.
11  L. Farde, E. Ehrin, L. Eriksson, et al., Proc. Natl. Acad. Sci. USA 82
    (1985) 3863-3867.
12  D.O. Keisewetter, W.C. Eckelman, R.M. Cohen and S.M. Larson, Abstract at
    Am. Chem. Soc. Meeting, 1985.
13  E.S. Garnett, G. Firnau and C. Nahmias, Nature, 305 (1983), 137-138.
14  C.C. Chiueh, Z. Zukowska-Grojec, K.L. Kirk, and I.J. Kopin, J. Pharmacol.
    Exp. Ther., 225 (1983) 529-533.
15  E.S. Garnett, C. Nahmias and G. Firnau, Can. J. Neurol. Sci., 11 (1984)
    174-179.
16  C.C. Chiueh, R.S. Burns, I.J. Kopin, et al., in S. Markey, et al.,
    Proceedings on MPTP, Academic Press, N.Y., in press.
17  G. Firnau, R. Chirakal and E.S. Garnett, J. Nucl. Med., 25 (1984)
    1228-1233.

*Synthesis and Applications of Isotopically Labeled Compounds 1985.*
Proceedings of the Second International Symposium, Kansas City, MO, U.S.A.,
3—6 September 1985, R.R. Muccino (Ed.), 343—348
© 1986 Elsevier Science Publishers B.V., Amsterdam — Printed in The Netherlands

STUDIES OF HUMAN CALCIUM KINETICS WITH STABLE ISOTOPIC KINETICS

A.L. YERGEY[*], N.E. VIEIRA[*], D. COVELL[#], J. MUENZER[*]
[*]National Institute of Child Health and Human Development
[#]National Cancer Institute
Bethesda, Maryland 20205

INTRODUCTION

It is well known that isotopically enriched materials, either elements or
molecules, can be used as tracers of chemical and physical phenomena such as
reaction or mixing processes. Highly enriched stable isotopes are excellent
choices for such tracers, and today, with the exception of diagonstic imaging
techniques, are virtually mandated for studies of human subjects. While
measurement of stable isotopic tracers can be accomplished by a number of
techniques, each with particular advantages, the most commonly used analytical
method is mass spectrometry. There are several reasons for this predominance.
First, the molecular identity of the tracer can frequently be maintained while
yielding satisfactory sensitivity for the analysis. Second, there is a
sufficient variety of mass spectrometric techniques so that one is generally
able to employ any polyisotopic element as a tracer. Third, mass spectrometric
measurements of tracers are made as a ratio of the tracer to an unperturbed
isotope resulting inan inherent gain in measurement accuracy.

We have used one of the classic mass spectrometric techniques for the
determination of the whole body distribution kinetics of calcium in normal
children, infants, pregnant and lactating women and in several cases of calcium
metabolic disorders. We have used thermal ionization mass spectrometry to
follow the time dependent change in the isotope ratios of the two simultaneously
administered tracers, one oral the other intravenous.

METHODS
Mass Spectrometry

Initial work, including analysis of all patient samples to date, has been done
using a single filament thermal ionization technique[1]. The recent acquisition
of a Finnigan MAT Thermal Ionization Quadrupole (THQ) instrument has allowed us
to adopt the more sensitive and precise dual filament technique. All calcium
samples, except water standards, are prepared as described in our earlier work[1]
by oxalate precipitation from basic solutions, which in the case of dietary and
fecal samples have been wet ashed, followed by collection and drying of the

samples. Approximately 15ug of $CaNO_3$ is placed on the evaporation filament and
is dried in two stages, the first to remove water of solution and the second to
remove water of crystallization and to stabilize the sample onto the filament.
Measurements are made by monitoring the center of each of four ion peaks in hte
Ca spectrum. Typically these are $^{42}Ca$, $^{43}Ca$, $^{44}Ca$ and $^{48}Ca$, where the first two
of these are used as tracers. The ratios are all determined relative to $^{48}Ca$
with the 43/48 ratio serving as a standard.

## Clinical

Subjects are admitted to the NIH Clinical Center and placed on a diet that
approximates their normal calcium intake. At the outset of a study they are
injected with $^{42}Ca$ (.6mg/kg) and given $^{44}Ca$ mixed in their breakfast milk
(2.5mg/kg). Six 5ml blood samples are drawn over the first 12 hours of the
study. The first 3-4 stools passed after the start of the study are collected,
and all urines, as 8hr pooled samples, are collected for the next three weeks.

## Mathematical Analysis

The SAAM (Simulation Analysis And Modeling) program[2] is used for analysis of the
error structure, determination of exponential fits and the compartmental
analysis of the isotope ratio data. The observed ratio data are converted to
delta % excess and used in that form or, in conjunction with total Ca
determinations, converted to mass of tracer excreted.

## RESULTS

Characterization of the dual filament technique and the THQ using water
solutions, serum and urine spiked with $^{42}Ca$ have shown that we can detect a
2-2.5% delta % excess with a relative standard deviation of about 1% or less.
In general this represents a 4-fold gain in sensitivity and a doubling in
precision, both of which lead to a greater ability to determine kinetic
processes with longer time constants.

The addition of the isotope spikes to water and serum samples yielded
isotope dilution curves that had slopes and intercepts very little different
from 1.0 and 0.0 respectively. The addition of spikes to urine samples resulted
in a curve that had slopes between 1.14 and 1.23. These indicate the spike was
being precipitated from urine more efficiently than the natural abundance
calcium, a phenomenon of incomplete equilibration of the spike in solution. The
equilibration can be effected by allowing the spiked urine sample to sit for 8
days at room temperature. (Figure 1). The major concern raised by the slow
equilibration is the possibility that the oral and i.v. tracers would not

equilibrate immediately in vivo, thus negating one of the major assumptions of the tracer technique. To test the assumption of immediate equilibration, a subject was injected with a tracer and blood samples drawn at 5 and 20 min. after injection. These samples were split into four aliquots. Two portions were put into ice and two were left at room temperature. An iced and room temperature aliquot were each analyzed immediately for tracer level, and the other two samples left for 8 days. There were no differences in the observed 42Ca/ 48Ca ratios from any of the samples. Thus , to limit of our measurements, there is an immediate equilibration of an intravenous tracer with the circulating calcium.

The single filament technique has been used to measure the time dependence of tracers in 8 normal children, a child with an inborn error of metabolism of unknown etiology that leads to calcification of soft tissues. The isotope ratio data are analyzed using both compartmental and non-compartmental models. Data from the intravenous tracer curves of several of these studies in children will be used to illustrate some properties of these models. A sum of exponentials, as shown in Equation 1, is the typical non-compartmental model.

$$y(t) = \sum_i A_i \exp(a_i t) \qquad\qquad (1)$$

The SAAM program uses initial values of the parameters selected by the user, then proceeds to minimize the sum of squares between the calculated function of Eq. 1 and the observed data. There are $2n$ possible free parameters for an $n$-term exponential expression. An initial value is selected for each exponent and for $n-1$ coefficients. The sum of coefficients is used as the final free parameter. We have found that typically three exponential terms are required to fit the intravenous tracer curves. The quality of the non-compartmental model can be assesed by the precision of the parameter fit estimated by the SAAM program. Table I shows the results of the exponential fit for one of the children. It is apparent that the quality of the fit is high since the average estimated error of the parameters, as shown by the fractional standard deviation (FSD), is less than 10%. The sum of the coefficients is equal to the zero time isotope dilution. This sum is similar in meaning to the extrapolation of an initial slope to the time axis, but uses the entire data set to achieve the goal. If the $t_0$ isotope dilution is known, then the mass of the rapidly mixing component, typically extracellular fluid (ECF) including blood can be calculated. Conversely, the dimension of this component of calcium distribution can be estimated from purely physiological considerations. Table II compares the delta % excess values for three subjects calculated from exponential fits and physiological estimates. It also shows the delta % excess value of the first measurements for these subjects, typically taken about 5 min. into a study. It can be seen that (1) the estimates of isotope dilution calculated by two methods agree reasonably well for subjects 1 and 3, with the physiological estimates being high; (2) the exponential calculation and the first measured values appear to be related in a consistent masnner, as might be expected from the way the calculations were performed; (3) the two estimates for the $t_0$ dilution are substantially different for subject 2. Since actual rather than ideal body weight was the basis of the physiological estimate of $t_0$ dilution, and since these children were all formerly obese and all slightly overweight at the time of the study, and since fat has no ECF associated with it, the physiological estimate may tend to underestimate the size of this component for calcium distribution. Such an underestimate would lead to larger than expected values of $t_0$. It is interesting to note that subject 2 was the "chunckiest" of these three subjects.

The compartmental modeling that is done with these dat sets has as its goal the explaination of calcium distribution in physiological pools. The compartments that are used in modeling do not, however relate directly to any specific physiological pool, although some deductions seem reasonable. Figure 2 shows the model currently in use. Compartments 1,2, 3 and 8 are internal and are considered to correspond to blood and other ECF, soft tissue, surface of bone and deep bone respectively. Compartments 5,6 and 7 are external and are sites for irreversible tracer losses and correspond to bladder, bowel and gut respectively. Flows into 5 and 6 can be measured directly using the dual tracer technique, and the flow 7-1, the fraction absorbed, can be measured using the ratio of both tracers in urine. In general the fractional transfer rates between compartments 1 and 2 as well as 1 and 3 can be estimated with FSDs of about 10% or less, as might be expected from the quality of the exponential fits. The transfer into and out of bone, transfers 3-8 and 8-3 of the model, are much slower than the other exchanges. Based on the data obtained in a three week study these parameters cannot be estimated with confidence. If one were able to extend the time over which the i.v. tracer's presence in urine could be measured, the quality of the estimate for the latter two parameters would be improved. Figure 3 shows an example of this. The real data of the study stop at 450 hrs (18.8 days), and the FSD estimates for the bone turnover parameters are meaninglessly large. If data are simulated out to 36 days, the precision of the parameter estimates improves remarkably and becomes quite reasonable. The ability to define these parameters has not existed previously, and all previous studies have gone for 19 days at most. The improved analytical capability that the THQ instrument affords us may permit the definition of these parameters.

LITERATURE CITED

1. Alfred Yergey, Nancy Vieira, James Hansen, <u>Anal.</u> <u>Chem.</u>, <u>52,</u> 1811 (1980).

2. M. Berman, M. Weiss, SAAM Manual, NIH Special Publication 78-180, (1978), Washington, DC

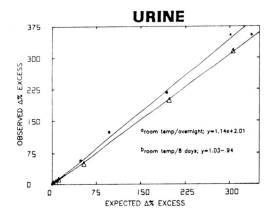

Figure 1

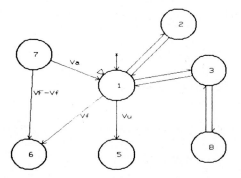

Figure 2

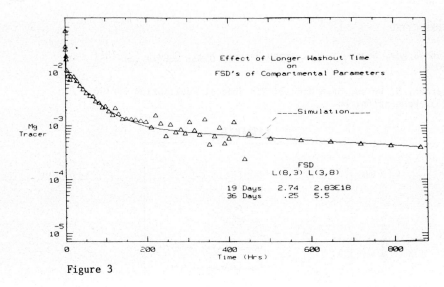

Figure 3

Table I

Reliability of Exponential Fit

|  |  | Value | FSD |
|---|---|---|---|
| Exponent | 1 | 3.0 | .045 |
|  | 2 | .027 | .072 |
|  | 3 | .0033 | .135 |
| Coefficient | 1 | 125.1 | --- |
|  | 2 | 762.7 | .130 |
|  | 3 | 27.2 | .034 |
| Sum of Coeff. |  | 915.0 | .029 |

Table II

Delta % Excess

(t=0)

| Subject | Exponential Fit | Physiological Estimate | First Meas. |
|---|---|---|---|
| 1 | 915 | 1112 | 774 |
| 2 | 712 | 1348 | 526 |
| 3 | 265 | 320 | 216 |

*Synthesis and Applications of Isotopically Labeled Compounds 1985.*
Proceedings of the Second International Symposium, Kansas City, MO, U.S.A.,
3—6 September 1985, R.R. Muccino (Ed.), 349—354
© 1986 Elsevier Science Publishers B.V., Amsterdam — Printed in The Netherlands

CLINICAL STUDIES IN PREMATURE INFANTS USING FOOD CONSTITUENTS LABELED WITH
STABLE ISOTOPES

M.J. Arnaud

Nestlé Research Department, Nestec Ltd., Avenue Nestlé 55, CH-1800 Vevey
(Switzerland)

ABSTRACT

The use of stable isotopes in clinical nutrition is particularly well
adapted for studying the fate of nutrients during pregnancy and in the neon-
ate. Whole body protein synthesis using repeated oral administration of
$^{15}$N-glycine and medium chain triglycerides oxidation using $^{13}$C-trioctanoin
have been studied in premature infants while iron absorption using $^{58}$Fe and
fecal isotope balance is under investigation.

INTRODUCTION

In reviewing the literature, it appears that the use of stable isotopes in
clinical research and nutrition has increased over the last decade. The explanation for this growing interest lies certainly in the development of less
tedious analytical methods, the availability of new stable-isotope-labeled
compounds and also in ethical considerations leading clinicians to replace
radiotracers. Stable isotopes are particularly convenient in clinical research
concerning high risk groups such as child-bearing women, neonates, children
and young adults. Neonates and, among them, premature infants, represent a
challenge to clinical medicine and nutrition because of the immaturity of
enzymatic systems and organ functions, the common medical complications encountered and the high growth and metabolic rates observed. Consequently, the
quantitative as well as the qualitative aspects of the needs for energy, protein and minerals in premature infants have to be investigated as well as the
interactions of all the nutrients, using a safe and non-invasive methodology.
This communication deals with three important research areas in the premature
infant : protein metabolism using $^{15}$N-glycine, energy metabolism using
$^{13}$C-medium chain triglyceride and mineral metabolism using $^{58}$Fe.

Protein Metabolism

$^{15}$N-Glycine has been the most widely used amino-acid in the evaluation
of protein turnover in clinical research. In premature infants, since the
first work (1) published in 1970, 11 other studies have been reported where
$^{15}$N-glycine was administered either orally or intravenously, by single or

continuous dosage (Table 1). Important variations in the weight of the infants, weight gain, gestational age and diet render comparison difficult and explain the observation that the greatest discrepancies between different studies in absolute rates of protein turnover were found in preterm low-birthweight infants (13). The majority of the studies used repeated oral administration for 30-72 hours and stochastic analysis of the plateau enrichment obtained in urinary urea (14) and in few cases, ammonia (15).

Calculated protein synthesis ranged from 4.7 to 26.3 g/kg/day for urea and 4.9 to 10.9 for ammonia. In repeated administration of glycine for 30-36 hours, urinary urea $^{15}$N-plateau was not achieved (3) and the estimate of the plateau value showed a wide range of variability. The use of the three last data points led to the overestimation of protein synthesis.

Birth weight and intrauterine nutritional status were shown to modify protein turnover (5) while casein or whey predominant diets (4), diets supplemented with MCT(5) and diets with different protein quality or different energy intake did not affect protein synthesis (7) but had an effect on the fraction of the flux coming from protein synthesis or breakdown. However, diets appeared to modify protein synthesis as the highest values were reported for breast milk when compared with infant formula (6,9). The most surprising finding was the failure to observe $^{15}$N enrichment in urea (8). In this study the repeated administration of a very low dose of $^{15}$N-glycine (0.1mg/kg/day) can explain the absence of a significant labeling. This observation has been recently confirmed after the repeated administration of 50 times higher dose of $^{15}$N-glycine (12). In the two studies, all of the infants with unlabeled urea except 2 were fed breast milk. For the last study the estimation of total glycine intake (mean ± SD) was 80.0±11 mg/Kg/day for the 11 studies showing urea labelling and 63.3±7.6 in the 5 cases with no enrichment. The presence of urea in breast milk cannot explain the effect observed in one subject on formula, neither in the case of the two infants breast fed where urea was labeled. When total protein intake was calculated taking into account that approximately 25% of nitrogen in breast milk is non-protein nitrogen, it appears that urea enrichment can be related to total protein intake. The intakes were 0.427±0.088 and 0.298±0.068 gN/kg/day in infants with labeled and unlabeled urea respectively. Table II shows that calculated protein intake for two subjects analyzed 3 times seemed to support this explanation .

When protein intake was reduced, in children, the excretion of endogenously synthesized urea was shown to fall as in premature infants (Table II) while urea retained was more extensively used for protein synthesis or other metabolic processes (16). The absence of urea labeling can be explained by the complete use of dietary glycine for the synthesis of protein as suggested previously (8). Other hypothesis are possible, such as the presence of two distinct urea pools : one labeled with glycine, located in the splanchnic area, where urea nitrogen recycling and excretion will be dependent on the protein intake and another pool which will have other amino acids as precursors.

As it was stated previously, [15]N-glycine $NH_3$/urea end product method

TABLE 1

Studies on protein turnover performed in Premature infants using [15]N Glycine

| No. of Studies | Dose of [15]N glycine mg/[15]N/kg/day(1) mg/[15]N/kg(2) | Diet * | Protein Synthesis g/kg/day | | Refs |
|---|---|---|---|---|---|
| | | | Urea | $NH_3$ | |
| 3 | 4.0 (2) | F | 4.7±1.0 | 5.6±1.1 | 1 |
| 10 | 0.5 (1) | unknown | 17.4±7.9 | – | 2 |
| 10 | 0.6 (1) | F(9);BM(1) | 26.3±7.0 | – | 3 |
| 30 | 0.6 (1) | F | 13.1±3.1 | – | 4 |
| | | F | 12.4±3.2 | – | |
| | | BM | 18.4±4.8 | – | |
| 40 | 0.6 (1) | F | 12.8±2.7 | – | 5 |
| | | | 19.8±4.6 | – | |
| 20 | 0.6 (1) | F | 14.4±3.9 | – | 6 |
| 24 | 0.6 (1) | F | 6.8±1.0 | – | 7 |
| | | | 8.9±1.3 | – | |
| 8 | 0.1 (1) | F(1);BM(7) | – | 10.9±3.4 | 8 |
| 30 | 0.6 (1) | F | 14.5±1.0 | 9.4±0.3 | 9 |
| | | F | 12.8±1.0 | 8.8±0.4 | |
| | | BM | 18.7±1.5 | 8.9±0.2 | |
| 10 | 3.7 (2) | F | 7.9±2.1** | | 10 |
| | | BM | 7.8±2.7 | | |
| 12 | 0.93(2) | BM+F | 7.9±2.2 | 4.9±2.1 | 11 |
| 16 | 5 (1) | F (10)BM(6) | 11.2±3.5 | 5.8±1.5 | 12 |

* F: infant formula; BM: breast milk; ** Cumulative renal [15]N excess.

TABLE II

Effect of protein intake on urinary urea excretion and [15]N enrichment of nitrogen end products.

| Subjects | Diet | Protein intake gP/kg/day | Glycine intake mg/kg/day | Urinary urea excretion in mg/ml | [15]N plateau enrichment | |
|---|---|---|---|---|---|---|
| | | | | | Atom urea | % excess $NH_3$ |
| FM 1 | EBM[1] | 2.20 | 69.7 | 1.77 | 0.413 | 0.542 |
| 2 | EBM[1] | 1.79 | 61.9 | 1.02 | 0* | 0.304 |
| 3 | EBM[1] | 1.58 | 57.7 | 0.99 | 0.135 | 0.710 |
| YR 1 | EBM[2] | 2.13 | 68.5 | 1.23 | 0* | 0.377 |
| 2 | F[3] | 3.22 | 89.6 | 3.06 | 0.269 | 0.497 |
| 3 | F[4] | 2.53 | 73.8 | 1.88 | 0* | 0.680 |

EBM =Expressed breast milk from their own mother (1) or supplemented with other milk (2). F = Formula Alprem-MCT (3) and Nan (4). * = Urea was significantly labeled in some urine samples.

give useful results for comparative purposes (17) and these data in con-
tradiction with the expected results must be explained and will certainly
lead to an improvement of the model.

Energy Metabolism :

The use of $^{13}$C-labeled compounds is well documented in human clinical studies. $^{13}$C-Trioctanoin breath test was applied in children to
detect fat malabsorption (18), the % of the dose collected in the 6 hours
following the oral administration in expired $CO_2$ was 27.6±10.3% in
normal children. Since this study, no work was subsequently published and
the oxidation, metabolism and storage of medium chain triglycerides (MCT)
is unknown and must be assessed in premature infants.

Every four hours, five infants received a formula containing 40% of
fat as MCT through a naso-gastric tube. On the second day of a three-day
nutrient balance, 160mg of $^{13}$C-trioctanoin was administered as a single
dose, producing an increase of 35-42% of trioctanoin present in the
formula. Indirect calorimetry was performed during the 24hrs following the
ingestion with the simultaneous collection and purification of expired
$CO_2$ to measure $^{13}$C enrichment (19). As no significant enrichment was
observed in urine and feces, the metabolic fate of MCT must proceed
through oxidation to provide energy and incorporation into fat stores or
other body constituents. Similar patterns of $^{13}$C enrichment in expired
$CO_2$ were recorded however with wide quantitative variations from one
infant to another. The fractions of the dose recovered range from 6.5 to
44 %. Even if we consider that in older infants, no more than 60% of $^{13}$C
which enters bicarbonate pool can be recovered in expired $CO_2$ (20), 28
to 90% of the administered dose seemed to be eliminated by non-respiratory
routes. Carbon recycling in premature infants in unknown and important
individual variations may explain the results obtained. The analysis by
GC-MS of blood medium chain fatty acids, free and in triglycerides, showed
the presence of $^{13}$C-octanoic acid and a low but significant labeling of
C12:0. Preliminary results reported C10:0 and C12:0 storage in adipose
tissues of infants in relation with dietary intake while C8:0 did not and
thus was reported to be more completely oxidized (21). The biosynthesis of
C12:0 and its storage in adipose tissues of premature infants cannot be
estimated in this study but must be considered in the total recovery.
Other hypotheses to account for a low recovery are the losses of medium
chain fatty acids and ketone bodies through breath and the skin. The
correlation obtained between total $^{13}CO_2$ collected and the area under
the plasma concentration curves of $^{13}$C-octanoic acid indicates possible
uncontrolled variations in the dose administered recently observed in MCT

supplementation(22).

Mineral Metabolism :

There are few reports in the literature where mineral metabolism was investigated in the newborn infant using stable isotopes. In the premature infants, four studies investigated calcium metabolism with $^{46}$Ca and $^{48}$Ca and one study evaluated zinc bioavailability with $^{70}$Zn. In spite of the prevalence of anaemia in childhood, the bioavailability of $^{58}$Fe has not yet been reported in the infant. Radioiron absorption tests performed in adult humans to measure the absorption from infant foods (23) gave results which cannot be extrapolated to the infant situation. A study using radioactive iron in the infants (24), showed the accuracy and validity of fecal isotope balance compared with the recovery of radioactivity in blood. Such a study would not now be accepted by an ethical committee and methodology using stable isotopes have to be developed.

Absorption of iron in young men studied by monitoring excretion of $^{58}$Fe in feces has already been reported (25). We confirmed these results using also neutron activation for the analysis of $^{58}$Fe in stools collected every day for 5 days, after the oral administration of 0.75 mg $^{58}$Fe. Cumulative fecal excretion of $^{58}$Fe amounted to 98% of the dose and most of the label was recovered on the first two days (Fig. 1).

This non-invasive technique gave us excellent recovery in adult subjects but as already stated (25) will be unsatisfactory for quantitative iron absorption in adult subjects with absorption lower than 5%. Moreover, we can questioned the physiological significance of such small variations in healthy subjects. In neonates where 20% or more of iron intake was

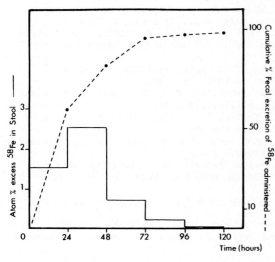

Fig. 1: Atom % excess in stool and cumulative fecal excretion of $^{58}$Fe fed to an adult volunteer.

shown to be absorbed, $^{58}$Fe fecal balance must be the method of choice and extrinsic label will give the availability of iron salts added to infant formula. Analysis of stable isotope in blood samples must be developed in order to correlate these results with the double radioisotope extrinsic tag method taken as a reference.

However, these experiments will be conducted with some limitations because of the expense of these isotopes and also the limited availability of different salts. This observation is also applicable to other studies performed with $^{15}$N and $^{13}$C labeled compounds.

REFERENCES

1. J.F. Nicholson, Pediatr. Res., 4 (1970) 389-397.
2. V.R. Young, W.P. Steffee, P.B. Pencharz, J.C. Winterer and N.S. Scrimshaw, Nature, 253 (1975), 192-193.
3. P.B. Pencharz, N.P. Steffee, W. Cochran, N.S. Scrimshaw, W.M. Rand and V.R. Young, Clin. Sci. Mol. Med., 52 (1977), 485-498.
4. P.B. Pencharz, L. Farri and A. Papageorgiou, Pediatr. Res., 15 (1981), 544, A 620.
5. P.B. Pencharz, M. Masson, F. Desgranges and A. Papageorgiou, Clin. Sci., 61 (1981), 207-215.
6. P.B. Pencharz, H. Parsons, K. Motil and B. Duffy, Medical Hypotheses, 7 (1981), 155-160.
7. D. Duffy, T. Gunn, J. Collinge and P. Pencharz, Pediatr. Res., 15 (1981), 1040-1044.
8. A.A. Jackson, J.C.L. Shaw, A. Barber and M.H.N. Golden, Pediatr. Res., 15 (1981), 1454-1461.
9. P. Pencharz, L. Farri, R. Clarke and A. Papageorgiou, Pediatr. Res., 17(1983), 298A, 1213.
10. W. Heine, C. Plath, I. Richter, K. Wutzke and J. Töwe, J. Pediatr. Goastroenterol. Nutr., 2 (1983), 606-612.
11. I. Nissim, M. Yudkoff, G. Pereira and S. Segal, J. Pediatr. Gastroenteral. Nutr. 2 (1983), 507-516.
12. C. Catzeflis, Y. Schutz, J.L. Micheli, C. Welsch, M.J. Arnaud and E. Jequier, Pediatr. Res., 19(1985) 679-687.
13. D. Halliday and M.J. Rennie, Clin. Sci., 63(1982), 485-496.
14. D. Picou and T. Taylor-Roberts, Clin. Sci., 36(1969), 283-296.
15. J.C. Waterlow, P.J. Garlick and D.J. Millward, (1978), in Protein Turnover in Mammalian Tissues and in the Whole Body, Amsterdam: North Holland Publishing Co.
16. D. Picou and M. Phillips, Am. J. Clin. Nutr. 25(1972), 1261-1266.
17. J.C. Waterlow, Proc. Nutr. Soc. 40(1981), 317-320.
18. J.B. Watkins, P.D. Klein, D.A. Schoeller, B.S. Kirschner, R. Park and J.A. Perman, Gastroenterology, 82(1982), 911-917.
19. G. Putet, M.J. Arnaud, A.-L. Thélin, G. Philippossian, R. Liardon, J. Santerre and B. Salle, unpublished results.
20. C.S. Irving, C.H. Lifschitz, W.W. Wong, T.W. Boutton, B.L. Nichols and P.D. Klein, Pediatr. Res. 19 (1985), 358-363.
21. P. Sarda, G. Lepage and P. Chessex, Pediatr. Res., 18(1984), 211A,691
22. N.R. Mehta, M. Hamosh, J. Bitman and D.L. Wood, Pediatr. Res. 19 (1985), 227A, 698.
23. T.A. Morck, S.R. Lynch, B.S. Skikne, and J.D. Cook, Am. J. Clin. Nutr. 34(1981), 2630-2634.
24. J. Schulz and N.J. Smith, Amer. J. Dis. Child., 95(1958), 109-119.
25. M. Janghorbani, B.T.G. Ting and V.R. Young, J. Nutr. 110(1980), 2190-2197.

*Synthesis and Applications of Isotopically Labeled Compounds 1985.*
Proceedings of the Second International Symposium, Kansas City, MO, U.S.A.,
3—6 September 1985, R.R. Muccino (Ed.), 355—360
© 1986 Elsevier Science Publishers B.V., Amsterdam — Printed in The Netherlands

## EXPERIENCES WITH $^3$H-NMR

F.M. KASPERSEN, C.W. FUNKE, G.N. WAGENAARS

Scientific Development Group, Organon International B.V.

P.O. Box 20, 5340 BH Oss, The Netherlands

Abstract

Several applications of $^3$H-NMR are discussed. For the determination of the position of tritium $^3$H-$^1$H shift correlation NMR spectroscopy can be applied. Discrimination between mono- and multitritiated species is possible on basis of the upfield shift caused by the tritium isotope effect.
The interference of radiolysis is discussed together with the application of $^3$H-NMR in the measurement of the specific activity. The measurement of the optical purity by $^3$H-NMR spectroscopy using Pirkle's alcohol is also illustrated.

## Introduction

Especially thanks to the work of the group at Amersham International/University of Surrey[1] $^3$H-NMR has become an established and essential technique in the analysis of tritiated compounds. Since 90% of the investigations with labelled compounds at our company is done with tritiated material we extended in 1981 our Bruker 200 MHz NMR spectrometer with a tritium probe, followed in 1984 by the installation of such a probe in our Bruker 360 MHz instrument. In this paper an overview of our experiences with $^3$H-NMR is given. The following topics will be discussed:

1. Determination of position of the label
2. Determination of distribution of labelled species
3. Determination of radiochemical purity
4. Determination of specific activity
5. Determination of enantiomeric purity

## Determination of the position of the label

In simple molecules location of the tritium is possible using the $^3$H chemical shift and/or the $^1$H-$^3$H coupling constants. In more complex systems $^3$H-$^1$H shift correlations[2] can be applied. Dependent on the pulse sequences used we see either all coupling constants (c.f. a normal COSY experiment[3]), a spectrum decoupled in the triton domain or measure a spectrum decoupled both in the proton and triton domain (c.f. a normal heteronuclear shift correlation experiment[4]. Usually the $^3$H$_m$-$^1$H$_n$ spin system forms part of a larger $^1$H spin system and this prohibits the choice of correct parameters in the latter two sequences; therefore the first pulse sequence should be preferred[2]. A drawback of shift-correlation spectroscopy is the large amount of radioactivity needed: 300 MBq/labelled position.

## Determination of the distribution of labelled species

Geminally or vicinally multitritiated compounds can be distinguished from monotritiated compounds on basis of the small upfield shift of the signals because of the tritium isotope effect [5]. For bepridil tritiated in the pyrrolidine ring by reduction with $^3$H$_2$ of the 3-pyrroline-analogue (Figure 1) we could not readily distinguish the mono- and multitritiated species; due to the interaction of the asymmetrically substituted β-C-atom of the propyl chain with the asymmetrical C-atoms in the pyrrolidine-ring formed upon introduction of tritium a very complicated spectrum was obtained.

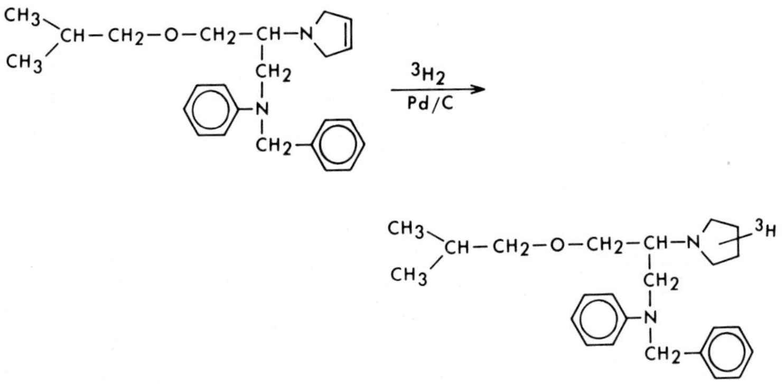

Figure 1: Synthesis of [pyrrolidine-$^3$H]-bepridil.

By measurement of the ratio monotritiated/ditritiated material by F.D. mass spectrometry and fractionation of the material by HPLC, it was possible to interpret the NMR spectrum as a mixture of the spectra of two diastereomeric forms of [pyrrolidine -3-$^3$H] bepridil (two singlets), [pyrrolidine-cis-3,4-$^3$H$_2$]- bepridil (one diastereomer, an AB pattern), a small amount of [pyrrolidine-trans-3,4-$^3$H$_2$]-bepridil (two diastereomers, two singlets), [pyrrolidine-2-$^3$H]-bepridil (two diastereomers, two singlets) and [pyrrolidine-2,3-$^3$H$_2$]-bepridil plus [pyrrolidine-2,3,4-$^3$H$_3$]-bepridil (complex signals)[6].

Determination of the radiochemical purity

The information obtained from a $^3$H-NMR spectrum about the radiochemical purity is limited. The $^3$H signals should coincide with signals in the proton spectrum of the unlabelled compound, but as shown in Figure 2 such a fulfilment does not guarantee a good radiochemical purity, especially for multitritiated compounds.

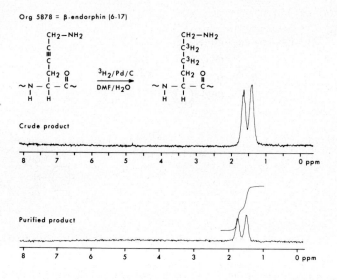

Figure 2: [3]H-NMR spectra ([1]H-decoupled) of [lysine-[3]H]-endorphin-(6-17)[7]

A: crude product (purity 50%)

B: purified product (purity 97%)

By interference of radiolysis inside the NMR tube [8], wrong conclusions might be drawn about radiochemical purity and position of the label. To circumvent such problems we usually record the spectra in the presence of 5 mg amounts of unlabelled carrier.


Determination of the specific activity

The measurement of specific activities between 100 GBq.mmol$^{-1}$ and 1000 GBq.mmol$^{-1}$ is possible by a combination of [1]H- and [3]H-NMR by measurement of the decrease in the intensity of the [1]H-signals. Even if a [1]H-NMR spectrum of good quality is obtained, the precision of such a measurement is worse than for a measurement by F.D. or FAB mass spectrometry [9].

In case of some exchange reactions the specific activity can be calculated from the $^3$H NMR spectrum alone[8] by measurement of the ratio ditritiated/monotritiated material under NOE suppressed conditions.

## Determination of the optical purity

Using chiral additive such as Pirkle's alcohol, the enantiomeric purity can be determined by NMR spectroscopy because of splitting of the signals. This method is also applicable for tritiated compounds. However, an NMR machine with a good resolution is needed because the tritium usually is not located in the regions with maximum splitting. This is illustrated in Figure 3 for a number of tetracyclic amines: the splitting observed for the N-methyl group is always larger than the splitting observed for the tritium resonances. The application for the measurement of the enantiomeric purity of [$^3$H]-(+)-bepridil will be published elsewhere.[6]

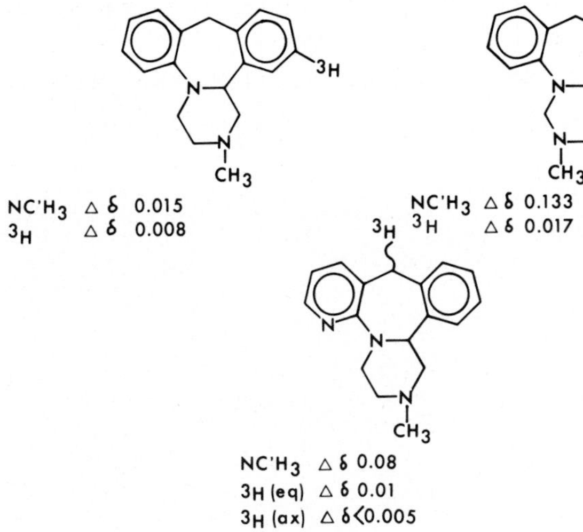

Figure 3: Splitting of resonances of the signals of the enantiomers of a number of tetracyclic amines on addition of Pirkle's alcohol.

360

Acknowledgement:
We thank Mr. F. van Rooy, Mr. E. Sperling and Mr. J. Wallaart for their contributions to this study.

REFERENCES

1. J.A. Elvidge, in J.A. Elvidge and J.R. Jones (eds) Isotopes: Essential Chemistry and Applications. The Chemical Society, London, 1980, pp 123.
2. C.W. Funke, G.N. Wagenaars, F.M. Kaspersen, Magn. Reson. Chem., submitted for publication.
3. W.P. Aue, F. Bartholdi, R.R. Ernst, J. Chem. Phys. 64, 2229 (1976).
4. A. Bax, Ph. Thesis, University of Delft, 1981.
5. J.P. Bloxsidge, J.A. Elvidge, J.R. Jones, R.B. Mane, M. Saljoughian, Org. Magn. Res. 12, 574 (1979).
6. F.M. Kaspersen, C.W. Funke, E.M.G. Sperling, F.A.M. van Rooy, G.N. Wagenaars, J.C.S. Perkin Trans II, in press.
7. F.M. Kaspersen, F.M. van Rooy, J. Wallaart, C. Funke, Recl. Trav. Chim. 102, 450 (1983).
8. C.W. Funke, F.M. Kaspersen, J. Wallaart, G.N. Wagenaars, J. Labelled Comp. Radioph. 20, 843 (1983).
9. W.D. Lehmann, F.M. Kaspersen, J. Labelled Comp. Radioph. 21, 455 (1984).

*Synthesis and Applications of Isotopically Labeled Compounds 1985.*
Proceedings of the Second International Symposium, Kansas City, MO, U.S.A.,
3—6 September 1985, R.R. Muccino (Ed.), 361—364
© 1986 Elsevier Science Publishers B.V., Amsterdam — Printed in The Netherlands

# THE USE OF $^3$H NMR IN THE PREPARATION OF TRITIATED NEUROCHEMICALS

C.N. FILER

E. I. DuPont de Nemours and Co., NEN Products

549 Albany St., Boston, Massachusetts 02118

ABSTRACT

Tritium has emerged as an advantageous radiolabel in biological research, and the past decade has witnessed the growing use of this isotope in neuroscience. High specific activity tritiated radioligands in receptor binding assay have proved invaluable to study the function of neurotransmitter receptors. The development and routine use of $^3$H NMR has clearly facilitated the preparation and characterization of tritiated neurochemicals. Specific examples highlight the ability of $^3$H NMR to confirm radiolabeling specificity as well as to ascertain tritiated radioligand specific activity.

During the past decade, the use of tritiated compounds in neuroscience and especially high specific activity radioligands in receptor binding assay experiments has proved to be a valuable means to study neurotransmission at the receptor level (ref. 1). The development of $^3$H NMR and its exploitation on a routine basis has greatly facilitated the preparation and characterization of tritiated neurochemicals. In particular, $^3$H NMR has been employed to probe tritiation specificity and determine radioligand specific activity.

A most important role for $^3$H NMR in the preparation of neurochemicals has been to reveal the exact position of tritiation. We have reported on the use of $^3$H NMR for this purpose in the cases of (-)-[N-propyl-$^3$H] N-propylnorapomorphine (ref. 2), (-)-[8,9-$^3$H] apomorphine (ref. 3), (±)-[N-methyl-$^3$H] mianserin (ref. 4) and certain [N-allyl-2,3-$^3$H] radioligands (ref. 5). $^3$H NMR was also able to convincingly demonstrate that [$^3$H] histamine (1) and [$^3$H] haloperidol (2) were specifically radiolabeled although prepared by general exchange conditions (Figs. 1 and 2).

The example of [14,15-$^3$H] dihydroforskolin (3) (ref. 6) illustrates the wealth of unique and subtle information about tritiation specificity that $^3$H NMR can afford. Radioligand 3 was prepared by the catalytic tritiation of olefin precursor forskolin. Since the 14-position methylene tritiums of 3 are proximate to a chiral center, they can be distinguished in the $^3$H NMR (Fig. 3) as separate downfield peaks (δ 1.45 and 1.65 ppm) due to residing in different chemical and magnetic environments. $^3$H NMR discloses that during tritiation the catalyst has essentially equal access to both sides of the olefin of forskolin and that there is restricted rotation about the 13,14-bond of 3.

$^3$H NMR and radiolabeling specificity considerations can also at times support or cast doubt on the radiochemical purity of a tritiated neurochemical. A tritiated radioligand may appear to be chromatographically homogeneous, but the appearance of an unexpected and unassignable peak in its $^3$H NMR may indicate the presence of an undetected impurity.

Besides the confirmation of tritiation specificity, $^3$H NMR also proves useful to determine specific activity, especially in cases where other methods such as UV spectroscopy or field desorption mass spectrometry (ref. 7) fail. Since it is so often necessary to know the exact molar concentration of a tritiated radioligand in solution, the precise determination of specific activity is crucial to neurochemists. The example of [21,22-$^3$H] dihydrostrychnine (4) prepared from the catalytic tritiation of strychnine illustrates how easy specific activity can be measured by $^3$H NMR. The $^3$H NMR of 4 (Fig. 4) shows the presence of a ditritiated species as indicated by two doublets at δ 2.35 ppm (21-position) and δ 1.90 ppm (22-position), and two monotritiated species appearing as singlets superimposed upon the doublets. Integrating and summing the contribution for each species provides a specific activity value of 31 Ci/mmol for 4. The same integration and summing process can be applied to even more complicated $^3$H NMR spectra for the calculation of specific activity.

In summary, $^3$H NMR has emerged as a useful tool in the preparation and characterization of tritiated neurochemicals. Its ability to reveal radio-labeling specificity is unique and it also compliments other existing methods to determine the specific activity of tritiated neurochemicals.

REFERENCES

1  H.I. Yamamura, S.J. Enna and M.J. Kuhar (Eds.), Neurotransmitter Receptor Binding, Raven Press, New York, 1978.
2  C.N. Filer, D.G. Ahern, F.E. Granchelli, J.L. Neumeyer and S.J. Law, J. Org. Chem., 45 (1980) 3465.
3  C.N. Filer and D.G. Ahern, J. Org. Chem., 45 (1980) 3918.
4  C.N. Filer, R. Fazio and D.G. Ahern, J. Org. Chem., 46 (1981) 3344.
5  C.N. Filer, D.G. Ahern, R. Fazio and R.J. Seguin, J. Org. Chem., 46, (1981) 4968.
6  R.-j. Ho and Q.-h. Shi, J. Biol. Chem., 259 (1984) 7630.
7  H.D. Beckey and H.R. Schulten, Angew. Chem. Int. Ed., 14 (1975) 403.

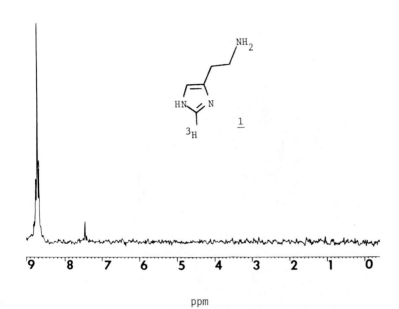

Fig. 1. $^1$H Decoupled $^3$H NMR (CD$_3$OD,D$_2$O,DCl) of $\underline{1}$.

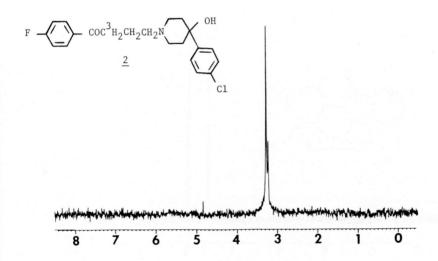

ppm

Fig. 2. $^1$H Decoupled $^3$H NMR (CD$_3$OD) of $\underline{2}$.

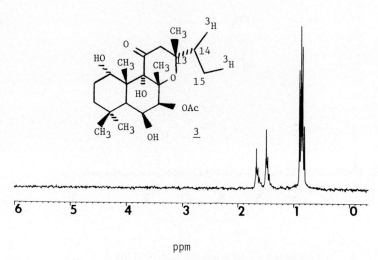

Fig. 3. $^1$H Decoupled $^3$H NMR (CDCl$_3$) of $\underline{3}$.

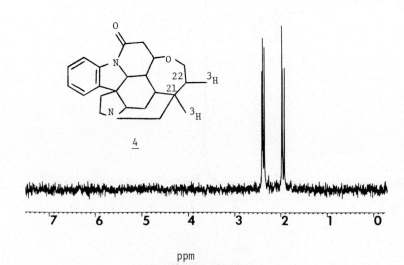

Fig. 4. $^1$H Decoupled $^3$H NMR (CDCl$_3$) of $\underline{4}$.

*Synthesis and Applications of Isotopically Labeled Compounds 1985.*
Proceedings of the Second International Symposium, Kansas City, MO, U.S.A.,
3—6 September 1985, R.R. Muccino (Ed.), 365—370
© 1986 Elsevier Science Publishers B.V., Amsterdam — Printed in The Netherlands

# $^3$H-NMR: THE CUSTOMER'S POINT OF VIEW

DEREK E. BRUNDISH

CIBA-GEIGY Pharmaceutical Division, Research Centre, Horsham, West Sussex, RH12
4AB, England*

ABSTRACT

Examples are given where $^3$H-NMR spectroscopy assists in (a) elucidating
unexpected results, (b) allowing simpler labelling procedures to be selected,
(c) clarifying metabolic studies, (d) planning radiochemical syntheses and even
(e) determining the structure of an unlabelled precursor molecule. The varied
advantages of routinely using the technique are seen to justify the costs involved.

INTRODUCTION

$^3$H-NMR is claimed to have as advantages:

1) It allows the assignment of $^3$H-NMR distribution without the need for time-
   consuming chemical degradation studies (Ref. 1) which, in any case may be
   subject the error through isotope redistribution.

2) It is non-destructive, allowing recovery of labelled material (Ref. 1).

3) It often allows generally-labelled compound to be declared adequate for use
   in a particular study, i.e. a one-step exchange preparation may be used instead of a multi-stage synthesis to produce unambiguously a specifically-
   labelled compound (Ref. 1).

4) It can assist in planning syntheses (Ref. 2).

However, other powerful and more sensitive analytical techniques exist, especially in the peptide field. Also, the cost of obtaining spectra can be quite
high, particularly when small amounts of sample require long acquisition times.
Thus, probably, a decision whether to use $^3$H-NMR may depend on the particular
molecule under study. The following examples illustrate some of our experiences, which have allowed our current 'point of view' to emerge.

RESULTS AND DISCUSSION

Elucidating unexpected results

For analysing the distribution of tritium label amongst the amino acid resi-

---

* Current address: CIBA-GEIGY AG, Central Research Laboratories, R-1060.1.12,
CH-4002 Basle, Switzerland

dues of a peptide which has been prepared from a synthetic precursor, the standard techniques of amino analysis after both acidic and enzymic hydrolysis coupled with scintillation counting are exquisitely sensitive (e.g. Ref. 3) and far beyond the range of [3]H-NMR. For [3]H-peptides to be useful in in vivo studies, it is not essential to know exactly the site of labelling within residues, and this can be assumed fairly safely from the structure of the precursor taken for labelling.

When we prepared [[3]H-Leu[2]] locust adipokinetic hormone (LAKH) (1) by reduction of the analogous decapeptide containing a 4,5-dehydroleucine residue (2), the product had a specific activity of 115 Ci/mmol (Ref. 4). Theoretical activity for the saturation of a double bound is 58 Ci/mmol.

$$\text{Glp-Leu-Asn-Phe-Thr-Pro-Asn-Trp-Gly-Thr-NH}_2 \quad (1)$$

Under such conditions, classical analytical techniques have little to offer.

$$(2) \qquad\qquad (3)$$

Proton-decoupled [3]H-NMR of [[3]H] LAKH showed tritium located in the approximate ratio of 6:1 in the δ(methyl) and γ(methine) positions of the leucine residue (3) at 0.9 and 1.6 ppm respectively. This suggested a mixed exchange and saturation mechanism with the former process being very rapid. From a consideration of the splitting pattern and from the results of deuteration studies on model compounds, we were confident that no methylene labelling was present (the signal would have overlapped with the methine signal). Our conclusions were confirmed by an independent study (Ref. 5) in which N-acetyl-dehydroleucine was partially reduced and then examined by [3]H-NMR. Signals at 4.9 and 1.7 ppm for vinylic and allylic tritium (2) indicated that exchange labelling reactions preceed saturation. This mechanism is consistent with our observations.

## Assessment of simple (i.e. exchange) labelling procedures

Again, from the peptide field, we observed that peptides containing histidine could be exchange-labelled with an efficiency that was inversely related to size (i.e. governed by steric hindrance) (Ref. 6). [3]H-NMR showed TRF (a tripeptide) and a C3a pentapeptide to be labelled exclusively at the C-2 position (7.8 ppm) of histidine (4), thus giving a specifically-labelled compound without the need for synthesis of a specifically-designed precursor.

We showed that 'exchange-out' of label was slow enough as to be negligible under physiological conditions, while C-5 label appeared to be completely stable to exchange. Other workers reported that histidine accepts tritium by exchange into both the C-2 and C-5 positions and that both sites are labile to 'exchange-out' (refs. 7,8).

Histidine exchange reactions have been described as 'fairly exceptional' (i.e. as regards obtaining a specifically located label) and unpredictable (Ref. 7). Results are known to be dependent on solvent pH and on gas pressure (Ref. 7) and must also be influenced by the choice of catalyst and solvent and possibly also by the structure of the peptide substrate. The literature on these subjects, both 'exchange-in' and 'exchange-out' (Refs. 6-9) is conflicting and the many variables require careful and systematic investigation. $^3$H-NMR would be a key technique in these studies.

(4)                          (5)

Metabolic studies

[$^3$H]Diclofenac (5) was prepared by debromination of a synthetic bromo-derivative (Ref. 10) which allowed labelling at a position known, from extensive studies using $^{14}$C-labelled material, to be free from metabolic hydroxylation (Ref. 11). Animal excretion studies, however, showed a few per cent of isotope transformed into tritiated water. $^3$H-NMR revealed, in addition to the expected signal at 7.09 ppm (5), a minor signal (2.6 %) at 7.19 ppm which could be specifically assigned to a position activated towards exchange labelling. This position (5) was a known primary site of metabolism by hydroxylation. With this knowledge, the compound became fully acceptable for in vivo use as corrections could now be made to metabolic data.

Synthesis route planning

A hot semi-synthesis of [$^3$H]MTP-cephalin (6) from [$^3$H]DMP (7) labelled in the N-acetyl group (Ref. 12) gave a product which yielded some tritiated water in an animal excretion study. An alternative synthesis was, therefore, required.

(6)  R = — NH ⟨CH₃⟩ CONH ... O—P—OCH₂ ... (structure)

(7)  R = — OH

It was known, from $^3$H-NMR studies, that exchange-labelling of MDP (7) introduced label into the N-acetyl group (2.0 ppm) and the anomeric position (5.1 and 4.7 ppm) (Ref. 13). To avoid exchange-labelling at the N-acetyl position, which would manifest in metabolism to tritiated water, it was decided to use a labelling substrate bearing a protecting group at the amino position of the S-substituted cysteine derivative to yield [$^3$H]L-alanine, which conversion had recently been reported (Ref. 6). This idea was quickly shown to be so complex as to be impracticable. However, work on the reductive desulphurisation approach, using model compounds, showed that they yielded the corresponding L-alanine compounds bearing $^3$H predominantly at the β-position (1.39 ppm) with no more than 0.3 % of D-alanine arising via the putative unsaturated intermediate as evidenced by label at the α-position (4.31 ppm) (Ref. 14). These results invalidated the earlier study (Ref. 6) which had suggested (by reverse isotope dilution analysis) that the L-alanine was equally labelled at the α- and β-positions. This had appeared rather improbable and had sugge-

(Scheme 1)

sted a novel mechanism. The new results obtained by [3]H-NMR now demonstrated a quite credible mechanism (Scheme 1), though it should be remembered that the outcome (i.e. hydrogenolysis vs. β-elimination) will probably depend on variables such as catalyst, solvent, protecting group, temperature etc. in each case studied.

Encouraged by this finding, we reduced a β-chloroalanine analogue of MDP. In this instance, the [3H]alanine residue was racemised perhaps to the extent of 10 % (signal at 4.32 ppm), however separation of the MDP's containing L- and D-alanine is very simple by high pressure liquid chromatography. Signals at the anomeric positions were seen but, surprisingly, N-acetyl exchange labelling was absent. This unexpected result validated β-chloroalanine[1]-MDP as a simple precursor for [3H]MTP-cephalin devoid of the unwanted metabolically labile N-acetyl label.

Now the [3]H-NMR had resolved the mechanism of alanine generation from S-tritylcysteine, we returned to the original somatostatin tridecapeptide derivative and again carried out an exchange-labelling. Spectroscopy showed a signal at 1.39 ppm (alanine $CH_3$). So little material was available that the failure to see a signal at 4.31 ppm (alanine CH) was no surprise, especially as it was probably present at below 0.5 % of the methyl label. The original work (Ref. 6) has shown exchange labelling of phenylalanine to around 20 % of that in alanine in purified fractions from somatostatin trideca- and tetradecapeptides. In the [3]H-NMR-spectrum in the present instance, no signal was observed for any proton in phenylalanine (Ref. 15). Accordingly, the sample was recovered (another claimed advantage of [3]H-NMR, it is a non-destructive technique (Ref. 1)) and analysed classically by hydrolysis, amino acid analysis and scintillation counting. The ratio of tritium associated with the alanine and phenylalanine residues was approximately 3:1. Spectroscopy had failed to give this information. Although the limited amount of material available makes it uncertain whether the phenylalanine signals should have been seen, the overall comparatively poor sensitivity of the spectroscopy relative to counting after separation cannot be denied.

## Structure determination

Acetylation of bromomaleic hydrazide would be expected to yield compound 8, a precursor for the preparation of [3H]maleic hydrazide (Ref. 16). The [1]H-NMR spectrum of the product shows two sharp signals; 2.28 ppm (acetyl) and 8.10 ppm (ring), but this last signal is, in isolation, no help in deciding between structures 8 and 9.

After tritiation (which was to around 70 % abundance), the [3]H signal was at 7.03 ppm and the [1]H spectrum of the tritiated material gave a pair of doublets centered (by calculation) on 7.00 and 7.40 ppm (J=9.9 cps). This readily

Br—⟨OAc⟩ (8)   Br—⟨OAc⟩ (9)   7.43 ppm / 7.03 ppm ⟨OAc⟩ (10)

demonstrated structure 8 as the acetylation product (Ref. 17).

ACKNOWLEDGEMENTS

$^3$H-FTNMR spectra were obtained by Dr. J.R. Jones, Surrey University, using a Bruker WH90 96 MHz machine. I am indebted to Mrs. S.M. Garman, Mr. B.E. Evans and Mr. M. McDonnell for technical assistance and to Dr. R. Wade for helpful discussion and encouragement.

REFERENCES

1   J.A. Elvidge, 'Isotopes - Essential Chemistry and Applications', J.A. El-vidge and J.R. Jones (Eds), The Chemical Society, London (1980) 123-194.
2   R. Voges, H. Andres, H.R. Loosi and E. Schreier, 'Synthesis and Applications of Isotopically Labeled Compounds', Proc. Internat. Symp., Kansas City, W.P. Duncan and A.B. Susan (Eds), Elsevier, Amsterdam (1983) 331-336.
3   D.E. Brundish and R. Wade, J. Labelled Compounds Radiopharm., 28 (1980) 1123-1133.
4   P.M. Hardy, P.W. Sheppard, D.E. Brundish and R. Wade, J. Chem. Soc. Perkin I (1983) 731-734.
5   G.L. Guilford, E.A. Evans, D.C. Warrell, J.R. Jones, J.A. Elvidge, R.M. Lenk and Y.S. Tang, 'Synthesis and Applications of Isotopically Labeled Compounds', Proc. Internat. Symp., Kansas City, W.P. Duncan and A.B. Susan (Eds), Elsevier, Amsterdam (1983) 327-330.
6   D.E. Brundish, M.G. Combe and R. Wade, J. Labelled Compounds Radiopharm., 20 (1983) 869-886.
7   H. Levine-Pinto, P. Pradelles, J.L. Morgat and P. Fromageot, J. Labelled Compounds Radiopharm., 17 (1979) 231-246.
8   H. Levine-Pinto, J.L. Morgat and P. Fromageot, J. Labelled Compounds Radiopharm., 21 (1980) 171-182.
9   E. Klauschenz, M. Bienert, H. Egler, U. Pleiss, H. Niedrich and K. Nikolics, Peptides, 2 (1981) 445-452.
10  Dr. A. Sallmann, CIBA-GEIGY AG, Basle (unpublished).
11  W. Riess, H. Stierlin, P. Degen, J.W. Faigle, A. Gerardin, J. Moppert, A. Sallmann, K. Schmid, A. Schweizer, M. Sulc, W. Theobald and J. Wagner, Scand. J. Rheumatol. Suppl., 22 (1978) 17-29.
12  G. Baschang, D.E. Brundish, A. Hartmann, J. Stanek and R. Wade, J. Labelled Compounds Radiopharm., 20 (1983) 691-696.
13  D.E. Brundish and R. Wade, J. Labelled Compounds Radiopharm., 22 (1985) 29-35.
14  D.E. Brundish, F. Harkness and J. Vadolas (unpublished).
15  J.M.A. Al-Rawi, J.A. Elvidge, J.R. Jones, V.M.A. Chambers and E.A. Evans, J. Labelled Compounds Radiopharm., 12 (1976) 265-271.
16  D.E. Brundish, Poster - Session B, this meeting.
17  T.J. Batterham, 'NMR Spectra of Simple Heterocycles', E.C. Taylor and A. Weissberger (Eds), John Wiley and Sons, New York (1973) 89-91.

*Synthesis and Applications of Isotopically Labeled Compounds 1985.*
Proceedings of the Second International Symposium, Kansas City, MO, U.S.A.,
3—6 September 1985, R.R. Muccino (Ed.), 371—376
© 1986 Elsevier Science Publishers B.V., Amsterdam — Printed in The Netherlands

TRITIATED COMPOUNDS FOR **IN VIVO** INVESTIGATIONS:
CAMP AND [3]H-NMR-SPECTROSCOPY FOR SYNTHESIS PLANNING AND PROCESS CONTROL

R. VOGES*[1], B.R. VON WARTBURG[2], H.R. LOOSLI[1]

[1]Pharmaceutical Department, Sandoz Ltd., CH-4002 Basle, Switzerland

[2]Sandoz Research Institute, A-1235 Vienna, Austria

ABSTRACT

[3]H-nmr spectroscopic determination of the tritium distribution and computer
metabolism programs help to predict the label's biological fate. This facilitates the introduction of tritium into metabolically less risky positions so that
tritiated compounds can be used for **in vivo** studies more widely in the future.

In the past, the use of tritiated compounds for in vivo studies has been limited. This is due to the potential biological instability of C-T bonds and the
frequently unpredictable distribution of the label. These disadvantages have now
been decisively diminished since computer programs - as for example CAMP and
XENO 4 (ref.1) - have been developed that can predict metabolites' structure and
their pathways of formation and local tritium concentrations can be detected by
[3]H-nmr spectroscopy. The combined application of both methods allows planning
and monitoring of the introduction of tritium into positions that are indicated
as metabolically stable. The CAMP-program (COMPUTER ASSISTED METABOLISM PREDIC-
TION) (ref. 2) we use is a modification of a well established computer program
for organic synthesis called CASP (COMPUTER ASSISTED SYNTHESIS PLANNING)
(ref.3). The framework of CASP was adapted to the needs of CAMP by exchanging
the large database of the programmed chemical reactions with a library of more
than 200 metabolic transforms (=programmed metabolic reaction types). These
transforms rely on the knowledge published in textbooks of metabolism and a
careful analysis of the human metabolism literature on approximately 1200 selected compounds. As CASP is a retrosynthetic program, whereas metabolic problems are normally forward problems, the use of the CASP-framework required a
retro-programming of the metabolic reactions.

CAMP is an interactive system using graphical images for communication. After
input of the target molecule, the system checks all transforms to find out those
that can be executed with the entered structure and displays the corresponding
potential metabolites on the terminal screen. This knowledge gives the presumably biologically stable positions of the compound and facilitates the selection

of the most suitable precursor for the introduction of the tritium label. Accordingly, the synthesis of tritiated compounds for **in vivo** investigations routinely starts with the following procedure:

- use CAMP for the finding of the metabolically less risky positions and the selection of the most suitable precursor
- introduce the label
- determine the distribution of the label by $^3$H-nmr spectroscopy
- reevaluate - in the case of isotopic scrambling - the potential biological stability of the label
- discard the material if the label (or a substantial part of it) is incorporated into risky positions.

The tritiation sequence for the dopamine agonist MESULERGINE 1 was the first multistep synthesis to which this approach was applied. The most probable biotransformation pathways, as predicted by CAMP, were N-demethylation of the side chain, N-demethylation at position 6, oxidation of the N-methyl group at position 1 to a relatively stable hemiaminal and subsequent cleavage to the corresponding nor-compound, N-oxidation at position 6, formation of the 12,13- and 13,14-arene oxides and, finally, oxidation of position 2 to the amide. They indicated that only the positions 4,5,7,8,9 and 10 could be expected to be inert to metabolic processes. Accordingly, the two isomeric lysergic acid methyl esters 2

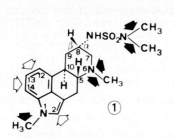

Fig. 1: MESULERGINE: CAMP-DIAGRAM
Structure and predicted Biotransformation Pathways of

◆ high priority    △ low-medium priority

and 3 were selected as precursors, of which the $\Delta^{7,8}$-isomer 2 was given preference since its hydrogenation in DMF in the presence of Pt and catalytic amounts of HClO$_4$ led immediately to the required 8$\alpha$-configurated ester 2a (Fig. 2). The material isolated from the reduction of 2 with tritium gas, however, showed a distribution of the label which was unsuitable for the biological purposes foreseen (Fig. 3). Due to isotopic scrambling 67 % of the tritium was attached to the metabolically risky positions 2 (42 %) and 14 (25 %) and only 33 % to the presumably stable positions 7ß (7 %) and 8ß (26 %). On the contrary, a high regioselectivity of the tritium addition was observed for the reduction of the $\Delta^{9,10}$-ester 3 (Fig. 4). The $^3$H-nmr spectrum of the resulting ester 3a revealed that more than 97% of the label was located at the proposed positions 9$\alpha$ and 10$\alpha$ and only 2.5% at the risky positions 2 (2%) and 14 (0.5%). Thus, only the - from the synthetic point of view - less favourable precursor, the $\Delta^{9,10}$-ester 3, proved to be suitable for the preparation of biologically-stable labelled [$^3$H]MESULERGINE. The following conversion of 3a including POLONOVSKY-oxidation

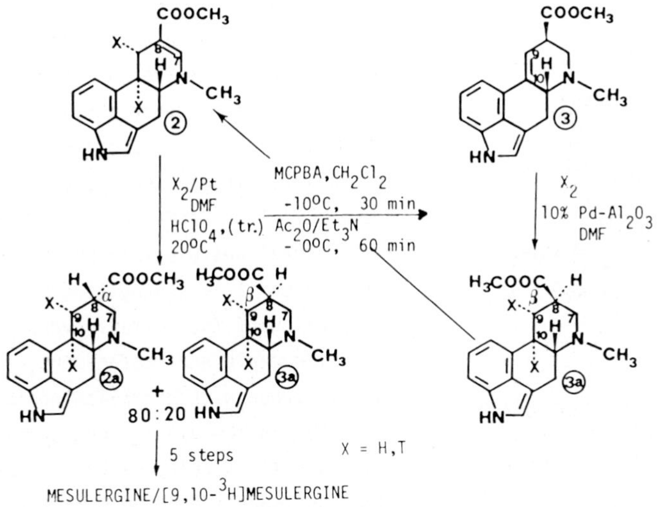

Fig. 2: Synthesis of MESULERGINE/[9,10-3H]MESULERGINE
Hydrogenation/Tritiation of $\Delta^{7,8}$ and $\Delta^{9,10}$-lysergic acid
methyl ester

to the $\Delta^{7},8$-[3H]ester 2, reduction to the saturated $8\alpha$-[3H]ester 2a, CURTIUS-de-gradation of the ester-group, N-methylation at position 1 and acylation of the $8\alpha$-amino group with dimethylsulfamoyl chloride has already been published (ref.4). It yielded a preparation for which less than 2 % HOT could be detected in all animal and human studies.

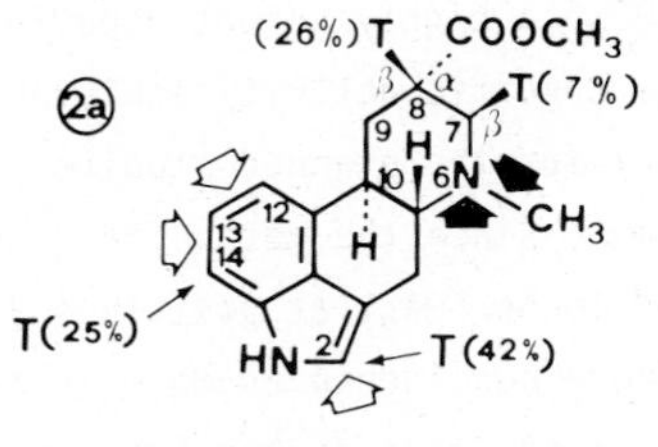

Fig.3: 9,10-dihydro-8α-lysergic
acid methyl ester:
Tritium Distrib. and predicted
Biotransf.Pathways (Mesulergine)

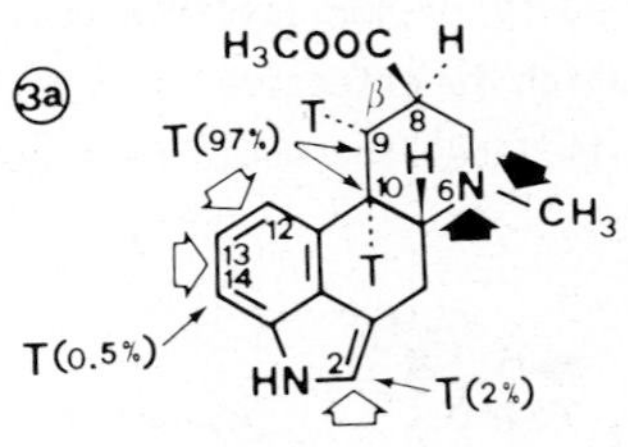

Fig.4: 9,10-dihydro-8β-lysergic
acid methyl ester:
Tritium Distrib. and predicted
Biotransf.Pathways (Mesulergine)

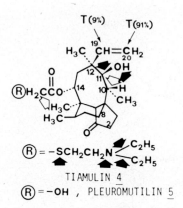

Fig. 5: TIAMULIN: CAMP-DIAGRAM
Structure, T-distribution and
pred. Biotransform Pathways

For TIAMULIN **4** (Fig.5), a semi-synthetic antibiotic with antibacterial activity against gram-positive bacteria, CAMP predicted an intensive metabolism of the thioglycolic acid side chain and recommended a labelling of the bicyclo[4.3.0]nanonone skeleton. TIAMULIN is a derivative of the natural antibiotic PLEUROMUTILIN **5**, from which it is synthesized by selective tosylation of the primary hydroxy group of the side chain and replacement of the tosyloxy group with diethylaminoethanethiol (ref.5). As the vinyl group promised to be biologically stable, exchange labelling of the positions 19 and 20 with a deficit of tritium gas in the presence of 10% Pd-C according to the CEPR-method (Catalytic Exchange Labelling by Partial Reduction) was tried. This method is based on the observation that catalytic reduction of olefinic substances with a deficit of tritium gas often leads to a labelling of the unreduced starting material with the tritium preferentially located in the vinylic and allylic positions. The proton-decoupled $^3$H-nmr spectrum of **5** confirmed that the label was exclusively incorporated into the desired positions: 9% was found at position 19 and 91 % at position 20. No tritium was attached to the risky positions 2 and 11. The material obtained after conversion of **5** to **4** showed no formation of appreciable amounts of HOT in all **in vivo** studies (ref. 6).

The incorporation of tritium exclusively into metabolically stable positions is often not feasible. In these cases a complete T/H re-exchange from the biologically unfavourable positions in a followig step is essential and can easily be monitored by $^3$H-nmr spectroscopy. For CV 205-502 **6**, a highly potent dopamine agonist, which is effective in very low doses, the specific activity achievable by carbon-14 labelling would have been insufficient for the planned studies in animal and man. Since the metabolic risk was predicted to be least at positions 2 and 4, both were considered as most suitable for the introduction of the tritium label. Position 3 was excluded since a biological hydroxylation seemed to be possible, although it was never observed for analogous ergoline compounds. Reduction of the key intermediate, the α,β-unsaturated ester **7**, to the ester **8** with tritium gas

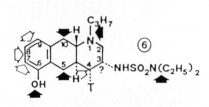

Fig. 6: CV 205-502: CAMP-DIAGRAM
Structure, T-distribution and
pred. Biotransformation Pathways

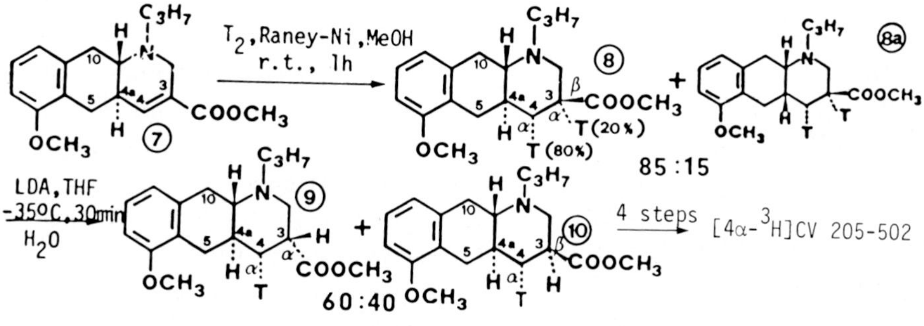

Fig. 7: Labelling sequence for CV 205-502

in methanol, in the presence of Raney-Ni led to a regioselective incorporation of more than 98 % of the label into the position 3α (20%) and 4α (80%) (Fig.7). Little or no tritium was found in the benzylic positions 5 and 10 and in the formerly allylic position 4a, although 15 % isomerization was observed. The tritium in position 3 was completely removed by repeated treatment of 8 with LDA in THF at - 35°C and quenching the resulting lithium ester enolate with water. Simultaneously, an epimerization at position 3 occurred giving predominantly the required 3α-ester 9. The final conversion of 9 to [4α-$^3$H]CV 205-502 was accomplished by similar steps as for [9.10-$^3$H]MESULERGINE 1 including CURTIUS-degradation of the ester group and acylation of the 3α-amine with diethylsulfamoyl chloride. Control experiments in rats confirmed the biological stability of the label: only 1% HOT was detected compared to 15 % for a CV 205-502 preparation labelled in the aromatic position 9 (ref.7).

Base-catalyzed T/H-reexchange from positions adjacent to carbonyl or carboxyl groups are normally not a serious problem. No general methods, however, are available if the tritium is located at other positions so that solutions have to be found individually. Tritiation of Δ$^9$,10-lysergic acid methyl ester 3 to 3a led in some cases to a partial labelling of the undesired positions 2 (0-5%), 4 (0-2%) and 14 (0-3%). The presence of polar groups and π-bonds promised to fix the substrate at the catalyst's surface and thus to enable a T/H-reexchange. Actually, post-treatment of 3a with H$_2$ in DMF in the presence of 10 % Pd-Al$_2$O$_3$ yielded a complete removal of the tritium from these positions. The moderate decrease of the specific activity by 25 % indicated that the tritium content of the positions 9 and 10 was not decisively diminished.

Although the present version of CAMP is applicable to most xenobiotics there are still a number of classes of compounds (peptides, macrolides etc.) for which the knowledge of metabolism is very small, so that the predictions are not yet satisfactory. CYCLOSPORIN A 11, a highly selective immunosuppressant which overcomes graft vs. host reactions in organ transplantation, is one example for

376

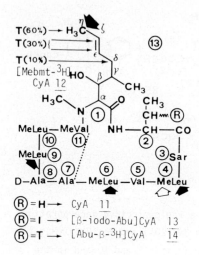

T(60%) → H₃C
T(30%)
T(10%)
[Mebmt-³H]
CyA 12

Ⓡ = H → CyA 11
Ⓡ = I → [ß-iodo-Abu]CyA 13
Ⓡ = T → [Abu-ß-³H]CyA 14

Fig. 8: CYCLOSPORIN A
Structure, T-distribution and
observed Biotr. Pathways (Man)

which the support of the metabolic investigations by CAMP was poor. Proceeding
from the elaborated structures of the
main metabolites (ref. 8), however,
³H-nmr-analysis of differently labelled
preparations allowed a more comfortable
access to tritiated CYCLOSPORIN A for
further in vivo and in vitro investigations. The material that was first used
was labelled biosynthetically from
[methyl-³H]methionine. The achievable
specific activities were low, varying
between 70 and 280 mCi/mmol, and the
radiochemical yields were less than 15 %.
The label was attached to the 7 N-methyl
groups and the γ-methyl group of the
olefinic amino acid No. 1. CEPR-labelling
of CYCLOSPORIN A with a deficit of tritium
gas in the presence of 10% Pd-C led to an
increase in the specific activity to 20 Ci/mmol and to a tritium incorporation
into the vinylic ε,ζ-positions (30%), the δ-position (10%) and, unfortunately,
into the metabolically highly risky η-methyl group (60%). [³H]CYCLOSPORIN A 14
at 10 Ci/mmol and specifically labelled at biologically stable positions could
finally be obtained by catalytic deoidination of [ß-iodo-Abu]CYCLOSPORIN A 13
with tritium gas in DMF. Poisoning the catalyst (10% Pd-CaCO₃) with a 10-fold
molar excess of triethylamine stopped the T₂-addition to the double bond and
enabled the selective I/T-replacement. The ³H-nmr spectrum confirmed that simultaneously no H/T-exchange into the olefinic amino acid had occurred: 95 % of the
tritium was found in the former iodine position and 5 % in the metabolically
stable N-methyl group of the sarcosine.

References
1  W.T. Wipke, G.I. Ouchi, J.T. Chou in L. Goldberg (Ed.), Struct.-Act.
   Correl. Predict. Tool Toxicol., Hemisphere, Washington (1983),151-169
2  B.R. v. Wartburg, R. Voges, W. Sieber, 9e Congrès Europ. Métabolisme du
   médicament, Pont-à-Mousson, France, Résumé (1984), 6-7
3  A.K. Long, S.D. Rubenstein, L.J. Joncas, C&EN 61 (May 1983), 22-30
4  R. Voges, H. Andres, H.R. Loosli, E. Schreier in W.P. Duncan, A.B. Susan
   (Eds.), Synth. and Appl. of Isotopically Labelled Compounds, Elsevier,
   Amsterdam (1983), 331-336
5  H. Egger, H. Reinshagen, J. Antibiotics 29 (1976), 925-927
6  J. Dreyfuss, S.M. Singhvi, J.M. Shaw, J.J. Ross, R. Czok, M. Nefzger,
   F. Battig, F. Schmook, J. Antibiotics 32 (1979), 496-503
7  J.M. Jaffe, ADME-studies with CV 205-502 in animal, Sandoz Res. Inst.,
   East Hanover, N.J. (unpubl. results)
8  G.Maurer,H.R.Loosli,E.Schreier,B.Keller, Drug Metab.Disp. 12 (1984),120-126

*Synthesis and Applications of Isotopically Labeled Compounds 1985.*
Proceedings of the Second International Symposium, Kansas City, MO, U.S.A.,
3—6 September 1985, R.R. Muccino (Ed.), 377—388
© 1986 Elsevier Science Publishers B.V., Amsterdam — Printed in The Netherlands

APPLICATIONS OF [3]H and [2]H NMR SPECTROSCOPY IN STUDIES OF β-LACTAM ANTIBIOTIC
BIOSYNTHESIS

D.H.G. CROUT[1] and P.J. MORGAN[2]
[1]Dept. of Chemistry, University of Warwick, Coventry, CV4 7AL, England
[2]Cambridge Research Biochemicals Limited, Harston, Cambridge, CB2 5NX, England.

ABSTRACT

Stereochemical studies have been invaluable in illuminating the mechanisms of
enzymatic reactions. The formation of cephalosporin C from penicillin N is a
biological process of fundamental importance in relation to cephalosporin C production. During this transformation, two methyl groups in penicillin N, (originally the two methyl groups of the precursor L-valine) are converted into methylene groups. One is involved in the ring expansion - sulphur migration step,
the other in the formation of the acetoxymethyl side chain. By synthesizing
'chiral methyl' valine in which both methyl groups were stereospecifically labelled with deuterium and tritium, and by using [3]H and [2]H n.m.r. to analyse the
valine, and the cephalosporin C produced from it biosynthetically, it has been
possible in a single experiment to elucidate the stereochemical changes taking
place during the transformations of both methyl groups. The results obtained
support the hypothesis that both transformations involve radical intermediates.

The use of isotopes in tracing the fate of labelled metabolites in biological
systems has stimulated the search for ever simpler and more reliable methods for
their detection and estimation. In proportion to the practical simplicity of
the technique, n.m.r. provides the biooganic chemist with the greatest amount
of information on the nature, extent and stereochemistry of isotopic labelling
in both biological intermediates and the end products of biological pathways.
The investigations to be described here provide an example of the application
of n.m.r. to the simultaneous investigation of two outstanding mechanistic problems in the biosynthesis of the β-lactam antibiotic cephalosporin C (5). The
power and simplicity of the method will become apparent when it is contrasted
with the alternative methods that might be used to solve these same problems.

The later stages in the biosynthesis of cephalosporin C in *Cephalosporium*
*acremonium* are shown in Scheme 1. The tripeptide (L-α-amino-δ-adipyl)-L-cyst-
einyl-D-valine (2) is cyclised to isopenicillin N (3, R = L-α-amino-δ-adipyl).
Isopenicillin N is epimerised to penicillin N (3, R = D-α-amino-δ-adipyl) which
undergoes ring expansion to desacetoxycephalosporin C (4). Hydroxylation of the
C-3' methyl group followed by acetylation gives cephalosporin C (5).

Both the ring expansion and the side-chain hydroxylation are oxidative processes. In spite of their apparent dissimilarity the enzymes catalysing these

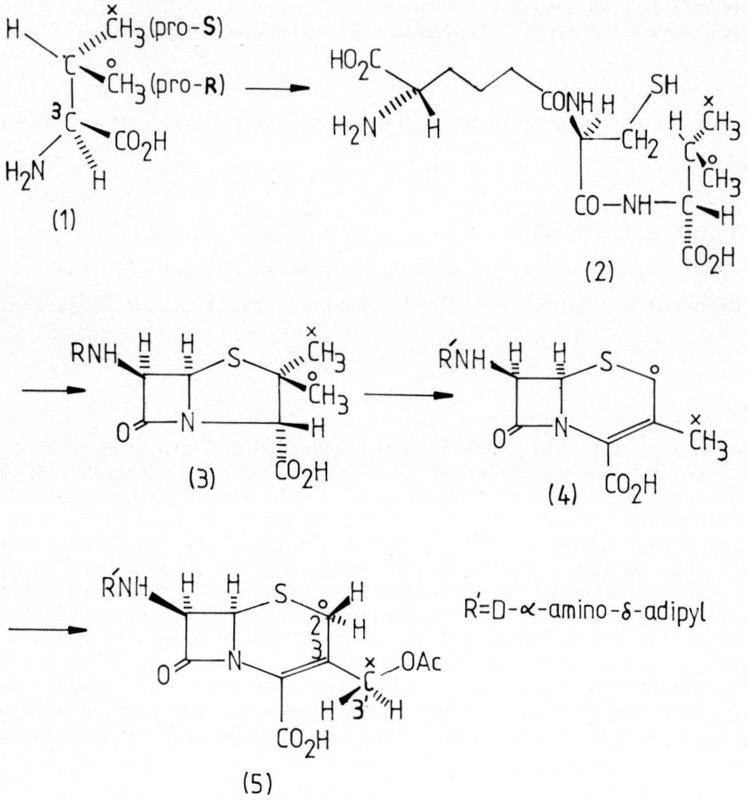

Scheme 1

respective steps have much in common. Thus both are 2-oxoglutarate-dependent dioxygenases with a requirement for iron (II) and a reducing agent (ref.1,2). The two steps also have in common the feature that in each a methyl group is converted into a methylene group bearing diastereotopic hydrogen atoms. In stereochemical terminology, a pro,prochiral centre is converted into a pro-chiral centre in each case. It was thus clear that an investigation of the stereochemistry of these transformations would shed light on the chemistry of these processes and provide important information on the biological mechanisms operating in the biosynthesis of these important substances.

Essential to any such investigation would be a means of generating a sample of penicillin N (3, R = D-α-amino-δ-adipyl) in which both methyl groups of the thiazolidine ring were chiral by virtue of stereospecific labelling with hydrogen, deuterium and tritium. Also essential would be a method for elucidating the configuration at the prochiral centres C-2 and C-3' in the product cephalosporin C (5). In principle, various solutions to the latter problem were possible; these might have included chemical, enzymatic or spectroscopic techniques or any combination of these. Since the initial elegant demonstrations of the use of chiral methyl groups in investigations of biological processes by Cornforth (ref.3) and by Arigoni (ref.4) and their respective collaborators, most investigations involving chiral methyl groups have relied on combinations of chemical and enzymatic techniques for the analysis of the results. However the prospect of using spectroscopic methods, and n.m.r. in particular, would offer the possibility of direct observation of the results, without recourse to chemical or enzymatic manipulation of the product. Further, and most significantly with respect to the proposed investigation, in an overall transformation affecting two methyl groups, it should be possible *to study both processes simultaneously and in a single incorporation experiment.*

As noted previously, the C-2 and C-3' methylene groups in cephalosporin C (5) bear diastereotopic hydrogen atoms. It only remained to confirm that the nonequivalence of the respective proton nuclei was sufficiently great to make the n.m.r. analysis possible. Inspection of the proton n.m.r. spectrum, observed at 300 MHz (Fig.1) showed this to be the case. The C-2 and C-3' methylene groups

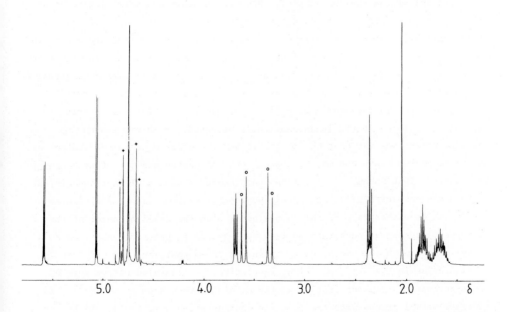

Fig. 1. $^1$H n.m.r. spectrum of the sodium salt of cephalosporin C (5) in $^2$H$_2$O (400 MHz) showing the AB quartets due to the protons of the C-3' (+) and the C-2 (o) methylene groups.

each give rise to a well-defined AB quartet. Leaving aside for the moment the precise way in which the stereochemical problem could be solved by analysis of the tritium n.m.r. spectrum of biosynthesised cephalosporin C, it remained to devise a way of generating a sample of penicillin N (3, R = D-α-amino-δ-adipyl) bearing chiral methyl groups. The synthesis of 'chiral methyl penicillin N' would have been a formidable task. However, it was known that the relevant portion of the molecule was derived from L-valine (1), the precursor of the D-valine component of the tripeptide (2). Moreover, it was known that the incorporation of L-valine into cephalosporin C was completely stereospecific with respect to events involving the isopropyl system. Thus the *pro-S* and *pro-R* methyl groups of L-valine (1) become the C-3' and C-2 methylene groups respectively of cephalosporin C (5).

It was therefore proposed to synthesise 'chiral methyl valine' and incorporate this into cephalosporin C. Further, since the two methyl groups of L-valine are dispatched to quite different destinations during cephalosporin C biosynthesis (*cf* Scheme 1), it was possible to consider an experiment in which both methyl groups of valine were labelled simultaneously, as noted previously.

The required labelled L-valine might have been prepared by separately synthesising L-valine with a chiral methyl group in both the *pro-R* and the *pro-S* positions and mixing the two samples. However, another and more elegant solution suggested itself. This would take advantage of the principle of 'linked configurations', whereby two stereochemically informative centres are generated in such a way that the configurations of the two centres are unambiguously related. If, in a biological system, the isomer having a particular configuration at one of these centres is selected enzymatically for further transformation, or if a particular diastereotopic group is selected, then a particular configuration at the related centre is automatically selected. Both centres may be chiral centres; one may be a chiral centre and the other a prochiral centre, or, as in the present case one may be a pro,prochiral centre and the other a prochiral centre. Thus Scheme 2 illustrates the result of adding HT stereospecifically to a stereospecifically deuterated isopropenyl system. Since addition may take place on either face of the double bond, with the (E)-isotopomer of the isopropenyl system as substrate an isopropyl system is generated that bears methyl groups with the *R*-configuration in the *pro-S* position, and with the *S*-configuration in the *pro-R* position, respectively. (The alternative mode of addition that would place tritium at the methine carbon atom is ignored). To generate methyl groups with the opposite configurations, it would only be necessary to use as substrate the Z-isotopomer of the starting deuterated isopropenyl system.

Solution of the immediate problem thus required the preparation of the isotopomers (8) and (11) of an appropriate derivative of isodehydrovaline (Scheme 3).

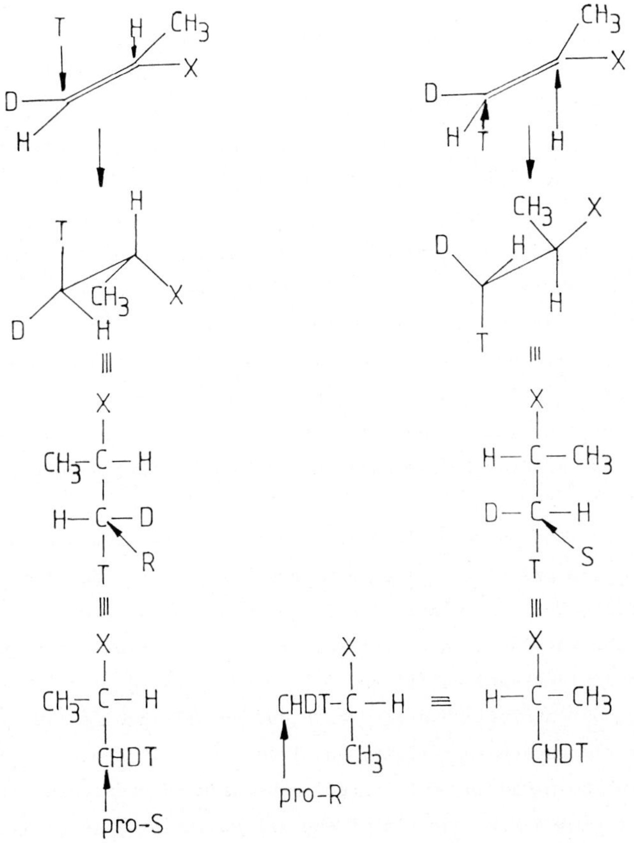

Scheme 2

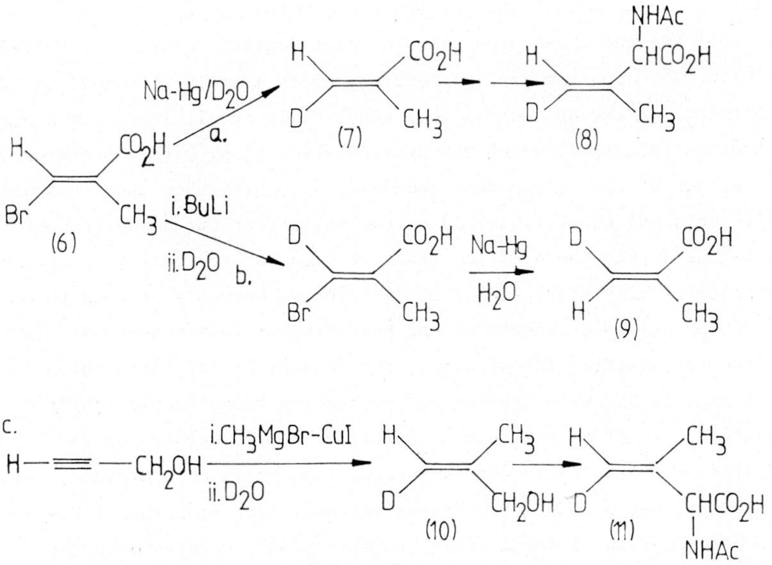

Scheme 3

The synthetic route envisaged for the preparation of these substances started from methacrylic acid or the corresponding alcohol. The methods ultimately developed for the crucial introduction of deuterium into these starting materials are shown in Scheme 3. Generation of the (E)-deuteriomethacrylic acid (7) relied on the observation of strict stereospecificity in the reductive substitution of bromine in (E)-3-bromomethacrylic acid (6) (Scheme 3a) (ref.5). The corresponding (Z)-isomer (9) was obtained by taking advantage of the kinetic acidity of H-3 in (E)-3-bromomethacrylate (6), which makes possible the exchange procedure illustrated in Scheme 3b. (This proton is sufficiently acidic to be removed by aqueous alkali). However, since the synthetic scheme required reduction of the methacrylic acid to methacryl alcohol (2-methyl-2-propen-1-ol, as (10)), advantage was taken of the cuprate addition to propargyl alcohol shown in Scheme 3c, which in our hands was developed into a highly stereospecific procedure (ref.6).

These deuterated substrates were elaborated to the racemic deuterated $N$-acetylisodehydrovalines (8) and (11), using a method based on the Neber rearrangement of the appropriate $N$-chloroimidates (ref.6). Substrates were thus in hand which would permit the introduction of tritium at the penultimate step in the synthesis. The $N$-acetylderivatives (8) and (11) were prepared since it was proposed to use homogenous catalytic hydrogenation, using Wilkinson's catalyst, to be assured of the strict stereospecificity required, and this demanded the use of a derivative soluble in the solvent system to be used (benzene:ethanol).

The proton and tritium n.m.r. spectra of the valine isolated after hydrogenation of the (E)-isotopomer (8) with an equilibrated mixture of $H_2$ and $T_2$ (7:1), followed by hydrolysis, is shown in Fig. 2. Both spectra show marked non-equivalence of labelling of the methyl groups, the *pro-S* methyl group bearing 95% of the deuterium label and the *pro-R* group 5%. A complementary result is revealed in the deuterium n.m.r. spectrum (Fig.3) of corresponding material obtained by hydrogenation (with $D_2$) of the unlabelled substrate. This result indicates a high degree of asymmetric induction during the hydrogenation step, with a preference for 3-*re*, 4-*si* attack on the *S*-component and 3-*si*, 4-*re* attack on the *R*-component (Scheme 4). This may be attributable to the ability of the amide group to function as a ligand during the hydrogen transfer steps of the catalytic cycle. However, a consequence is that the label is distributed unevenly between the methyl groups of the L- and D-isomers of the resulting valine (Scheme 4). In order to equalise the distribution of label, the product $N$-acetylated valines from subsequent experiments were "racemised" by heating in an acetic anhydride-acetic acid mixture. In fig 4 are shown the tritium n.m.r. spectra of samples of valine prepared by hydrogenation of deuterated $N$-acetylisodehydrovaline with carrier-free tritium, before and after "racemisation". The spectrum of Fig 4b shows the even distribution of label after "racemisation" compared with the

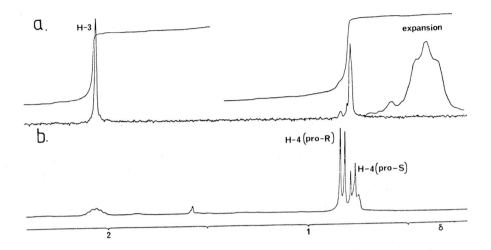

Fig.2. (a) $^{3}$H n.m.r. spectrum (320 MHz); (b) $^{1}$H n.m.r. spectrum of the valine produced by hydrogenation of DL-(E)-[4-$^{2}$H]-2-acetylamino-3-methyl-3-butenoic acid (8) with an equilibrated mixture of H$_2$ and $^{3}$H$_2$ (7:1) in the presence of Wilkinson's catalyst, followed by hydrolysis.

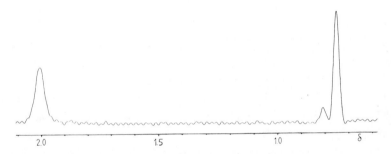

Fig.3. $^{2}$H n.m.r. spectrum (61.4 MHz) of the valine produced by hydrogenation (with $^{2}$H$_2$) of DL-2-acetylamino-3-methylbut-3-enoic acid (N-acetylisodehydroval-ine) in the presence of Wilkinson's catalyst, followed by hydrolysis.

unequal distribution in material obtained by hydrolysis of the N-acetyl derivatives directly after hydrogenation (Fig.4a). Evident in Fig.4a is the expected
deuterium-tritium spin-spin splitting pattern (also to be seen in the product
obtained by hydrogenation with HT, Fig.2a). It should be noted that because
ethanol was used as a co-solvent for the hydrogenations, some hydrogen-tritium
exchange occurred, so that in these broad-band proton-decoupled spectra, there
are superimposed doublet and singlet patterns for the signals attributable to
each methyl group, arising from components of the mixture with tritium or protium, respectively at C-3. Complementary effects are seen in the signals attributable to H-3. (See structure (1), Scheme 1). The final appearance of the spectra is also influenced by the upfield shift of signals due to tritium in those
components of the mixture bearing two tritium atoms per molecule. The isotopic

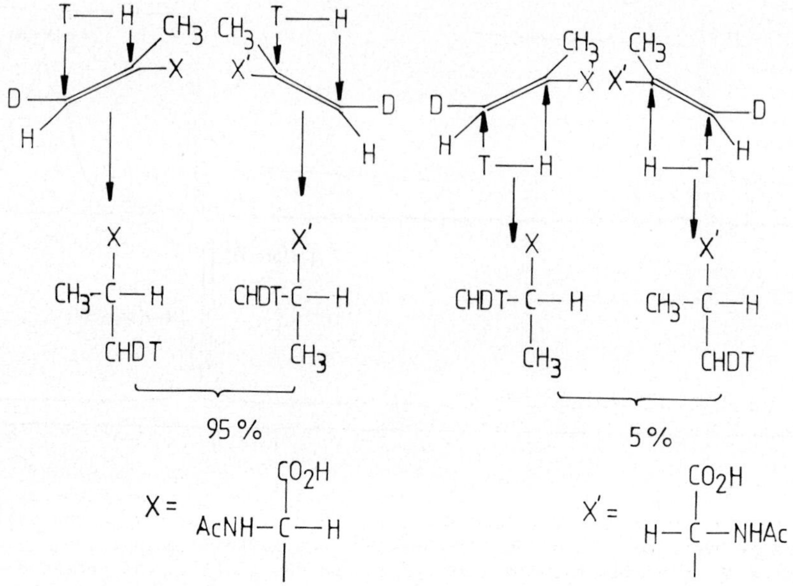

Scheme 4

complexity of the product mixture in no way affects the outcome of the final experiment, since H-3 in valine (cf (1)) is lost during biosynthesis of cephalosporin C(5). Further, the only species informative in the final analysis are those carrying tritium in the methyl groups and it is only necessary to bear in mind that in more than 88% of such species, deuterium was also present.

The principle of the analysis of the result of incorporating "chiral methyl valine" into cephalosporin C is exemplified in Fig.5. The assignments of the signals due to the diastereotopic protons $H_A$ and $H_B$ in the putative product are assumed to be as shown. For purposes of illustration, a methyl group having the $S$-configuration is illustrated as undergoing a stereospecific hydroxylation with retention of configuration. The signals arising from species in which deuterium and hydrogen are replaced in the tritium n.m.r. spectrum of the product (without broad-band proton decoupling) would be as shown in Fig. 5 a,b, respectively. These would be combined in the overall spectrum shown in Fig.5c, consisting of a downfield triplet and an upfield doublet. If the hydroxylation were to proceed with inversion of configuration, this pattern would be reversed. Complementary patterns would be obtained starting from a methyl group with the $R$-configuration. Tritium n.m.r. analysis thus provides an *absolute* method for the elucidation of the stereochemistry of the product, not dependent on kinetic H/D isotope effects. However, if an H/D kinetic isotope effect were to operate, the relative intensities of the signals would alter in the sense shown in Fig. 5d. In the extreme, the signal due to the -CHTOH species would disappear altogether and only signals

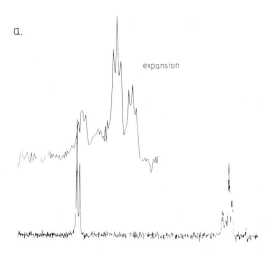

a.

expansion

b.

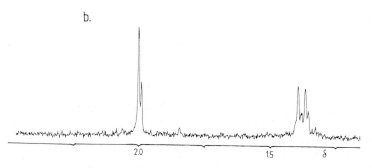

2.0                1.5        δ

Fig.4. $^3$H n.m.r. spectra (320 MHz, broad band proton decoupled) of DL-valine obtained by tritiation    of (a) DL-(E)-[4-$^2$H]-2-acetamido-3-methyl-3-butenoic acid (11) and (b) of DL-(E)-[4-$^2$H]-2-acetamido-3-methyl-3-butenoic acid(8) fol-lowed by (a) hydrolysis, (b) 'racemisation' followed by hydrolysis.

attributable to -CDTOH species would be visible, and these, depending on resolu-tion, might appear either as a 1:1:1 triplet as shown, or as an apparent singlet. These last remarks anticipate the actual outcome of the incorporation experiment which will now be described.

Samples of "chiral methyl valine" were prepared by hydrogenation of the deu-terated derivatives (8) and (11) of isodehydrovaline with carrier-free tritium (10 Ci batches) as described previously, and adminstered to *Cephalosporium acremonium*. After several abortive experiments two factors were identified as being crucial for success.

(i) Use of tritium gas immediately on receipt from the manufacturers. Stor-age of tritium for periods of more than a few weeks resulted in loss of material presumably by radiolytic effects resulting in adsorption of tritium on to the glass walls of the vials.

386

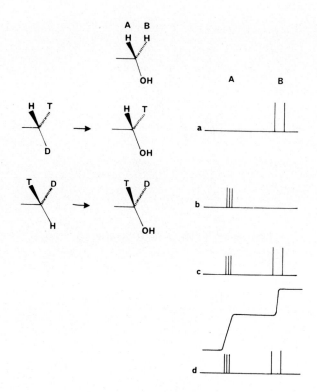

Fig.5. Principle of the stereochemical analysis by n.m.r. of chiral methyl groups.

(ii) Administration of the labelled valine to *C. acremonium* immediately following preparation. The product proved to be highly susceptible to radioautolysis and was completely destroyed after 2-3 weeks.

With these factors identified, it was possible to plan experiments so that tritium gas was used as soon as received and the product valine immediately administered to *Cephalosporium acremonium*. The tritium n.m.r. spectra of the samples of cephalosporin C produced are illustrated in Fig.6. To produce these spectra 2.2 and 2.55 Ci of "chiral methyl valine" were used giving rise respectively to 3.04 and 3.15 mCi of tritiated cephalosporin C. These spectra, which were acquired without broad-band proton decoupling, reveal only signals due to CDT species and the resolution is such that the signals appear as singlets rather than 1:1:1 triplets. From the observed signal-to-noise ratio, it can be estimated that for the signals due to CHT species to disappear into the noise, a kinetic H-D isotope effect of at least 5 must be operating with respect to the side-chain hydroxylation, and of at least 3 with respect to the sulphur insertion.

The spectra fulfilled all the expectations with respect to the provision of stereochemical information. After making allowance for the small (~ 5%) amounts

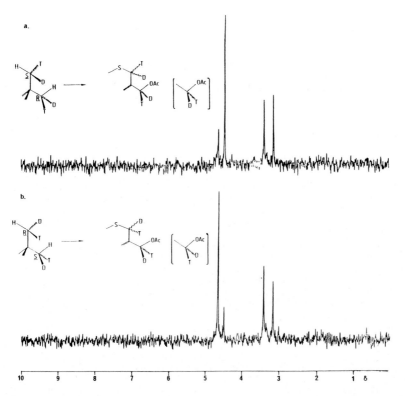

Fig.6. $^3$H n.m.r. spectra (320 MHz) of cephalosporin C derived from 'chiral methyl valine'. The configurations of the precursors are indicated in the figure.

of incorrectly labelled deuterated isodehydrovalines present in the material subjected to catalytic tritiation, the relative intensities of the signals due to
the protons of the C-3' methylene group show that the hydroxylation of desacetoxycephalosporin C proceeds with 87-90% stereospecificity, whereas the sulphur
insertion during the ring expansion step proceeds, within experimental error,
with complete lack of stereospecificity. These results are striking in view of
the similarities between the enzymes catalysing these two processes, noted previously. The stereochemical evidence provides strong support for a radical mechanism for the sulphur insertion process (ref.7). Because the signals due to the
C-3' methylene group have not been assigned, the experiments described here do not
define the absolute stereochemistry of the hydroxylation, but complementary experiments by Townsend (ref.8) have shown that the predominant mode is retention,
in line with numerous other biological hydroxylations (ref.7).

388

Acknowledgments

The incorporation experiments were carried out in collaboration with Professor Sir Edward Abraham and his colleagues Dr. C-P. Pang and Dr. R.L. White of the Sir William Dunn School of Pathology, University of Oxford.  The tritium n.m.r. spectra were determined by Lady Richards and Dr. A.E. Derome of the Dyson Perrins Laboratory, University of Oxford, through the kind cooperation of Professor J.E. Baldwin.

REFERENCES

1   J. Kupka, Y.Q. Shen, S. Wolfe and A.L. Demain, FEMS Microbiol. Lett. 16 (1983) 1-6.
2   C.M. Stevens, E.P. Abraham, F.C. Huang and C.J. Sih, Fed. Proc. Fed. Am. Soc. Exp. Biol., 34 (1975), 623; M.K. Turner, J.E. Farthing and S.J. Brewer, Biochem. J., 173 (1978) 839-850.
3   J.W. Cornforth, J.W. Redmond, H. Eggerer, W. Buckel and C. Gutschow, Nature, 221 (1969) 1212-1213.
4   J. Lüthy, J. Rétey and D Arigoni, Nature 221 (1969) 1213-1215.
5   D.H.G. Crout and J.A. Corkill, Tetrahedron Letters (1977) 4355-4357.
6   D.H.G. Crout, M. Lutstorf and P.J. Morgan, Tetrahedron, 39 (1983) 3457-3469.
7   C-P. Pang, R.L. White, E.P. Abraham, D.H.G. Crout, M. Lutstorf, P.J. Morgan and A.E. Derome, Biochem. J., 222 (1984) 777-788.
8   C.R. Townsend and E.B. Barrabee, J.C.S. Chem. Comm. (1984) 1586-1587.

*Synthesis and Applications of Isotopically Labeled Compounds 1985.*
Proceedings of the Second International Symposium, Kansas City, MO, U.S.A.,
3—6 September 1985, R.R. Muccino (Ed.), 389—393

# STUDIES OF CATALYST SELECTIVITY BY ³H-NMR SPECTROSCOPY

L. CARROLL[1], J.R. JONES[1] and W.J.S. LOCKLEY[2]

[1]Chemistry Department, University of Surrey, Guildford, GU2 5XH (UK)

[2]Fisons Pharmaceuticals, Bakewell Road, Loughborough, LE11 0RH (UK)

ABSTRACT

³H-Nmr studies have confirmed that highly regioselective ortho-tritiation of arylcarboxylic acids and of arylcarboxamides may be conveniently achieved in a single step by rhodium(lll) chloride catalysed exchange with tritiated water. The studies point to factors which could in some cases lower the overall regioselectivity of the labelling process and which can affect the specific radioactivity or radiochemical purity of the product.

Metal-catalysed exchange with isotopic water has been extensively utilised in the preparation of deuterated and tritiated organic compounds (refs.1-4). Initial studies utilised heterogeneous Group 8 metal catalysts (refs.5,6) but the discovery of aromatic exchange homogeneously catalysed by tetrachloro-platinate II (ref.7) opened the way to investigations with the chloro-complexes of other second and third row Group 8 metals such as iridium (ref.8) and rhodium (ref.9).

Initial studies of the labelling regioselectivity obtained with these homogeneous catalysts utilised ¹H-nmr for the assignment of labelling sites, in conjunction with mass spectrometric quantitation of isotopic abundance (ref.10). ²H-Nmr has occasionally been used, as in the case of the homogeneous platinum system (ref.11) although it was necessary to employ lanthanide shift reagents in order to obtain the maximum information on regioselectivity.

The advent of ³H-nmr made it possible to study the orientation of labelling produced by various catalysts with good quantitation, high detectability (by comparison with other nuclei) and excellent spectral dispersion. The technique has consequently been extensively applied to the assignment of labelling regioselectivity for a number of heterogeneous metal catalyst systems (refs.4, 12-15). Comparatively few studies have however been reported (ref.16) where the technique has been applied to homogeneous metal catalysts.

This paper describes the use of ³H-nmr to study the ortho-labelling of aromatic carboxylic acids and amides by rhodium(III) chloride exchange with tritiated water. Previous studies with this catalyst have demonstrated highly regioselective ortho-labelling of aromatic and α,β-unsaturated acids (refs.18,

$$R \xrightarrow{\overset{\bullet}{H_2O} \; \backslash \; RhCl_3}_{\text{D.M.F.} \; \backslash \; 107^0} \quad \overset{\bullet}{H} \text{---} R \text{---} H^{\bullet}$$

$$R = CO_2H, CO_2Na, CONH_2, CONHR',$$

$$CH_2NH_2, CH_2NHR', CHMeNH_2, NHCOR'.$$

$$S = \text{Many substituent groups}$$

19) and of C-aryl and N-arylcarboxamides (refs.20,21). However, these employed the deuterium isotope and regioselectivity was assigned largely from [1]H-nmr studies although [2]H- and [13]C-nmr was applied in particular instances (refs.20,21) Since tritium labelling by the rhodium(III) chlcride technique has proved to be both simple to perform and applicable to a wide variety of substrates (ref.22) [3]H-nmr studies were initiated in order to investigate the factors which govern the regioselectivity of the procedure.

The results from a number of tritiation reactions are summarised in Table 1. In general the regioselectivity of the procedure was found to be extremely high. In eight of the ten cases studied (substrates 1,2,3,6,7,8,9,10) no resonances associated with lack of regioselectivity were detected. Estimates of the minimum regioselectivity in these cases have been made by consideration of the extent of random spectroscopic noise which could be obscuring very small resonances. Overall the results for these eight substrates are consistent with previous [1]H- and [2]H-nmr studies (refs.19,20) and confirm the ability of the procedure to achieve regioselectivity quite comparable with more traditional synthetic methods.

By contrast, the results obtained for two substrates (4 and 5) were not consistent with those previously obtained using [1]H- and [2]H-nmr studies. Whilst a reduction of regioselectivity had been noted (refs.18,19,21) with compounds containing groups (OH and $NH_2$) which strongly activate the molecule towards electrophilic exchange this was small and less than 10%. In the current [3]H-nmr studies this was however not the case, some 34% of the total tritium was present at positions ortho and para to the hydroxyl group in 2-hydroxybenzamide, whilst in the case of 2-hydroxybenzoic acid more than 90% of the tritium was present at the electrophilically activated 3 and 5 positions. It is unlikely that the disagreement between the results of the tritium and deuterium studies arises from isotopic differences, rather, the cause may be sought in the type of reaction conditions dictated by each isotope. Although deuterium oxide may be utilised in large quantity and in large molar excess to ensure labelling of the substrate at high atom percentage abundance, exchange reactions with tritiated water often pose a choice between good radiochemical incorporation and high specific radioactivity. Thus, whilst 4-oxo-4H-chromene-2-carboxylic acid may be labelled using 0.32 mol of tritiated water per mole of substrate,

TABLE 1

Regioselectivity of $^3$H-labelling for various substrates assigned by $^3$H-nmr spectroscopy.

| | Substrate | Positions labelled (% of $^3$H) |
|---|---|---|
| 1. | Benzamide | 2, 6 (97%)[a] |
| 2. | Benzoic acid | 2, 6 (99%)[a] |
| 3. | 2-Ethoxybenzamide | 6 (96%)[a] |
| 4. | 2-Hydroxybenzamide | 6 (66%), 3,5 (34%) |
| 5. | 2-Hydroxybenzoic | 6(9%), 3,5 (91%) |
| 6. | 4-Methoxybenzamide | 2,6 (99%)[a] |
| 7. | 2-Methoxybenzoic | 6 (98%)[a] |
| 8. | 3-Methylbenzoic | 2,6 (98%)[a] |
| 9. | 4-Methylbenzoic | 2,6 (99%)[a] |
| 10. | 4-Oxo-4H-chromene-2-carboxylic acid | 3 (97%)[a] |

[a]No resonances associated with tritiation at other positions were detected. Estimates of the minimum regioselectivity are based upon signal/noise ratio in the $^3$H-nmr spectra.

with the utilisation of over 5% of the available tritium, the specific radio-activity is only ca 20% of the theoretical equilibrium value. Alternatively, utilisation of a large excess (ref.22) of tritiated water leads to incorporation of less than 0.4% of the tritium employed, but does yield a specific radio-activity very close to the theoretical maximum under the circumstances. The $^3$H-nmr studies described herein utilised the former conditions so as to maximise tritium utilisation. Under these almost anhydrous conditions the stability of the rhodium(III) chloride catalyst is compromised. In the presence of phenolic compounds decomposition occurs with the precipitation of rhodium metal. It seems likely therefore that the lowered regioselectivity observed with the phenolic compounds reflects rapid catalyst decomposition followed by labelling of the electrophilically activated sites by a competing substitution process.

In addition to providing information about the regioselectivity of the reaction $^3$H-nmr demonstrated that the tritiated substrates were of good radio-chemical purity even after only a simple work-up procedure. Only in the case of tritiated 2-methoxybenzoic acid was contamination with a tritium labelled impurity detected. Here the $^3$H-nmr spectrum displayed a small (<10%) resonance at δ 7.85 in addition to the expected ortho-triton resonance at δ 7.70. Examination of both the $^3$H- and $^1$H-nmr spectra of the mixture enabled a tentative identification of the minor impurity as ortho-tritiated 2-hydroxybenzoic acid. Since no dealkylation of this type was observed with 4-methoxybenzamide or with 2-ethoxybenzamide it may be that the demethylation side-reaction is observed only with activated methoxyl groups of the salicylate type.

In summary the application of the $^3$H-nmr technique to studies of rhodium(III) chloride catalysed tritiation has enabled verification of the high regio-selectivity of the procedure and has allowed identification of conditions and substrates which might give rise to reduced regioselectivity. Additionally, the reaction has been shown to be largely free from labelled by-product formation, though a potential demethylation side-reaction has been identified. It is most unusual to observe a catalyst, either heterogeneous or homogeneous, capable of such high regioselectivity. Consequently the method could, in appropriate circumstances, rapidly replace the more conventional synthetic procedures.

REFERENCES

1    E.A. Evans, Tritium and its Compounds, Butterworths, London, 1974, pp 794.

2    J.R. Jones in Isotopes: Essential Chemistry and Applications,
     J.A. Elvidge and J.R. Jones (Eds.), Special Publication No.35,
     The Chemical Society, London, 1979, pp 349-400.

3    J.L. Garnett, Proc. 2nd Int. Conf. Methods Prep. Storing Lab. Comp.,
     (1968) 709-711.

4    J.L. Garnett and M.A. Long in Synthesis and Applications of Isotopically
     Labelled Compounds,  W.P. Duncan and A.B. Susan (Eds.), Elsevier,
     Amsterdam, 1983, pp 415-420.

5    L.C.Leitch, Can. J. Chem., 32 (1954) 813-814.

6    for a review see G.E. Calf and J.L. Garnett, Adv. Heterocycl. Chem.,
     15 (1973) 137-185.

7    R.J. Hodges and J.L. Garnett, J. Phys. Chem.. 72 (1968) 1673-1682.

8    J.L.Garnett, M.A. Long, A.B. McClaren and K.B. Peterson,
     J. Chem. Soc. Chem. Commun., (1973) 749-750.

9    M.R. Blake, J.L. Garnett, I.K. Gregor, W. Hannan, K. Hoa and M.A. Long,
     J. Chem. Soc. Chem. Commun., (1975) 930-932.

10   J.L. Garnett, R.J. Hodges, R.S. Kenyon and M.A. Long, J. Chem. Soc. Perkin
     II., (1979) 885-890.

11   P.A. Colfer, T.A. Foglia and P.E. Pfeffer, J. Org. Chem., 44 (1979) 2573-
     2575.

12   J.L.Garnett, M.A. Long and C.A. Lukey, J. Chem. Soc. Chem. Commun., (1979)
     634-635.

13   J.L. Garnett, M.A. Long, C.A. Lukey and P.G. Williams, J. Chem. Soc.
     Perkin II., (1982) 287-289.

14   M.A. Long, J.L.Garnett and P.G. Williams in Synthesis and Applications of
     Isotopically Labelled Compounds, W.P. Duncan and A.B. Susan (Eds),
     Elsevier, Amsterdam, 1983, pp 315-320.

15   J.A. Elvidge, J.R. Jones and M. Saljoughian, J. Pharm. Pharmacol.,
     31 (1979) 508-511.

16   E.A. Evans, D.C. Warrell, J.A.Elvidge and J.R. Jones, Handbook of Tritium
     NMR Spectroscopy and Applications, J. Wiley and Sons, Chichester,
     1985, pp 249.

17   J.M.A. Al-Rawi, J.A. Elvidge, J.R. Jones, R.B. Mane and M. Saieed, J. Chem.
     Res(S)., 1980, 298-299.

18   W.J.S. Lockley in Synthesis and Applications of Isotopically Labelled
     Compounds, W.P. Duncan and A.B. Susan (Eds.), Elsevier, Amsterdam, 1983,
     pp 427-428.

19   W.J.S. Lockley, Tetrahedron Lett., 23 (1982) 3819-3822.

20   W.J.S. Lockley, J. Lab. Comp. Radiopharm., 21 (1984) 45-57.

21   W.J.S. Lockley, J. Lab. Comp. Radiopharm., 22 (1985) 623-630.

22   W.J.S. Lockley, J.Chem. Res(S)., 1985, 178-179

*Synthesis and Applications of Isotopically Labeled Compounds 1985.*
Proceedings of the Second International Symposium, Kansas City, MO, U.S.A.,
3–6 September 1985, R.R. Muccino (Ed.), 395–400
© 1986 Elsevier Science Publishers B.V., Amsterdam — Printed in The Netherlands

TRITIUM AND DEUTERIUM NMR STUDIES OF ZEOLITE CATALYZED ISOTOPE EXCHANGE
REACTIONS

J.L. GARNETT, M.A. LONG and P.G. Williams
School of Chemistry, University of New South Wales, Kensington,
N.S.W. 2033, Australia.

ABSTRACT
    The use of $^3$H and $^2$H nmr spectroscopy in studies of hydrogen isotope exchange
over zeolites and metal loaded zeolites is important for both development of new
catalytic methods of producing labelled compounds and for investigation of the
mechanisms of catalysis over zeolites, as selected examples illustrate.

INTRODUCTION

    The ability to determine hydrogen isotope orientation in a compound labelled
by some form of catalytic exchange is fundamentally important for two reasons.
Firstly, the user of the compound may require a knowledge of the specificity of
the isotope to interpret subsequent reaction studies with the labelled
substrate. Secondly, the isotope orientation provides fundamental information
about the mechanism of the catalytic reaction and the nature of the active
centres in the catalytic surface or soluble catalytic entity.

    For these reasons both $^3$H and $^2$H nmr spectroscopy have become useful tools
in the hands of the catalytic chemist and the procedures are being applied
extensively to the important commercial zeolite catalysts[1]. Tritium nmr has
the advantage over deuterium nmr in its high sensitivity, high resolution and
the wealth of spin coupling data available for immediate use in interpretation
of what in general are simple spectra. Nevertheless, higher levels of isotope
incorporation are possible with deuterium and the advent of high field nmr
instruments provides for deuterium spectra which frequently have adequate
resolution for many purposes.

    Small isotope effects in chemical shifts of tritium when referenced to a
particular internal standard are now well documented[2], but in general proton
shift data is immediately applicable for peak assignment purposes, and it is
only when peaks are very close that a combination of isotope effect and solvent
effect may lead to a reversal of peak orders and thus wrong assignments, as has
been noted[3].

    Zeolites are used commercially to catalyse a large number of organic
reactions. Perhaps the most important involve hydrocarbon skeleton synthesis,

isomerisation and cracking reactions as utilised in the petroleum industry. The catalytic activity for such reactions is associated with several properties of the zeolites including the nature of the cationic sites which may be strongly acidic, the nature of Lewis acid type centres, and the geometry of their pore structure at the molecular size level(4). Mechanisms proposed for carbon skeleton reactions commonly involve protonation type reaction steps and hence can be explored with tritium or deuterium tracers. Metal ions introduced at cationic sites may or may not be involved.

Results reported in this paper relate to aspects of these mechanistic studies of zeolite catalysis. Examples have been chosen to indicate the usefulness of nmr spectroscopy.

RESULTS AND DISCUSSION

H-Mordenite Catalysed Exchange of Aromatic Compounds

Typical results obtained by exchanging an organic compound over H-mordenite in the presence of a trace of high specific activity tritiated water are summarised in Table 1. Aromatic compounds exchange readily and the $^3H$ nmr spectra show the orientation to be typical of electrophilic aromatic substitution such as might be expected from an acidic catalyst. Little exchange is observed in alkyl substituents except where branched at the alpha carbon atom such as in sec-butylbenzene, and then the alkyl activity is confined to the beta carbons. The interpretation of this exchange pattern has been discussed elsewhere in terms of hydride transfer between carbonium ion and reactant molecule(5).

TABLE 1

Tritium Labelling of Aromatic Compounds over H-mordenite

| Compound | Isotope Source | Time (h) | Temp (C) | Incorp % | % of Tritium per site |
|---|---|---|---|---|---|
| toluene | HTO | 24 | 125 | 76 | o 29, m 1.7, p 39, Me <1 |
| cumene | HTO | 48 | 125 | 64 | o 25, m 7, p 23, Me 2, CH<1 |
| s-butylbenzene | HTO | 48 | 125 | 56 | o 16, m 3, p 31,CH<1,$CH_2$ 7,βMe 6,γMe <1 |
| naphthalene | HTO | 24 | 125 | 83 | α 19, β 6 |
| bromobenzene | HTO | 54 | 150 | 30 | o 19, m <1, p 62 |
| toluene | $T_2$ | 48 | 180 | <1 | |
| toluene | $C_6H_5T$ | 24 | 100 | 58 | o 18, m 20, p 24, Me<1 |

reaction conditions: 25mg catalyst,0.1ml substrate,5microlitres HTO(40Ci/g) or 500mCi $T_2$ or 0.1ml $C_6H_5T$(5Ci/g)

If tritium gas is used as isotope source in place of HTO, exchange is undetectable except at higher temperatures over long periods. In contrast, the use of high specific activity tritiated benzene, (or $C_6D_6$ ), as isotope source for exchange into a molecule such as toluene leads to a close to random distribution of isotope in the aromatic ring. This remarkable difference in isotope distribution based on choice of isotope source was explored in more detail in a set of experiments, summarised in Figure 1, in which the exchange of specifically para-tritiated toluene with benzene was studied utilising both tritium and deuterium nmr and mass spectrometry.

Firstly, randomisation of isotope from the para position of toluene in the presence of benzene was followed to ascertain the rate of exchange of benzene relative to the ortho and meta positions in toluene. In the same experiment it could be determined if these two toluene positions had different rates under these essentially anhydrous conditions. Two results are shown in Figure 1 for this type of experiment. One shows the result of the reactants reaching an equilibrium situation (sample 1), and the distribution of isotope is approximately random amongst all positions in the exchange system. Earlier in the exchange process, (sample 2), the different rates of each of the exchanging positions is evident, and this result is a better guide to the situation under initial exchange conditions.

Secondly, the effect of water on the rate of randomisation of isotope, and on the individual rates of the meta and ortho positions was assessed. This reaction is shown by sample 3 in Figure 1, and it can be seen that the rate of uptake of isotope in the ortho position greatly exceeds that in the meta position. Additionally, after the same time of reaction as sample 1, the orientation is still very clear - suggesting that the overall activity of the catalyst has been lowered by the presence of the water in the reaction mixture.

Thirdly, it was necesssary to elucidate the path of isotope redistribution in toluene, i.e. whether it proceeded intermolecularly, or by some intramolecular mechanism. Hence the redistribution of tritium from the para position in toluene was followed by $^3H$ nmr at the same time as redistribution of deuterium from perdeuterotoluene to the essentially unlabelled p-$^3H$-toluene. If tritium randomisation occurred whilst tritium redistribution did not, the process would have been intramolecular only. If in the initial stages of reaction, tritium randomisation exceeded that of deuterium, but both were present, then it would indicate that both inter- and intramolecular processes were active.

The results of this type of reaction are shown by samples 4 and 5 in Figure 1. Sample 4 shows almost random distributions of both tritium and deuterium in the toluene. However, in sample 5 the para position still contains about 85% of the tritium, the $D_0$ and $D_8$ peaks still being the largest in the mass spectrum. Qualitatively these results show that exchange is not solely intramolecular.

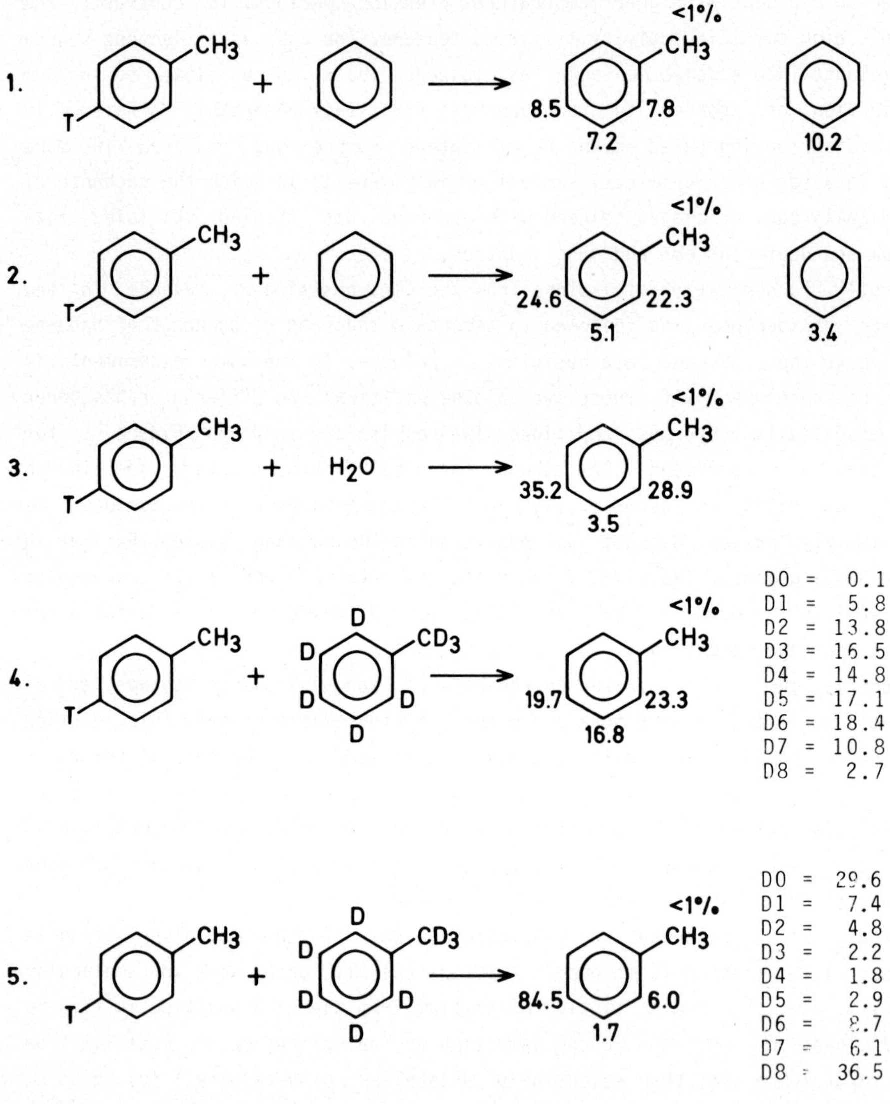

Fig. 1. Randomisation reactions of p-[3]H-toluene over H-mordenite. Tritium distribution in products is shown as % of incorporated tritium per H site. Deuterium mass spectral distributions are % peak heights. Reaction conditions: 25mg H-mordenite, 25mg p-[3]H-toluene, 0.1ml substrate (samples 1,2,4,5), 5 microlitres water (sample 3), at 125°C. Reaction times 96h (samples 1,3,4), 24h (samples 2,5).

They do not conclusively establish whether exchange is totally intermolecular, but at best the intramolecular contribution is small.

Consideration of the orientations of the tritium in samples 1 to 3 in Figure 1 show that the selectivity of exchange for the ortho position in toluene in preference to the meta position is retained, if not enhanced, when water is present. Also, even under conditions when water is not specifically added to the reaction mixture, isotope is incorporated more quickly at the ortho than the meta position of toluene. The rate of exchange at either of these positions under these zeolitic conditions is greater than at a single position in benzene.

Hence the lack of orientation of tritium in the aromatic centres of alkylbenzenes in experiments where isotopic benzene is the isotope source, (Table 1) may be explained by the probability that the substrate may exchange many times with the zeolite surface before more isotope is deposited on the surface by the benzene. In effect, isotope randomises within the substrate being labelled at a rate greater than entry of isotope.

## Metal Loaded Mordenite Exchange

Table 2 contains the results of exchange of a number of representative compounds over palladium loaded mordenite with tritium gas as isotope source. A result for exchange of toluene with HTO over Pd-Y is included for comparison purposes.

TABLE 2

Tritium Exchange over Palladium-mordenite

| Compound | Isotope Source | Incorp % | % of tritium per site |
|---|---|---|---|
| toluene* | HTO | 43 | o 1, m <1, p 2, Me 32 |
| toluene | $T_2$ | 55 | o 10, m 3, p 19, Me 18 |
| cumene | $T_2$ | 44 | o 14, m 2, p 19, CH 19, Me 5 |
| chlorobenzene | $T_2$ | 36 | o 11, m <1, p 77 |
| pyridine | $T_2$ | 31 | o 50, m <1, p <1 |
| n-hexane | $T_2$ | 4 | C1 7, C2 7.4, C3 7.3 |
| 2,3 di-me-butane | $T_2$ | 69 | CH 6.2, Me 7.3 |

reaction conditions: 96h at $100^{\circ}$C, 25mg catalyst,0.2ml substrate,500mCi $T_2$ or 5microlitres HTO(40Ci/g) except where otherwise indicated.

* catalyst Pd-Y zeolite, 72h at $150^{\circ}$C

The following important features are apparent:

(a) Exchange over Pd-Y zeolite with HTO leads to ortho-para distribution within an aromatic centre but, in contrast to H-mordenite or H-Y zeolite, more general alkyl exchange is also observed.

(b) Tritium gas is readily activated as an isotope source in contrast to exchange over H- forms of zeolites and tritium distributions are similar to those with HTO as isotope source.

(c) A wider range of compounds are activated over Pd-mordenite including saturated alkanes and labelling occurs at temperatures where little isomerisation of the carbon skeleton is observed.

It is thus apparent that the loading of zeolites with catalytically active noble metals leads to an efficient method of labelling many organic compounds and high specific activities are possible where tritium gas is the isotope source. However, the use of a metal loaded zeolite rather than a bulk metal as catalyst(6) yields an isotope distribution pattern which is different from that of either the zeolite or the metal on its own. Nor is it just an "average" of the two patterns but quite unique. The mechanistic interpretation in terms of activation of tritium on the metal with accompanying "spillover" to the zeolite active centres has been discussed elsewhere(7,8).

The results presented illustrate the great value of $^3$H or $^2$H nmr spectroscopy in developing methods of hydrogen isotope labelling(9) and also its value in probing catalytic mechanisms.

We thank the Australian Institute of Nuclear Sciences and the Australian Research Grants Scheme for support.

REFERENCES

1 M.A. Long, J.L. Garnett and P.G. Williams, J.Chem.Soc. Perkin Trans. 2, (1984) 2105-9, and refs. therein.
2 E.A. Evans, D.C. Warrell, J.A. Elvidge and J.R. Jones, Handbook of Tritium NMR Spectroscopy and Applications, John Wiley and Sons, Chichester, 1985, pp. 11-12.
3 M.A. Long, J.K. Saunders, P.G. Williams, A.L. Odell and R.W. Martin, Org. Mag. Reson., 22 (1984) 665-7.
4 S.M. Csicsery, Chem. in Britain, 21 (1985) 473-7.
5 M.A. Long, J.L. Garnett, P.G. Williams and T. Mole, J.Amer. Chem. Soc., 103 (1981) 1571-2.
6 J.L. Garnett, M.A. Long, C.A. Lukey and P.G. Williams, J.Chem.Soc. Perkin Trans. 2, (1982) 287-9.
7 M.A. Long, J.L. Garnett, and P.G. Williams, Aust. J. Chem., 35 (1982) 1057-9.
8 G.M. Pajonk, S.J. Teichner and G.E. Germain (Eds.), Spillover of Adsorbed Species, Elsevier, Amsterdam, 1983.
9 J.A. Elvidge and J.R. Jones (Eds.), Isotopes: Essential Chemistry and Applications, The Chemical Soc. Special Publ. 35, London, 1980.

*Synthesis and Applications of Isotopically Labeled Compounds 1985.*
Proceedings of the Second International Symposium, Kansas City, MO, U.S.A.,
3—6 September 1985, R.R. Muccino (Ed.), 401—408
© 1986 Elsevier Science Publishers B.V., Amsterdam — Printed in The Netherlands

DETERMINATION OF OPTICAL PURITY BY $^3$H NMR SPECTROSCOPY

J A ELVIDGE[1], E A EVANS[2], J R JONES[1] and LI MING ZHANG[1]

[1]Chemistry Department, University of Surrey, Guildford, Surrey GU2 5XH

[2]Amersham International plc, Amersham, Bucks HP7 9NA

ABSTRACT

Compounds that are optically active as a result of isotopic substitution find wide application in the life sciences. Consequently the first half of this paper will be concerned with the various methods that are employed to prepare optically active tritiated compounds. The second half will be concerned with the various methods that are employed to measure optical activity and in particular $^3$H nmr spectroscopy. The work will refer especially to a series of secondary alcohols which have been labelled by a catalytic exchange procedure and whose optical purity has been determined by $^3$H nmr measurements in the presence of a chiral lanthanide shift reagent tris(3-hepta-fluorobutyryl-d-camphorato)europium(III).

INTRODUCTION

Tritium labelled compounds which are optically active and stereospecifically labelled provide an essential armoury of radiotracers for use in scientific research.[1] Such compounds are especially important in elucidating the mechanisms of chemical and biochemical reactions.[2] The latter studies are of particular importance in furthering knowledge of disease states many of which are related to malfunction of enzymes.

In the uses of such tracer compounds it is essential to have accurate knowledge of the regio- and stereo-specificity of the labelled atoms, as well as the "radiooptical" purity in the case of optically active labelled compounds. The "radiooptical" purity may be defined as that proportion of the labelled molecules which are in the stated optical form of the compound.

Tritium nmr spectroscopy provides the ideal analytical method for establishing these important parameters in the application of tritium labelled compounds as tracers.[3]

GENERAL LABELLING METHODS

Methods for the useful practical labelling of organic compounds with tritium have been reviewed[1,3,4] as well as a review relating to compounds stereospecifically labelled with the hydrogen isotopes deuterium and tritium.[5] The methods fall into three general categories as follows:

(1)    Chemical synthesis

(2)    Biochemical methods

(3)    Hydrogen isotope exchange reactions

Optically active compounds labelled with tritium can be prepared by any of these general methods although the emphasis in this short paper is on isotope exchange labelling of secondary alcohols. Some examples illustrate the principles of the methods.

(1)    Chemical Synthesis

Labelling by use of optically active precursors normally gives the desired optically active tritium compound provided no change has occurred through, for example, exchange with inversion at the asymmetric carbon atoms(s) or chiral centres. For example, reduction of p-chloro-L-phenylalanine with tritium gas using a palladium catalyst in methanolic potassium (or sodium) hydroxide yields L-[4-$^3$H]phenyl-alanine with full retention of optical activity.[6]

Chemical synthetic methods which involve the formation of an asymmetric centre containing the label usually provide mixtures of (R)- and (S)-labelled products. For example the reduction of a ketone $R_1R_2C=O$ with sodium borotritide yields a mixture of D- and L-labelled alcohols. It should be noted that if $R_1$ or $R_2$ is a hydrogen atom, introduction of tritium by reduction then leads to the formation of a chiral centre. There are many such examples in the literature[1] including the preparation of tritium labelled carbohydrates.[1,7]

In the preparation of optically active tritium compounds by such chemical synthetic methods it is often possible to predict with accuracy not only the position of the labelled atom(s) but also the regio- or stereospecificity of the label. It should be noted however that simple reactions can sometimes result in the inversion of optical activity. An example is the qua ternization of (+)-bicuculine using [$^3$H]methyl iodide which reverses the optical rotation to give 1S,9R-(-)-[N-methyl-$^3$H]bicuculine methiodide.[8]

Recently, more use has been made of chiral homogeneous catalysts to prepare optically active amino acids and peptides by reduction with tritium gas of unsaturated intermediates[4,9,10] For example, the reduction of (Z)-N-acetyldehydrophenylalanyl-(S)-phenylalanine methyl ester with the catalyst $L_2RhCl$ where $L_2$ is a chiral diphosphine such as (+)diop.[11]

(+)diop

In this example reduction with tritium resulted in 88 per cent of the rotamer (1) and 12 per cent of (2)

(2)    Biochemical Methods

Labelling of organic compounds with tritium employing biochemical methods such as the use of enzymes usually results in the retention or production of stereospecifically labelled products.[1,3,5]

(3)    Isotope Exchange

Hydrogen isotope exchange labelling reactions can be applied to a very wide variety of compounds[1,3] including those which are optically active. In this case it is difficult to predict with any accuracy either the position of the labelled atoms or the stereo-specificity of the labelling reaction, unlike in chemical synthetic methods. Methods fall into three general categories as follows:

- exchange with tritium gas
- catalysed exchange in solution with tritium gas
- catalysed exchange in tritiated solvents

the details and peculiarities of which are well described in the literature[1]. Hydrogen isotope exchange reactions in solution using heterogeneous and homogeneous metal catalysts are well studied.[1,13] In this study we have labelled a number of alcohols by exchange in tritiated water in the presence of tris(triphenylphosphinyl) ruthenium dichloride as homogeneous catalyst. In such exchange reactions both D- and L-rotamers become labelled with the production of tritiated racemic mixtures.

The principal features of the hydrogen-tritium exchange labelling of alcohols in THO at 200°C for 1 to 3 hours under nitrogen using the homogeneous catalyst tris(triphenylphosphinyl) ruthenium dichloride, are as follows:

(1)  For primary alcohols either specific or nearly specific labelling occurs at the α-position. Longer reaction times favour a more generally labelled product

(2)  The mechanism of tritium incorporation is thought to proceed by an oxidation-reduction type:

$$R_1R_2CHOT \rightleftharpoons R_1R_2CTOH$$

The initial step being the formation of an alkoxy-bound ruthenium complex followed by hydrogen (tritium) transfer:

$$R_1R_2CHOH \;+\; (Ru) \rightleftharpoons R_1R_2C\!\overset{H}{\underset{}{-}}O - (Ru)$$

$$(Ru) \;+\; R_1R_2CTOH \xleftarrow{\;\;T^+\;\;} R_1R_2CO\ldots.RuH$$

(3)  Some labelling in the beta position is observed probably due to the fact that exchange also takes place in the aldehyde or ketone formed as intermediate

(4)  Secondary alcohols give generally labelled products

(5)  Tertiary alcohols such as adamantol are not labelled.

Table 1 shows the relative incorporation of tritium in a number of primary alcohols as determined by tritium nmr spectroscopy and by liquid beta scintillation counting.

TABLE 1

Position and relative incorporation of tritium in Primary Alcohols[+]

| Alcohol | Molar Specific Activity | Relative % Tritium positions | | |
| --- | --- | --- | --- | --- |
| | mCi/mmol | alpha | beta | other |
| Ethanol | 54 | 100 | . | . |
| 1-Heptanol | 115 | 86 | 14 | . |
| 3-Phenyl-1-propanol | 136 | 96 | 4 | . |
| 1-Octadecanol | 180 | 88 | 4 | 8 |
| Benzyl alcohol | 82 | 100 (benzylic) | | |

+Experimental conditions: Alcohol (0.3g), $RuCl_2(PPh_3)_3$ (5 mg) and THO (10μl at 50Ci/ml) in a sealed tube under nitrogen were heated 200°C for 1-3 hrs.

Using the same labelling procedure the pattern of labelling in a number of secondary alcohols is shown in table 2.

TABLE 2

Position and relative incorporation of tritium in Secondary Alcohols as determined by $^3$H NMR spectroscopy[+]

| Alcohol | Chemical Shift $\delta$(ppm) | Relative intensity % | Assignment |
|---------|------------------------------|----------------------|------------|
| 2-Pentanol | 1.16 | 48 | 1-Me |
| CH$_3$(CH$_2$)$_2$CH(OH)CH$_3$ (3 2 1) | 1.36 ⎫ 1.45 ⎭ | 38 | 3-H$_B$ 3-H$_A$ |
| | 3.74 | 14 | $\alpha$-H |
| 2-Decanol | 1.17 | 49 | 1-Me |
| CH$_3$(CH$_2$)$_7$CH(OH)CH$_3$ | 1.37 ⎫ 1.46 ⎭ | 34 | 3-H$_B$ 3-H$_A$ |
| | 3.73 | 18 | $\alpha$-H |
| 2-Hexadecanol | 1.18 | 47 | 1-Me |
| CH$_3$(CH$_2$)$_{13}$CH(OH)CH$_3$ | 1.40 ⎫ 1.45 ⎭ | 33 | 3-H$_B$ 3-H$_A$ |
| | 3.76 | 20 | $\alpha$-H |

+ $^1$H decoupled spectra in CDCl$_3$ solvent at 25°C.

All three secondary alcohols show a similar pattern of labelling.

## ANALYSIS

Optical purity is usually measured by polarimetry; chromatography (gas, liquid or high performance/pressure liquid); Nmr spectroscopy using (a) a chiral solvent (b) conversion of, for example, chiral alcohols and amines to diastereomeric esters and amides with an enantiomerically pure chiral acid chloride or (c) using chiral lanthanide shift reagents; specific enzymes reactions (acylases or oxidases) and reverse isotope dilution analysis for isotopically labelled compounds. Overall retention of optical purity of a sample as measured by polarimetry for example, following hydrogen-tritium exchange labelling does not necessarily indicate a high radiooptical purity.

Much of the radioactivity could be associated with a very small chemical weight of the unexpected rotamer as impurity often found for example in Wilzbach labelling.[1,12,14,15] In such cases reverse isotope dilution analysis has been employed for example for determination of the radiooptical purity of labelled amino acids.[16] However, even this method has its drawbacks and is dependent on not only having chemically pure enantiomorphs for the dilution but also being able to separate the impurity. Such difficulties are avoided by the use of $^3$H nmr spectroscopy and a suitable shift reagent.

The principles of chiral lanthanide shift reagent usage involves an equilibrium reaction. Under normal conditions the equilibrium between the substrate and the lanthanide shift reagent (LSR) is rapid on the NMR time scale:

$$\left\{ \begin{array}{l} (R) - Substrate \\ (S) - Substrate \end{array} \right\} \quad + \ 2(R)-LSR$$

$$\Big\Updownarrow K_R \ (or \ K_S)$$

$$(S) - Substrate-R-(LSR) \quad + \quad (R) - Substrate-R-(LSR)$$

$$A \qquad\qquad\qquad\qquad\qquad\qquad B$$

Therefore only a single time-averaged spectrum results from the average of complexed and uncomplexed substrate molecules. The two complexes formed as a result of the binding of an enantiomerically pure LSR to the two enantiomers are diastereomeric and can have different averaged chemical shifts. This may arise (a) because $K_S$ and $K_R$ are not the same and (b) A and B may differ in their geometry, thus causing a difference in the induced shift for corresponding signals in the two complexes. Usually chemical shift differences are large enough for complete separation of at least one set of enantiotopic signals and the optical purity can be determined directly by integration of the resolved signals.

Some widely used chiral LSR's are:

(a)    Tris(3-t-butylhydroxymethylene-d-camphorato)europium (111)  Eu(bhmc)$_3$

(b)    Tris(3-heptafluorobutyryl-d-camphorato)europium (111)  Eu(hfbc)$_3$

(c)    Tris(3-trifluoroacetyl-d-camphorato)europium (111)  Eu(facam)$_3$

(d)    Tris(d,d-dicampholymethanato)europium (111)  Eu(dcm)$_3$

Resolution enhanced $^3$H nmr spectra in the measurement of optical purity of the tritiated secondary alcohols can be made on the basis of the α-H, 1-Me and 3-H signals.

Typical spectra using this technique are shown in Figure 1 (without LSR) and in Figure 2 (with LSR) for 2-[G-$^3$H]decanol.

Figure 1          $^3$H Nmr ($^1$H decoupled) of [G-$^3$H]Dodecanol in CDCl$_3$

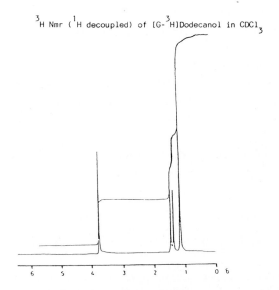

Figure 2          $^3$H Nmr ($^1$H decoupled) of [G-$^3$H]-
Dodecanol in CDCl$_3$ in the
presence of Eu(hfbc)$_3$ - note
the α-H signal is now split
into 2 singlets representing
the d & l forms: splitting of
the Me signal is also evident

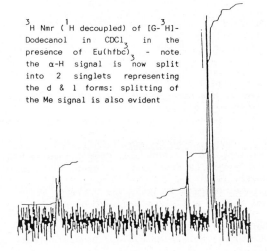

408

CONCLUDING REMARKS

The current use of tritium nmr spectroscopy not only provides a check on the patterns of labelling but also on the proportions of tritium present in optical isomers through the use of europium (lanthanide) shift reagents. For example, the advantages of $^3$H nmr spectroscopy for the examination of chiral centres, including chiral methyl groups (-CHDT) is already well established[3], such compounds finding increasing application in studies of biosynthesis. The latter necessarily implicates the use of tritium and the benefits of tritium nmr spectroscopy as an analytical tool[3,17-19].

Our technique presented here for the analysis of secondary alcohols labelled with tritium is being extended for the analysis of other labelled optically active tritium compounds such as amino acids.

REFERENCES

1  E A Evans, Tritium and Its Compounds, 2nd ed, Butterworths, London, 1974
2  cf. Radiotracer Techniques and Applications, Volumes 1 and 2, E A Evans and M Muramatsu eds, Marcel Dekker, Inc, New York and Basel, 1977
3  E A Evans, D C Warrell, J A Elvidge and J R Jones, Handbook of Tritium NMR Spectroscopy and Applications, John Wiley and Sons Ltd., Chichester, 1985
4  E A Evans, Synthesis and Applications of $^3$H-Labeled Compounds, Proc. International Symposium on Synthesis and Applications of Isotopically Labeled Compounds, Kansas City 6-11 June 1982. W P Duncan and A B Susan eds. Elsevier, Amsterdam 1983, p.1
5  D W Young, Stereospecific syntheses of Tritium Labelled Compounds using Chemical and Radiochemical Methods, Chapter 4 in Isotopes in Organic Chemistry Vol. 4 Tritium in Organic Chemistry, E Buncel and C C Lee eds (1978) p.177-294
6  J M A Al-Rawi, J A Elvidge, J R Jones, V M A Chambers and E A Evans, J Label Compds Radiopharms, 12, (1976) 265
7  J A Elvidge, J R Jones, R B Mane, V M A Chambers, E A Evans and D C Warrell, J.Label Compds Radiopharms, 15, (1978) 141
8  J Kardos, G Blasko, P Kerekes, I Kovacs and M Simonyi, Biochem Pharmacol, 33 (1984) 3537
9  W S Knowles and N J Sabachy, Chem Communs (1968) 1445
10  W S Knowles, N J Sabachy and B D Vineyard, Chem Communs (1972) 10
11  H Levine-Pinto, J L Morgat, P Fromageot, D Meyer, J C Poulin and H B Kagan, Tetrahedron, 38 (1982) 119
12  J H Parmentier, J.Label Compds, 1 (1965) 93; 2 (1966) 367
13  E A Evans, D C Warrell, J A Elvidge and J R Jones, J.Radioanalyt.Chem., 64 (1981) 41
14  H Simon, G Mullhofer and H D Dorrer in J Sirchis ed Proc.Conf on Methods for Preparing and Storing Marked Molecules, Brussels 1963. Euratom Pub. EUR 1625e, 1964, p.997
15  H Simon, K Schmidt, G Mullhofer, W Eder and R Medina, Z.Naturforsch, 23b (1968) 778
16  R J Bayly, Proc.Symp.Radioisotopes Phys.Sci.Ind, IAEA Vienna 2 (1962) 305 (see also reference 1 page 544)
17  L J Altman, C Y Han, A Bertolino, D Laurigeri, W Muller, S Schwarz, D Shanker, W H de Wolf and F Yang, J.Amer.Chem.Soc., 100 (1978) 3235
18  H G Floss and M D Tsai, Adv.Enzymology, 50 (1979) 243
19  E Abraham, C-P Pang, R L White, D H G Crout, M Lutstorf, P J Morgan and A E Derome, J.C S.Chem.Communs (1983) 723

*Synthesis and Applications of Isotopically Labeled Compounds 1985.*
Proceedings of the Second International Symposium, Kansas City, MO, U.S.A.,
3—6 September 1985, R.R. Muccino (Ed.), 409—414
© 1986 Elsevier Science Publishers B.V., Amsterdam — Printed in The Netherlands

SYNTHESIS OF ISOTOPICALLY LABELED THREAT AGENTS*

DONALD G. OTT, MARTIN J. REISFELD, AND THOMAS W. WHALEY
Toxicology Group, Life Sciences Division, Los Alamos National Laboratory,
University of California, Los Alamos, New Mexico, 87545

ABSTRACT

The blister agents, bis(2-chloroethyl) sulfide (HD or sulfur mustard) and
dichloro(2-chlorovinyl)arsine (L or Lewisite) were prepared with carbon-14 at
all carbon atoms. The synthesis of HD proceeded from 2-bromoethanol. In the
Lewisite synthesis, chloro(2-chlorovinyl)mercury, from acetylene, was converted to L, along with the bis- and tris-(chlorovinyl) compounds, which were
separated by thin layer chromatography. The nerve agents, isopropyl methylphosphonofluoridate (GB or sarin) and pinacolyl methylphosphonofluoridate (GD
or soman) were labeled in the methyl group attached to phosphorus with either
deuterium, tritium, or carbon-14 starting from the labeled iodomethane.

INTRODUCTION

We have been engaged in a project to develop methods for the synthesis of
isotopically labeled chemical threat agents. This paper summarizes some of
our work to date. We have developed procedures for the synthesis of
isotopically labeled bis(2-chloroethyl) sulfide (1, sulfur mustard, HD),
dichloro(2-chlorovinyl)arsine (2, Lewisite, L), isopropyl methylphosphonofluoridate (3, sarin, GB), pinacolyl methylphosphonofluoridate (4, soman, GD).

$$ClCH_2CH_2SCH_2CH_2Cl$$

1

$$\begin{matrix} Cl & & H \\ & C=C & \\ H & & AsCl_2 \end{matrix}$$

2

$$CH_3\overset{O}{\underset{F\quad CH_3}{\overset{\|}{P}}}OCHCH_3$$

3

$$CH_3\overset{O}{\underset{F\quad CH_3}{\overset{\|}{P}}}OCHC(CH_3)_3$$

4

Our primary emphasis has been on the preparation of radioactively labeled
materials; however, the procedures can also be applied to labeling with stable
isotopes. The radiolabeled chemical threat agents were to be used in a
variety of biological studies. Accordingly, labeling at biologically stable
positions with relatively high specific activities (1 Ci/mmol for tritium and
50 mCi/mmol for carbon-14) was a prime consideration.

METHODS AND RESULTS

Synthesis of bis(2-chloroethyl-$^{14}C_2$) sulfide (1) was carried out by the
two-step sequence given in Equation 1. 2-Bromoethanol-$^{14}C_2$ (5) was trans-

$$HOCH_2CH_2Br \xrightarrow{\text{Na}_2\text{S}} (HOCH_2CH_2)_2S \xrightarrow{\text{HCl}} (ClCH_2CH_2)_2S \qquad (1)$$

5         6         1

*This project was supported by the U.S. Army Medical Research and Development
Command and conducted under the auspices of the U.S. Department of Energy.

ferred on a vacuum line into a frozen aqueous solution of sodium sulfide (1.05 equivalents), which was then warmed to room temperature and magnetically stirred for·2 hours. Because the bis(2-hydroxyethyl-$^{14}$C$_2$) sulfide (6) is very soluble in water, the water had to be completely removed from the mixture before the product could be extracted from the inorganic salts into an organic solvent. Most of the water was removed by lyophilization, the last traces by azeotropic distillation with chloroform. With the aid of a filter stick, the residue was repeatedly extracted with chloroform. The extract was shown by $^1$H-NMR to contain only the thiodiglycol, which was quantitated by radio-activity analysis of aliquots (88% yield). In a published, large-scale preparation of the thiodiglycol (ref. 1), 2-chloroethanol was used, rather than the bromo compound. The product was extracted from the sodium chloride residue (after evaporation of the water) with hot absolute ethanol, and finally purified by distillation. However, 2-bromoethanol, which was the available starting material for the labeled preparation, produces sodium bromide that is soluble in ethanol.

It has long been known that treatment of the thiodiglycol with hydrochloric acid readily produces sulfur mustard in quantitative yield (ref. 2). The chloroform extract of 6 was evaporated in a screw-cap tube containing a magnetic stirring vane. Concentrated hydrochloric acid (40 equivalents) was introduced through the Teflon septum-valve cap, and the mixture was stirred at 65-70$^{\circ}$C for an hour (an insoluble phase was evident after the first few minutes). After the tube had cooled, the product 1 was extracted into benzene, and the extract was washed with water, dried over molecular sieve, and transferred with benzene washings to a small volumetric flask. Samples of this final solution of product were taken into hexane containing 1,6-dichlorohexane as an internal standard for quantitation and analyzed by capillary column gas chromatography. No impurities were detected. Quantitation was also made by radioactivity analysis of aliquots taken into methanolic sodium hydroxide (84% yield). The overall yield of 1 from 5 was 74%.

Conditions for the production of dichloro(2-chlorovinyl-$^{14}$C$_2$)arsine (2) on a large scale using mercuric chloride catalyzed condensation of arsenic trichloride with acetylene were extensively studied (ref. 3). The chemical reactions were as shown in Equation 2, although the mercuric chloride was used

$$HC{\equiv}CH \xrightarrow[\text{HCl}]{\text{HgCl}_2} ClCH{=}CHHgCl \xrightarrow{\text{AsCl}_3} \begin{array}{l} ClCH{=}CHAsCl_2 \quad\quad 2 \\ + \\ \left(ClCH{=}CH\right)_2AsCl \quad 9 \\ + \\ \left(ClCH{=}CH\right)_3As \quad 10 \end{array} \quad (2)$$

7 ·· 8

in only catalytic amounts, and the intermediate 2-chlorovinylmercuric chloride (8) was not isolated. For labeling purposes it was felt that isolation of the intermediate 8 as a pure compound could lead to a higher purity for 2, as well as simplify introduction of the isotopic acetylene. A mercuric chloride solution (4 $\underline{M}$, 2 equivalents), which was also 4 $\underline{M}$ in sodium chloride and 0.05 $\underline{M}$ in hydrochloric acid, was placed in a glass, O-ring sealed, pressure reaction tube and attached to a vacuum line. The acetylene-$^{14}C_2$ was vacuum transferred into the frozen solution, and the tube was closed, thawed, and warmed to $30^{\circ}C$ to redissolve the inorganic salts. A precipitate developed in the magnetically stirred mixture, and the pressure decreased from above atmospheric pressure to about 0.2 atmosphere over 16 hours. The thick grayish-white slurry (which had always been white in nonradioactive trial preparations) was frozen with liquid nitrogen, and by-product acetaldehyde-$^{14}C_2$(0.25 equivalents) was transferred to a storage vial along with a small amount of water. The tube was opened, and the product was extracted with benzene. The extract was washed with water, dried over molecular sieve, and transferred to a Reactivial with evaporation in a stream of nitrogen. The product 8 was obtained in 61% yield as a white crystalline solid, which soon turned gray and continued to darken with time. Again, this decomposition had not occurred in development trials using nonlabeled acetylene.

Arsenic trichloride (14 equivalents) was added, along with a magnetic stirring vane, to the Reactivial containing 8 and the solution was stirred at room temperature for 4 days. Thin layer chromatography showed no 8 remained. Hexane was added, and the solution was extracted 3 times with 6 $\underline{N}$ hydrochloric acid to remove the arsenic trichloride. The hexane solution was streaked onto preparative thin layer chromatography plates (2-mm silica gel layer), which was developed with 5% methanol in benzene. Three well separated bands (A,B, and C), visualized under ultraviolet light, had $R_f$ values of 0.3, 0.76, and 0.88, respectively. The bands were scraped and collected (separately) on a fritted glass vacuum filter assembly and transferred to centrifuge cones.

In trial runs the products were eluted from the plate scrapings with benzene. Utilizing tracer carbon-14 and elemental analyses, it was shown that the product from band A had chlorine:arsenic:vinyl ratios of 1:1:1, band B had 2:1:2, and band C had 3:1:3. The relative molar amounts in the bands, A:B:C, were approximately 90:10:1. It appears that the reaction products Lewisite-1 (2) and Lewisite-II (9) had further reacted with methanol during chromatography resulting in removal of the chlorine attached to arsenic [the Lewisite-III (10) was, of course, not affected]. It was not established whether these materials were the arsenite esters, acids, oxides, or other compounds. However, after treatment with concentrated hydrochloric acid, the products from bands A and B were reconverted to 2 and 9, having the correct analytical

ratios for chlorine:arsenic:vinyl of 3:1:1 and 3:2:1, respectively. No inert
(non-alcohol containing) solvent systems, with either silica gel or reverse
phase plates, were found that would separate the three original reaction
products. Also, the use of larger excesses of arsenic trichloride in the
reaction had no significant effect on decreasing the amounts of 9 and 10
produced, contrary to what might have been expected.

The plate scrapings from band A were treated with concentrated hydrochloric
acid, and the slurry was extracted with benzene; centrifugation was used to
aid in separation of the phases. The benzene solution of 2 was dried over
molecular sieve and transferred to a vial that had been calibrated for volume.
Aliquots were taken and appropriately diluted for radioactivity analysis,
which gave a yield of 33% from 8 (20% overall yield from 7). Thin layer
chromatography showed only one spot with $R_f$ identical to authentic 2.

Two additional agents we sought to prepare were the cholinesterase inhibitors isopropyl methylphosphonofluoridate (3) and pinacolyl methylphosphonofluoridate (4). The methyl group of the phosphonofluoridate group is the only
biologically stable position for labeling with tritium or carbon-14. Both
sarin and soman can be prepared from a common precursor, methylphosphonic
difluoride. The reactions employed in the synthesis of methylphosphonic
difluoride are shown in Equation 3 (ref. 4).

$$CH_3I \xrightarrow{P(OPh)_3} CH_3\overset{+}{P}(OPh)_3\ I^- \xrightarrow{EtOH} CH_3\overset{O}{\underset{\|}{P}}(OPh)_2 \xrightarrow[\text{2. HCl}]{\text{1. LiOH}}$$

$$\quad\quad\quad\quad 11 \quad\quad\quad\quad\quad\quad\quad 12 \quad\quad\quad\quad\quad\quad\quad 13$$

$$CH_3\overset{O}{\underset{\|}{P}}(OH)_2 \xrightarrow{SOCl_2} CH_3\overset{O}{\underset{\|}{P}}Cl_2 \xrightarrow[\text{18-crown-6}]{KF} CH_3\overset{O}{\underset{\|}{P}}F_2 \quad\quad (3)$$

$$\quad\quad 14 \quad\quad\quad\quad\quad\quad\quad 15 \quad\quad\quad\quad\quad\quad\quad 16$$

The phosphonium salt 12 was prepared by heating triphenyl phosphite (1.08
equivalents) and the isotopically labeled methyl iodide (11) in a sealed tube
at 120-130°C for 40 hours. The resulting viscous brown liquid could be
induced to crystallize when triturated with ether, yielding the phosphonium
salt 12 in 95% yield. When dissolved in ethanol at room temperature, the
phosphonium salt underwent a rapid ester interchange and Arbusov reaction to
afford diphenyl methylphosphonate (13) in quantitative yield. From the weight
of the phosphonium salt and the radioactivity in the ethanol, it was
possible to calculate a reasonably accurate specific activity. It is possible
to remove the equivalent of phenol, which was produced in the previous
reaction, by a simple extraction procedure and obtain a pure sample of the
diester 13; however, this operation is not necessary because additional phenol
is produced in the subsequent saponification step. After evaporation of the

ethanol and ethyl iodide, the residue of the diester 13 and phenol was treated
with 6 equivalents of 1N lithium hydroxide solution and heated at 110–120°C
with stirring overnight. After cooling and acidification with concentrated
hydrochloric acid, the reaction mixture was extracted with chloroform to
remove phenol. Most of the water from the resulting solution of methylphosphonic acid (14) and lithium chloride was evaporated in a stream of air.
The last traces of water were removed under reduced pressure after the
reaction flask was attached to a vacuum manifold.

While it was possible to isolate methylphosphonic acid from the mixture of
the diacid 14 and lithium chloride by a somewhat laborious extraction with
acetone, there is no particular advantage in isolating the pure diacid. The
diacid 14 was readily converted to methylphosphonic dichloride (15) by
treating the mixture of the diacid and lithium chloride with a 15-fold excess
of thionyl chloride containing a catalytic amount (about 1 mole %) of
N,N-dimethylformamide and heating the resulting mixture at 80°C with stirring
overnight. Isolation of pure methylphosphonic dichloride was accomplished by
fractionation on a vacuum manifold. After attaching the reaction flask to the
manifold, all of the volatile material was vacuum transferred to a second
flask. By careful fractionation of the thionyl chloride from the thionyl
chloride–methylphosphonic dichloride mixture it was possible to obtain pure
dichloride 15 as a solid which was then transferred to a product tube on the
vacuum manifold. Methylphosphonic dichloride was obtained in 65–70% overall
yield from the starting methyl iodide with an additional 5–10% of the
dichloride being carried over with the thionyl chloride. A relatively
non-volatile residue containing radioactivity equivalent to the amount of
dimethylformamide used in the dichloride-forming reaction was left in the
second flask. Approximately 20% of the starting radioactivity remained in the
lithium chloride residue. This activity is probably a non-volatile polyphos-
phonate residue. At this stage, it was possible to obtain an accurate
specific activity from an accurately weighed sample of the pure dichloride.

The conversion of the dichloride 15 to methylphosphonic difluoride (16) was
conducted on a vacuum manifold. A solution of the dichloride in benzene (23
wt% dichloride) was vacuum transferred into a tube containing a previously
dried mixture of potassium fluoride and 18-crown-6, and the mixture was
stirred vigorously for 2 days at 30°C. The molar ratio of dichloride to
potassium fluoride to crown ether was 1:2.25:0.1. In order to insure complete
conversion of the dichloride to the difluoride it was important to maintain
the top of the reaction tube at about 10°C in order to keep the contents of
the tube in contact with the potassium fluoride–crown ether mixture and away
from the joint on the vacuum manifold. (Trace impurities were seen in the

difluoride when this precaution was not taken). At the end of the reaction period, the benzene–difluoride mixture was vacuum transferred to a screw-cap vial which would serve as the reaction flask for conversion to sarin or soman. Careful manipulation of the benzene–difluoride solution was essential to avoid losses of the volatile difluoride. The yield of the difluoride 16 from the dichloride 15 was about 95%. The difluoride in this solution was shown to be pure by NMR spectroscopy using either $^1$H, $^2$H, $^3$H, $^{13}$C, $^{19}$F, or $^{31}$P observation.

Conversion of the benzene solution of the difluoride to sarin (3) or soman (4) (Equation 4) was accomplished by adding a mixture containing one

$$CH_3PF_2 \xrightarrow[Et_3N]{ROH} CH_3POR \qquad \begin{array}{l} 3 \quad R = (CH_3)_2CH- \\ \\ 4 \quad R = (CH_3)_3CCHCH_3 \end{array} \tag{4}$$

16 ... F

equivalent of triethyl amine and one equivalent of the appropriate alcohol (isopropyl alcohol for sarin and pinacolyl alcohol for soman) and stirring at room temperature for 2 hours. After washing the benzene solution of the phosphonofluoridate with a hydrochloric acid-sodium chloride solution and drying the benzene solution over molecular sieve, the benzene solution of the phosphonofluoridate was transferred with benzene washings to a flask calibrated for volume. An aliquot of this solution was taken into hexane containing diethyl ethylphosphonate as an internal standard for quantitation and analyzed by capillary column gas chromatography. Quantitation was also made by radioactivity analysis of an aliquot of this hexane solution taken into methanolic sodium hydroxide containing carrier methylphosphonic acid. The only detectable impurity in either of the products was a small amount of pinacolyl alcohol in the soman preparation. Typical yields from the difluoride 16 were 60% for sarin and 75% for soman. This synthesis has been carried out with deuterium, tritium, and carbon-14 labeling.

REFERENCES

1 E.M. Faber and G.E. Miller, Organic Syntheses, Coll. vol. II (1943) 576–578.
2 H.T. Clarke, J. Chem. Soc., 101 (1912) 1583–1590.
3 W.E. Jones, R.J. Rosser, and F.N. Woodward, J.S.C.I., 68 (1949) 258–262.
4 D.G. Ott, M.J. Reisfeld, and T.W. Whaley, J. Labelled Compds. and Radiopharm., (in press).

*Synthesis and Applications of Isotopically Labeled Compounds 1985.*
Proceedings of the Second International Symposium, Kansas City, MO, U.S.A.,
3—6 September 1985, R.R. Muccino (Ed.), 415—420
© 1986 Elsevier Science Publishers B.V., Amsterdam — Printed in The Netherlands

SOMAN'S ACTIONS ON THE BRAIN:  A 2-[$^{14}$C]DEOXYGLUCOSE STUDY

T.L. Pazdernik, F.E. Samson, and S.R. Nelson

Ralph L. Smith Research Center, University of Kansas Medical Center, Kansas

City, Kansas  66103 (USA)

ABSTRACT

Rats were pretreated with either diazepam, atropine, benactyzine, scopolamine or mecamylamine 10 min prior to soman exposure. Local cerebral glucose use
(LCGU) was determined during the seizure phase (15 min post soman) or the
pathology phase (72 hr post soman). Soman's effects on LCGU are complex;
stimulation of LCGU is associated with soman-induced seizures whereas soman-
induced inhibition of LCGU may have functional, metabolic and/or pathological
components.  Studies with pretreatment agents suggest that soman affects
muscarinic, nicotinic and non-cholinergic systems in the brain.

INTRODUCTION

The 2-[$^{14}$C]deoxyglucose (2-DG) method is a quantitative autoradiographic
technique that provides both a pictorial and a quantitative representation of
the rate of local cerebral glucose use (LCGU) of the entire brain (1). Soman
(0-1,2,2-trimethylpropyl methylphosphonofluoridate), a potent cholinesterase
inhibitor, produces repetitive seizures and a 2-5 fold increase in LCGU in many
brain areas (2). 24-72 hr post soman, LCGU is reduced in most brain regions
(35-80% of control) and conspicuous damage occurs in piriform cortex, amygdala
and dorsal thalamus (3). The aim of this report is to discuss the application
of the 2-DG technique towards understanding soman's actions on the brain. The
impact of 5 pretreatment agents on the pictorial representation of LCGU after
soman exposure are presented.

METHODS

Male Wistar rats (3-9/group; 250-300 g; Charles River Breeding
Laboratories, Wilmington, MA) were pretreated i.m. with diazepam (DZP; 3.2
mg/kg), atropine sulfate (Atr; 3.2 or 10 mg/kg), benactyzine hydrochloride (Bz;
1.0 or 3.2 mg/kg); scopolamine hydrobromide (Sco; 0.32 or 1.0 mg/kg) or
mecamylamine hydrochloride (Mec; 1.0 or 3.2 mg/kg) 10 min prior to injection
(sc) of soman 0.9 LD$_{50}$. In addition, LCGU was determined in appropriate
controls. LCGU autoradiograms were determined during the seizure phase (15 min
post soman) or the pathology phase (72 hr post soman). Details of the procedure

have been previously described by Pazdernik et al. (4); the 2-DG labeling period was 45 min.

RESULTS

Representative photographs of autoradiograms from control rats, soman exposed rats and from rats pretreated with Dzp, Atr, Bz, Sco or Mec prior to soman exposure are shown in Fig. 1 (2-DG given 15 min post soman; seizure phase) and Fig. 2 (2-DG given 72 hr post soman; pathology phase). Autoradiograms obtained from rats given the pretreatment agent alone were similar to control autoradiograms. A brief description of each group follows.

Soman exposure

LCGU increased dramatically in most brain structures during soman-induced seizures. This correlates with large increases in neuronal activity associated with overt convulsions. 72 hr post soman exposure, LCGU was markedly reduced in most brain areas; reduction was most prominent in areas where extensive damage was obvious such as the piriform cortex.

Diazepam pretreatment plus soman exposure

Dzp pretreatment abolished the overt convulsions associated with soman exposure and prevented the large LCGU increases observed 15 min post soman exposure. However, LCGU was still elevated in certain striopallidonigral structures, such as dorsal lateral caudate, globus pallidus, substantia nigra and ventral pallidum. LCGU patterns 72 hr post soman were similar to control and no brain damage was observed.

Atropine pretreatment plus soman exposure

Atr pretreatment with either 3.2 or 10 mg/kg did not abolish soman-induced convulsions, although the duration of convulsions was reduced, especially with the 10 mg/kg dose. LCGU with Atr (3.2 mg/kg) 15 min post soman exposure was similar to that with soman alone, whereas LCGU levels with Atr (10 mg/kg) were more similar to controls. However, the pattern of LCGU differed from controls in that there was a slight generalized suppression but LCGU remained elevated in a few structures such as basolateral amygdala and substantia nigra. When LCGU was determined 72 hr post soman exposure, LCGU values were at control levels (3.2 mg/kg) or slightly depressed (10 mg/kg). The characteristic brain damage was prevented with both doses.

Benactyzine pretreatment plus soman exposure

Bz pretreatment (1.0 or 3.2 mg/kg) protected against soman-induced convulsions. However, these rats were asthenic but responsive to stimuli. LCGU values 15 min post soman exposure were near normal with the low Bz dose and

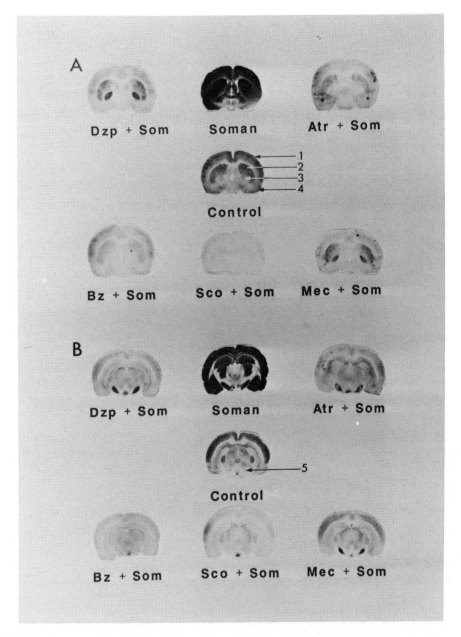

Fig. 1. Representative 2-DG autoradiographs showing local cerebral glucose use during the seizure phase. 2-DG was given 15 min post soman (SOM). Numbered structures are: 1 = frontal cortex, 2 = caudate, 3 = globus pallidus, 4 = piriform cortex, 5 = substantia nigra. A = Frontal brain level; B = Midbrain level.

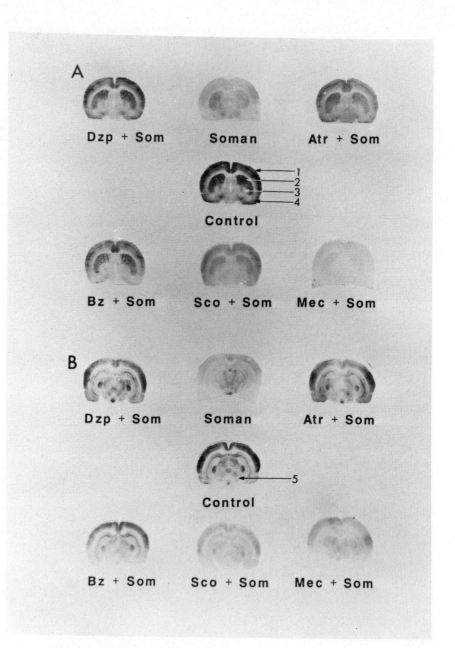

Fig. 2. Representative 2-DG autoradiographs showing local cerebral glucose use during the pathology phase. 2-DG was given 72 min post soman (SOM). Numbered structures are: 1 = frontal cortex, 2 = caudate, 3 = globus pallidus, 4 = piriform cortex, 5 = substantia nigra. A = Frontal brain level; B = Midbrain level.

generally depressed in most brain structures with the high dose. LCGU values 72 hr post soman exposure were near normal with the low Bz dose and slightly depressed with the higher Bz dose. Again, extensive brain damage was not detected in Bz pretreated rats exposed to soman.

## Scopolamine pretreatment plus soman exposure

Sco pretreatment (0.32 or 1.0 mg/kg) protected against soman-induced convulsions and rats remained alert at all times post soman exposure. LCGU values 15 min post soman exposure were markedly depressed and the localization of radiolabel was diffuse. LCGU values 72 hr post soman were still suppressed but not as much as at 15 min post soman exposure. Again, brain damage was not detected in Sco pretreated rats exposed to soman.

## Mecamylamine pretreatment plus soman

Pretreatment with Mec (3.2 mg/kg) did not prevent soman-induced seizures. In spite of the seizures, the LCGU in Mec pretreated rats was not greatly increased. Indeed, the autoradiograms resembled those from rats pretreated with Dzp prior to soman exposure. LCGU autoradiograms 72 hr post soman exposure were similar to those obtained 72 hr after soman exposure alone and brain damage may even be greater in the Mec pretreated rats.

## DISCUSSION

The 2-DG procedure evaluates regional brain metabolism. Under many conditions, there is a close coupling between metabolic activity and brain functional activity (5). However, studies with pretreatment agents prior to soman exposure, demonstrated that soman's actions on brain metabolism are more complex than expected and that brain metabolism under certain conditions is not tightly coupled with brain functional activity. In general, pretreatment with antimuscarinic agents (eg. Atr, Bz, Sco) prior to soman exposure produces a marked reduction in brain metabolism that does not correlate with the behavioral activity of the rats. This is most notable with Sco pretreatment, where LCGU is suppressed even greater than with general anesthesia although the animals were alert. This suppression of LCGU persists even 72 hr post soman exposure. In a recent experiment, Atr (32 mg/kg) pretreatment prior to soman exposure also produced a marked degree of LCGU suppression even though the animals remained alert. This suppressive effect of soman on brain metabolism following pretreatment with antimuscarinics needs further study since they are primary therapeutic agents used for organophosphate intoxication.

Normally, glucose-6-phosphatase activity is low in brain (5) and thereby 2-deoxyglucose-6-phosphate accumulates over the 45 min 2-DG experimental period in relation to glucose metabolism, giving autoradiograms which have a sharp demarcation between structures proportional to glucose use within a structure. In contrast, 2-DG autoradiograms from rats pretreated with Sco prior to soman exposure have a diffuse suppressed appearance. One possibility is that the 2-deoxyglucose-6-phosphate may be degraded over the 45 min experimental period under these conditions.

Dzp pretreatment blocks soman-induced seizures and the marked increase in LCGU associated with soman-induced seizures. However, LCGU still remains elevated in certain striopallidonigral structures. Since Dzp is known to have a greater impact on the spread of electrical activity in the brain than on epileptogenic foci per se, this suggests that striopallidonigral pathways are important epileptogenic foci for soman-induced seizures. Surprisingly, experiments with Mec (nicotinic antagonist) pretreatment (3.2 mg/kg), which had no effect on overt convulsions induced by soman, gave autoradiograms that were indistinguishable from those obtained from rats pretreated with Dzp prior to soman exposure.

Soman-induced seizures initiates a complex pathological sequela that results in extensive damage to some brain regions (eg. piriform/entorhinal cortex, amygdala, dorsal thalamus, hippocampus). LCGU is markedly reduced 72 hr post soman exposure, especially in damaged structures. At this time, rats are behaviorally depressed. Thus, during the pathology phase, reduced LCGU may reflect functional, metabolic and/or pathological changes. Rats pretreated with Dzp, Atr, Bz or Sco prior to soman exposure had no obvious brain damage and LCGU values approached control values 72 hr post soman exposure, except in rats pretreated with Sco (1.0 mg/kg) where metabolic suppression of LCGU was still evident 72 hr post exposure. In contrast, with Mec pretreatment, damage appeared to be more severe and LCGU reduction was more pronounced than with soman alone 72 hr post soman exposure.

## ACKNOWLEDGEMENTS

This research was supported in part by U.S. Army Contract DAMD17-83-3242.

## REFERENCES

1   L. Sokoloff, M. Reivich, C. Kennedy, M. Des Rosiers, C. Patalack, K. Pettigrew, O. Sakurada and M. Shinohara, J. Neurochem, 10 (1977) 897-916.
2   J. McDonough, B. Hackley, R. Cross, F. Samson and S. Nelson, Neurotoxicology 4 (1983) 203-210.
3   T. Pazdernik, R. Cross, M. Giesler, S. Nelson, F. Samson, and J. McDonough, Neurotoxicology, 6 (1985) 61-70.
4   T. Pazdernik, R. Cross, M. Giesler, F. Samson and S. Nelson, Neuroscience, 14 (1985) 823-835.
5   L. Sokoloff, Metabolic Probes of Central Nervous System Activity in Experimental Animals and Man, Magnes Lecture Series, Vol. I, Sinauer Associates Inc., Sanderland, MA, 1985.

*Synthesis and Applications of Isotopically Labeled Compounds 1985.*
Proceedings of the Second International Symposium, Kansas City, MO, U.S.A.,
3—6 September 1985, R.R. Muccino (Ed.), 421—426
© 1986 Elsevier Science Publishers B.V., Amsterdam — Printed in The Netherlands

# UTILIZATION OF $^{13}$C AND $^{14}$C ISOTOPES IN TOXICOLOGICAL STUDIES WITH ORGANO-PHOSPHORUS COMPOUNDS

T. R. FUKUTO[1] and C. M. THOMPSON[2]

[1]Department of Entomology, University of California, Riverside, CA 92521 (USA)
[2]Department of Chemistry, Loyola University, Chicago, IL 60626 (USA)

## ABSTRACT

The mechanism of action of methamidophos, a toxic organophosphorus compound of relatively poor anticholinesterase activity, was investigated with the aid of O-methyl and S-methyl $^{13}$C- and $^{14}$C-labeled methamidophos. Use of [SCH$_3$-$^{14}$C]- and [OCH$_3$-$^{14}$C]methamidophos showed that the P-S bond was cleaved in the reaction leading to methamidophos inhibition of acetylcholinesterase. The m-chlorobenzoic acid oxidation of methamidophos to the corresponding S-oxide, a possible activation product, was demonstrated by means of [SCH$_3$-$^{13}$C]methamidophos and $^{13}$C NMR. However, toxicokinetic studies with $^{14}$C labeled material provided evidence which indicated that metabolic activation was not required to account for the high toxicity of methamidophos.

## INTRODUCTION

Methamidophos (O,S-dimethyl phosphoramidothioate) is a broad-spectrum contact and systemic insecticide which currently finds widespread application in the control of a variety of insect pests. Although methamidophos has been in agricultural use for a number of years, relatively little is known about its mechanism of action. For example, it is highly toxic to insects and mammals which exhibit typically cholinergic signs of poisoning, yet is a relatively poor *in vitro* anticholinesterase (refs. 1,2). Further, owing to the nature of the structure of methamidophos it is not clear which bond to the phosphorus atom

$$CH_3O \diagdown \underset{CH_3S \diagup}{P} \overset{\diagup O}{\diagdown NH_2}$$

is being cleaved in the reaction leading to the inhibition of the cholinesterase enzyme by methamidophos (ref.3). The discrepancy between weak anticholinesterase activity and high toxicity also raises the possibility that methamidophos is being activated to a metabolic intermediate of high anticholinesterase potency (ref.4). This report summarizes results of a study concerned with the elucidation of the mechanism of action of methamidophos using $^{13}$C and $^{14}$C isotopically labeled materials (refs.2,3,5,6).

MATERIALS AND METHODS

$\underline{O}$-Methyl and $\underline{S}$-methyl $^{13}C$ and $^{14}C$ labeled methamidophos were prepared from isotopically enriched $^{13}C$ or $^{14}C$ methanol and $^{13}C$ or $^{14}C$ methyl iodide or methyl methanesulfonate (refs.2,3,5,6). Procedures used in this investigation are described in the same references.

RESULTS AND DISCUSSION

Inhibition of acetylcholinesterase

In order to identify the bond which is broken in the reaction between electric eel acetylcholinesterase (AChE) the enzyme was incubated with either excess $[OCH_3-^{14}C]$- or $[SCH_3-^{14}C]$methamidophos and the reaction mixture was subjected to Sephadex G-25 chromatography (ref.3). Reaction of $[OCH_3-^{14}C]$methamidophos with AChE, followed by Sephadex chromatography resulted in the chromatographic profiles of radioactivity presented in Fig. 1a. The small peaks, representing fractions 9-14 (peak A, 500 units of AChE) and fractions 12-17 (peak A', 1000 units), correspond to AChE. The second large peaks, representing fractions 16-32 (peak B) and fractions 19-37 (peak B'), correspond to methamidophos. The fractions representing peak A and A' were examined for AChE activity and little or no activity was detected.

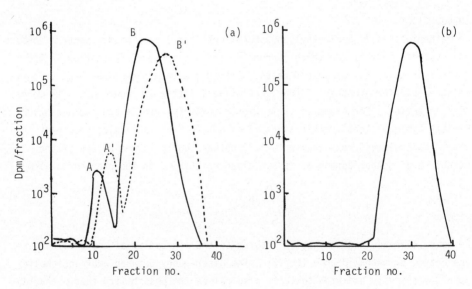

Fig. 1. Plots showing $^{14}C$ dpm/fraction vs fraction number following incubation of $[^{14}C]$methamidophos and 500 units AChE (   ) and 1000 units AChE (   ). (a) $[OCH_3-^{14}C]$methamidophos and (b) $[SCH_3-^{14}C]$methamidophos.

In contrast, incubation of AChE (500 units) with $[SCH_3-^{14}C]$methamidophos resulted in the chromatographic profile presented in Fig. 1b.  In this case, only one radioactive peak was observed which corresponded to methamidophos.

These results strongly suggest P-S bond cleavage in the reaction between methamidophos and AChE, as depicted in equation 1.  In the equation E-OH repre-

$$E-OH \quad + \quad \begin{matrix} CH_3O \\ \diagdown \\ CH_3S \end{matrix} P \begin{matrix} \diagup O \\ \diagdown \\ NH_2 \end{matrix} \quad \longrightarrow \quad \begin{matrix} CH_3O \\ \diagdown \\ E-O \end{matrix} P \begin{matrix} \diagup O \\ \diagdown \\ NH_2 \end{matrix} \quad + \quad CH_3SH \quad\quad\quad (1)$$

sents AChE with OH representing the serine hydroxyl moiety in the enzyme.

## Oxidation of methamidophos

Owing to the high toxicity and low anticholinesterase activity of methamido-phos, the formation of a metabolic activation product of high inhibitory potency against acetylcholinesterase has been suggested in the mode of action of this compound (refs.4,7). Moreover, based on indirect evidence, methamidophos S-oxide has been proposed as the structure of the metabolic intermediate (ref.4) although the S-oxide has never been isolated.  In order to establish the existence of methamidophos S-oxide, the products resulting from the oxidation of [SCH$_3$-$^{13}$C]-methamidophos with m-CPBA (m-chloroperbenzoic acid) were characterized by $^{13}$C NMR (ref.5).

The $^{13}$C NMR spectrum ($^{1}$H decoupled, broad band) of [SCH$_3$-$^{13}$C]methamidophos gave an upfield doublet at $\delta$ 12.46 ppm with J = 4.27 Hz attributable to $^{13}$C-S-$^{31}$P coupling.

The $^{13}$C NMR spectrum of products obtained 16 h following addition of 2 equiv of m-CPBA to 1 equiv of $^{13}$C methamidophos in CDCl$_3$ solvent is presented in Fig.2.

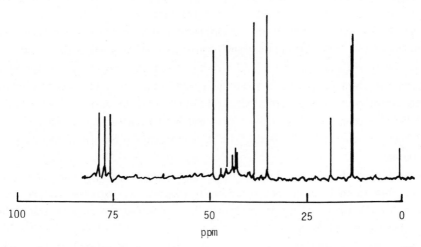

Fig. 2. $^{13}$C NMR of the products formed 16 h following reaction of [SCH$_3$-$^{13}$C]-methamidophos and m-CPBA.

The peaks for the major products 1a and 1b were observed as two doublets centered at 36.37 (J = 75.7 Hz) and 47.11 (J = 82.4 Hz) ppm. A $T_1$ experiment revealed that the four resonances modulated as two distinct doublets. Other minor peaks at 18.25 and 42-43 ppm were attributed to side products resulting from cleavage of the $^{13}CH_3$S-P bond. Significant amounts of methamidophos (12.46 ppm) were still present which was confirmed by TLC and HPLC. The triplet in the region of 75-77 ppm is attributable to the solvent $CDCl_3$.

The principal oxidation products 1a and 1b were concluded to be the diastereomers of methamidophos as indicated in the Newman projections shown below. Sup-

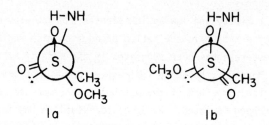

la                                      lb

port for this conclusion is presented as follows. To begin with, the two doublets, which are attributed to $^{13}C$ and $^{31}P$ coupling and are indicative of an intact C-S-P moiety, appear in the known sulfoxide chemical shift region. Further, since the phosphorus center in methamidophos is chiral, introduction of a sulfoxide chiral center by oxidation of the sulfur atom will give rise to diastereomers (1a and 1b).

Although other Newman rotamers are possible, the diastereomers are presented as 1a and 1b to explain the large difference in chemical shifts between the two doublets observed. Since the tendency of sulfoxides to enter into hydrogen bonding is well established (refs.8,9), intramolecular hydrogen bonding between the amido hydrogen and the sulfoxide oxygen is proposed which gives rise to the eclipsed Newman rotamers 1a and 1b. In 1b the $^{13}C$ methyl moiety is eclipsing the oxygen and the electronegative environment would induce an anisotropic effect large enough to cause an upfield shift (ref.5 and refs. therein). The unusually large $^{13}C$-S-$^{31}P$ coupling constants of 75.7 and 82.4 Hz were attributed to geminal coupling and the influence of the electronegative oxygen in the sulfoxide moiety.

Treatment of methamidophos S-oxide with the oxygen scavenger trimethyl phosphite resulted in substantial return of methamidophos, as indicated by the disappearance of the two doublets at 36.37 and 47.11 ppm and increase in the methamidophos absorption at 12.46 ppm.

The above results provide evidence for the existence of methamidophos S-oxide as an oxidation product of methamidophos, therefore, lending support to the possibility of metabolic activation in the mode of action of this compound. However, attempts to isolate the S-oxide intermediate were unsuccessful.

## Toxicokinetics of [SCH$_3$-$^{14}$C]methamidophos in the rat

Distribution of radioactivity in the rat. Owing to its high toxicity relative to its weak anticholinesterase activity, methamidophos either is metabolically activated to a more potent anticholinesterase, e.g., the S-oxide, or it
persists at sufficiently high concentrations in the poisoned animal to produce
toxicity (ref.10). The distribution and excretion of [CH$_3$S-$^{14}$C]methamidophos
after intravenous administration of a toxic dose to the rat was determined to
establish levels of methamidophos in rat tissue and to relate these levels to the
degree of cholinesterase inhibition in erythrocytes, plasma, and regions of the
central nervous system (ref.2).

Following intravenous injection of a toxic but nonlethal dose of 8 mg/kg of
$^{14}$C methamidophos, radiolabeled material was rapidly distributed to all rat tissues in more or less similar amounts with peak levels achieved within one to ten
min in most tissues. Between 20-60 min were required to reach peak levels of
radiolabeled material ($\sim$40 nmol/g methamidophos equivalents, see Fig. 3) in the
central nervous system (cerebellum, cerebrum, and combined spinal cord and brain
stem) and the peripheral nervous system (sciatic nerve), a period when poisoning
signs were most severe. The level of radioactivity in the nervous system was
generally lower than most of the other tissues except for white and brown fat.

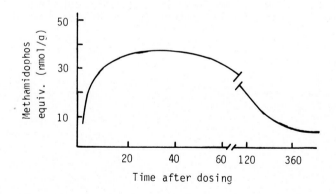

Fig. 3. Approximate levels of radiolabeled material as methamidophos equivalents
in the central nervous system or peripheral system.

Cholinesterase inhibition. Determination of cholinesterase activity in plasma,
erythrocyte, and central nervous system following intravenous administration of
8 mg/kg methamidophos showed inhibition occurring as early as one min following
treatment with maximum levels of inhibition being reached after 30-60 min when
poisoning signs were most severe. The degree of inhibition in the central ner-

426

vous system was 80-85% that of the control value during this period.

When concentrations of methamidophos similar to those found in the nervous system, i.e., $5 \times 10^{-5}$ M, were incubated with brain, plasma or erythrocyte cholinesterase, similar levels of inhibition as found in vivo were observed over the same time course. These results suggest that the high toxicity of methamidophos is attributable to the accumulation of high enough concentrations of methamidophos in the nervous system to inhibit acetylcholinesterase. Although metabolic activation of methamidophos cannot be completely ruled out, the toxicokinetic data indicate that activation is not required to explain its toxicity to insects and mammals (refs.2,10).

REFERENCES

1 G.B. Quistad, T.R. Fukuto and R.L. Metcalf, J. Agric. Food Chem., 18 (1970) 189-194.
2 A.J. Gray, C.M. Thompson and T.R. Fukuto, Pestic. Biochem. Physiol., 18 (1982) 28-37.
3 C.H. Thompson and T.R. Fukuto, J. Agric. Food Chem., 30 (1982) 282-284.
4 M. Eto, S. Okabe, Y. Ozoe and K. Maekawa, Pestic. Biochem. Physiol., 7 (1977) 367-377.
5 C.M. Thompson, S. Castellino and T.R. Fukuto, J. Org. Chem., 49 (1984) 1696-1699.
6 C.M. Thompson, T. Nishioka and T.R. Fukuto, J. Agric. Food Chem., 31 (1983) 696-700.
7 E.M. Bellet and J.E. Casida, J. Agric. Food Chem., 22 (1974) 207-211.
8 D. Bernard, J.M. Fabian and H.P. Koch, J. Chem. Soc., (1949) 2442-2454.
9 C.A. Kingsbury and D.J. Cram, J. Am. Chem. Soc., 82 (1960) 1810-1819.
10 A.M.A. Khasawinah, R.B. March and T.R. Fukuto, Pestic. Biochem. Physiol., 9 (1978) 211-221.

*Synthesis and Applications of Isotopically Labeled Compounds 1985.*
Proceedings of the Second International Symposium, Kansas City, MO, U.S.A.,
3—6 September 1985, R.R. Muccino (Ed.), 427—430
© 1986 Elsevier Science Publishers B.V., Amsterdam — Printed in The Netherlands

# INTERACTIONS WITH HYDROLASES AND THE BIOCHEMICAL SELECTIVITY OF ORGANOPHOSPHINATES

T. M. BROWN[1]

[1]Entomology Dept., Clemson University, Clemson, SC 29634-0365 (USA)

ABSTRACT
    An abridged synthesis of 4-nitrophenyl diphenylphosphinate is described in which this isotopically labeled compound could be prepared in 2 steps. Stereospecificity and biochemical selectivity of organophosphinates is reviewed with regard to acetylcholinesterase, arylester hydrolase, carboxylester hydrolase and α-chymotrypsin. Isotopically labeled procaine, aspirin, and acetic acid were employed in investigations of possible organophosphinate-drug interactions in mice.

INTRODUCTION

    Organophosphinates are potential pretreatment agents for protection against organophosphate poisoning. This is due to the favorable properties of organophosphinates in phosphinylation of the active site of acetylcholinesterase; i.e. certain organophosphinates are very rapid inhibitors (ref. 1), certain phosphinylated acetylcholinesterases recover rapidly either spontaneously or with oxime treatment (ref. 2), and phosphinylated acetylcholinesterase is not subject to o-dealkylation (aging) reactions known to hinder reactivation of phosphorylated acetylcholinesterase.

    Isotopically labeled organophosphinates would be useful for investigations of pharmacokinetics in experimental animals and for studies of interactions of these compounds with acetylcholinesterase and other hydrolases, including stereochemical mechanisms. Organophosphinates have been synthesized previously (ref. 2,3,4). An alternative route of synthesis is available now for certain organophosphinates and it is described here as assembled and performed from known reactions.

    Recent investigations of the spectrum of hydrolases interacting with organophosphinates, and the stereoselectivity of these hydrolases with chiral organophosphinates are reviewed.

METHODS

    Synthesis of 4-nitrophenyl diphenylphosphinate (DPP) was performed in 2 steps; first, diphenylphosphinyl chloride was prepared from diphenylphosphinous chloride (ref. 5) and then diphenylphosphinyl chloride was used to prepare DPP (ref. 3). In a 100 ml 3-neck flask, 53.9 mmol diphenyl phosphinous chloride (Stauffer Chemical Co., Westport, CN) in 40 ml benzene was exposed to oxygen which was passed through at 4 bubbles/s for 6h with condenser attached. Solvent was removed by distillation, then product was distilled in a short path apparatus with vacuum at 63.2% yield. Product Rf was 0.34 by silica gel thin layer chromatography (TLC) in chloroform, methanol and water (80:30:0.5) which agreed with an authentic standard of diphenylphosphinyl chloride (Chemical Dynamics Corp., South Plainfield, NJ).

Synthesis of 4-nitrophenyl diphenylphosphinate (DPP) from diphenylphosphinyl chloride and sodium 4-nitrophenoxide (Aldrich Chem. Co., Milwaukee, WI) was performed according to a previously described method (ref. 3) with modifications. In a 100 ml 3-neck flask, 20 mmol sodium 4-nitrophenoxide was stirred with 20 mmol water and 20 ml acetone until completely yellow; then 18 mmol diphenyl-phosphinyl chloride in 12 ml acetone was added dropwise. The mixture was refluxed 3.5 h, stirred overnight, filtered and acetone removed in vacuo. Residue was dissolved in dichloromethane, washed with 0.5% sodium bicarbonate, then water, then dried through sodium sulfate. Dichloromethane was removed in vacuo and yield of oil was 94.1 ± 5.7%. Oil was 63.1% title compound by octylsilyl reversed-phase high performance liquid chromatography (HPLC) with 50% acetonitrile in water (ref. 6). Product was crystallized from tetra-hydrofuran and cyclohexane (1:1) and crystals melted at 127-140°. Any attempt to perform these 2 reactions in sequence in the same flask should be approached with caution because any unreacted diphenyl phosphinous might react violently with water or with sodium nitrophenoxide.

For drug interaction studies in mice (ref. 7), [carboxyl-$^{14}$C]-procaine was synthesized from diethylaminoethyl chloride and 4-aminobenzoic acid (ref. 8) and a closed respiration apparatus was used to trap [$^{14}$C]-carbon dioxide from [acetyl-1-$^{14}$C]-aspirin. For stereoselectivity studies with hydrolases (ref. 9), the chiral-phase HPLC concept was applied (ref. 10). For studies of phosphinate hydrolysis by arylester hydrolase (ref. 11), the enzyme was partially purified from rabbit serum (ref. 12). For reactivation experiments with carboxylesterase (ref. 13), the gel permeation techniques were adapted from previous studies with acetylcholinesterase (ref. 2).

## RESULTS AND DISCUSSION

The final yield of DPP by the synthesis described was 37% of theoretically possible yield. This could be improved by optimization of the first reaction to convert sufficient diphenyl phosphinous chloride to allow continuation with the second reaction in the same vessel.

An advantage of this method is the potential for incorporating isotopes of oxygen into the molecule using the first reaction; isotopes of oxygen have been useful in stereoanalysis of phospho transfer enzymes (ref. 14). Methylphenyl-chlorophosphine is commercially available for the possible synthesis of 4-ni-trophenyl methyl(phenyl)phosphinate (MPP) by this scheme.

The use of isotopically labeled drugs provided the opportunity to investigate organophosphinate effects on drug metabolism in mice. Physiologically realistic doses of [carboxyl-$^{14}$C]-procaine and [carboxyl-$^{14}$C]-aspirin were administered to phosphinate-pretreated mice. Analysis by HPLC separation and liquid scintillation counting demonstrated that pretreatment with DPP increased the procaine concentration in blood by 3-fold over control levels (ref. 7); however, MPP had no significant effect.

Aspirin hydrolysis was not reduced by either DPP or MPP pretreatment (ref. 7). This was initially indicated by salicylic acid levels in blood, which were not decreased, and later confirmed in an experiment employing [acetyl-1-$^{14}$C]-aspirin. Pretreatment with DPP or MPP had no effect on the expiration of [$^{14}$C]-carbon dioxide from mice after ip administration of [acetyl-1-$^{14}$C]-aspirin.

Enantiomers of 4-nitrophenyl ethyl(phenyl)phosphinate (EPP) and 4-nitrophenyl isopropyl(phenyl)phosphinate (IPP) were isolated by chiral-phase HPLC and stereoselectivity of enzyme inhibition was assessed as the ratio of activity ($r_a$) found by dividing the bimolecular reaction constant of the P(+) enantiomer by that of the P(-) enantiomer (ref. 9). Inhibition of electric eel acetyl-cholinesterase was stereoselective with $r_a$ values of 35 for EPP and 7.8 for IPP (ref. 9). Opposite stereoselectivity was observed in the inhibition of bovine pancreatic $\alpha$-chymotrypsin with $r_a$ values of 0.0845 for EPP and 0.198 for IPP. In both cases, stereoselectivity was greater for the more rapid inhibitor which was EPP.

Stereoselectivity of $\alpha$-chymotrypsin inhibition was confirmed by exposing this enzyme to racemic IPP and then performing chiral-phase HPLC analysis of the reaction product using a column of covalently bonded D-3,5-dinitrobenzoyl-phenylglycine (D-DNBPG) (ref. 9). The result obtained by analysis of this product with the L-DNBPG column is presented here (see Fig. 1).

Hydrolysis of EPP enantiomers catalyzed by arylester hydrolase was also stereoselective ($r_a$ = 0.115) and the enantiomer hydrolyzed more rapidly was P(-) EPP (ref. 9.). This was the more inhibitory enantiomer toward $\alpha$-chymo-trypsin, but it was the lesser inhibitory enantiomer toward acetylcholinesterase.

Four series of diverse 4-nitrophenyl organophosphinates were examined as sub-strates for rabbit serum arylester hydrolase (ref.11). Ten of 13 compounds tested were substrates and all substrates were observed to have lower Michaelis constants than paraoxon which was 0.609 mM. Specific activities of arylester

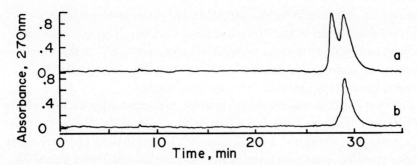

Fig. 1. Stereoselective reaction of 0.34 mM IPP with 0.34 mM chymotrypsin at 37° monitored by L-DNBPG chiral-phase HPLC. (a) Extract of control mixture without enzyme at 40 min. (b) Extract of mixture with enzyme at 6 min.

hydrolase for MPP and EPP were 2.9 and 0.65 μmol/min/mg protein, respectively. There was no activity detected with IPP nor with DPP.

Spontaneous reactivation of phosphinylated rabbit liver carboxylester hydrolases varied with the chemistry of the phosphinyl group (ref. 13). The reactivation rate constant was 0.00048 $min^{-1}$ following inhibition by EPP, and this rate increased 2-fold with addition of TMB-4 oxime. Although DPP and 4-nitrophenyl dithienylphosphinate were slow acetylcholinesterase inhibitors (ref. 1), they were very potent against carboxylester hydrolase.

## ACKNOWLEDGEMENTS

This was technical contribution No. 2460 of the South Carolina Agricultural Experiment Station and the research was performed under contract DAMD17-82-C-2193 of the U.S. Army Medical Research and Development Command.

## REFERENCES

1 C.N. Lieske, J.H. Clark, H.G. Meyer, L. Boldt, M.D. Green, J. Lowe, W. Sultan, P. Blumbergs and M.A. Priest, Pestic. Biochem. Physiol., 22 (1984) 285-294.
2 C.N. Lieske, J.H. Clark, H.G. Meyer, M.A. Lawson, J.R. Lowe, P. Blumbergs and M.A. Priest, Pestic. Biochem. Physiol., 17 (1982) 142-148.
3 T.R. Fukuto, R.L. Metcalf and M.Y. Winton, J. Econ. Entomol., 54 (1961) 955-62.
4 G.M. Kosolapoff, J. Amer. Chem. Soc., 71 (1949) 369-370.
5 D.A. Tyssee, L.P. Bausher and P. Haake, J. Amer. Chem. Soc., 95 (1973) 8066.
6 T.M. Brown and J.R. Grothusen, J. Chromatogr., 294 (1984) 390-396.
7 J.M. Joly and T.M. Brown, Toxicol. Appl. Pharmacol., in press.
8 R. Guiliano and M.L. Stein, Il Farmaco, 11 (1956) 3-9.
9 J.R. Grothusen and T.M. Brown, Pestic. Biochem. Physiol., in press.
10 W.H. Pirkle, J.M. Finn, J.L. Schreiner and B.C. Hamper, J. Amer. Chem. Soc., 103 (1981) 3964-3966.
11 J.R. Grothusen, P.K. Bryson, J.K. Zimmerman and T.M. Brown, J. Agric. Food Chem., in press.
12 J.K. Zimmerman and T.M. Brown, J. Agric. Food Chem., in press.
13 P.K. Bryson and T.M. Brown, Biochem. Pharmacol., 34 (1985) 1789-1794.
14 J.R. Knowles, Fed. Proc., 41 (1982) 2424-2431.

*Synthesis and Applications of Isotopically Labeled Compounds 1985.*
Proceedings of the Second International Symposium, Kansas City, MO, U.S.A.,
3—6 September 1985, R.R. Muccino (Ed.), 431—434
© 1986 Elsevier Science Publishers B.V., Amsterdam — Printed in The Netherlands

PREPARATION OF CARBON-14 AND TRITIUM LABELED COMPOUNDS USED FOR TREATMENT/
PROTECTION OF ORGANOPHOSPHORUS OR RADIATION POISONING

J.A. Kepler, C.E. Twine, and R.D. Austin

Chemistry and Life Sciences, P.O. Box 12194, Research Triangle Institute,

Research Triangle Park, North Carolina 27709 USA

ABSTRACT
    A new synthesis of [6,7-$^3$H$_2$]atropine (2), the synthesis of [2-$^{14}$C]pyrido-
stigmine bromide (13), [6-$^3$H]pyridostigmine (6) and S-[2-(3-aminopropylamino)-
[1,2-$^{14}$C]ethyl]phosphorothioic acid (18) are described. The $^3$H NMR of [6,7-
$^3$H]atropine and [6,-$^3$H]pyridostigmine are discussed.

    Atropine (13) is of current interest as an antichloinergic for treatment
of organophosphate poisoning. A sample of atropine labeled in the tropine
ring, but not in the N-methyl group, was required for biological studies.
[6,7-$^3$H$_2$]Atropine has been previously prepared (ref.1) in a multi-step process
using the classical Robinson (ref.2) synthesis and 2,5-dimethoxy[3,4-$^3$H$_2$]furan
as starting material. More recenlty Noyori's group has reported (ref.3) a
convenient synthesis of 6,7-dehydroatropine 1 which we used in a one step
preparation of [6,7-$^3$H$_2$]atropine 2 (Scheme 1). Thus catalytic tritiation of 1
afforded an excellent yield of 2 which was purified by HPLC using a Waters
Radial Pak SiO$_2$, 10μ column and CHCl$_3$-MeOH-Et$_3$N (800:200:0.8) as eluant. The
specific activity was 52 mCi/mmol. The 95.5 MHz proton decoupled $^3$H NMR of 2
showed an AB quartet (J = 14 cps) at δ 1.72 and 1.94 for the 6- and 7-tritons.
Also visible were singlets at δ 1.72 and 1.94 from singly labeled molecules.
There were no other triton resonances in the spectra. Because of the severe
steric hindrance of the α-side of the atropine ring by the axial tropic ester,
we expected that the tritons would be β- to the lower side of the ring as
shown. The asymmetry of the hydrogen and carbon NMR spectra of atropine and
scopolamine is well documented and is known to be due to the anisotropy of the
benzene ring of the tropyl ester (ref.4). The 250 MHz $^1$H NMR spectra of
atropine free base in CDCl$_3$ was too complicated to accurately assign the 6-
and 7-proton frequencies and so a direct comparison between the triton spectra
and the proton spectra was not possible. Feeney et al. (ref.4), however,
observed a 0.13 ppm difference between the 6β- and 7β-protons and a much
larger 0.53 ppm difference between the 6α- and 7α-protons of the cation of
atropine in D$_2$O. Furthermore, the differences in frequencies of the pairs of
protons 1- and 5-, 2β- and· 4β-, and 2α- and 4α- were 0.12, 0.06, and 0.21 ppm

respectively for the cation, and 0.12, 0.08, and 0.21 respectively for the free base. Therefore a direct comparison of the chemical shift difference between the 6- and 7-proton of the cation and the free base is not unreasonable. Consequently we believe that the relatively small (0.22 ppm) difference in the chemical shift of the triton is more in keeping with them being β-oriented (0.13 ppm difference in cation) rather than α-oriented (0.53 ppm difference in cation).

Pyridostigmine bromide is being investigated as a protective agent against organophosphate poisoning. We have prepared pyridostigmine labeled with tritium (Scheme 2) and labeled with carbon-14 (Scheme 3). The inter mediate 3 was prepared by reaction of N,N-dimethylcarbamoyl chloride with 2,6-dibromo-3-hydroxypyridine (ref.5). Catalytic reduction with tritium gas in the presence of magnesium oxide gave the tritiated carbamate 4. Quarternization of 4 with methyl bromide in acetone afforded [2,6-$^3$H$_2$]pyridostigmine bromide (5) which lost the 2-triton upon exchange with methanol to give [6-$^3$H]pyridostigmine bromide (6) with specific activity of 22 mCi/mmol. The 95.5 MHz proton decoupled $^3$H NMR showed a single resonance at δ 8.78 which compares to the 6-proton resonance at δ 8.80. The proton coupled $^3$H NMR showed a doublet with J = 7 cps confirming the assignment.

[2-$^{14}$C]pyridostigmine bromide (13) was prepared as shown in Scheme 3. The dried potassium salt of labeled furoic acid (7, ref.6) was treated with thionyl chloride and a catalytic amount of DMF to give the acid chloride 8. We obtained better yields of 8 using the carboxylate salt rather than the carboxylic acid for this reaction. The crude 8 was treated with CHCl$_3$ saturated with ammonia to afford a 73% yield (based on 7) of amide 9. Reduction of 9 with LAH gave 10 in 70% yield. Oxidative rearrangement of 10 (ref.7) gave 3-hydroxy[2-$^{14}$C]pyridine 11 in 68% yield. Carbamoylation of 11 followed by quarternization with methyl iodide gave [2-$^{14}$C]pyridostigmine bromide (13). The overall yield was 18% based on barium [$^{14}$C]carbonate and the specific activity was 18 mCi/mmol.

The phosphorothioate, S-[2-(3-aminopropylamino)][1,2-$^{14}$C]ethyl]phosphorothioic acid 18 (WR-2721), was prepared as shown in Scheme 4 (ref.8). Reaction of [$^{14}$C]ethylene oxide with a ten-fold excess 1,3-diaminopropane gave the amino alcohol 16 in 60% yield. Treatment of 16 with refluxing 48% hydrobromic acid gave the bromide 17 in 73% yield. Reaction of 17 with exactly one equivalent of freshly prepared trisodium thiophosphate gave WR-2721 in 50% yield with specific activity of 22 mCi/mmol. The quality and quantity of the trisodium thiophosphate is critical to the success of this reaction (ref.9). If this reagent is not pure, the product is extremely difficult to purify.

ACKNOWLEDGEMENT

This work was supported by USARMDC Contract Nos. DAMD17-78-C-8041 and DAMD17-84-C-4009.

REFERENCES

1   A. Jordan, L.M. Du Plessio, V.P. Joint, J. S. African Chem. Inst., 21 (1968) 22.
2   (a) R. Robinson, J. Chem. Soc., 111 (1917) 762.  (b) A. Schopf and G. Lehman, Ann., 518 (1935) 5.
3   Y. Hayakaw, Y. Baba, S. Makino, and R. Noyori, J. Amer. Chem. Soc., 100 (1978) 1786.
4   J. Feeney, R. Foster, E.A. Piper, J. Chem. Soc. Perkin II (1977) 2016.
5   H.S. Den Hertog, F.R. Schepman, J. De Bruyn and G.J.E. Thysee, Recueil., 69 (1950) 1281.
6   L.F. Elson and D.R. Hawkins, J. Label. Comp. and Radiopharm., 14 (1978) 799.
7   N. Elming, S.V. Carlston, B. Lennart and I. Ohlsson, Brit. 862,521 (1961).
8   J.R. Piper, C.R. Stringfellow, Jr., R.D. Elliot and T.P. Johnston, J. Med. Chem., 12 (1969) 236.
9   J.R. Piper, private communication.

Scheme 1

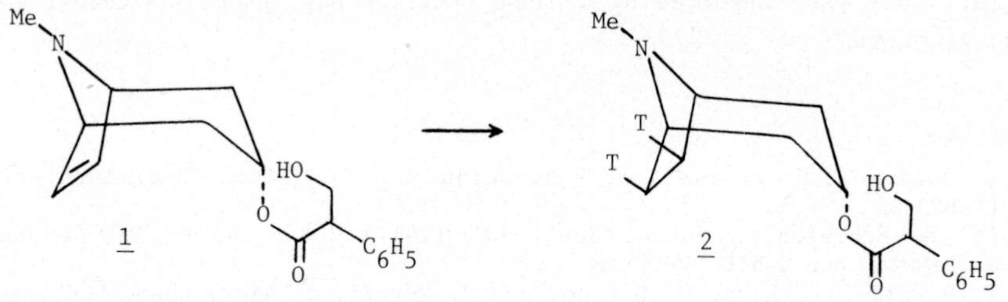

Scheme 2

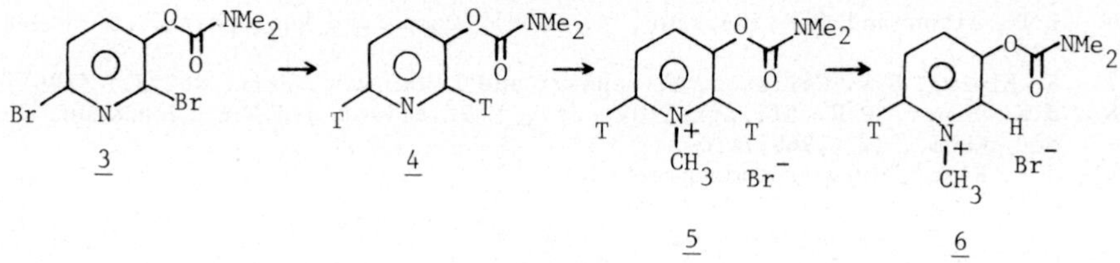

Scheme 3

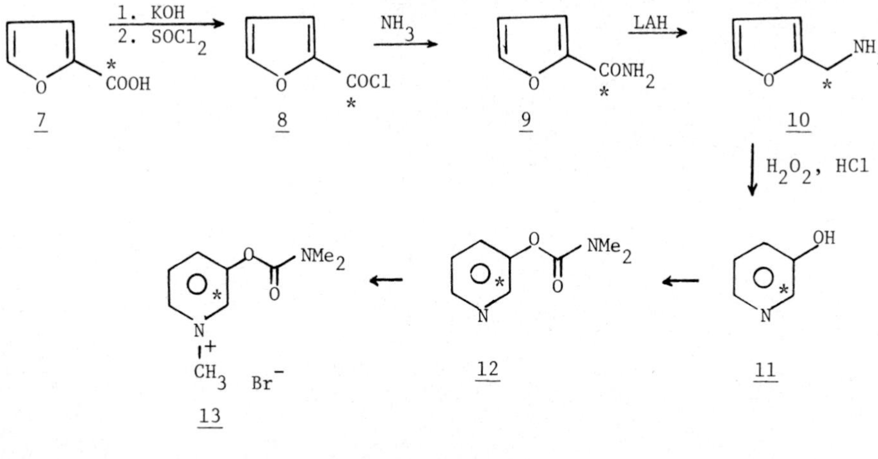

Scheme 4

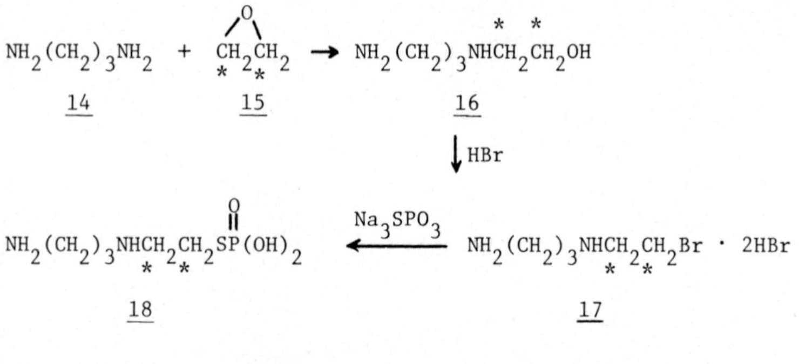

$$NH_2(CH_2)_3NH_2 \quad + \quad CH_2CH_2 \quad \rightarrow \quad NH_2(CH_2)_3NHCH_2CH_2OH$$

14      15      16

$$\downarrow HBr$$

$$NH_2(CH_2)_3NHCH_2CH_2SP(OH)_2 \quad \xleftarrow{Na_3SPO_3} \quad NH_2(CH_2)_3NHCH_2CH_2Br \cdot 2HBr$$

18                17

*Synthesis and Applications of Isotopically Labeled Compounds 1985.*
Proceedings of the Second International Symposium, Kansas City, MO, U.S.A.,
3—6 September 1985, R.R. Muccino (Ed.), 435—440
© 1986 Elsevier Science Publishers B.V., Amsterdam — Printed in The Netherlands

# RECENT ADVANCES IN MASS SPECTROMETRIC SYSTEMS FOR MEASURING THE RELATIVE ABUNDANCES OF STABLE ISOTOPES, AT NATURAL ABUNDANCE LEVELS, OR AS ENRICHED OR DEPLETED FOR LABELLING PURPOSES*

LEONARD F. HERZOG, II
Nuclide Corporation, 642 E. College Ave., State College, PA 16801

## ABSTRACT

Isotope ratio measurement mass spectrometers of high accuracy have now been in use for over 40 years. Although the essential emenents of such systems — multiple sample/standard inlets and multiple-isotope simultaneous detectors — remain the same, interim developments have made such instruments much more "user friendly" and reliable, while automated sample introduction, MS control and signal digitizing and data processing systems permit high throughput rates with little operator time per sample. Also, techniques which permit very small samples to be analyzed, and background and/or memory to be "erased" have been developed. Herein, the state of the art is ducussed, with some emphasis on certain less-well-known advances such as interpolative inlet systems, on-line sample preparation, ion counting, switchable multi-collectors, and synchronous source/detector background suppression; and the use of thermionic, crucible and plasma sources for analyzing elements such as K, Ca, Rb and Pb as their solid salts.

## INTRODUCTION

Applications of stable isotopes in organic chemistry, biochemistry and medicine include (a) tracing molecules, (b) labelling a specific atom in a molecule so that a fragment containing it can be followed through a series of reactions, (c) quantitative analysis by "isotope dilution", (d) metabolic studies, and (e) studies using the small variations in isotope abundances that exist in nature. Stable isotope tracers can be used for in vivo studies in humans for which radioactive isotopes cannot. And, in environmental and agricultural studies, the byproduct "dominant-isotope-enriched" tracers make large-scale experiments inexpensive.

This is a summary of a more extensive paper, which is available from the author.

## APPLICATIONS OF STABLE ISOTOPES

### Locating Elements of Interest by Isotopic Labelling

Stable isotope labelling was introduced before 1935, but has been used infrequently in organic and biochemistry until recently, primarily because, to use "classical" isotope ratio instruments, one has to convert samples into simple molecules such as $CO_2$ or KCl. This introduces the possibility of isotope fractionation. Alsó, an isotopic label may become too diluted by normal isotopic abundance material to detect. However, today it is often unnecessary to change the chemical form of a sample before MS analysis, since, through the use of a high resolution mass spectrometer the label-isotope can,

---

*Nuclide Contribution No. 2203-0985

sometimes, be determined by studying only a fragment-ion in the mass spectrum of the molecule of interest.

Elements in which the abundance of a minor isotope has been greatly "enriched" can be used as tags to e.g., follow the course of substances of interest containing such elements through complex chemical processes via mass spectra.

## Quantitative Analysis by Isotope Dilution

Enriched stable isotopes were used as internal standards for the determination of H and N as early as 1940— $^2$H to determine fatty acids, and $^{15}$N for amino acids, after processing samples to $H_2$ and $N_2$ for analysis. But with modern MSs one can often apply the method to intact molecules, to make routine clinical determinations of drug concentrations in human plasma and urine, by adding the isotopically-labelled drug, in known amount, to the "raw" sample before GC-MS analysis.

As an example, nortryptyline (NT) containing an M/(M+3) doublet prepared by mixing normal NT with NT in which two protium ($^1$H) atoms had been replaced by deuterium ($^2$H), and one $^{14}$N by $^{15}$N, has been used to determine the drug's residence time in the human body, and also, which substances (GC peaks) in urine were the drug's metabolites (1). Such studies can be carried out with very small doses.

## Determining natural variations in isotope ratios

It was found soon after isotopes were discovered that the relative abundances of the isotopes of many elements vary, depending on the source. Attempts to explain these observations caused many new fields of research to open, in geo-, cosmo-, inorganic, and organic chemistry.

Some applications of isotopic analysis require determination of the **absolute abundance** of an isotope, while for others (e.g., "before" and "after" studies) the **difference** in isotope ratio between two samples is all one needs to know. Moreover, one can derive absolute abundances by comparing an unknown's isotope ratio to that of a standard of known absolute isotopic composition.

Many biomedical applications do not require high accuracy; sometimes all that is necessary is that the element have an isotopic "fingerprint" that makes its ions stand out in spectra. Of course there are also cases when only the highest possible precision and accuracy will suffice. Hence, over the past 30 years, analysts have developed instruments and techniques through which very high reproducibility in ratio measurements and absolute accuracy in isotopic abundance determinations can be achieved consistently. Such instruments have made it possible to achieve, for simple gases, single-run internal precisions of ±10 ppm of the isotope ratio and agreement with other labs to within 50 ppm (0.005%), even for ratios of 1/100 or less, such as natural $^{13}C/^{12}C$, $^{15}N/^{14}N$ and $^{18}O/^{16}O$.

An example is the isotopic analysis of carbon in honey, as a test of adulteration. The $^{13}C/^{12}C$ ratio in real honey is sufficiently different from that in cane or beet sugar to permit one to determine the percentage of adulteration rather accurately (2).

For elements that have no convenient gaseous compounds, such as K, Ca, Rb, Li, etc., achieving high reproducibility is more difficult; but still, careful workers using thermionic source MSs have achieved ±100 ppm of the isotope ratio or better.

## Determining Isotope Ratios of Transient Species

When samples are introduced into a MS from a gas chromatograph, sometimes only a few seconds are available to collect data on a GC peak of interest, and the amount of compound present changes rapidly. If a mass spectrometer has only a single ion detector, only one ion species can be measured at a time; and if too much time is required to measure several species of interest the "raw" intensity ratios may be substantially in error. For such applications, **the ideal is a system with simultaneous collection by N collectors;** while for single-collector MSs, a detection system with a time-constant of a few milliseconds, and having a comparably small settling time after a mass-switch, best approaches the ideal, since, in this case, only instabilities or pressure changes comparable (in speed) to the switching-rate will affect the abundance measurements.

Quadrupole mass filters and TOF MSs are sufficiently "fast" for such use, but single-collector magnetic-analyzer MSs that also meet these criteria have existed for many years - e.g., with **ion accelerating voltage** slewing (scan) rates up to $10^8$ volts/sec and settling times after a step to within $\pm 0.1\%$ of a final value in 50 microseconds. In addition, there are available MSs with **laminated magnets** which can slew at rates as high as 0.1 sec/mass decade. However, some magnetic analyzer MSs are available which achieve the ideal of measuring two or more species simultaneously.

## "On line" sample preparation

Breath is another important sample in which constituent composition varies rapidly, and which contains some constituents (e.g., $H_2O$ and organics) which cause problems in the isotopic analysis of others, such as $O_2$ and $CO_2$. Recently, "on line" processing trains, by which the gas of interest can be separated-out, after which it is piped directly into a fast-response-amplifier dual-collector MS for isotopic analysis, have been developed (3).

## CHOICE OF AN ION ANALYZER

Although today, magnetic, mass filter (quadrupole and monopole), and time-of-flight ion analyzers are all available, for applications demanding high reproducibility, until now, magnetic analyzer MSs have proven best. Hence, hereinbelow, only magnetic MSs will be discussed.

## ISOTOPE RATIO MEASUREMENT SYSTEMS

### Scanning, jump scanning and peak stepping (S.I.M.)

In conventional mass spectrum **scanning,** much time is spent collecting unwanted information— baseline and species of no interest. A substantial improvement in efficiency can be made by **"jump scanning",** in which the MS scans rapidly until reaching a peak of interest, then slows down and records data while traversing it. But **"peak-stepping",** in which one focuses the analyzer successively only onto m/e where there are species of interest, is more efficient. By stepping the ion accelerating voltage, it is feasible to e.g., step through four preselected m/e of interest cyclically ten or more times per second.

### Simultaneous Collection of Two or More Ion Beams

Ions of different m/e follow different radii in a magnetic field, hence a magnetic MS can collect two or more species **simultaneously,** and when "n" species are detected simultaneously, considerably more than n times as much information - perhaps 2n can be obtained in a given time!

Dual collector instruments were first used before 1940. In the past 5 years or so, instruments with 3 or more Faraday collectors have become more common - making it possible to, e.g., simultaneously measure $^{16}O/^{18}O$ and $^{13}C/^{12}C$ in $CO_2$ at m/e 44/5/6.

Another important improvement in multi-collector mass spectroscopy is the integrating digital ratiometer. Some can compute two or more ratios simultaneously. As a result of these improvements, today, one can e.g., detect differences in near-natural HD/HH ratios (about 1/3300) as small as $\pm 0.01\%$; or, for 0.3% to 1% isotopes (such as $^{18}O$ and $^{13}C$) achieve an internal precision to $\pm 0.001\%$, and reproducibly measure ratio-differences smaller than $\pm 0.01\%$.

## Mass Spectrographs/EOID Detector

Simultaneous ion collection reaches its fullest expression in mass spectrographs, which can simultaneously detect all species present in a mass range as broad as, e.g., M to 50M. "Electronic photoplates" utilizing arrays of thousands of miniaturized electron multipliers are now under development. These will revolutionize not only selected ion monitoring but also obtaining mass spectra in general, by eliminating all need to scan, in many cases.

## Multiple Inlet Systems

"Multiplexing" inlet systems makes it possible to measure differences in ratios more reproducibly because instrument operating conditions can be kept more closely identical for sample and standard. Dual inlets for gas samples have two reservoirs, for standard (S) and unknown (U), and one adjusts flow rates through the viscous leaks until the ion current of the major isotope remains constant to $\lesssim \pm 1\%$ when valves are switched, causing "S" to flow into the "waste" pump and "U" into the MS, or vice versa. Flow rates for full sensitivity are $10^{13}$-$10^{15}$ molecules/sec - i.e., as a minimum about $10^{-6}$ std ml/sec; for $CO_2$ this is about $10^{-9}$ g/s. **For dual viscous inlet/dual F-cup collector systems, when measuring small differences, interlab reproducibility can approach the best intralab reproducibility (<0.005%), even including uncertainties introduced in all steps of sample preparation.**

For dual inlet systems, as ratios become more different, a systematic error due to "memory" increases. This problem can be reduced by using two, bracketing standards, and interpolating between them. Such **"triple inlets"** have recently also been applied to analyses of highly spiked $N_2$, $H_2$, etc. with good success (4).

Although the multi-inlet concept is difficult to apply to studies of transient species, multiple-collector systems are ideally suited to such studies. Accordingly, direction-focusing MSs with up to six collectors have been built, e.g., for breath analysis.

## Analyzing Very Small Gas Samples

Classical dual-inlet systems using viscous leaks can be used for small samples if both sample and standard are mixed with a "carrier" gas - e.g., argon-until the pressures and volumes in the inlet reservoirs are in the normal range; dilutions of up to about X100 have been used. Of course, the ion current is reduced, so one must take data longer. Also, even though the conductance of a **molecular** leak is mass dependent, pairs of conventional "batch inlets" with **matched molecular leaks** have been used successfully for 0.1 ml to 0.001 ml samples, since the fractionation the leak causes can be corrected-for.

However, the most common method for analyzing small samples is by using a

**"micro" reservoir.** For gases such as $CO_2$, which condense at $LN_2$ temperatures, transfer into a tiny reservoir is readily accomplished. Alternatively, one can admit most of the sample into a relatively large reservoir, and then decrease it's volume to, e.g., 0.2 ml by filling it with mercury in a controlled fashion. This **variable volume micro-reservoir** method has the advantage that it can be used with all gases except such as react with Hg, glass or the metal used; and, it requires no expenditure for coolants.

### Erasing Background - the Synchronous Source and Detector System

The analysis of small amounts of common gases such as $N_2$ is often impossible because MS "background" contains too much of the same gas, or another (e.g., CO) of the same m/e. But there is a measurement system which can very dramatically reduce such interferences - e.g., by a factor as high as $10^4$. To achieve this, one admits the sample in regular pulses, so that while the background remains a continuous, d.c. signal, the sample signal becomes an a.c. component superimposed on it. The detector is a "lock in" amplifier, or digital circuitry, synchronized to the valve cycle.

### Ion Counting, and Hybrid Detector Systems

Ion beam intensities can be measured by counting ion arrivals, using an "electron multiplier" (EM) as a pulse amplifier. Hayes et al applied ion counting to microgram and smaller samples of $CO_2$, using a dual-inlet MS with a single EM detector for 0.1 µg ($5 \times 10^{-5}$ std ml) of $CO_2$ (5).

Unfortunately, one loses precision rapidly after ion arrival rates exceed about $3 \times 10^6$ cps ($\sim 5 \times 10^{-13}$A). However, if one uses a Faraday cup detector at a different radius to measure the major species and the multiplier for the minor ones, this restriction is overcome. In these **"hybrid"** detector instruments, data for species other than those at m/e which the multiple collectors are set to detect can be obtained by peak stepping.

### DESKTOP COMPUTER AND MINICOMPUTER SYSTEMS

A recent development is the use of desktop computers to control peak stepping, valve switching, data gathering, ion source focusing and data analysis. A typical system solves the MS equation to approximately locate operator-selected peaks, finds their exact centers, changes the ion accelerating voltage (or the magnetic field) to step from peak to peak, takes data at each position, and then processes it. Computers can of course also be instructed to have the instrument do many other things, to completely automate MS operation; a full discussion will not be attempted here.

### OTHER TYPES OF ION SOURCE

Electron bombardment, the traditional method of ionization of gases for IRMS, is rather well known. However some methods of ionizing liquids and solids deserve mention:

### Thermionic Source

Ionization of atoms by contact with a surface is the basis of the so-called "thermionic" source. In **multi-filament** "TI" sources, vaporization and ionization temperatures can be optimized individually. Today, fully developed T.I. source MSs with vacuum lock or "carousel" sources are available for analyzing K, Li, Ca, Sr, Pb, Zn, etc. However, TI sources do have some special problems, such as the tendency to fractionate isotopes; also there are very great ($10^6$) ionization efficiency differences for various elements. At least one manufacturer offers MSs equipped for both EB and TI studies (6).

## Crucible Source

A sample heated in a crucible in which the ratio of internal area to orifice is small maintains an equilibrium mixture of vapor species. A molecular beam effusing from its orifice can be ionized by either EB or TI.

## Plasma Source

Recently, "plasma-source MS" has been applied to isotope dilution determinations of trace elements important in nutrition, e.g., Fe, Zn, Cu, Se, Li and Rb (7). For plasma MS analysis, samples are prepared as dilute solutions, which are nebulized and "desolvated" en route into a plasma chamber, adjacent to the MS source, at normal atmospheric pressure. Ions are formed, and pass into the source through differentially-pumped pinhole "leaks". Ratio measurement precision and reproducibility are nominal, but the fact that the sample is handled outside the MS and that sample "clearout" times are measured in seconds makes application of the technique convenient, and also makes possible the achievement of quite high throughput rates.

## SUMMARY

Isotope ratio measurements by mass spectroscopy have already demonstrated great utility in biochemistry and organic chemistry for studies involving elements which have convenient gaseous compounds. Recent developments have made it much easier to carry out such analyses. Now the field is being expanded also by studies of elements like K and Ca, as solids or liquids. Instruments and techniques for such applications are also available, thanks to earlier application to other fields, such as geochemistry.

## References

(1) D. R. Knapp et al, J. Pharm. Exp. Thera. 80 (1972) 784-790
(2) W. D. Landis and J. W. White Jr., Science 197 (1977) 891-2
(3) D. A. Schoeller, Am. Soc. M.S. Abstracts 30 (1982) 178-9
(4) M. F.Estep and T. C. Hoering, Geo. et Cosmo. Acta 44 (1980) 1197-1206
(5) D. A. Schoeller and J. M. Hayes, Anal. Chem. 47 (1975) 408-415
(6) Nuclide Corp. Pub 2204-0885 "A New MS system for rapid isotope ratio determinations of elements prepared as solid as well as gaseous compounds - Model 12-90-RMS/SU"
(7) M. Janghorbani et al, Am. J. Hematology (in press, 1985): "Erthrocyte Incorporation of Ingested Stable Isotope of Iron ($^{58}$Fe)."

*Synthesis and Applications of Isotopically Labeled Compounds 1985.*
Proceedings of the Second International Symposium, Kansas City, MO, U.S.A.,
3—6 September 1985, R.R. Muccino (Ed.), 441—446
© 1986 Elsevier Science Publishers B.V., Amsterdam — Printed in The Netherlands

TUNABLE DIODE LASER SPECTROSCOPY OF STABLE ISOTOPIC TRACERS - DETECTION AND
MEASUREMENT OF RELATIVE ABUNDANCE OF ISOTOPIC CARBON MONOXIDE

Peter S. Lee[1] and Richard F. Majkowski[2]

[1]Biomedical Science Dept., General Motors Research Labs, Warren, MI 48090

[2]Physics Dept., General Motors Research Labs, Warren, MI 48090

## ABSTRACT

A molecular absorption system using a tunable diode laser and a dual path
length sample cell for stable isotopic tracer analysis has been developed.
The high spectral resolution and power density of the laser allow real-time
simultaneous detection of different isotopes with great specificity. And, the
matched absorption path length cell simplifies signal processing and improves
the accuracy in quantitative measurement by maintaining the same signal to
noise ratio for vastly different isotopic concentrations. The principle and
operation of the system are described using isotopic oxygen analysis in carbon
monoxide as an illustrative example. The method is applicable to any sample
that is or can be converted into an infrared active gas.

## INTRODUCTION

Radioisotopes have been extensively used as tracers. Many other
investigations, however, preclude their use either because no suitable
radioisotope is available or radiation health concerns may limit their use.
Routine applications of stable isotopes, however, have been hindered by the
lack of a detection method as versatile and simple as that used for radiation
detection (e.g., scintillation counting). The small frequency shift in the
molecular vibration-rotation spectra due to isotopic substitution can be used
to detect and measure isotopic abundance. Infrared emitting diode lasers,
because of their frequency tunability, high spectral resolution and power
density, provide a good probe for isotopic analysis. The principle and
operation of a tunable diode laser spectroscopic system for stable isotope
analysis is described using isotopic carbon monoxide as an example. However,
this general method can be applied to any sample gas that has or can be
converted to have infrared active modes.

## PRINCIPLE

The infrared spectrum of diatomic molecules normally consists of two series
of approximately equidistant vibration-rotation transitions, the R-branch
extending from $\nu_o$ (frequency of the pure vibrational transition) toward higher

frequencies, and the p-branch extending from $\nu_o$ toward lower frequencies (1). This is shown schematically in Figure 1.

When an atom in a molecule is substituted with an isotope of the same element, there is a shift in the vibration-rotation transitions due to changes in the internuclear distances in the various vibrational levels and the moments of inertia (2). The resulting frequency shift in the vibration-rotation spectra due to isotopic substitution forms the basis of the laser spectroscopic isotopic analysis system. In the case of carbon monoxide, there are six possible isotopic forms of the CO molecule -- $^{12}C^{16}O$, $^{12}C^{17}O$, $^{12}C^{18}O$, $^{13}C^{16}O$, $^{13}C^{17}O$, $^{13}C^{18}O$. Consequently, there would be six sets of overlapping vibration-rotation spectral lines. Within a 1 cm$^{-1}$ region, there can be lines from several isotopic molecules with adjacent spectral lines $\sim$0.1 to $\sim$0.001 cm$^{-1}$ apart. This, however, presents no problem for a diode laser system. The spectral resolution (laser linewidth) is typically 10$^{-4}$ cm$^{-1}$ (3) which is orders of magnitude better than the isotopic line spacings. Since the laser line is tunable, it can be centered in regions where the absorption lines of several isotopic molecules can be scanned within a single longitudinal laser mode.

In a system with two optical path lengths, the transmitted laser intensities, $I_1$ and $I_2$, for two isotopic spectral lines are given by the Beer-Lambert law:

$$I_1 = (I_o)_1 \, e^{-\alpha_1 P_1 \ell_1} \tag{1}$$

$$I_2 = (I_o)_2 \, e^{-\alpha_2 P_2 \ell_2} \tag{2}$$

where $I_o$ is the incident laser intensity, $\alpha$ is the spectral absorption coefficient (torr$^{-1}$ cm$^{-1}$), P is the partial pressure (torr), and $\ell$ is the path length (cm).

From Eq. (1) and Eq. (2), the isotopic ratio $\left(\frac{P_1}{P_2}\right)$ can be obtained

$$\left(\frac{P_1}{P_2}\right) = \frac{\ln\left(\frac{I_o}{I}\right)_1}{\ln\left(\frac{I_o}{I}\right)_2} \Big/ \left(\frac{\alpha_1}{\alpha_2}\right)\left(\frac{\ell_1}{\ell_2}\right) \, . \tag{3}$$

Thus, if the spectral absorption coefficients are known, the isotopic abundance and the abundance ratio can be determined from experimental measurement of I and Io.*

---

*The absorption coefficient is a function of the line profile (4), thus the absorptivity should be integrated over the entire spectral line. At low pressure where the Doppler effect dominates the line shape, the peak absorptivity may be used.

EXPERIMENTAL

The tunable diode laser isotopic analysis system is shown schematically in Fig. 2. A PbEuSeTe quantum well diode laser, housed in a closed cycle helium refrigerator, provided the IR radiation. The laser was developed and fabricated at GMR (5, 6). The infrared emission from the laser could be broadly tuned from 1600 cm$^{-1}$ to 2290 cm$^{-1}$ for CW operation by varying the heat sink temperature of the laser. At the fixed temperature, the frequency of the laser mode can be fine tuned by varying the injection current. A typical single mode covered 1-2 cm$^{-1}$ with a tuning rate of ~30 cm$^{-1}$/amp.

The laser radiation was focused onto the slit of a half meter grating monochromator. The monochromator was used primarily to filter out unwanted laser modes and to provide approximate wavelength identifications. The radiation was collimated through the sample cell, and focused onto a liquid N$_2$ cooled InSb (3 mm) detector. For experimental set-up, the detector signal was displayed on an oscilloscope. For quantitative measurements, the laser radiation was optically chopped, and the output of the detector was processed by a lock-in amplifier and displayed on a strip chart recorder.

To eliminate the problem associated with isotopic molecules of vastly different concentrations, an optical absorption cell with two interconnected compartments and a common gaseous sample was used. Ideally, the ratio of the path lengths should be matched to the ratio of spectral intensities. For example, with $^{12}C^{16}O$ P(6) line and $^{12}C^{18}O$ R(7) line where the natural abundance ratio is about 480 and a line strength ratio is about 0.9, a path length ratio of ~400 would be required for optimization of spectral signals. Because of the difficulty in fabrication of the glass cell, a path length ratio of 114.0 was the best that could be obtained for the present experiment.

RESULTS AND CONCLUSION

The diode laser system was successfully used to detect isotopic spectral lines of carbon monoxide. Fig. 3a shows an oscilloscope trace of an unabsorbed laser mode centered at approximately 2082 cm$^{-1}$. Figures 3b and 3c show the oscilloscope trace of the mode absorbed over a 10 cm path cell with BaF$_2$ windows (1" diameter and 3 mm thick). The partial pressure-path length product was 2550 torr-cm (Fig. 3b) and 240 torr-cm (Fig. 3c), respectively. Four isotopic CO molecular spectral lines extending within 1 cm$^{-1}$ can be clearly resolved and detected in this mode. They are: $^{12}C^{18}O$ P(3) at 2081.039 cm$^{-1}$, $^{13}C^{16}O$ P(4) at 2081.169 cm$^{-1}$, $^{12}C^{17}O$ P(9) at 2081.368 cm$^{-1}$, and $^{12}C^{16}O$ P(15) at 2082.003 cm$^{-1}$. It is clear from Fig. 3b that there was considerable pressure broadening at 255 torr, which diminished as the pressure was reduced (Fig. 3c).

The signal from isotopic lines, although present in the sample in vastly different concentrations ($^{16}O/^{18}O$ ~480), can be equalized by optimizing the absorption path. This would eliminate the problem associated with processing signals of vastly different intensities. An equally good signal to noise ratio can thus be obtained for the less abundant isotopic molecule as the more abundant isotopic molecule. With a non-optimized fixed dual length prototype of the matched variable absorption path cell, the improvement in the detection of $^{12}C^{16}O$ P(6) and $^{12}C^{18}O$ R(7) spectral lines can be clearly seen in Fig. 4. The enhanced absorption (Fig. 4b) of the low concentration $^{12}C^{18}O$ is due to the longer absorption path. The total CO pressure (4.96 torr) was the same for both the short and the long path compartments.

The relative abundance of isotopic CO, determined from the peak spectral absorption data and reported spectroscopic parameters (7, 8), ranged from 0.002031 to 0.002039 for $^{12}C^{18}O$ relative to $^{12}C^{16}O$. These abundance ratios apply only to the particular experimental sample. There is no CO reference sample derived from primary standards such as SMOW (Standard Mean Ocean Water) or PDB (Pee Dee Belemnite) to enable us to do an intercomparison study. The consistency of this method using a non-optimized prototype system, however, can be determined from the individual values used to determine a particular ratio. At 2 torr pressure, 7 measurements of the $^{12}C^{18}O$ R(7) line (long cell) and 12 measurements of the $^{12}C^{16}O$ P(6) line (short cell) gave a $^{12}C^{18}O/^{12}C^{16}O$ ratio of 0.002039 ± 0.000005 (mean ± SD). Similarly, 3 measurements of the $^{12}C^{17}O$ R(0) line and 3 measurements of the $^{12}C^{16}O$ P(6) line at 4.96 torr gave a $^{12}C^{17}O/^{12}C^{16}O$ ratio of 0.000375 ± 0.000010 (mean ± SD).

In conclusion, we have described an infrared laser spectroscopic system for analysis of stable isotopic tracers. This system uses a high resolution quantum well PbEuSeTe diode laser fabricated at GMR, and a sample cell with path lengths matched to the expected isotopic spectral intensities. Presently, the system is being applied to measure stable oxygen isotopes in biological tissue samples that can be converted into CO. The method is applicable to any sample which can be converted into an IR active gas.

ACKNOWLEDGMENT

The authors wish to express their sincere thanks to Dale L. Partin and Christopher M. Thrush for providing the diode laser. They also wish to express their appreciation to Jeffrey A. Sell, Richard M. Schreck and the late Wayne Lo for stimulating discussions.

REFERENCES

1    G. Herzberg, Molecular Spectra and Molecular Structure, I. Spectra of Diatomic Molecules, D. Van Nostrand, New York, 1965, 111 pp.

2    S. Walker and H. Straw, Spectroscopy, Vol. 2, MacMillan, New York, 1962, 263 pp.

3    W. Lo and D. L. Partin, in A. Bernhardt (Ed.), New Lasers for Analytical and Industrial Chemistry, Proc. SPIE 461 (1984), 5-10.

4    B. H. Armstrong, J. Quant. Spectrosc. Radiat. Transfer, 7 (1967), 61-88.

5    D. L. Partin, R. F. Majkowski, and D. E. Swets, J. Vac. Sci. Technol., B3 (1985), 576-580.

6    D. L. Partin, R. F. Majkowski, and C. M. Thrush, J. Appl. Phys., 55 (1984), 678-682.

7    G. Guelachvili, J. Mol. Spectrosc., 75 (1979), 251-269.

8    C. Chackerian, Jr., G. Guelachvili and R. H. Tipping, J. Quant. Spectrosc. Radiat. Transfer, 30 (1983), 107-112.

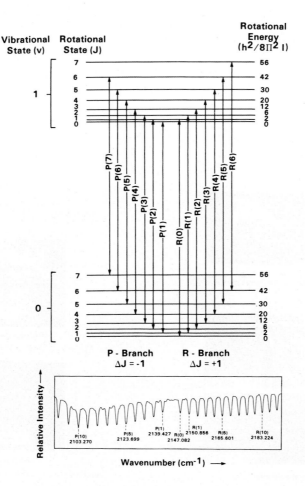

Fig. 1   The vibration-rotation transitions for a diatomic molecule with the observed $1 \leftarrow 0$ spectrum of CO showing the components and some transition frequencies in cm$^{-1}$ (for $^{12}C^{16}O$).

446

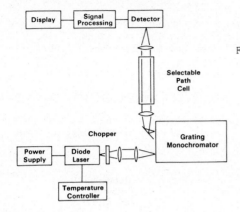

Fig. 2  Schematic diagram of the diode laser isotopic analysis system. The laser radiation is collimated through the sample cell which may contain two or more selected absorbing paths. The path lengths are optimized to give comparable absorption for different isotopic transitions.

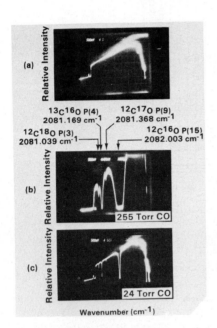

Fig.3  Oscilloscope trace of an unabsorbed laser mode (3a), and the mode absorbed by 255 torr (3b) and 24 torr (3c) of normal tank CO in a 10 cm cell.

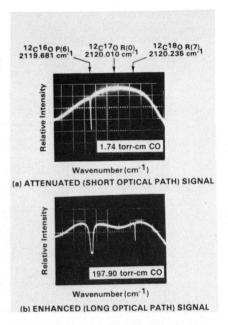

Fig. 4  Enhanced detection of the $^{12}C^{18}O$ R(7) transition by adjusting the optical paths at equal pressure (4.96 torr).

*Synthesis and Applications of Isotopically Labeled Compounds 1985.*     447
Proceedings of the Second International Symposium, Kansas City, MO, U.S.A.,
3—6 September 1985, R.R. Muccino (Ed.), 447—452
© 1986 Elsevier Science Publishers B.V., Amsterdam — Printed in The Netherlands

# ON-LINE RADIOACTIVITY FLOW DETECTOR FOR HPLC

M. J. Kessler, Ph.D.
RadioAnalytic, Inc., 5102 S. Westshore Blvd., Tampa, FL   33611,
U.S.A.

## ABSTRACT

An on-line radioactivity flow detector allows the direct
quantitation of beta and low energy gamma emitters separated by
HPLC. Two radioisotopes with different energies can be quantitated simultaneously, on-line in real time. The methodology
used in the flow detector is the same as that used in a liquid
scintillation counter using coincidence counting and dual pulse
height analyzers for distinguishing of radioisotopes of various
energies. The data obtained by the flow detector is permanently stored on disk and can be reprocessed and graphically plotted at any later time.

## INTRODUCTION

The combined use of radioactivity and HPLC for the analysis
of various metabolic products has been used increasingly in the
last 20 years. The early method for quantitation of the radioactive peaks eluting from HPLC was the fraction collection -
liquid scintillation counting method. This technique involved
setting up a fraction collector to collect fractions at preset
times. Aliquots were then removed from each fraction, placed
in scintillation vials and scintillation fluid added. The
vials were capped and shaken, labeled and transported to the
liquid scintillation counter for quantitation. This entire
process required an average of 10 hours for complete analysis
on each sample. Thus, this technique was not easily adaptable
to the large number of samples that could be generated by
HPLC.

The technique of on-line radioactivity flow detection was
introduced (1,2) to enable the investigator to circumvent this
problem and get immediate results of radioactivity eluting from
HPLC in real time with no delay. The original radioactivity
flow detector required a solid (heterogeneous) anthracene flow
cell for quantitation of high energy beta emitting isotopes.
The technique permitted low sensitivity quantitation of $^{14}C$ and
higher energy beta emitters  but suffered from contamination
problems. The next major advance occurred a few years later,
with the introduction of the homogeneous flow cell in which the
HPLC effluent is mixed on-line with scintillation solution

448

(3,4). This enabled the user to quantitate low and high energy beta-emitters without contamination problems and with a large increased sensitivity. Finally in the last 5 years, the on-line quantitative technique for radioactive peaks eluting from HPLC has become increasingly popular because of its increased sensitivity and computerized data reduction incorporated into the flow detector. This permits large numbers of radioactive samples to be analyzed unattended by an automated HPLC system and a radioactive flow detector.


DISCUSSION
    The modern use of the flow through radioactivity detector will be investigated by answering the following questions: How is radioactivity detected and quantitated? How is the radioactivity eluting from the HPLC graphically presented in real time? Why use a radioactivity detector for quantitation of radioactive peaks eluting from HPLC?
    The first question to address is how radioactivity is detected in a flow detector? This is accomplished in the FLO-ONE/Beta (Fig. 1) by the technique of scintillation counting using either a heterogeneous (solid) or mixing with scintillation solution (homogeneous) flow cell. The beta particles emitted by the radionuclide activate a solvent molecule in the

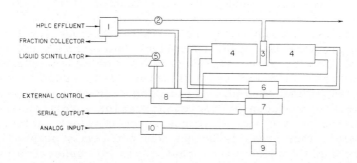

1. Electronic Stream Splitter
2. Static Fluid Mixer
3. Flow Cell
4. Photomultiplier Tubes
5. Scintillator Pump
6. Pulse Height Analysis Board
7. Controller Board
8. High Voltage/Pump Driver
9. Computer
10. Analog Board

    Fig. 1. A complete block diagram of the FLO-ONE/Beta radioactive flow detector

liquid scintillation solution. The activated molecules transfer their energy to a fluor molecule. The fluor converts the energy of each beta particle directly to a flash of light, whose intensity is directly proportional to the energy of the original beta particle. Because the energy (10-1500 KeV) of the beta particle, is extremely small (low light intensity), a pair of photomultiplier tubes are used to measure the light flashes. The resultant pulses are then sorted by a pulse height analysis board. This results in an energy spectrum for each radionuclide present in the sample. The information is finally sent to a computer for analysis, calculations, and graphic presentation of a radiochromatograph (5,6).

In addition to the features just presented, several others help to increase the overall versatility of the radioactivity flow detector. The first feature is a built-in electronic stream splitter. This permits the scientist to obtain maximum sensitivity using a homogeneous (scintillation solution) flow cell and to save a percentage of the sample for future analysis. Second, an electronically controlled HPLC-quality pump for delivery of the scintillation solution permits a precise and controlled flow rate of scintillation solution. Third, an analog signal from various HPLC detectors (UV, fluorescense, electrochemical, etc.) can be presented on the same graph as two radioactive channels. Fourth, electronically controlled radioisotope discriminator windows permit the scientist to determine the best counting channels by using a special software program – Spectrum Analysis (Fig. 2). This feature allows the investigator to accurately set windows for single or dual radiolabeled samples. In Figure 2 sample windows of 1-40 and 40-100 would be used to obtain maximum efficiency of tritium and $^{14}$C and minimum crossover of $^{14}$C into the tritium channel.

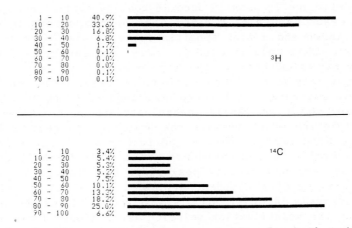

Fig. 2. Energy Spectrum presentation for both tritium and $^{14}$C obtained using the Spectrum Analysis Program of the FLO-ONE/Beta radioactivity flow detector.

The second question to be addressed is the method of quantitating radioactivity in a flow detector. Two basic factors contribute to the sensitivity and resolution of radioactive peaks eluting from the HPLC: cell type and residence time. The first is the type of flow cell used in the detector. Three different cells (solid, liquid, high energy isotope) can be used with the sensitivity and resolution greatly dependent on the cell volume and cell type (Table 1). The liquid cell is the most commonly used because it has the highest sensitivity and best resolution for all beta and low energy gamma emitters.

TABLE 1 Flow cells used in radioactivity flow detectors

| "QUICK-CHANGE" RADIOACTIVITY DETECTOR FLOW CELLS | | |
|---|---|---|
| STANDARD liquid | SOLID XE, Glass, Plastic | SPECIAL HEI |
| SCINTILLATOR TYPE | | |
| Internally mixed with FLO-SCINT I, II or III Depending on HPLC Solvent | Europium Activated $CaF_2$ (100 micron) Lithium Activated Glass (70-80 micron) Scintillator in Plastic (200 micron) | No Solid Support - Plastic Scintillator Window |
| ISOTOPE & % EFFICIENCY | | |
| $^3H > 45\%$ $^{14}C > 90\%$ | $^3H \approx 3\%$, $^{14}C > 90\%$ $^3H \approx 0.1\%$, $^{14}C > 25\%$ $^3H \approx 0.1\%$, $^{14}C > 25\%$ | $^{32}P \approx 50\%$ $^{99m}Tc \approx 40\%$ $^{125}I \approx 25\%$ |
| MINIMUM DETECTABLE LIMITS | | |
| $^3H \approx 70$ dpm $^{14}C \approx 30$ dpm | $^3H \approx 5000$ dpm, XE only $^{14}C \approx 300$ dpm $^{14}C \approx 750$ dpm $^{14}C \approx 750$ dpm | $^{32}P \approx 200$ dpm $^{99m}Tc \approx 300$ dpm $^{125}I \approx 500$ dpm |

The solid cell type is usually used in quality control analysis where the exact nature of the radioactive components in the sample are known and a high specific activity sample is being quantitated. This cell is used for only high energy beta and low energy gamma emitters. The high energy isotope cell is used to count only very high energy beta emitters ($^{32}P$) and low energy gamma emitters. It has the advantage of using no solid scintillator, which can easily contaminate and no liquid scintillation solution which permits the scientist to recover his radioactive HPLC peaks. The second factor affecting sensitivity is a factor termed residence time. This is the amount of time that each radioactive peak is in the flow cell. The residence time is directly dependent on the size of the flow cell and inversely dependent on the total flow rate of the HPLC effluent and the scintillation solution (if a liquid flow cell is used). Therefore, for maximum sensitivity a large flow cell and/or a slow total flow rate should be used (7,8).

The third question is what method of data reduction can be achieved in a flow through radioactivity detector? This detector presents a real time on-line graphics presentation of two channel of radioactivity and one analog input signal on the same graphic presentation (Fig. 3). The graphic results and data summary can be presented in net counts, cpm, dpm isocratic, and dpm corrected for variable quench in the gradient mode.

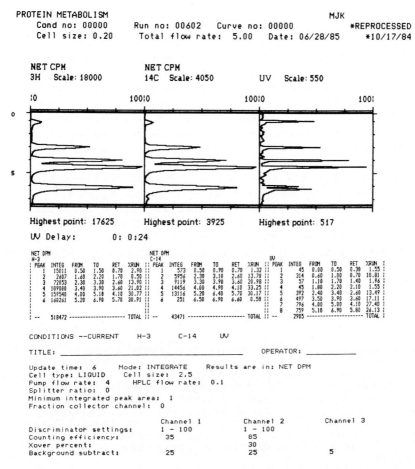

Fig. 3. The graphic presentation of the data reduction software used in the FLO-ONE/Beta radioactivity detector for tritium, $^{14}$C, and UV signal from the HPLC.

Each peak is numbered, the retention time given, the total area determined, the time for the integration start and stop points, and percentage that each peak is of the total radioactivity is printed on the data summary.

452

The raw data from each HPLC separation run is stored permanently on a floppy disk and can be reprocessed, replotted, background subtracted, and corrected for quench. The radioactivity flow detector can be controlled by an external HPLC data system and injector, and store up to twenty hours of data on a floppy disk and thirty days using a 10 megabyte hard drive. A special data reduction package allows the investigator to selectively subtract background, skims minor peaks, smooth data, expand a region of interest, and manual setting of integration pointers.

Now that the questions of how a flow detector quantitates radioactivity and how the data is calculated and graphically presented have been answered, the final question is why use a flow through radioactivity detector? There are fundamentally two reasons for the use of a radioactivity flow detector for quantitation of radioactive peaks eluting from HPLC. The first reason is that of time. The traditional method of fraction collection-scintillation requires about 10 hours for the analysis of a single HPLC run but the flow through radioactivity detector quantitates radioactivity in real time and on-line from the HPLC. The second reason is that of cost. The radioactivity flow detector requires only a solid cell or mixing with scintillation solution at a cost of approximately $3.00/sample. Whereas, the alternative method of fraction collection-scintillation counting requires over ten separate steps and cost $30.00/sample. Therefore, the use of an on-line radioactivity detector is over ten times faster for analysis of the samples and at a cost of about ten percent of the alternative method.

REFERENCES

1.  E. Rapkin and J. Gibbs, Nature 194 (1962) 43-49.
2.  E. Schram and R. Lombaert, Anal. Biochem 3 (1962) 68-74.
3.  J. Hunt, Anal. Biochem., 23 (1968) 289-294.
4.  M. J. Kessler, J. Liq. Chromatogr., 5 (1982) 313-325.
5.  M. J. Kessler, Amer. Lab., 8 (1982) 52-63.
6.  M. J. Kessler, J. of Chromatogr., 255 (1983) 209-217.
7.  M. J. Kessler, J. of Chromatogr. Sci., 20 (1982) 523-527.
8.  M. J. Kessler, J. Liq. Chromatogr., 5 (1982) 313-325.
9.  K. C. Cundy and P. S. Crooks, J. Chromatogr., 281 (1983) 17-33.
10. H. K. Webster and J. M. Whaun, J. Chromatogr., 209 (1981) 283-292.
11. J. C. Nolan, W. Pickett, K. English, A. L. Oronsky, and S. S. Kerwar. Prostaglandin, 24 (1982) 443-449.
12. N. Ozawa and F. P. Guengerish, Proc. Natl. Acad. Sci., 80 (1983) 5266-5270.

*Synthesis and Applications of Isotopically Labeled Compounds 1985.*
Proceedings of the Second International Symposium, Kansas City, MO, U.S.A.,
3—6 September 1985, R.R. Muccino (Ed.), 453—458
© 1986 Elsevier Science Publishers B.V., Amsterdam — Printed in The Netherlands

INCREASING ROLE OF HIGH PERFORMANCE LIQUID CHROMATOGRAPHY (HPLC) IN RADIOPHAR-
MACEUTICAL ANALYSIS

T.E. BOOTHE, R.D. FINN, M.M. VORA, A.M. EMRAN, P.J. KOTHARI and S. WUKOVNIG

Cyclotron Facility, Mount Sinai Medical Center, Miami Beach, Fl.  33140 (U.S.A.)

ABSTRACT
    HPLC can provide valuable information regarding the identification and
quantification of radiolabelled starting materials, including anion and cation
analyses; synthesis of labelled intermediates; and subsequent preparation of
useful radiolabelled compounds.

INTRODUCTION
    HPLC is experiencing a rapidly increasing role in the development of radio-
pharmaceuticals.  Some possible uses in the analysis of radiochemical and radiopharmaceutical preparations are:  1) analysis of radiolabelled starting
materials;  2) determination of reaction products, both labelled and
non-labelled; 3) optimization of reaction conditions; 4) purification, including
separation from both chemical and radiochemical impurities; 5) determination of
specific activity; 6) quality assurance, including chemical and radiochemical
purity (ref. 1); 7) stability of radiolabelled products during synthesis,
purification, and storage (ref. 1); and 8) determination of decomposition
products and/or metabolites.
    We have utilized HPLC in many of these categories with $\gamma$-emitting radio-
nuclides having half-lives as short as $10m(^{13}N)$ to as long as $241.6d(^{153}Gd)$.
Applications to several radiochemical systems are presented.  In several
instances comparisons are made to thin-layer chromatography (TLC) as a tool for
analysis and quality control.  Concerted efforts have been made to utilize and
develop methods using reversed-phase columns, as these are economical and
readily available to most chromatographers.

METHODS
    The basic liquid chromatographic system is shown in Fig. 1.  A switching
valve is incorporated to allow injections either onto an appropriate column or
into a Teflon reference tube (2m x 1mm i.d.).  A three-way valve directs the
eluate flow from the appropriate source to a NaI(Tl) crystal attached to a
counting system using a Nuclear Data Model 60A multichannel analyzer operated in
the multichannel scaling (MCS) mode.  The reference tube allows the use of

"on-line" standard counting and provides a rapid direct comparison of any eluted
radioactive peak from the column to the total radioactivity injected.

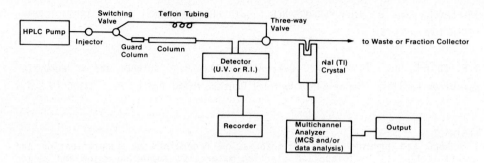

Fig. 1.  Liquid Chromatographic System.


RESULTS AND DISCUSSION

Preparation of 2-[$^{18}$]fluoro-2-deoxy-D-glucose (2-$^{18}$FDG)

The reaction of $^{18}$F$^-$($t_{\frac{1}{2}}$ = 109.8m) with methyl 4,6-0-benzylidene-2-3-0-
cyclic sulfato-$\beta$-D-mannopyranoside (ref. 2) was utilized to prepare 2-$^{18}$FDG.
Due to the complexity of products, HPLC purification was necessary to achieve
consistently high radiochemical purity (ref. 3).  A typical radiochromatogram is
shown in Fig. 2.  The system, which uses two preparative columns in series was
capable of resolving numerous radiolabelled compounds from the desired product.
Some compounds eluted before 2-$^{18}$FDG; others which were retained on the columns,
could be removed by water.  Occasionally, a radiolabelled impurity co-eluted

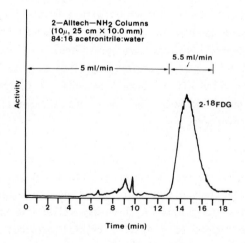

Fig. 2 Radiochromatogram showing preparative purification of 2-$^{18}$FDG.

with the $2-^{18}$FDG. This was usually associated with too large injection volume (>500 $\mu$l) or gradual degradation of the column system after ~40 injections. TLC methods using phosphate-impregnated (ref. 4) and boric acid-impregnated (ref. 5) silica gel were found to resolve $2-^{18}$FDG from the impurity (Fig. 3). The $R_f$

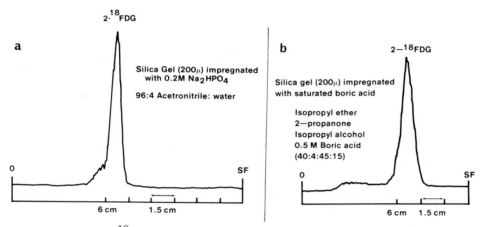

Fig. 3. TLC of $2-^{18}$FDG radiopharmaceutical on a ) phosphate-impregnated silica gel and b) boric acid-impregnated silica gel. Plates were developed to 6 cm, dried, and successionally developed and dried an additional 1.5 cm, up to seven times; 0 = origin, SF = solvent front.

of the impurity in Fig. 3a was approximately the same as that obtained for $2-[^{18}$F]fluoro-2-deoxy-D-mannose, $2-^{18}$FDM (ref. 4). Gas chromatographic analysis of the final radiopharmaceutical (ref. 6) did not confirm the presence of $2-^{18}$FDM. Although the identity of the impurity is unknown, we do not believe it to be $2-^{18}$FDM (ref 3). These TLC systems were not capable of resolving $2-^{18}$FDG from many of the other radiolabelled compounds formed during the preparation.

An Alltech C18 column (10$\mu$ , 25cm x 4.6mm), using a mobile phase of 98:2 acetonitrile: water with 2.23mM tetradecylamine (ref. 7) at a flow rate of 1.5 ml/min, was employed with limited success for the analysis of $2-^{18}$FDG (retention time = 5.1 min).

## Anion Analysis

Many useful radiolabelled precursors are anions. Reversed-phase $C_{18}$ columns are suitable for anion separations (ref. 8) and have been utilized (ref. 9) for the analysis of several radiolabelled anions (Table 1). This system has been used to investigate such areas as: 1) $^{13}NO_2^-/^{13}NO_3^-$ formation in the $^{16}O(p,a)^{13}N$ reaction including specific activity as a function of target

TABLE 1

Anion analysis using reversed-phase $C_{18}$ columns. [a,b]

---

Anion (radiolabel, retention time in min.)

---

$CN^-$([11]C, 2.5), $HCO_3^-$([11]C, 4.3), $OCN^-$([11]C, 8.9)

$NO_2^-$([13]N, 9.7), $NO_3^-$([13]N, 12.4)

$F^-$([18]F, 6.7), $Br^-$([82]Br, 9.1), $IO_3^-$([131]I, 7.0) $I^-$([123]I,[131]I, 16.0)

$MoO_4^{2-}$(8.0)[b]

$TcO_4^-$([95m]Tc, [99m]Tc, 10.2)[b]

---

[a]LiChrosorb RP-18 column (10$\mu$, 25cm x 4.6mm); 0.01M octylamine, pH = 4.7($H_3PO_4$), 2.0 ml/min; U.V. detection at 200-235nm.

[b]Alltech C18 column (10$\mu$, 25cm x 4.6mm), 20% acetonitrile added to above mobile phase, pH = 5.2.


conditions (ref. 9); 2) oxidation reactions of [11]$CN^-$ prepared from the [14]$N(p,a)$[11]$C$ reaction (ref. 10); 3) alkaline hydrolysis of $O$[11]$CN^-$ to $H$[11]$CO_3^-$ (ref. 10) and 4) pertechnetate formation in the work-up of the [nat]$Mo(p,xn)$[95m]$Tc$ reaction and subsequent separation of the [95m]$TcO_4^-$ from $MoO_4^{2-}$ (ref. 11).

The system has also been used to analyze radioiodide solutions (ref. 9). The specific activity of [131]$I^-$ solutions which were claimed to be "carrier-free" were occasionally found to be as low as 450 mCi/$\mu$mol (at manufacturer's calibration time). The specific activity of [123]$I^-$ solutions was much higher (~5 Ci/$\mu$mol). An impurity often found in radioiodide solutions is radioiodate and is usually determined by TLC procedures (ref. 9 and ref. 12). We have demonstrated that in typical [123]$I^-$ or [131]$I^-$ solutions, the iodate determined by TLC methods ranged from 0.2% on Whatman #1 paper to as high as 2.7% on silica gel, even when the solution contained antioxidant. However, no detectable radioiodate could be found using HPLC. The iodate found using TLC could possibly arise from air oxidation of the radioiodide on the TLC surface.

A polymer-based anion exchange column (ref. 13), the Hamilton PRP-X100 column (10$\mu$, 25cm x 4.1 mm), was eluted with 1.5mM potassium hydrogen phthalate at 2.0ml/min. With "indirect-U.V." detection at 285 nm, the system provided a means for the determination of the specific activity of [18]$F^-$ (retention time = 2.8 min) produced from the [18]$O(p,n)$[18]$F$ reaction.

## Cation Analysis

We have used reversed-phase $C_{18}$ columns with post-column reaction for the analysis of several cations (Tables 2 and 3). The conditions listed in Table 2,

TABLE 2

Cation analysis using reversed-phase $C_{18}$ columns. [a,b]

| Cation (retention time in min.) |
| --- |
| $Ga^{3+}$ (1.1), $Cu^{2+}$(1.7), $Pb^{2+}$(2.2), $Zn^{2+}$(3.7) |
| $Ti^{4+}$(3.8), $Ni^{2+}$(4.1), $Cd^{2+}$(7.3), $Fe^{3+}$(7.8) |

[a] Altex Ultrasphere-ODS ($5\mu$, 25cm x 4.6mm); 0.01M sodium hexanesulfonate, 0.045M tartaric acid, pH = 3.4 (NaOH) at a flow rate of 2.0 ml/min.

[b] Detection was U.V. - vis. at 520nm using post-column reaction with 0.2mM 4-(2-pyridylazo)resorcinol (PAR), 2M $NH_4OH$ and 1M $NH_4OAc$ at a flow rate of 2.0ml/min.

TABLE 3

Separation of Tb and Gd using reversed-phase $C_{18}$ columns. [a,b]

| Species (radiolabel) | Retention time (min.) |
| --- | --- |
| $Na_2Gd$-DTPA ($^{153}Gd$) | 1.5 |
| $Tb^{3+}$ ($^{153-160}Tb$) | 4.8 |
| $Gd^{3+}$ ($^{153}Gd$) | 5.8 |

[a] Alltech C18 ($10\mu$, 2.5 cm x 4.6mm); 5mM sodium octanesulfonate, 0.075M $\alpha$-hydroxyisobutyric acid, pH = 4.8(NaOH) at a flow rate of 1.5 ml/min.

[b] Detection was U.V.-vis at 653 nm using post-column reaction with 0.15mM Arsenazo III at a flow rate of 1.5 ml/min.

which were adapted from the literature (ref. 14), have been used to: 1) perform trace metal analysis in radiochemical and radiopharmaceutical preparations, e.g. trace metals in $^{67}GaCl_3$ solutions; 2) follow $^{68}Zn$, used in the $^{68}Zn(p,2n)^{67}Ga$ reaction through a production cycle: a) target plating, b) proton irradiation, c) chemical separation of $^{67}Ga$ and d) ion exchange recovery of $^{68}Zn$; and 3) determine Ni concentrations in $^{18}F^-$ solutions prepared from the $^{18}O(p,n)^{18}F$ reaction on $^{18}O$-enriched water using a nickel-lined target.

Using $^{153}Gd$ as a radiotracer, we have recently begun to investigate the preparation of Gd complexes such as Gd-diethylenetriaminepentaacetic acid (Gd-DTPA) for magnetic resonance imaging (MRI) (ref. 15). The preparation of the "no-carrier-added" $^{153}Gd$ was performed using the $^{nat}Ga(p,xn)^{153-160}Tb$ reaction. The Tb radioisotopes are separated from Gd by ion exchange. The $^{153}Tb(t_{\frac{1}{2}} = 2.3d)$ decays to $^{153}Gd$, which is purified and separated from the remaining Tb radioisotopes. The HPLC system (ref. 16) shown in Table 3 can be used to follow various aspects of this procedure. A separation of bound Gd, as in $Na_2Gd$-DTPA, to unbound $Gd^{3+}$ can also be studied.

CONCLUSIONS

HPLC is an invaluable tool in many areas of radiochemical synthesis, radiopharmaceutical development, and quality control. HPLC and TLC still remain complimentary techniques, each having specific advantages. However, the sole reliance upon any one method should be avoided particularly during the initial phases of developing techniques for analysis of various stages of radiochemical and radiopharmaceutical preparation.

REFERENCES

1  T.D. Bell, in W.P. Duncan and A.B. Susan (Eds.), Synthesis and Applications of Isotopically Labeled Compounds, Elsevier, Amsterdam, 1983, pp. 217-222.
2  T. Tewson, J. Nucl. Med., 24 (1983) 718-721.
3  M.M. Vora, T.E. Boothe, R.D. Finn, P.J. Kothari, A.M. Emran, S.T. Carroll and A.J. Gilson, J. Label. Compd. Radiopharm. (in press).
4  C. Van Rijn, J. Herscheid, G. Visser and A. Hoekstra, Int. J. App. Radiat. Isot., 36 (1985) 111-115.
5  M. Ghebregzabher, S. Rufini, G.M. Sapia and M. Lato, J. Chromatogr., 180 (1979) 1-16.
6  C.-Y. Shiue, J.S. Fowler, A.P. Wolf, D. Alexoff and R.R. MacGregor, J. Label. Compd. Radiopharm., 22 (1985) 503-508.
7  C.H. Lochmuller and W.B. Hill, Jr., J. Chromatogr., 264 (1983) 215-222.
8  N.E. Skelly, Anal. Chem., 54 (1982) 712-715.
9  T.E. Boothe, A.M. Emran, R.D. Finn, P.J. Kothari and M.M. Vora, J. Chromatogr., 333 (1985) 269-275.
10  T.E. Boothe, A.M. Emran, R.D. Finn, M.M. Vora and P.J. Kothari, Int. J. Appl. Radiat. Inst., 36 (1985) 141-144.
11  R. Finn, T. Boothe, J. Sinnreich, E. Tavano, A. Gilson, and A.P. Wolf, in Radiopharmaceuticals and Labelled Compounds-1984, IAEA, Vienna, 1985, pp. 47-54.
12  T. Phan and R. Wasnich, Practical Nuclear Pharmacy, Banyan Enterprises, Honolulu, HI, 1981, 116pp.
13  D.P. Lee, J. Chromatogr. Sci., 22 (1984) 327-331.
14  R.M. Cassidy and S. Elchuk, Anal. Chem., 54 (1982) 1558-1563.
15  D.H. Carr, Physiol. Chem. Phys. and Med. NMR, 16 (1984) 137-144.
16  C.H. Knight, R.M. Cassidy, B.M. Recoskie and L.W. Green, Anal. Chem., 56 (1984) 474-478.

*Synthesis and Applications of Isotopically Labeled Compounds 1985.*
Proceedings of the Second International Symposium, Kansas City, MO, U.S.A.,
3—6 September 1985, R.R. Muccino (Ed.), 459—464
© 1986 Elsevier Science Publishers B.V., Amsterdam — Printed in The Netherlands

IMAGING SCANNERS FOR THE ANALYSIS OF RADIOLABELED TLC AND OTHER BIOLOGICAL
SAMPLES

S.D. Shulman[1] and Y. Kobayashi[2]

[1]Bioscan, Inc. 4590 MacArthur Blvd. Washington, DC 20007 (USA)

[2]KOBY Associates, 60 Audubon Rd., Wellesley, MA 02181 (USA)

ABSTRACT

Since their introduction several years ago, Imaging Scanners have become
important quantitative tools for the analysis of radioisotopes on TLC, gels,
and paper chromatograms. In addition, there is growing interest in applications of this instrumentation in new areas of biotechnology. Imaging Scanners
have recently been demonstrated to provide rapid quantitation of tritiated
molecular probes for viral DNA and human IgG factor.

Over the past two decades, a great deal of effort in X-ray and high energy
physics has gone into the development of new large format imaging
detectors.[1,2] These detectors provide a direct digital readout of the particle
or X-ray positions permitting vast amounts of data to be accumulated rapidly
by digital computers which can process and store the position information.
These new detectors have made possible many recent discoveries in particle
physics and in X-ray diffraction studies of complex molecules.

As these detectors were being developed, researchers in Europe and the
U.S. realized that there were important applications for them in the biomedical
sciences. Several groups investigated their use for radiological imaging while
others were interested in laboratory applications requiring faster, more
accurate quantitation of radiolabeled samples.[3,4] The first laboratory
applications to be examined were the analysis of radiolabeled chromatograms and
gels.

For TLC and gel applications the basic requirements of an imaging detector
system include: a 20 cm long 1-dimensional detector capable of imaging a
complete standard TLC lane; windowless operation so that the common low energy
isotopes, $^3H$ and $^{14}C$, can be counted with high efficiency; and resolution on
the order of 1-2 mm in the chromatography direction. In actual practice, all
instruments use gas proportional counters with either a delay line or resistive
anode position readout system.

460

Imaging Scanners are direct replacements for older, mechanical scanners. Instead of counting activity from only a few millimeters of the chromatogram at a time, they can detect all betas emitted anywhere along the lane. This advantage alone makes them 50-100 times more sensitive than the older scanners. Imaging detectors, however, have additional advantages. The background count-rate is very low because the position of background events is also measured. Backgrounds of less than 0.2 counts/min/mm are routinely obtained. In analyzing a spot of 5 mm width, the background in corresponding adjacent regions is less than 1 cpm.

One further advantage of the Imaging Scanner, is the digital approach to data storage and data analysis. These systems are routinely interfaced to microcomputers which provide direct quantitative results as well as complete graphical documentation of the chromatograms. Thus, they provide results comparable to plate scraping and scintillation counting, but eliminate almost all of the labor and require much shorter counting times than are usually needed for the large number of liquid scintillation samples generated by scraping.[5]

To date, the majority of Imaging Scanner systems are in use in metabolite studies in pharmacology, toxicology, and plant sciences. One of the most common applications is in connection with lipids which are routinely separated on TLC. Figure 1 shows a lipid fraction which has been separated on TLC after incorporation of [14]C-oleate. The Imaging Scanner is easily able to quantitate components containing less than 1% of the total radiolabeled material. The required analysis time for this sample was only 10 minutes.

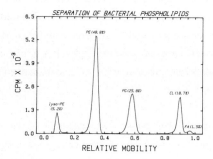

Fig. 1. TLC separation of lipids incorporating [14]C-oleate.

Another routine metabolite separation is shown in Figure 2. Here a [3]H label
was used and the analysis time required was still only 10 minutes. In the top
plot, only one peak is visible, but the digital storage and recall capabilities
of the computer system, allow the same data to be plotted with an expanded
scale as shown in the bottom plot. With the expanded scale, two more compounds
are seen near the origin each with about 1% of the total activity. More
labeled material, with about 2.5% of the activity, is seen just below the main
product peak which contains 92.5% of the total activity.

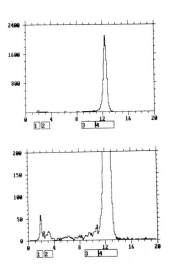

Fig. 2. (TOP) TLC analysis of tritiated compound. (BOTTOM) Y-axis expanded by
x 12 to show trace impurities.

Imaging Scanners are now being used with all types of radioactivity. Even
gamma emitters produce significant numbers of energetic electrons so that these
instruments are used in nuclear medicine to check intermediate and ultimate
product purities for [99m]Tc, [18]F, and short lived isotopes of Indium, Gallium,
and [131]I. Other routine applications currently include enzyme assays for which
substrate and product can be separated on TLC and [3]H and [125]I labeled gels.

With the growth of molecular biology and biotechnology, several new radiolabeled techniques have become quite common. Some involve blotting techniques
as shown schematically in Figure 3. In the Southern or western blot (right), a
mixture of macromolecules is separated by gel electrophoresis and then
transferred out of the gel onto the surface of a nitrocellulose or nylon
membrane. In the dot blot (left), samples are deposited directly onto the

membrane. With the molecules of interest bound to the membrane, a labeled probe is placed in contact with surface of the membrane. For DNA, this is usually a complementary strand of DNA which will bind only to one specific genetic sequence which is under investigation. When the excess labeled probe is removed, only the target molecular species remains labeled.

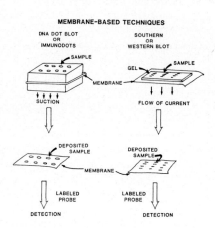

Fig. 3. A schematic diagram of membrane-based blotting techniques.

To date, most molecular probes have been labeled with $^{32}P$ or $^{125}I$, and autoradiography is used to detect the presence of the labeled complex of probe and target species. Other, low energy, longer half-life radioisotopes have not been used because of the difficulty and length of time required to obtain a reasonable autoradiographic exposure. With the use of the Imaging Scanner, however, it has been possible to rapidly detect even $^{3}H$ labeled probes.

In order to count $^{3}H$ labeled blots, certain conditions must be met: 1) the label must be on the surface because the mean free path for tritium betas in air is only about 2 mm; 2) the sample must be dry because any moisture will absorb the betas; and 3) the sample must be flat so that the same fraction of betas reach the detector from all parts of the sample. With these conditions in mind, several experiments have been carried out to test the maximum possible sensitivity achievable using $^{3}H$ labeled probes detected with the Imaging Scanner. In the first test, a series of seven spots with varying amounts of label were dried on a glass plate. The activity ranged from a high

of $10^4$ dpm to a low of 50 dpm.  The lane was analyzed for 10 minutes, and all
spots are clearly detected including the <u>smallest spot containing only 50 dpm</u>
of activity.

Next, similar tests were carried out to check the sensitivity of the Imaging
Scanner for a tritium labeled molecule bound to a nylon membrane.  In these
tests, 100 dpm were detectable in 10 minutes.  From this information and the
fact that $^3H$ is available at a specific activity of 100 curies per millimole,
one can calculate the minimum number of labeled molecules detectable with
a tritium labeled probe.  The result is a remarkable theoretical sensitivity
limit of 1 femtomole $(1 \times 10^{-15})$!

The above results were obtained under very idealized conditions.  The next
experiments were designed to provide some data on the sensitivity of tritium
labeled probes under actual laboratory conditions.  In one experiment, various
amounts of viral DNA, ranging from 200 nanograms to 100 picograms were "dot
blotted" onto a nylon membrane.  The probe was the same viral DNA which had
been nick translated to incorporate the $^3H$.  Approximately, 1.5 microcuries of
labeled probe were used.  The 100 picogram spot was detected in a 15 minute
analysis with the Imaging Scanner.  The same test done with a $^{32}P$ labeled probe
using autoradiography required a 2 hour exposure to detect 1 nanogram of viral
DNA.

A similar experiment was carried out in the area of immunochemistry.  Human
IgG, in amounts ranging from 1 microgram to 1 nanogram, was bound to a nylon
membrane and probed for with tritiated Protein A.  Because Protein A is not
readily available labeled at high $^3H$ specific activities, only 0.2 microcuries
of activity were used for this test.  The results are shown in Figure 4.

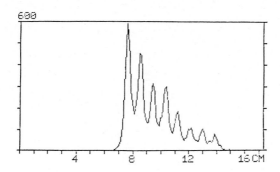

Fig. 4.  Analysis of human IgG probed with tritiated Protein A.

464

In an 18 second analysis, the 1 nanogram spot (at the far right - 14 cm) is easily detected. Even with this low specific activity probe, the Imaging Scanner sensitivity is within the range required for many immuno-diagnostic tests.

Ultimately, tritiated probes combined with the sensitivity of the Imaging Scanner offer many advantages for this type of analysis: 1) conformation - tritium is chemically bound and does not alter the structure of the labeled probe as may be the case with iodine or other fluorescent molecule labels; 2) sensitivity - the combination of $^3$H and the Imaging Scanner offer analysis times of minutes versus hours or days for autoradiography; 3) safety - tritium is a very safe isotope to handle, and in fact can be safely handled with far less training and special equipment than other higher energy isotopes; 4) stability - because of its long half-life, the shelf-life of tritiated probes will be limited by the chemical stability, not the isotope decay as is currently the case with $^{32}$P and $^{125}$I labeled probes.

REFERENCES

1. Borkowski, C.J. and Copp, K. (1968) Rev. Sci. Inst. 39, 1515.
2. Breskin, A., Charpak, G., Sauli, F., and Santiard, J.C. (1974) Nucl. Instrum. Methods 119, 1.
3. Gabriel, A. and Bram, S. (1974) FEBS Lett. 39, 307.
4. Baird, W.M., Diamond, L., Borun, T.W., and Shulman, S. (1979) Analytical Biochem. 99, 165.
5. Shulman, S. (1983) J. Liquid Chrom. 6(1), 35.

*Synthesis and Applications of Isotopically Labeled Compounds 1985.*
Proceedings of the Second International Symposium, Kansas City, MO, U.S.A.,
3—6 September 1985, R.R. Muccino (Ed.), 465—472
© 1986 Elsevier Science Publishers B.V., Amsterdam — Printed in The Netherlands

# DIRECT QUANTITATIVE MEASUREMENT OF RADIO CHROMATOGRAMS AND ELECTRO-PHEROGRAMS WITH POSITION SENSITIVE WIRE CHAMBERS

H. Filthuth

Laboratorium Prof. Dr. Berthold, 7547 Wildbad (West Germany)

## ABSTRACT

In this paper we describe the technique of position sensitve wire chambers and their application for the evaluation of Radio Thin Layer Chromatography and Electrophoresis. We report the experience with this technique in different laboratories. The results with the most frequently used isotopes are presented, e.g. H-3, P-32, S-35, I-125, I-131, Tc-99m. High spatial resolution down to 0.5 mm for H-3 and 1 mm for C-14 can be obtained.

## INTRODUCTION

Since the "Geiger counter" (1921) particle and gamma-radiation is being detected with gas-filled detectors, i.e. Geiger counters, proportional counters and multi-wire chambers, cloud chambers, spark chambers. The particles, resp. the radiation, ionize the traversed gas in the detector. The produced charges along the trajectories of the particles are collected at special electrodes producing electrical pulse signals which can be detected with the appropriate electronics, or the ionization is visualized with cloud or spark formation. To measure the spatial distribution of the radiation special position sensitive detectors have been developed in the last 15 years. This development got its momentum from particle physics. The technically most advanced multi-wire chamber detector has been developed by CERN, Geneva, to search for the "heavy light quanta" of the weak interaction, the intermediate vector bosons, $W^{\pm}$ and $Z^{o*)}$. If protons collide with antiprotons of 500 GeV energy (equ. of 500 proton masses) these vector bosons are produced at a very low rate of about 1 in $10^9$ collisions (1).

The $W^{\pm}$ and $Z^{o}$ are detected by their charged decay products, $W^{\pm} \rightarrow e^{\pm} \, \partial$ and $\mu^{\pm} \, \partial$, $Z^{o} \rightarrow e^+ e^-$ and $\mu^+ \mu^-$ ( $\partial$ = neutrinos, $\mu$ = mu-meson). In general about 40 particles are produced in the $p\bar{p}$-collision.

Therefore the experimental problem consists of the detection of very few electrons and $\mu$-mesons from the decay of the $W^{\pm}$ and $Z^{o}$, 1 in $10^9$ to $10^{10}$. The detector has a volume of 25 m³ surrounding the $p\bar{p}$-collision region. About 25,000 wires are distributed inside the detection volume to detect the charges generated along the trajectories of the particles which allows reconstruction of the particle tracks in space and the identification of the vector bosons, which is only possible with the most advanced electronics and very sophisticated computer programs. Fig. 1 and 2 give you an impression of this phantastic detector and Fig. 3 shows the decay of a $Z^{o}$-particle.

---

*) In analogy to the electronmagnetic interaction, where the accelerated electric charge emits photons, in the weak interaction the accelerated weak charge (lepton) emits "heavy photons", the intermediate vector bosons, which are about 100 times heavier than the proton.

466

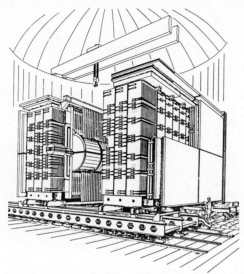

Fig. 1: The large multiwire chamber of CERN, Geneva, UA1 experiments.

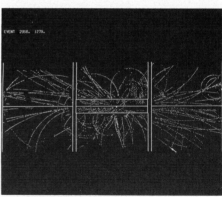

Fig. 2: The detection of a p̄p-collision of 500 GeV energy. The production of about 100 charged particles is "seen" electronically by the wires of the chamber.

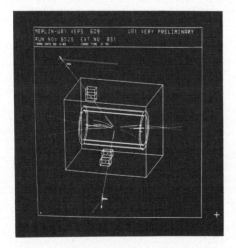

Fig. 3: Detection of the intermediate vector boson $Z^0$ (heavy photon of the weak interaction, about 100 times heavier than the proton), by its decay $Z^0 \rightarrow \mu^+\mu^-$. The $Z^0$ is being produced in the collision of protons with antiprotons of 500 GeV energy.

# THE LINEAR ANALYZER

As described earlier (2,3,4,5,6), we have developed a very simple position sensitive detector, the Linear Analyzer, with modern technology to measure the surface distribution of radio chromatograms and electropherograms, to detect particle and gamma-radiation.

To remind you, the detector is a position sensitive proportional counter, resp. wire chamber, with delay line read out. Beta-particles and gamma-rays emitted from the chromatogram enter the counter from the bottom through a 250 x 15 mm open entrance window. This configuration allows the detection of low-energy beta-particles, such as those emitted by H-3 and I-125. Also gamma rays, i.e. from Tc-99m and I-123, are detected, being converted into electrons by photo- and compton-effect inside the counter.

We have three Linear Analyzer Systems:
The Manual System or Tracemaster, (Fig. 4), a chromatogram track is positioned manually below the diaphragm of the detector head. If the measurement is comple-ted the next chromatogram has to be positioned again manually. We have two auto-matic systems: the one-plate-system automatically measures one chromatogram plate with up to ten tracks, with the multiplate system, four standard TLC-plates (20 cm x 20 cm) can be measured automatically.
In principle any data system or multichannel analyzer can be connected to the Linear Analyzer for data acquisition and analysis. Special software for this application has been developed for the BERTHOLD data system LB 510, LB 511, for the Apple II and IBM PC/XT/AT.

## PERFORMANCE OF THE LINEAR ANALYZER

### Sensitivity

The detection efficiency for low energy beta-particles is practically 100 %. But due to their absorption in the thin layer only a small fraction enters the counter. For a thin layer of 20 mg/cm² we have:
C-14: 3% to 15% depending on "electronic collimation" (50 dpm detected in 10 min)
P-32: up to 40% cpm/dpm
The detection efficiencies for the most commonly used isotopes are summarized in Table I.

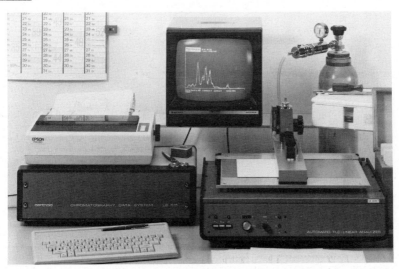

Fig. 4: Linear Analyzer System, Tracemaster.

## Resolution

The resolution is limited due to the isotropic emission of the radiation and due to the thin layer thickness. One obtains 0.5 mm for H-3, 1.0 mm for C-14 and P-32. The background radiation is 50 cpm / 250 mm = 0.20 cpm/mm.

## Lower detection limit

The lower detection limit is related to the background radiation and the statistics of the detected counts. If one measures long enough one can detect very low activities. Fig. 5 gives you an example of detecting 100 dpm of 14-C in 10 min. The measuring time necessary to detect a certain activity can be estimated very easily. If B (cpm) is the background and S (cpm) the radiation signal, one will have a clear signal above background if the error distribution of background and signal are separated by $3\sigma_B$ and $3\sigma_S$, i.e. the following relation holds: $B \cdot T + 3\sqrt{B \cdot T} = (B + S) \cdot T - 3\sqrt{(B + S) \cdot T}$. To detect 1 cpm with these criteria one has to measure T = 900 min.

Table I

Total detection efficiency, $\varepsilon_1 \cdot \varepsilon_2$, from thin layer plate of 200 µ thickness.

| Nuclide | emitter | E(max) | half live | cpm/dpm |
|---------|---------|--------|-----------|---------|
| H-3 | beta- | 18 Kev | 12 y | 2% |
| I-125 | gamma-beta (Auger) | 30 Kev | 60 d | 2.5% |
| I-131 | beta- gamma | 608 Kev 723 Kev | 8 d | up to 20% |
| C-14 | beta- | 155 Kev | 5736 y | up to 20% |
| S-35 | beta- | 167 Kev | 87.5 d | up to 20% |
| P-32 | beta- | 1.7 Mev | 14.3 d | up to 40% |
| P-33 | beta- | 200 Kev | 25.3 d | up to 20% |
| Tc-99m | gamma- | 140 Kev | 6 hr | 5% |
| I-123 | gamma- | 159 Kev | 13 hr | 5% |
| Tl-201 | gamma- | 75 Kev | 76 hr | ~ 5% |
| Cr-51 | gamma- | 321 Kev | 27.7 d | > 5% |
| Co-58 | gamma- | 811 Kev | 70.8 d | > 5% |
| Fe-59 | gamma- | 1.10 Mev | 44.6 d | > 5% |

$\varepsilon_1$ is the fraction of beta-particles penetrating the surface of TLC-plate

$\varepsilon_2$ is the detection efficiency with LB 283, 50 % for H-3, 90 % for C-14, P-32.

# QUANTITATIVE MEASUREMENTS

As described earlier (2 - 6), the present system permits quantitative analysis of beta- and gamma- sources from TLC-plates and electrophoresis gels. The technique avoids the limitations inherent in quantitation using a scintillation counter. For example, results for analysis of material labelled with H-3 and C-14 show the amount of radioactivity introduced into the thin layer (Fig. 5).

An important factor for deducting the final result, dpm of the compound, from the number of cpm is the correct data analysis.

We analyze the data with standard $x^2$-fitting methods. We assume that the peak has a gaussian shape and the background can be approximated by a polynominal up to 2nd order.

This analytical method has the advantage to define precisely the position boundaries and area of compound. It is also capable of identifying two overlapping compounds even if they are visually not clearly separated. Instead of assuming a gaussian peak one can, of course, approximate its shape by a different expression.

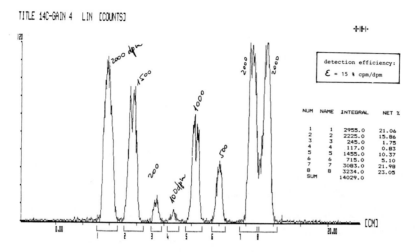

TITLE 14C-GAIN 4  LIN [COUNTS]

detection efficiency:

$\mathcal{E}$ = 15 % cpm/dpm

| NUM | NAME | INTEGRAL | NET % |
|---|---|---|---|
| 1 | 1 | 2955.0 | 21.06 |
| 2 | 2 | 2225.0 | 15.86 |
| 3 | 3 | 245.0 | 1.75 |
| 4 | 4 | 117.0 | 0.83 |
| 5 | 5 | 1455.0 | 10.37 |
| 6 | 6 | 715.0 | 5.10 |
| 7 | 7 | 3083.0 | 21.98 |
| 8 | 8 | 3234.0 | 23.05 |
| SUM | | 14029.0 | |

Fig. 5: Detection efficiency for C-14.

## EXPERIMENTS

In the following I would like to describe a few applications of the Linear Analyzer:

1. Measurement of pathways of metabolites: metabolism of 1-0-Octadecyl-2-methoxy-rac-glycero-3-phosphocholine in Raji cells (7)
(This experiment is described in detail at this conference (see index).
The most studied compound, 1-0-Octadecyl-2-metoxy-rac-glycero-3-phosphocholine (OM-G3PC, Et 18 OCH$_3$ in earlier literature) has been reported to be an efficient inhibitor of cell growth of various tumor cells in vitro and in vivo. This was explained by a detergent-like effect of OM-G3PC on the cells. However, Fleer, Kim, Unger and Eibl (7) found that OM-G3PC is not a substrate for the O-alkyl cleavage enzyme in living cells. The aim of their study was to follow the fate of OM-G3PC in living cells using a radiolabelled (H-3) compound.

The ether lipid 1-0-Octadecyl-2-methoxy-rac-glycero-3-phospho-(methyl-H-3)-choline was incubated at sub-lethal doses (2.5 µg/ml) with Raji cells.

Cell growth and cell viability are decreased after longer incubation times with the lipid, leading to about 35 % cell death after 72 hrs. Lipid extracts of the cells were examined for presence of metabolites of the ether lipid. Besides the presence of the original compound, only 1,2-diacyl-sn-glycero-3-phospho-(methyl-H-3)-choline was formed during incubation (Fig. 6). No relation between cell death and amount of incorporated radiolabel could be detected.
However, a direct correlation was found between the amount of diacyl-phospho-(methyl-H-3)-choline formed and cell death. The authors therefore conclude that 1-0-Octadecyl-2-methoxy-rac-glycero-3-phosphocholine itself is not harmful for the cells. However, one of its metabolites, most likely 1-0-Octadecyl-2-methoxy-glycerol, causes cell death.

In summary, the result of this communication shows for the first time a possible pathway for the degradation of OM-G3PC, leading to the formation of a powerful cell toxin. This indicated that OM-G3PC is actually the precursor of the real toxin. This toxin is formed from OM-G3PC in the lipid bilayer by the action of an enzyme with substrate properties similar to phospholipase C.

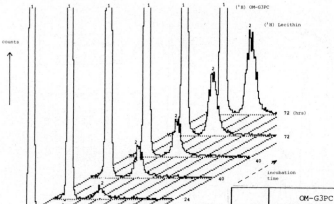

| | OM–G3PC incorp./$10^6$ cells | lecithin formed/$10^6$ cells |
|---|---|---|
| 24 hrs | 150 ± 10 nCi 810 ± 50 pmol | 3.1 ± 0.1 nCi 16.8 ± 0.5 pmol |
| 40 hrs | 140 ± 10 nCi 760 ± 50 pmol | 6.4 ± 0.6 nCi 35.0 ± 3 pmol |
| 72 hrs | 140 ± 20 nCi 760 ± 100 pmol | 11.1 ± 0.9 nCi 60 ± 5 pmol |

Fig. 6: Formation of radiolabelled lecithin (peak 2) in Raji cells incubated with (H–3) OM–G3PC (peak 1). The formation of lecithin is linear over at least 3 days of incubation and it indicates the simultaneous generation of 1-0-Octadecyl-2-methoxy-glycerol.

## 2. Determination of the radiochemical purity of radiopharmaceuticals

As described earlier different measuring methods to examine the purity of radiopharmaceuticals have been investigated by Hammermaier et. al. (8). The Linear Analyzer was found to be a very suitable instrument to detect the impurities. The same group investigated the radiochemical purity and stability of I-131/I-125/ I-123 ortho-iodohippuric acids (9).

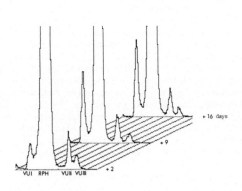

Fig. 7: Decomposition with time of I-131 ortho-iodohippuric acid (RPH) into iodide (VUI), ortho-iodobenzoic acid (VUII) and an unknown impurity (VUIII), measured with Linear Analyzer.

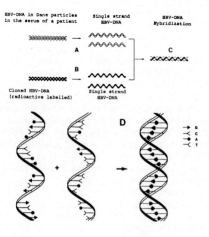

Fig. 8: Principle of detection of HBV-DNA in patient serum by DNA hybridization.

Some marketable I-131/I-125/I-123 o-iodohippuric acids were analyzed from March to June 1984 with regard to their radiochemical purity and stability. As method of analysis thin layer chromatography was chosen and as method of measurement a TLC Linear Analyzer was used (see Fig. 7).

At the same time the in vitro stability of the listed radiopharmaceuticals was taken into consideration. It turned out that the I-131 products are subject to a great decomposition. Fig. 7 shows the effect of decomposition with time of the products.

A comparison drawn from several HPLC-measuring methods showed that the selected method of thin layer chromatography led to a far better separation of the radiochemical impurities.

## 3. 32-P labelled DNA for Diagnosis of Hepatitis B-Virus

Hepatitis-B-Virus-DNA-Hybridization - an advance in the diagnosis of Hepatitis B (10,11): The determination of the hepatitis B virus DNA by means of hybridization with cloned HBV-DNA has resulted in a decisive improvement in the diagnosis of hepatitis B infections. Sophisticated techniques make possible the detection of HBV-DNA in ranges corresponding to the infectious dose, and in which HBs-Ag is no longer detectable with radio-immunological methods. The principle is shown in Fig. 8.

Double helix HBV-DNA from circulating Dane particles is dissociated and bound to nitrocellulose filter (A). In coli-E bacteria cloned HBV-DNA is marked with 32-P and also dissociated in single strands (B). At the hybridization the complementary DNA sequences of the unlabelled and the 32-P labelled DNA associate (C). The very specific detection of HBV-DNA is guaranteed by the association of only complementary bases (D).

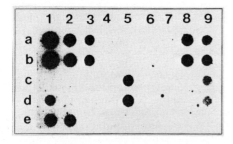

Fig. 9: Autoradiography of 32-P labelled HBV-DNA bound on nitrocellulose

a, b, 1 - 5:  standard with 30, 10, 3, 1, 0.1 pg HBV-DNA
a, b, 6, 7:  negative controls
a, b, 8, 9:  positive controls of HBe-Ag and HBs-Ag
c, d, e, 1 - 9: serum of patients

The lower limit with autoradiography of 20 hrs is about 0.1 pg HBV-DNA, corresponding to 3000 Dane particles. The Linear Analyzer is at least 1000 times more sensitive (see Fig. 10).

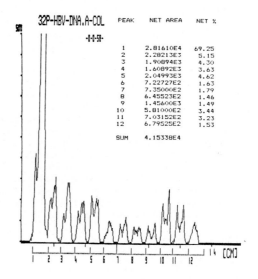

| PEAK | NET AREA | NET % |
|------|----------|-------|
| 1 | 2.81610E4 | 69.25 |
| 2 | 2.28213E3 | 5.15 |
| 3 | 1.90894E3 | 4.30 |
| 4 | 1.60892E3 | 3.63 |
| 5 | 2.04993E3 | 4.62 |
| 6 | 7.22727E2 | 1.63 |
| 7 | 7.35000E2 | 1.79 |
| 8 | 6.45523E2 | 1.46 |
| 9 | 1.45600E3 | 1.49 |
| 10 | 5.81000E2 | 3.44 |
| 11 | 7.03152E2 | 3.23 |
| 12 | 6.79525E2 | 1.53 |
| SUM | 4.15338E4 | |

Fig. 10: Detection of bound 32-P labelled DNA with the Linear Analyzer, 1 minute measuring time. The detection limit is here 1000 times lower than with autoradiography.

472

The bound radioactive labelled DNA can be detected on the nitrocellulose filter by autoradiography (Fig. 9) and/or by the Linear Analyzer (Fig. 10). With
the Linear Analyzer a very sensitive and quantitative result can be obtained in
a few minutes compared to a day exposure time with the autoradiography, which is
not quantitative. The 32-P label of the DNA could be replaced by a 3-H label
using as detector the Linear Analyzer.

REFERENCES

1  Armison, G., et. al. (UA 1 collaboration), Phys. Lett. 122 B, 1983, p. 103;
   Phys. Lett. 126 B, 1983, p. 398.
2  Filthuth, H., Linear Analyzer improves Detection in Radio-TLC Tests, Indust.
   Res. & Dev., June 1981.
3  Filthuth, H., State of the Art in Scanning TLC. Detection of Radiochromatograms and Electropherograms with position sensitive wire chambers, Synthesis
   and Applications of Isotopically Labeled Compounds, Proceedings of an International Symposium, Kansas City, 6-11 June, 1982, W.P. Duncan and A.B. Susan
   (Eds.), Elsevier Publishing Company, Amsterdam, 1983, pp. 447-452.
4  Filthuth, H., Radioscanning of TLC, Advances in Thin Layer Chromatography,
   ch. 7, J.C. Touchstone (Ed.), John Wiley & Sons, New York, 1982.
5  Filthuth, H., New Methods in Analyzing Radiochromatograms and Electropherograms, Techniques and Applications of Thin Layer Chromatography, ch. 10, J.C.
   Touchstone (Ed.), John Wiley & Sons, New Yorck, 1985.
6  Filthuth, H., Detection of Radio-Chromatograms and Electropherograms with position sensitive wire chambers, Analytical and Chromatographic Techniques in
   Radiopharmaceutical Chemistry, ch. 4, D.H. Wieland, T.J. Mangner, M. Tobes
   (Eds.), Springer Verlag, New Yorck, 1985.
7  Fleer, E.A.M., Kim, D.-J., Unger, C., and Eibl, H., Metabolism of
   1-0-Octadecyl-2-methoxy-rac-glycero-3-phosphocholine in Raji cells, Max Planck
   Institut für Biophysikalische Chemie, preprint 1985, to be published in
   Chemistry and Physics of Lipids.
8  Hammermaier, A., Reich, E., Bögl, W., IHS-Report 36, February 1984, Institut
   für Strahlenhygiene des Bundesgesundheitsamtes, Neuherberg/München.
9  Hammermaier, A., Reich, E., Bögl, W., IHS-Report 48, August 1984, Institut
   für Strahlenhygiene des Bundesgesundheitsamtes, Neuherberg/München.
10 Seelig, R., Metzger, B., Spohr, U., Metzger, P., Renz, M. and Seelig, H.P.,
   Hepatitis-B-Virus-DNS-Hybridisierung--ein Fortschritt in der Diagnostik der
   Hepatitis B, Privates Institut für Immunologie und experimentelle Pathologie
   GmbH, Karlsruhe, Klinikarzt, Heft 2/85, Verlag Straube, Erlangen, 1985.
11 Berninger, M., Hammer, M., Hoyer, B., and Gerin, J.L., An Assay for the Detection of the DNA Genome of Hepatitis B Virus in Serum, Journal of Medical
   Virology, Sept. 1982, pp. 57-68.
12 Jamet, P. and Thoisy, J.-Ch., Evaluation et Comparaison de la Mobilité de
   différents Pesticides par Chromatographie sur Couche Mince de Sol, Service
   de Chimie des Pesticides, Département de Phytopharmacie et d'Ecotoxiologie
   I.N.R.A., Versailles, preprint 1985.

ACKNOWLEDGEMENT

We would like to thank very much Prof. H. Eibl, Dr. E. Fleer, Prof. R. Seelig,
Dr. B. Metzger, Dr. A. Hammermaier, Dr. P. Jamet and Dr. J.-Ch. Thoisy for the
permission to publish their experiments in our paper.

*Synthesis and Applications of Isotopically Labeled Compounds 1985.*
Proceedings of the Second International Symposium, Kansas City, MO, U.S.A.,
3—6 September 1985, R.R. Muccino (Ed.), 473—478
© 1986 Elsevier Science Publishers B.V., Amsterdam — Printed in The Netherlands

1-O-OCTADECYL-2-O-METHYL-rac-GLYCERO-3-PHOSPHO [$^3$H-methyl] CHOLINE:
CHEMICAL PREPARATION AND METABOLISM IN LEUKEMIC RAJI CELLS

E.A.M. FLEER[1], D-J. KIM[1], C. UNGER[2], and H. EIBL[1]

[1]Max Planck Institut für Biophysikalische Chemie, Abt. Membranbiophysik (14)
Am Fassberg, Postfach 2841, D3400 Göttingen, West Germany.

[2]University of Göttingen, Dept. of Internal Medicine, Division of Haematology/
Oncology, Robert Koch Str. 40, D3400 Göttingen, West Germany.

ABSTRACT

The ether lipid 1-O-octadecyl-2-O-methyl-rac-glycero-3-phospho [$^3$H-methyl]-
choline (OM-G3PC) was prepared from the corresponding phosphatidylethanolamine,
using [$^3$H]methyliodide as methylation agent. The overall yield was 30%, based
on [$^3$H] methyliodide, with an about 2.5 times increase in specific radioactivity.
The radiolabeled OM-G3PC was then used in metabolic studies of ether lipids
in Raji cells. The main result of this investigation was the observation that
the labeled phosphocholine group was transfered from OM-G3PC to diacylglycerol
which results in the formation of phosphatidylcholine and 1-O-octadecyl-2-O-me-
thyl-rac-glycerol. This is a new observation, which shows that a phospholipase
C-like enzyme can catalyze the transfer of the intact phosphocholine group
from OM-G3PC to diacylglycerol.

INTRODUCTION

The compound 1-O-octadecyl-2-O-methyl-rac-glycero-3-phosphocholine (OM-G3PC)
(ET18OCH3 in the earlier literature) is among the most studied alkyl lysophospho-
lipids (ref. 1-11). It has been reported to be an efficient inhibitor of
neoplastic cell growth in vitro (ref. 2-6) and in vivo (ref. 7,8). It is
suggested that its property of cell growth inhibition is due to its stability:
because of its resistance to phospholipases it is accumulated in the cell
membrane with fatal consequences. Normal cells are supposed to be more resistant to OM-G3PC than neoplastic cells, due to the presence of the so-called
cleavage enzyme. Neoplastic cells have none - or only low levels - of this
enzyme. The enzyme supposedly cleaves off the long fatty alcohol from the
ether lipid, destroying the lytic properties of the lipid to the bilayer.

However, in earlier studies of the cleavage enzyme we (10) and others (11)
have shown that the cleavage enzyme is not able to degrade OM-G3PC in in vitro

experiments. Therefore, the above explanation for a difference in toxicity
of OM-G3PC to neoplastic cells is doubtful . To search for a valid explanation
of the cytotoxic effects of OM-G3PC we have performed metabolic studies with
radiolabeled OM-G3PC.

MATERIALS AND METHODS

1-O-Octadecyl-2-O-methyl-rac-glycero-3-phosphoethanolamine was prepared in our
laboratory (ref. 12,13). [3H]methyliodide was from NEN (Boston,Mass.,USA).
Dimethylsulphate, silicagel, and silicagel TLC-plates were from Merck (Darmstadt
FRG). Other chemicals were of the highest purity available and used without
further purification.

Raji cells (B-lymphoblastic lymphome) were grown in RPMI 1640 medium
(GIBCO), supplemented with 10% Fetal Calf Serum (Biochrom). Streptomycin
(128 mg/l),indomethacin (0.5 mg/ml), and penicillin ($10^5$ IE/ml) were routinely
added to the culture medium.

Synthesis of 1-O-octadecyl-2-O-methyl-rac-glycero-3-phospho [3H-methyl] choline

1-O-Octadecyl-2-O-methyl-rac-glycero-3-phosphoethanolamine (OM-G3PE) (50 mg,
0.1 mmol.) was brought in a stoppered (10 ml) reagent tube. [3H] methyliodide
(25 mCi, 37.5 mg, 0.26 mmol.) in a breakseal tube was dissolved in 0.5 ml
chloroform/methanol (1/1, v/v) and transfered to the reagent tube containing
OM-G3PE. The tube was washed four times with 0.5 ml chloroform/methanol to
ensure quantitative transfer of the methyliodide to the reagent tube. Subsequently 1.5 ml saturated potassium carbonate in water was added to the reaction
mixture and the mixture was kept at $40^{\circ}$C under vigorous stirring for about
20 hours. Then 0.5 ml dimethyl sulphate was added (630 mg, 5 mmol.)and the
mixture stirred for another six hours. The reaction mixture was then extracted
three times with chloroform, the chloroform fractions were combined and dried
on a rotation evaporator. The residue was dissolved in chloroform/methanol/wa-
ter (60/40/4, by vol.) and brought on a small silicagel column. The column
was eluted with the same solvent to remove apolar byproducts, then with
chloroform/methanol/water (35/35/10, by vol.) to collect the[3H]OM-G3PC.
The combined fractions were dried, dissolved in chloroform and brought on a
preparative TLC-plate. The plate was developed in chloroform/methanol/water
containing 2.5% NH3 (60/40/4, by vol.). The band corresponding to OM-G3PC
was scraped off and the OM-G3PC was eluted with chloroform/methanol/water
(35/35/10, by vol.). The yield was 18 mg OM-G3PC (30%) with a specific radioactivity of  220 mCi/mmol., based on [3H] counting in a Searle Mark III Analytic counter and phosphorous determination according to Eibl and Lands (16).

Incubation of Raji cells with OM-G3PC.

Raji cells (10 ml, $2.10^5$ cells/ml) were incubated with 2.5 ug OM-G3PC/ml
(220 mCi/mmol.). After 24, 48, or 72 hours of incubation, aliquots of the cell
suspension were counted in a Neubauer cell counting chamber and tested for
viability with the trypan blue dye exclusion test (ref. 14). The cell suspension was then diluted with 10 ml serum free medium  and the cells were centrifuged at 800 g for 10 minutes at room temperature. The supernatant was
collected and the pellet washed twice with 10 ml serum free medium. Of the
combined supernatants (40 ml) 100 ul aliquots were taken for $^3$H counting.
The cell pellet was extracted twice according to Bligh and Dyer (ref. 15).
The extracts were combined and 2.5 ml water and 2.5 ml chloroform were added
for phase separation. The chloroform layer (lower phase) was collected and
the water phase was reextracted with 5 ml chloroform. After phase separation
aliquots of the upper phase (water/methanol) were taken for $^3$H counting.
The chloroform phases were combined, dried under a stream of nitrogen, and
the residue was dissolved in chloroform/methanol (9/1 v/v). After taking
aliquots for $^3$H counting, the remainder was brought on a TLC-plate and the
plate was developed in chloroform/methanol/acetic acid/water (100/60/20/5,
by vol.). The plate was then dried and scanned for $^3$H activity in an Automatic
Linear Analyzer LB 284 complemented with Data System LB 500 (Berthold, Wildbad,
FRG). For comparison with reference spots of unlabeled OM-G3PC and phosphatidylcholine, the plates were stained in iodine vapor.

RESULTS AND DISCUSSION

Preparation of OM-G3PC

The overall yield of OM-G3PC was 30%, based on $[^3$H]methyliodide. The
specific radioactivity of the product was increased 2.5 times, from about
90 mCi/mmol. to 220 mCi/mmol. This fits the fact, that 0.1 mmol. OM-G3PC
was methylated by using 0.26 mmol. methyliodide. The total yield of 30% was,
however, rather low. Side products were detected on analytical TLC-plates
after the 20 hours reaction. Also, a sizeable amount of OM-G-phospho-(N-methyl
and N,N-dimethyl)-ethanolamines was formed. The amount of byproducts was
reduced by the addition of dimethylsulphate. It seems, that an equilibrium
exists between the phosphoethanolamines differing in the degree of N-methylation,
an equilibrium that seems to be dependent on the amount of methyliodide
present. In pilot experiments with unlabeled methyliodide it was found that
a large excess of methyliodide (to about 30 fold) was needed to convert the
phosphoethanolamine completely to phosphocholine. Raising the temperature
increased the yield. Another possible factor influencing completion of the

N-methylation could be the presence of enough base to keep the phosphoethanolamine deprotonated. We used a saturated solution of potassium carbonate
in water to neutralize the hydroiodic acid generated during the reaction.
It is possible that use of another base could result in higher yields with
less sideproducts.

Incubation of Raji cells with OM-G3PC.

The Raji cells were incubated with radiolabeled OM-G3PC and after Bligh
and Dyer extraction the extracted lipids were analyzed on TLC-plates. It was
found that only a fixed amount of radiolabel was incorporated in the Raji cells
(150 nCi/$10^6$ cells). Of course most of the radiolabel incorporated in the
cells was due to the presence of the OM-G3PC added. However, with time a second
radiolabeled lipid fraction could be detected, coinciding with the band of
normal lecithin (Fig. 1). When this second lipid product was scraped off

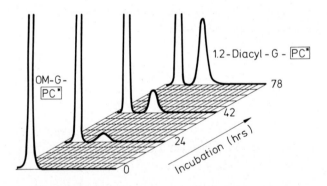

Fig. 1. Formation of radiolabeled lecithin in Raji cells incubated with
[$^3$H]OM-G3PC. Conditions of the incubation are described in the text.

and hydrolyzed with potassium tert. butylate in methanol, it was found that
more than 90% of the radiolabel in this fraction was watersoluble, indicating
that the radiolabel was (1.2 diacyl)-phosphatidylcholine which does not
contain  alkylether groups. Therefore it is concluded that an exchange reaction

takes place between the introduced synthetic radiolipid and lipids from the cell membranes. Most likely, phosphocholine is tranfered from OM-G3PC to diacylglycerol. This is the first time that such an exchange reaction is observed. Another type of transfer, the transfer of phosphocholine from sphingomyelin to diacylglycerol, has been described by Voelker and Kennedy (ref. 17). Simultaneously with the production of radiolabeled lecithin, the Raji cells showed a loss of viability in the trypan blue exclusion test. A direct correlation (corr. coeff. 0.904) was established between cell death and (1.2-diacyl)-lecithin formation, but not between uptake of OM-G3PC and cell death. Since lecithin is a normal compound in the cell membrane, its formation can not be toxic to the cells. Another compound formed during the production of lecithin could be the phosphatidic acid analog from OM-G3PC, 1-O-octadecyl-2-O-methyl-rac-glycero-3-phosphate. This compound is expected to have similar physical properties as compared to OM-G3PC and is therefore believed not to be toxic to the cells. Most likely, phospho-choline is transfered as a unit from OM-G3PC to (1.2-diacyl)-glycerol, generating 1-O-octadecyl-2-O-methyl-rac-glycerol (OM-G) and (1.2-diacyl)-phosphatidylcholine. It is our opinion that OM-G or metabolites thereoff are responsible for the death of the incubated Raji cells. Since no radiolabel was detected in the water/methanol phase of the Bligh and Dyer extract, it is unlikely that the phosphocholine group is first hydrolyzed from OM-G3PC and is then build in in the (1.2-diacyl)-glycerol. It is therefore concluded, that the radiolabeled phosphocholine found in the lecithin fraction is the result of a direct transfer reaction.

REFERENCES

1   Berdel, W. E., Greiner, E., Fink, U., Stavrou, D., Reichert, A., Rastetter, J., Hoffmann, D. R., and Snyder, F., Cancer Res. 43, (1983), pp 541-545.
2   Berdel, W. E., Schick, H. D., Fink, U., Reichert, A., Ulm, K., and Rastetter, J., Cancer Res. 45, (1985), pp 1206-1213.
3   Tidwell, T., Guzmann, G., and Vogler, W.R., Blood 57, (1981), pp 794-797.
4   Heffman, D.M., Barnes, K.C., Kinkade jr., J.M., Vogler, W.R., Shoji, M., and Kuo, J.F., Cancer Res. 43, (1983), pp 2955-2961.
5   Berdel, W.E., Greiner, E., Fink, U., Zänker, K.S., Stavrou, D., Trappe, A., Fahlbusch, R., Reichelt, A., and Rastetter, J., Oncology 41, (1984) pp 140-145.
6   Storme, G.A., Berdel, W.E., van Blitterswijk, W.J., Bruyneel, E.A., De Bruyne, G.K., and Mareel, M.M., Cancer Res. 45, (1985), pp 351-357.

7   Munder, P.G., Modolell, M., Bausert, W., Oettgen, H.F., and Westphal, O.,
    in: Augmenting Agents in Cancer Therapy, E. M. Hersch, M. A. Chirgos
    and M. J. Mastrangelo (Eds.), Raven Press, New York, (1981), pp 441-458.

8   Berdel, W.E., Blut 44, (1982), pp 71-78.

9   Soodsma, J. F., Piantadosi, C., and Snyder, F., J. Biol. Chem. 247,
    (1972), pp 3923-3929.

10  Unger, C., Eibl, H., von Heyden, H.-W., and Nagel, G. A.,
    Cancer Res. 45, (1985), pp 616-618.

11  Lee, T. C., Blank, M. L., Fitzgerald, V., and Snyder, F.,
    Arch. Biochem. Biophys. 208, (1981), pp 353-357.

12  Eibl, H., Angew.  Chemie 23, (1984), pp 257-271.

13  Eibl, H. and Westphal, O., Liebigs Ann. Chem. 709, (1967), pp 231-233.

14  Hudson, L. and Hay, F. C., Practical Immunology, Blackwell Scientific
    Publications, England, (1976), pp 29-32.

15  Bligh, E. G. and Dyer, W. J., Canad. J. Biochem. Physiol. 37, (1959),
    pp 911-917.

16  Eibl, H. and Lands, W. E. M., Anal. Biochem. 30, (1969), pp 51-57.

17  Voelker, D. R. and Kennedy, E., Methods in Enzymol. 98, (1983), pp 596-598.

*Synthesis and Applications of Isotopically Labeled Compounds 1985.*
Proceedings of the Second International Symposium, Kansas City, MO, U.S.A.,
3—6 September 1985, R.R. Muccino (Ed.), 479—484
© 1986 Elsevier Science Publishers B.V., Amsterdam — Printed in The Netherlands

# DEVELOPMENT OF THE RADIO-GLC AND RADIO-HPLC EQUIPPED WITH A SYNCHRONIZED ACCUMULATING RADIOISOTOPE DETECTOR

S. BABA

TOKYO COLLEGE OF PHARMACY

## ABSTRACT

We have developed a novel detector, synchronized accumulating radioisotope detector (SARD) for radio-GLC and radio-HPLC, which can improve the detecting efficiency without sacrificing chromatographic resolution. SARD is composed of counting tubes, switching units and accumulation counters. The working principle is that the detection signals of a small fragment in a sample are accumulated into the same accumulation counter by means of the switching unit. By this detector, radiochromatography can be used more successfully in terms of quantitative analysis. Application examples to the drug metabolism study are presented.

## INTRODUCTION

GLC and HPLC are the most frequently used methods for the separation of chemical compounds. In detecting radioactivity of radioactive substances flowing through (GLC or HPLC) or alongside (TLC) a radioisotope detector, a single counting tube has been commonly used. However, the use of a single counting tube does not permit a simultaneous improvement in both the detecting efficiency for the radioactivity and the resolving power. This paper describes a novel detector, synchronized accumulating radioisotope detector (SARD) for GLC (ref.1) and HPLC (ref.2) which can improve the detecting efficiency without sacrificing chromatographic resolution.

## WORKING PRINCIPLE OF SARD

The principle and the block diagram of SARD (n=3) applied to GLC are shown in Figs. 1 and 2, respectively. Gaseous radioactive components pass through the counting tubes $C_1$, $C_2$ and $C_3$ in times t=0 – $\underline{a}$, $\underline{a}$ – $2\underline{a}$ and $2\underline{a}$ – $3\underline{a}$, where $\underline{a}$ is defined as sampling time and equal to the volume of the counting tube divided by the flow-rate of the gas. These counting tubes have equal inner volumes and are connected longitudinally. The radioactivity signals of the first portion detected by $C_1$, $C_2$ and $C_3$ during the above time intervals are accumulated in the accumulation counter $A_1$ by the switching unit $B_1$. The accumulated counts are then sent to a recorder and recorded as the radioactivity of fraction 1. The same procedure is followed for the next portion entering the detector

480

assembly, the counts being accumulated in $A_3$, and recorded as the radioactivity of fraction 2. Each switching unit has one output terminal and three input terminals 1 – 3. The connection between the output terminal and one of the input terminals is electronically controlled according to a time interval based on the flow-rate of the radioactive substance. One of the advantages of the present method is that it is not necessary to ensure uniformity in the counting efficiency and background counts of each counting tube, since all portions of the gas are treated equally by all the counting tubes.

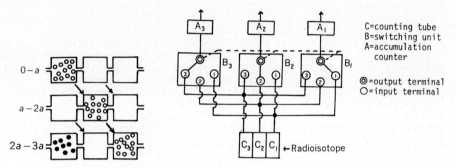

Fig. 1. Principle of SARD(n=3).     Fig. 2. Block diagram of SARD.

EXPERIMENTALS

Radio-GLC system

A schematic diagram of the radio-GLC system is given in Fig. 3. The column eluate is separated into two routes in an appropriate proportion. One route leads to FID. The other route leads to an oxidation-reduction furnace in which $^{14}C$- or $^{3}H$-labeled compounds in the gas stream are decomposed to produce $^{14}CO_2$ or $^{3}H_2$. After mixed with methane as a counting gas, the radioactive gas passes through the five counting tubes (an effective volume of 30 ml each), which are connected to each other by an anti-coincidence circuit and arranged as shown in Fig. 4. The radioactivity signals detected by each individual tube are accumulated in the manner as mentioned above. For comparing between the conventional and the present method, the first counting tube was used not only as a part of SARD but also as an independent conventional detector. With the exception of resolution experiments, all data were obtained by closing the route leading to FID. Unless otherwise stated, the operating conditions were as follows. The flow rates of carrier gas (nitrogen) and counting gas are 50 and 250 ml/min, respectively. Measurements were performed with a full scale of 1000 cpm at a time constant of 10 sec for the conventional method, and with a full scale of 300 counts per sampling time for the present method.

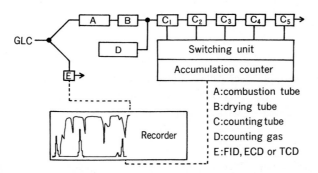

Fig. 3. Radio-GLC system equipped with SARD (n=5).

Radio-HPLC system

The column eluate (0.5 ml/min) is monitored by UV detector and then mixed
with a liquid scintillator [DPO: 4g, POPOP: 400mg dissolved in 1 liter of a
mixture of dioxane, toluene and cellosolve(15:3:2 v/v), 7.5 ml/min] and passed
through the five counting cells (an effective volume of 1.1 ml each) set
between a pair of photoelectron multiplier tubes.

RESULTS AND DISCUSSIONS

SARD was successfully applied to thin-layer chromatography at first (ref.3).
The usefulness of SARD as a detector for radio-GLC is largely dependent on how
much peak broadening occurs due to the prolonged residence time of the
radioactive substance in the multiple counting tubes placed in series. Another
problem is that an electron avalanche caused by the disintegration of a
radioactive nuclear within one counting tube might spread to the adjoining
counting tubes to give false counts.

The simultaneous measurement of the radioactivity emerging from GLC column
by operating the first and fifth counting tubes clarified that the multiplying
counting tubes did not result in an appreciable peak broadening. Fig. 5 shows
the radio-gas chromatograms obtained simultaneously by three operation modes.
The chromatogram A was obtained by using the first counting tube of SARD. B was
obtained by the five counting tubes without synchronized accumulating. C was
obtained by SARD. The comparison of these chromatograms demonstrates most
clearly the advantages of SARD. The peak width of C is comparable to that of A.
On the other hand, the integral intensity of C is fairly equal to that of B and
five times that of A. The reproducibility of the integral intensities of C is
much improved in comparison with that of A as shown in Table 1. These
experimental results suggest that the synchronized accumulation in SARD is
works exactly as theoretically predicted and the "infection" of electron
avalanche does not occur. The application of an anti-coincidence method to SARD
could reduce the background counts by about 50% as shown in Fig. 6. The

482

counting loss which might be caused by this device was proved to be negligible. The performance of the radio-GLC was examined by using [3H] and [14C]hexadecane. When the detection limit for SARD was defined as three times of S.D. of the total counts of three successive background fractions, it was approximately 15 pCi for 14C. The resolution time was 20 sec. The counting efficiencies for 14C and 3H were 95 and 56%, respectively.

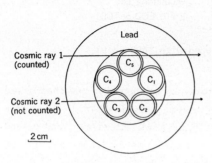

Fig. 4. Arrangement of counting tubes.

TABLE 1

Reproducibility of integral intensity ($cm^2$, n=10, from Fig. 5).

|  | Conventional (A) | (B) | SARD (C) |
|---|---|---|---|
| Detector volume (ml) | 30 | 150 | 30×5 |
| Mean | 0.65 | 3.33 | 3.48 |
| S.D. | 0.070 | 0.165 | 0.135 |
| C.V. | 10.8 | 5.0 | 3.9 |

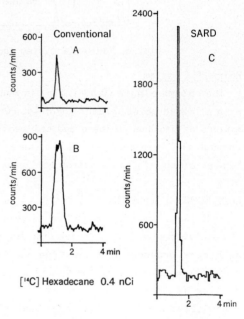

[14C] Hexadecane 0.4 nCi

Fig. 5. Effectiveness of SARD applied to radio-GLC.

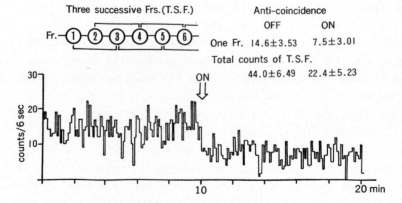

Three successive Frs.(T.S.F.)

Anti-coincidence

|  | OFF | ON |
|---|---|---|
| One Fr. | 14.6±3.53 | 7.5±3.01 |
| Total counts of T.S.F. | 44.0±6.49 | 22.4±5.23 |

Fig. 6. Effect of mutual anti-coincidence on background counts.

The measurement of the radioactivity in HPLC eluate has generally been performed by counting the radioactivity in each fraction of the eluate with a liquid scintillation counter, namely the off-line batch counting method. However, a continuous counting method has been available for 10 years (ref.4,5). This method is classified into two types. One is homogeneous counting in which the eluate is mixed with a liquid scintillator and the resulting solution is continuously passed through the counting cell set between a pair of photoelectron multiplier tubes. The other is heterogeneous counting in which the eluate is passed through a cell containing a solid scintillator. In this type, however, the counting efficiency was low and an appreciable peak broadening occurred by the multiplying counting cells. For these reasons, we studied mainly the homogeneous method. The use of multiple counting cells for radio-HPLC might result in a peak broadening, since liquid suffers from back diffusion more extensively than gas. The comparison of the chromatograms obtained by using simultaneously the first and fifth counting cells of SARD clarified that the peak broadening occurred to only a minor extent. This proved the applicability of SARD to HPLC. The performance of the radio-HPLC system equipped with SARD was examined by using [$^{14}$C] or [$^{3}$H]adenine. The counting efficiencies for $^{14}$C and $^{3}$H were 95 and 35%, respectively. The detection limit was estimated to be 45 pCi for $^{14}$C. The resolution time was approximately 45 sec. It may still be possible to improve the detection limit and the resolution time.

## APPLICATIONS OF THE RADIO-GLC AND RADIO-HPLC SYSTEMS EQUIPPED WITH SARD

These systems have two advantages. One is the improvement in the detecting efficiency without sacrificing chromatographic resolution. The other is to provide the radioactivity information in the digital form. The radio-GLC can be applied as follows; 1) searching radioisotopically labeled metabolites prior to the identification of metabolites by GLC-MS, 2) the estimation of GLC peak yield (ref.6), and 3) the quantitation of metabolites derived from a radioisotopically labeled drug (ref.1). One example of application will be mentioned. Fig. 7 shows the simultaneously recorded gaschromatograms of urinary metabolites of [$^{14}$C]suprofen administered rat. When FID was used as a detector, we found eight peaks. Only three of them, marked with stars, corresponded to metabolites of the drug in question(ref.7). It should be pointed out that peak 2 could be clearly identified as a metabolite by SARD. This peak might be ignored by FID. The radio-GLC makes it possible to exclude GLC peaks unrelated to the metabolites in question. This is advantageous for knowing in advance the behavior of a stable isotope tracer in GLC.

The rdio-HPLC system provides a useful tool for metabolism studies. In this case, the catch-up of metabolites is almost quantitative, although the

484

resolution is inferior to the GLC. This radio-HPLC system can be applied as follows. Radioisotopically labeled metabolites are easily identified among larger amounts of endogenous substances. This system can be used as a metabolic pattern analyzer. Time courses of plasma levels of each metabolite may be clarified without sacrificing such small experimental animals as rats(ref.8). An example of the radio-HPLC applied to the clarification of the metabolic pattern of a drug is shown in Fig. 8. Satisfactory results were obtained with a relatively small amount of radioactivity (3.8 nCi) and without such tedious procedures as fractionation followed by liquid scintillation counting.

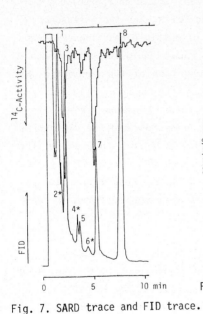

Fig. 7. SARD trace and FID trace.

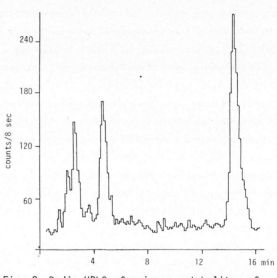

Fig. 8. Radio-HPLC of urinary metabolites of [$^{14}$C]suprofen administered guinea pig.

REFERENCES

1 S. Baba and Y. Kasuya, J. Chromatogr., 196 (1980) 144-149.
2 S. Baba, M. Horie and K. Watanabe, J. Chromatogr., 244 (1982) 57-64.
3 S. Baba, Y. Kasuya, M. Takeda and N. Tokunaga, J. Chromatogr., 168 (1979) 49-58.
4 M. J. Kessler, J. Chromatogr., 255 (1983) 209-217.
5 R. F. Roberts and M. J. Fields, J. Chromatogr., 342 (1985) 25-33.
6 S. Baba, K. Akira, M. Horie and Y. Mori, J. Chromatogr., 341 (1985) 251-259.
7 Y. Mori et al, Drug Metabolism and Disposition, 12 (1984) 767-771.
8 S. Baba, Y. Shinohara, H. Sano, T. Inoue, A. Masuda and M. Kurono, J. Chromatogr., 305 (1984) 119-126.

*Synthesis and Applications of Isotopically Labeled Compounds 1985.*
Proceedings of the Second International Symposium, Kansas City, MO, U.S.A.,
3—6 September 1985, R.R. Muccino (Ed.), 485—490
© 1986 Elsevier Science Publishers B.V., Amsterdam — Printed in The Netherlands

THE PRESENT STATUS OF MEDICAL APPLICATIONS OF STABLE ISOTOPES IN CHINA

ZONG-QIN XIA

Shanghai Second Medical College, 280 South Chong-gin Road, Shanghai, China

ABSTRACT
    Medical applications of stable isotopes in China are currently mainly
carried out in Beijing and Shanghai.   Efforts have been made to synthesize
tracers from homemade $^2$H or $^{15}$N precursors or imported $^{13}$C precursors.  A few
sets of gas isotope ratio MS and GC-MS systems are available in both cities.  A
micro-scale emission spectrometric method was established for $^{15}$N abundance.  A
clinical investigation has proved that $^{13}$C-methacetin breath test is valuable in
estimating the severity of hepatic malfunction.  Some other $^{13}$C breath tests are
being studied.   $^{15}$N-Glycine has been used in measuring total body protein
synthesis and breakdown of uremic patients and prematures.  A multiple tracer
method has been established for studying simultaneously the tracer kinetics of
aromatic and branched chain amino acids in hepatic failure and some other
diseases.

INTRODUCTION

    The medical applications of stable isotopes in China were started in the
late 1970's, and are up to now mainly carried out in several laboratories in
Beijing and Shanghai.  The emphasis is put on clinical research works according
to the requirements of clinical practice.

SOURCES OF LABELED COMPOUNDS

    Regarding the sources of stable nuclides, $^{15}$N and deuterium (D) are mainly
provided domestically.  A chemical exchange method (NO-HNO$_3$) for the enrichment
of $^{15}$N was established in the early 1970's by the Shanghai Research Institute of
Chemical Industry (1).   Various high abundance $^{15}$N inorganic compounds are
currently supplied by the Institute, and are used in several laboratories for
the synthesis of $^{15}$N-labeled organic compounds.  The Institute itself can also
provide some $^{15}$N-labeled organic compounds such as urea, glycine, L-glutamic
acid, L-tryptophan etc.  The raw materials of deuterium-labeled compounds are
mainly heavy water and deuterium gas.  The Beijing Chemical Engineering Factory
started the preparation of deuterium NMR reagents in 1973 (2).  Now, 16 such
reagents are being supplied commercially, and may be used as intermediates for
the synthesis of deuterium-labeled organic compounds.  As for the $^{13}$C-labeled
compounds, imported Ba$^{13}$CO$_2$ or $^{13}$C intermediates are the chief sources, although

the Shanghai Research Institute of Chemical Industry has recently established a technique for producing small amounts of high abundance $Ba^{13}CO_3$ (3).


MEASUREMENT OF STABLE ISOTOPES IN MEDICAL SAMPLES

For the measurement of stable isotopes in medical samples three methods have been adopted. One is the emission spectrometry for the analysis of $^{15}N$ samples. In addition to the ordinary scale method, a micro-scale method ($CaO-Al_2O_3$) has been developed by the Shanghai Research Institute of Chemical Industry (4). For $^{15}N$ amino acids, only 0.5 ml of plasma is required for one sample, the amount of nitrogen may be as low as 4-8 μg. The second method is the analysis of $^{15}N$ gas, $^{13}CO_2$ or $^2H$ gas with the gas isotope ratio mass spectrometer. The domestic equipment may be used for measuring $^{15}N$ with a precision of 0.02-0.05%, but $^{13}CO_2$ and $^2H$ are mainly measured with the MAT 251 system. The third method is to measure the isotope abundance directly in organic molecules with the GC-MS system. Techniques have been established in both Beijing and Shanghai, including some computer programs based on Biemann's method or its modification for the calculation of the abundance (5-8). In addition, proton NMR (9) and $^{13}C$ NMR (10) have also been used for the analysis of abundance or labeled position, but mainly for high abundance samples.


APPLICATION IN CLINICAL RESEARCH WORKS

Several clinical research works that have been or are being carried out in China are as follows:

The breath test for chronic hepatic malfunction

It is well known that among the commonly used laboratory examinations, there is no satisfactory index for the quantitative estimation of chronic hepatic malfunction. It is by this reason that the aminopyrine breath test has attracted the interest of many gastroenterologists. In 1979, Schneider et al. suggested that labeled methacetin might be better than aminopyrine. In our laboratory methacetin labeled with $^{13}C$ at the methoxy carbon (abundance: 90.25%; purity: 99%) was synthesized from $^{13}CH_3I$ (11), and the validity of this compound has been examined in 17 normal volunteers and 54 patients with non-alcoholic chronic liver damage (12-14). After an oral dose of 1.5 mg/kg, the exhaled $CO_2$ was collected with a liquid nitrogen trap at various intervals, and the $^{13}CO_2$ was measured with MAT 251 to give the δ value. The time-course curve revealed that the δ value reached a lower peak and declined slower in patients than in normal subjects. The more severe the disease the greater the difference. Various parameters were obtained from the time course curve. When judged by the percentage of overlap between normal and diseased, the Ω value appears to be better than the other parameters commonly used. The difference of this index between CAH and CPH, or between compensated and decompensated cirrhosis is statistically significant. No difference of the absorption rate constant between various groups was observed. Therefore, it was concluded that, the methacetin breath test was a safe, rapid, and convenient test for liver function, and the $\Omega$ value was recommended for clinical use.

Breath test for pancreatic insufficiency

There have been several reports in literature, that breath test with fatty acids labeled with $^{14}C$ or $^{13}C$ at the carboxyl carbon could be used for the examination of fat mal-absorption. In order to distinguish pancreatic fat mal-absorption from that due to other disease, a dual-labeled breath test has been established by Capital Nuclear Medicine Center (15). A single dose of $1-^{13}C$-palmitic acid and $1-^{14}C$-triolein was given to each patient and excretions of $^{13}CO_2$ and $^{14}CO_2$ were monitored. It was found that in patients with intestinal mucosal disease the excretion of both labeled $CO_2$'s were delayed, indicating a mal-absorption of free fatty acids. On the contrary, in patients with chronic pancreatitis only a delay of $^{14}CO_2$ excretion was observed, this may be explained by the fact that the pancreatic lipase is mainly related to the hydrolysis of triglycerides, but not the absorption of free fatty acids. This work is right now being continued. It seems to be a promising technique for the diagnosis of pancreatic insufficiency.

The use of $^{15}N$-glycine in the study of total body protein synthesis and breakdown rate in chronic renal failure

Clinical practice has proved that dialysis therapy is effective on the intoxication syndrome of chronic renal failure patients. However, it is ineffective on and may even be harmful to the disturbance of protein metabolism in such patients, and the patients often died of nutritional exhaustion. Therefore much attention has been paid to the nutritional therapy for chronic renal failure in recent years. Various prescriptions of amino acid mixtures have been designed in China. Their validity has been tested by three laboratories in Beijing and Shanghai, using $^{15}N$-glycine to study the total body protein synthesis and breakdown rate before and after treatment.

$^{15}N$-glycine was first synthesized in Capital Nuclear Medicine Center (16) and later in Shanghai Institute of Chemical Reagents (17).

All the three laboratories adopted the Picou-Taylor Roberts model, but their detailed experimental methods were different from each other. In Capital Nuclear Medicine Center, a single dose of $^{15}N$-glycine was injected intravenously, and the 48 hours cummulative urine excretion of total $^{15}N$ measured. An increase of the ratio of synthesis rate to breakdown rate was observed (18). In Shanghai Xin-Hua Hospital, repeated oral doses of $^{15}N$-glycine were given at a rate of 0.05 mg N/kg/3 hrs for 60 hours, and $^{15}N$-

plateau in the urine urea measured. By this method, both the synthesis rate and the breakdown rate of total body protein were found to be increased after a prescription of amino acid mixture. An increase of the utilization of amino acids in protein synthesis was also reported (19).

Shanghai Second Medical College and Shanghai Ren-Ji Hospital also found that both the synthesis rate and breakdown rate were increased by amino acid treatment. In this work [15]N-glycine was given orally at a rate of 0.9 mg N/kg/hr for 8 hours, and [15]N plateau in plasma total amino acids was determined (20).

It is apparent from the above results that important information can be obtained from stable isotope tracer experiments. However, since the excretion of NPN is usually impaired in renal failure patients, the optimal experimental method and metabolic model remains to be further studied.

The use of [15]N-glycine in the study of total body protein synthesis and breakdown of neonatals

Family planning has been carried out in China for years. In general, there is only one child for a couple. As a result, the health care of infants is becoming more and more important. A study of the total body protein metabolism of neonatals was therefore carried out in Shanghai Xia-Hua Hospital (1,22). The method of Waterlow was followed. A single dose of [15]N-glycine was given to each infant, the [15]N in urine ammonia was determined and the metabolic parameters were calculated again according to the Picou-Taylor Roberts model. The authors claimed that for neonatals the cummulative excretion of ammonia [15]N in 6 hours was most suitable for the calculation. Although the N balance was positive in all groups, the synthesis rate was much more rapid in small size mature neonatals and premature neonatals when compared with normal size neonatals. If there was malnutrition in premature neonatals because of inadequate feeding, the synthesis rate became slower. The authors concluded that more protein intake was necessary for small size and premature neonatals; but in case the premature neonatals were suffering from malnutrition, the increase of intake should be gradual.

The use of [13]C-leucine breath test for the study of total body protein synthesis and breakdown in severe burn

Negative nitrogen balance may happen in severe burn patients after the shock stage and may lead to death if not corrected. Estimation of the total body protein synthesis rate and breakdown rate is therefore required as a guide of nutritional treatment. Since large amounts of N compounds may be lost from the injured surface, the ordinary [15]N-amino acid method, although applicable, is not very suitable for such patients. Hence the [13]C-leucine breath test was established and its validity in severe burn was tested by a cooperative group in Shanghai (23).

1-$^{13}$C-DL-leucine was synthesized from K$^{13}$CN which in turn was prepared from Ba$^{13}$CO$_3$ by the Shanghai Institute of Chemical Reagents (24). It was then subjected to enzyme resolution to yield 1-$^{13}$C-L-leucine. The $^{13}$C abundance of the final product was 85% with a purity of 98%.

Each human subject was given a priming intravenous injection of NaH$^{13}$CO$_2$ together with 1-$^{13}$C-L-leucine followed by infusion of the labeled leucine for 4-6 hours, the infusion rate being 2.4 μmol/kg/hr.

The $^{13}$CO$_2$ abundance in exhaled air was measured with MAT 251 while the $^{13}$C abundance in plasma leucine was measured with a Finnigan GC-MS system, using 227/228 fragment of the TFA derivative which retained the carboxyl carbon. The plateau of either $^{13}$CO$_2$ in exhaled air or $^{13}$C-leucine in plasma appeared in about 2-3 hours, hence the experiment could be finished in 4-6 hours. A dual-labeled experiment revealed that the amino acid flux (Q), the synthesis rate (S), and the breakdown rate (C) obtained from $^{15}$N-glycine and $^{13}$C-leucine were consistent with each other. The results from rabbit experiment showed that Q, S, and C were all significantly higher in burned than in normal rabbits and the increase of breakdown is more prominent than the increase of synthesis.

A multiple tracer technique for the study of the metabolic kinetics of amino acids in severe hepatic failure

Recent clinical investigation has proved that the proportion of various amino acids in plasma may be changed in certain important diseases such as uremia, hepatic failure, burn, etc. Thus, there may be an increase of aromatic amino acids with or without a decrease of branched amino acids in plasma during hepatic failure. In order to study the mechanism of such an imbalance, a method for studying simultaneously the metabolic kinetics of several amino acids has been established by a research group in Shanghai. $^{15}$N-L-alanine, (α,β-$^2$H)-L-leucine, and (α,β-$^2$H)-L-phenylalanine were chosen as the representatives of non-essential, branched, and aromatic amino acids, respectively. The deuterated amino acids were prepared by a catalytic exchange method modified from Master and Richards (25). The abundance and purity of $^2$H-leucine were 96% and 99%, respectively, while those of $^2$H-phenylalanine were 98% and 99%, respectively. $^{15}$N-L-alanine was prepared at the Shanghai Institute of Industrial Microbiology by a biosynthesis process using two immobilized bacteria. Its abundance and purity were 96% and 98% (26).

To each subject a single dose of 40 mg $^{15}$N-alanine, 20 mg $^2$H-leucine, and 20 mg $^2$H-phenylalanine was injected intravenously. Using the Finnigan GC-MS system, the three amino acids in plasma were isolated and their abundances measured. From the time course of abundance, the kinetic parameters were calculated according to a two pool model modified from Jones and Kopple. Since the α-D was found to be unstable in vivo, a mathematical method has been used to resolve the $\alpha,\beta$-D abundance and only $\beta$-D abundance was used for the calculations of kinetic parameters. The preliminary results from 5 normal volunteers and 5 patients showed that the turnover rate constant of phenylalanine in pool A (plasma-related pool) was significantly smaller in hepatic failure than in normal (27). This phenomenon is in accordance with the elevation of phenylalanine content in plasma and may be explained by the fact that phenylalanine is mainly catabolized in hepatic cells. No significant change was observed in the turnover rate constants of the other two amino acids.

This work is still in progress. The authors claimed that the combined use of GC-MS technique and multiple tracers labeled with stable isotopes is of great potential.

In short, the medical applications of stable isotopes in China are still in the early stage. It is expected that, as a result of the progress of science and technology, the cost of stable isotope-labeled compounds and the measuring equipment will become cheaper in the coming years and the international scientific communications in this field will become more popular. We strongly believe, along with these changes, that the medical applications of stable isotopes in China will be developed more rapidly in the near future.

REFERENCES
1  Shanghai Research Institute of Chemical Industry,  The Third National Symposium on Stable Isotopes, Beijing, No. 7, (1983).
2  DZ. Qin, J. Stable Isotopes, 3 (1983) 25.
3  KH. Yang et al., J. Chemical Industry, 2 (1984) 112.
4  CM. Lu et al., The Third National Symposium on Stable Isotopes, Beijing, No. 11 (1983).
5  X. Zhang and RQ. Ding, J. Stable Isotopes, 1 (1981) 54.
6  YE. Hu et al., J. Stable Isotopes, 4 (1983) 17.
7  J. Jiang et al., Nuclear Electronics and Detection Technology, 4 (1984) 19.
8  TC. Dai et al., J. Stable Isotopes, 4 (1983) 35.
9  X. Zhang and RQ. Ding, J. Stable Isotopes, 3 (1983) 6.
10  YZ. Zhou and YP. Shi, J. Stable Isotopes, 4 (1984) 43.
11  YE. Hu et al., J. Stable Isotopes, 3 (1983) 20.
12  TC. Dai et al., J. Stable Isotopes, 3 (1983) 1.
13  YY. Qiu et al., Chinese J. Nuclear Med., 4 (3) (1984) 129.
14  ZQ. Xia et al., Nuclear Techniques, 3 (1985) 1.
15  XM. Zhu and SC. Wang, personal communication, (1985).
16  SC. Wang et al., Chinese J. Nuclear Med., 3 (4), (1983) 224.
17  YL. Zhang et al., J. Stable Isotopes, 1 (1983) 38.
18  J. Jiang et al., personal communication, (1985).
19  JN. Zuo et al., personal communication, (1985).
20  ST. Cheng et al., Chinese J. Nuclear Med., 5 (3) (1985) 149.
21  QC. Wu et al., J. Clin. Pediatrics, 1 (2) (1983) 65.
22  SM. Wu et al., personal communication, (1985).
23  WD. Zhou et al., to be published.
24  YX. Huo et al., J. Stable Isotopes, 4 (1984) 24.
25  TC. Dai et al., to be published.
26  GY. Huang et al., J. Stable Isotopes, 2 (1984) 1.
27  TC. Dai et al., to be published.

*Synthesis and Applications of Isotopically Labeled Compounds 1985.*
Proceedings of the Second International Symposium, Kansas City, MO, U.S.A.,
3—6 September 1985, R.R. Muccino (Ed.), 491—496
© 1986 Elsevier Science Publishers B.V., Amsterdam — Printed in The Netherlands

491

PROBLEMS WITH HIGH SPECIFIC ACTIVITY CARBON - 14 SYNTHESIS

D G Parker  —   Imperial Chemical Industries PLC
                Advanced Material Business Group
                P O Box No 90 Wilton Centre
                Middlesbrough
                Cleveland UK TS6 8JE

ABSTRACT

A frequent problem encountered in radiosynthesis is that the yield
obtained in cold or traced runs are not reproducible in the hot synthesis.
This paper highlights some of these problems during Carbon-14 Synthesis of
polymerisable monomers and reactions capable of reacting by two separate
mechanistic pathways, one of which is promoted by an internal radical source.

The effect of radiolysis on stored labelled compounds is well known and

documented (ref 1). Usually the most damaging effect is caused by secondary

decomposition, which results from the interaction of substrate (labelled

compound) with free radicals (or other excited species) produced by the

radiation. Secondary decomposition rates vary enormously and depend on, for

example, dispersion medium, susceptibility of substrate to radical attack,

chemical stability of subtrate, etc. The problem of radiolysis has usually

been approached in terms of the stability of radiolabelled compounds during

storage. The problem of what effect radiolysis has on the course of a chemical

reaction has been largely neglected.

A class of compounds which are obvious candidates for radical induced

'decomposition' are polymerisable monomers eg, vinyls, acrylates, styrene etc.

A notable example taken from our own experience of this problem is the

synthesis of [$^{14}$C] methylacrylate. We set out to prepare [$^{14}$C] methylacrylate

(50mCi, 10mCi/mmole) using classical Reppe chemistry (ref 2) <u>viz.</u>

$$CH \equiv CH \xrightarrow[\text{Ni(CO)}_4 \quad \text{HCl}]{\text{CH}_3\text{OH}} CH_2 = CHCOOCH_3$$

The reaction proved successful and the crude product was purified by

preparative glc. On standing in a sealed ampoule for 2 days the total sample

polymerised. On repeating the reaction, we observed polymerisation occurring

almost as soon as the methylacrylate had been prepared. The methacrylate was

used immediately for the next stage of synthesis. The intermediate formed was

stable and the overall radiochemical synthesis successfully completed.

Some examples of other polymerisable monomers which we have prepared with a $^{14}C$ label are shown in table 1. Problems with polymerisation occurred in almost all cases.

TABLE 1    POLYMERISABLE MATERIALS

| | |
|---|---|
| CH≡CH | $CH_2=CHCONH_2$ |
| $CH_2=CHCl$ | $CH_2=CHCO_2CH_3$ (CH₃ branch) |
| $CH_2=CHOCOCH_3$ | ⬡ $CH=CH_2$ |

In order to attempt to predict the inherent stability of some of the above monomers, we calculated anticipated rates of polymerisation (Rp) using the expression (ref 3).

$$Rp = \frac{K_p M \ (3.7 \times 10^{10} EG \ C)^{0.5}}{K_t^{\frac{1}{2}} \quad N} \quad (moles \ 1 \ sec)$$

where C is activity Ci/mole

    M is monomer concentration mole/l

    E is decomposition energy of $^{14}C$ (eV)

    G is g value molecules/100 eV

    N is Avogadros Number ($6.032 \times 10^{23}$)

    $k_p$ is propagation rate constant (1 mole$^{-1}$ sec$^{-1}$)

    $k_t$ is termination rate constant (1 mole$^{-1}$ sec$^{-1}$)

Data is available on a number of monomers, and we have calculated the time to 10% polymerisation, for these materials (Table 2). A specific activity of 10 Ci/mole has been used for each example.

TABLE 2 TIME TO 10% POLYMERISATION FOR [14C] MONOMERS

Fraction converted in t sec is $tR_p/M = Q$

Thus if T is time to 10% conversion we have

$$T = \frac{0.1 \ M}{R_p}$$

M = 1000 $\rho$ /$m_w$ where $\rho$ = density (g/ml), and $m_w$ = molecular weight

| MONOMER | G | TEMP | $c$ | $k_p$ | $k_t$ | $m_w$ | $10^5 R_p$ | T |
|---|---|---|---|---|---|---|---|---|
| Methyl Methacrylate | 5.5 | 25 | 0.938 | $2.1 \times 10^2$ | $1.5 \times 10^7$ | 100 | 6.1 | 4.3hrs |
| Methyl Methacrylate | 5.5 | 60 | 0.897 | 630 | $5 \times 10^7$ | 100 | 9.3 | 2.7hrs |
| Methyl Acrylate | 2.97 | 25 | 0.953 | 1580 | $5.5 \times 10^6$ | 86 | 22.5 | 1.4hrs |
| Vinyl Acetate | 1.4 | 25 | 0.932 | 1000 | $6.5 \times 10^6$ | 86 | 8.7 | 3.5hrs |
| Tetrafluorothylene Liquid | 2.97 | 50 | 1.52 | 9100 | 87 | 100 | $1.7 \times 10^5$ | 0.9hrs |
| TFE gas | 2.97 | 50 | 0.0045 | 9100 | 87 | 100 | 27 | 17sec |

[14C] Monomers at even modest specific activities are inherently unstable.

The problem of polymerisation is not restricted to the obvious polymerisable monomers mentioned above. An example where the 'monomer' was formed during reaction/storage is seen in a preparation of 3-Chloropropionyl chloride scheme (ref 4).

Shortly after it had been produced by reaction of thionylchloride on 3-chloropropionic acid (4) it was reacted further in the course of a synthesis of an ICI development compound. Little of the desired product was formed in the reaction. Much of the activity was found to be non-volatile under vacuum, and there was mass spectroscopic evidence that at least one of the isolated by-products (not found in the cold reaction) contained an acrylate function. These observations may be rationalised as shown in scheme 1 ie, elimination of HCl to give acroylchloride (2) which reacts further, thus forcing the equilibrium to the right.

The elimination reaction may well be catalysed by residual acid from the thionyl chloride reaction and/or from hydrolysis of (5) by impurity water. It should be noted that [14C] 3-chloropropionic acid itself is stable for reasonable periods of storage.

**SCHEME 1**

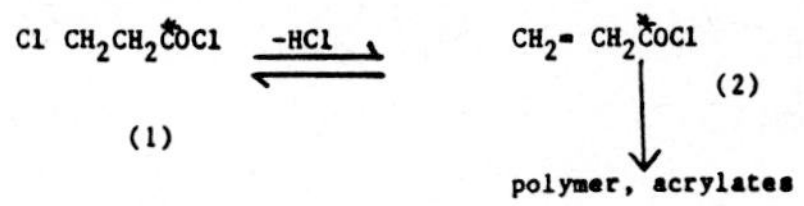

Cl CH₂CH₂COCl  —HCl→  CH₂= CH₂COCl (2)

(1)

polymer, acrylates

Competitive reductive elimination also proved problematical in the synthesis of an ICI herbicidal compound. A key step in the total radiolabelled synthesis is the copper catalysed reaction of trifluoromethyl iodide with 4-iodochlorobenzene (3) to yield 4-trifluoromethylchlorobenzene (4). In cold reactions reproducible yields of 90% were obtained. However, when (3) at 50 mCi/mmole was reacted the yield of (4) was reduced to 40%, the main product being chlorobenzene (ref 5).

|  | 90 | Trace |
|---|---|---|
| Cold |  |  |
| Hot (50mCi/mmole) 40 |  | 50 |

The realisation that [$^{14}$C] induced free radical side reactions might be affecting some hot synthesises prompted the hypothesis that;

"If a chemical reaction can procede by two or more pathways and one of these pathways involves the participation of free radicals, then the ratio of products formed by the differing pathways for the cold reaction may be altered in favour of the free radical route for a high specific activity hot run"(ref 6).

A catastrophic examples of a hot synthesis not following the course of its cold analogue was experienced in the course of an ICI pyrethriod synthesis. The route chosen involved a Claisen rearrangement reaction (5) $\longrightarrow$ (6) $\longrightarrow$ (7), which had been well characterised in a cold synthesis.

With [$^{14}$C] labelled (6), however, a much reduced yield of the desired (7) was obtained, the major reaction product being [2$^{14}$C] ethylacetate (ref 7). This may arise via an ene reaction

No rational explanation for this observation is offered although difficulties with Claisen rearrangement reactions of [$^{14}$C] labelled materials has been previously reported (ref 8).

As a final example of a hot reaction failing to yield the desired results obtained in its cold analogue, the following sequence was observed in a synthesis of [U-ring $^{14}$C] anthranilic acid. For this synthesis, we required [U-ring $^{14}$C] 2-bromoaniline at 40 mCi/mmole. We chose to synthesise this material via reaction of aniline with N-bromosuccinimide. Good yields of the desired o-isomer were obtained when the reaction was tested 'cold'. Unfortunately, when [U $^{14}$C] aniline was reacted the isomer ratio almost reversed viz (ref9).

SYNTHESIS OF 2-BROMOANILINE

| | | |
|---|---|---|
| cold | 30 | 6 |
| hot (40mCi/mmole) | 4 | 20 |

496

We did not investigate the reasons for this reversal, instead we prepared anthranilic acid by an alternative route. It is known that NBS can react _via_ a free radical or electrophilic pathway depending on reaction conditions (10) and it is interesting to speculate whether in this case the change in selectivity is due to the influence of $[^{14}C]$.

CONCLUSION

We have highlighted some of the problem syntheses experienced by ICI's labelled compounds team at the Billingham laboratories. We describe many instances of reactions where we have been unable to reproduce the yields found in pilot 'cold' studies in the 'hot' analogue, some disasterously so. Often the reason for failure is a mystery, however, we feel that sufficient evidence is presented to demonstrate that free radical pathways initiated by $^{14}C$ decay offers a plausible explanation.

REFERENCES
1. E A Evans Self - Decomposition of Radiochemicals
   Review 16 Amersham International PLC
2. W Reppe et al Ann., 1953, 582, 1
3. Communication from R A Jackson ICI
   Petrochemicals and Plastics Division, Wilton
4. H Schmid and A Schmid, Helv. Chim. Acta., 1952 35, 1879
5. D G Parker and D C Greenslade Unpublished results
6. D G Parker ICI Labelled Compounds Symposium, University of York,
   September 1983
7. D G Parker and S Gardner Unpublished results
8. E A Evans RCS Radiochemical Methods Group Symposism University of York,
   September 1980
9. D G Parker and P Hannah Unpublished results
10. D H Hey and W A Waters Chapt 11, Rodds 'Chemistry of Carbon Compounds'
    Ed S Coffey Elsevier 1964

*Synthesis and Applications of Isotopically Labeled Compounds 1985.*
Proceedings of the Second International Symposium, Kansas City, MO, U.S.A.,
3—6 September 1985, R.R. Muccino (Ed.), 497—500
© 1986 Elsevier Science Publishers B.V., Amsterdam — Printed in The Netherlands

# MECHANISTIC STUDIES OF CATALYTIC HYDROGENATION: GAS TRITIATION AND DEUTERATION OF 2-ACETAMIDOACRYLIC ACID AND ALPHA-ACETAMIDOCINNAMIC ACID

Y. S. TANG, H. MORIMOTO, S. UN and H. RAPOPORT

National Tritium Labeling Facility, Lawrence Berkeley Laboratory, Berkeley, CA.

## ABSTRACT

The difference of labeling in heterogeneous catalytic gas tritiations of 2-acetamidocinnamic acid and 2-acetamidoacrylic acid is demonstrated by $^3H$ NMR spectroscopy. The nonequivalent addition of tritium to the double bond of 2-acetamidoacrylic acid is due to simultaneous hydrogen-tritium exchange during adsorption on the catalyst surface. A new mechanistic interpretation has been proposed to explain the behavior of this substrate. These conclusions were substantiated by mass spectrometry results obtained using $D_2$ and deuterated solvents. Steric effects on vinylic exchange studied by GLRC were also reported.

## INTRODUCTION

The major products of heterogeneous hydrogenation of a double bond will depend on the effects of the concomittant hydrogenation, isomerization and exchange reactions, whichever predominates (ref. 1). Quite often, these unexpected products have greatly restricted the use of hydrogenation in organic synthesis. Thus, a rational approach to the design and modification of the hydrogenation reaction, must rest ultimately upon a detailed understanding of the heterogeneous catalytic mechanism.

## RESULTS

Reduction of 2-acetamidocinnamic acid using 5% Pd/BaSO$_4$ and carrier free tritium gas in redistilled THF affords N-acetyl [2,3-$^3H$] phenylalanine with specific activity of 60 Ci/mmol. Proton decoupled 287 MHz tritium NMR spectrum of the product (see fig. 1) showed two triton signals at δ3.2 (methylene) and δ4.6 (methine) with relative intensities of 54% and 46% distribution.

In great contrast to the above results, the proton decoupled tritium NMR spectrum of the reduction of 2-acetamidoacrylic acid showed that (see fig. 2) 95% of the tritium is incorporated at the δ1.36 (methyl) and only 5% at the δ4.35 (methine). Specific activity of the product was 85 Ci/mmol, the theoretical maximum for the complete addition of three tritium atoms. The enlarged spectrum of the methyl peak (see fig. 3) revealed multiple signals caused by the primary isotope effects $CT_3$- ($\delta 1.33$), $CT_2H$- ($\delta 1.35$), $CTH_2$- ($\delta 1.37$) and by triton-triton coupling $CT_3$-CT ($\delta 1.28$, $\delta 1.35$). If only 10% tritium in hydrogen were used, the probability of two tritons across the double bond would be very low (1%), as would be the highly tritiated $CT_3$-specie. The tritium NMR studies of such a reaction product (see fig. 4) showed the absence of the $\delta 1.28$ signal and a markedly reduced $CT_3$-methyl specie.

This extremely disparate addition of tritium across the double bond is the result of a vinylic exchange process (ref.2). When the substrate was deliberately under-reduced, the reduced N-acetyl $[2,3-^3H]$ alanine (as in fig. 2) and two additional signals at $\delta 5.90$ (cis- to N-acetyl moiety) and $\delta 6.32$ (trans-) appeared in the tritium NMR spectrum (see fig. 5.)

These studies suggested that two distingishable hydrogenation mechanisms may apply to the terminal vinylic substrate and to the aromatic substituted methine precursors. A primary alkyl intermediate adsorbed on the catalyst surface prior to the tritium-hydrogen exchanged mechanism is believed to occur in the hydrogenation (tritiation) of 2-acetamidoacrylic acid, while a $\pi$-alkyl complex formation-reduction mechanism is applied to the hydrogenation of $\alpha$-acetamidocinnamic acid.

Although the vinylic exchange mechanism may be the reason for the unevenly labeled N-acetyl $[2,3-^3H]$ alanine, there is still no satisfactory explanation with regard to the source of hydrogen at the methine position. Despite the efforts to exclude hydrogen on the catalysts by prereduction and exhaustively drying and pumping, the ratio between the $\alpha$- and $\beta$- positions remained unchanged. When a higher substrate: catalyst ratio (10:1) was used, the $\alpha$-methine peak also increased to 12% (see fig. 6). In addition, the specific activity of this reaction product is also higher ($\sim 96$ Ci/mmol).

These conclusions were further supported by the studies using deuterated solvent with predried glassware and catalyst. When using three fold weight of catalyst over substrate (see table 1.A) the mass spectroscopy studies of molecular ion peak of N-acetyl-alanine revealed that some (i.e. 10%) of the product has no deuterium incorporated. When the amount of catalyst used was reduced 30 fold (see table 1.E), the ratio of hydrogenated product decreased markedly and highly deuterated compounds were obtained. Similar results also occured with to 2-acetamidocinnamic acid (see table 2). A high degree of isotope incorporations also resulted when the catalyst was prereduced with deuterium gas prior to the reduction (see table 1.D and 2.C). The ratios of deuterium incorporations between different heterogeneous catalysts were also studied (see table 2.D, E, F), and 30% Pd/C was found to be most effective.

Work has been carried out to compare some structurally related styrenes, under the same tritiation conditions, towards vinylic exchanged reaction. Using a capillary gas-liquid-chromatography equipped with heat proportion counter, the ratios of reduction and exchanged products were measured (see table 3). These results showed that by introducing an aromatic system the amount of exchanged product was markedly decreased. And while 1,1-diphenylethylene has 22% exchanged product under this condition, there was only reduced product found in the case of trans-stilbene.

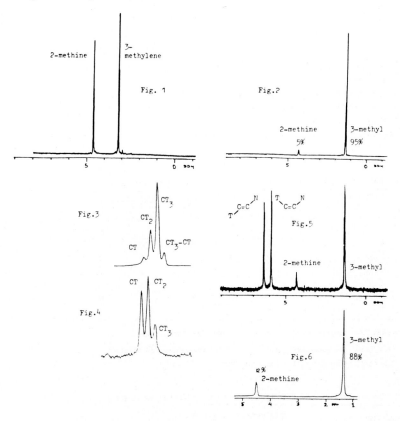

Figure 1-6 Tritium NMR spectra (with proton decoupled)

Fig.1. N-acetyl[2,3-³H]phenylalanine

Fig.2. N-acetyl[2,3-³H]alanine

Fig.3. Expanded 3-methyl peak of fig.2.

Fig.4. Expanded 3-methyl peak using 10%tritium

Fig 5. Partially reduced products of 2-acetamidoacrylic acid

Fig.6. N-acetyl[2,3-³H]alanine using catalyst:substrate ratio 1:10

REFERENCES:

1. S. J. Thompson and G. Webb, J. Chem. Soc., Chem. Comm., 5, (1976) 526 .
2. J. A. Elvidge, J. R. Jones, R. M. Lenk, Y. S. Tang, E. A. Evans,
   G. L. Guilford and D. C. Warrell, J. Chem. Research (S), (1982) 82.

TABLE 1

Mass spectroscopy results for the deuteration of 2-acetamidoacrylic acid

| conditions | Possible Structures/Relative % | | | | |
|---|---|---|---|---|---|
| | H H<br>H-C-C-NHCOCH₃<br>H CO₂H | D<br>-C-C- | D<br>D-C-C | D<br>D-C-C<br>D | D D<br>D-C-C<br>D |
| A | 10 | 25 | 35 | 25 | 5 |
| B | 3 | 10 | 20 | 35 | 32 |
| C | 2 | 5 | 19 | 34 | 37 |
| D | - | 5 | 13 | 42 | 40 |
| E | 2 | 8 | 22 | 35 | 33 |
| F | 16 | 22 | 23 | 22 | 17 |

5%Pd/BaSO₄ : Substrate    3:1 ,    99.98% d₈THF , 2 Hrs.

B : 100% d₄-MeOD

C : Pre-reduced 5%Pd/BaSO₄ in solution

D : Pre-reduced 5%Pd/BaSO₄ in dry form

E : 5%Pd/BaSO₄ : Substrate    1:10

F : 5%Pd/BaSO₄ : Substrate    1:10, in distilled THF


TABLE 2

Mass spectroscopy results for the deuteration of 2-acetamidocinnamic acid

| conditions | Possible Structures/Relative % | | | |
|---|---|---|---|---|
| | H H<br>Ph-C-C-NHCOCH₃<br>H CO₂H | D(D)<br>Ph-C-C- | D D<br>Ph-C-C- | D D<br>Ph-C-C-<br>D |
| A | 26 | 34 | 30 | 10 |
| B | 9 | 31 | 52 | 8 |
| C | 3 | 42 | 52 | 3 |
| D | 6 | 37 | 46 | 11 |
| E | 5 | 32 | 49 | 14 |
| F | 29 | 33 | 30 | 8 |

5%Pd/BaSO₄  : Substrate    3:1 ,    99.998% CDCl₃, 2Hrs.

B : 5%Pd/BaSO₄  : Substrate    1:10    C  :  Pre-reduced in solution

D : 30% Pd/C, ratio 3:1 , E : Raney Ni, D₂O    F : PtO₂

TABLE 3

Ratios of vinylic exchanged and reduction products as studied by radio-glc

| SUBSTRATES | %EXCHANGED | %REDUCED |
|---|---|---|
| ⬡-= | 42 | 58 |
| ⬡=′ | 25 (CH₃) | 75 |
| ⬡>- | 40 (CTH, CTH₂) | 60 |
| ⬡ (bicyclic) | 22 | 78 |
| ⬡ ⬡ | 7 | 93 |
| ⬡ =⬡ | 0 | 100 |

*Synthesis and Applications of Isotopically Labeled Compounds 1985.*
Proceedings of the Second International Symposium, Kansas City, MO, U.S.A.,
3—6 September 1985, R.R. Muccino (Ed.), 501—504
© 1986 Elsevier Science Publishers B.V., Amsterdam — Printed in The Netherlands

ANTIBODY/GC/MS:  A NEW FIELD OF APPLICATION FOR NON-RADIOACTIVE
LABELED COMPOUNDS

W. Krause, U. Jakobs and P.E. Schulze
Research Laboratories of Schering AG, Müllerstr. 170 - 178,
1000 Berlin 65, W. Germany

ABSTRACT

A new analytical principle has been developed combining the
features of both radioimmunoassay and GC/MS. Its application has
been tested in three areas, in eicosanoid analysis with iloprost,
in tetrahydrocannabinol measurement and in steroid analysis. Details are given on the determination in plasma of estradiol.
Therefore, the antibody, generally employed in RIA measurements,
was coupled to Sepharose 4 B and used as stationary phase for
extraction of the analyte. Variations in recovery were corrected
by using a deuterated analogue as internal standard. The samples
then were derivatized and quantitated by negative-ion chemical
ionization-mass spectrometry. Both sensitivity and specificity of
the new method are superior to radioimmunoassay.

INTRODUCTION

At present, the most sensitive analytical methods are radio-

immunoassay and gas chromatography-mass spectrometry. However,

for RIA the most serious drawback is its lack in specificity and

for GC/MS the tedious clean-up procedures generally necessary.

Antibody/GC/MS combines the simplicity of radioimmunoassay with

the specifity of gas chromatography-mass spectrometry. The deter-

mination of iloprost, a stable prostacyclin analogue, and of

11-nor-Δ9-tetrahydrocannobinol-9-carboxylic acid have been des-

cribed earlier (1,2). The present study gives details on the mea-

surement of estradiol.

METHODS

Synthesis of deuterated estradiol

500 mg of 1.3.5-estratrien-3-ol-17-one was given under an

atmosphere of nitrogen to a solution of 2.43 g of anhydrous potas-

sium acetate in 65 ml carbitol-$D_1$ (diethyleneglycol-mono-ethyl-

ether). The mixture was stirred until all components had dissolved

and heated at 70°C for 24 h under protection from light.

45 ml $D_2O$ was added and the solution subsequently extracted
three times with 50 ml dry ethyl acetate. The combined ethyl acetate phases were washed twice with 50 ml $D_2O$, dried with sodium
sulphate and evaporated to 5 ml. The crystals obtained were
washed with cold $D_1$-methanol. The yield was 425 mg(I) with a melting point of 245/246.5 - 247°C.

203 mg of (I) was dissolved under nitrogen in a mixture of 10
ml $D_1$-methanol and 3 ml dichloromethane (purified by filtration
through an $Al_2O_3$ column). After the addition of 30.5 mg $D_4$-sodium
borohydride and standing for half an hour, the solution was concentrated to 5 ml. Recrystallization from methanol yielded 170 mg
of $D_n$-1.3.5-estratrien-3-ol-17ß-ol with the following composition:
$D_0$ : 1.5 %, $D_1$ : 5.3 %, $D_2$ : 23.4 %, $D_3$ : 54.8 %, $D_4$ : 15.8 %.
Structural confirmation was performed by NMR, MS, TLC, and HPLC.

## Antibody - mediated extraction

For extraction of estradiol from plasma, the antibody used in
RIA measurements was coupled to Sepharose 4B as has been described
in the literature (3). Before extraction, 100 - 500 pg of the
deuterated analogue is added to the samples as internal standard.
The analytical procedure underlying Antibody/GC/MS is summarized
in Fig. 1.

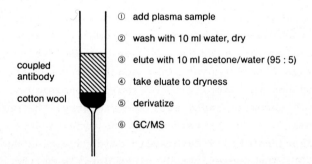

① add plasma sample

② wash with 10 ml water, dry

③ elute with 10 ml acetone/water (95 : 5)

④ take eluate to dryness

⑤ derivatize

⑥ GC/MS

coupled antibody

cotton wool

Fig. 1: Schematic representation of Antibody/GC/MS

## Gas chromatography - mass spectrometry

50 µl heptafluorobutyrylimidazol/xylol (1 : 2, v/v) is added
to the dry extracts. After heating at 80°C for 2 h, 300 µl octane/
dodecane (30 : 1, v/v) is added. Following mixing for 1 min and
cooling down to room temperature, the octane/dodecane phase is
taken to dryness and the residue is reconstituted in 10 µl xylol.
1 µl is used for GC/MS analysis.

The GC/MS system consisted of a Finnigan 4021 machine with a CP-Sil 5 CB fused silica capillary column (50 m, 0.20 mm ID, 0.11 μm; Chrompack). The carrier gas was helium at an inlet pressure of 24 PSI. Samples were injected by splitles injection at 280°C and the column was programmed from 180°C (4 min) to 300°C at 20°C/min. The retention time was 17 min. The operating conditions of the mass spectrometer were: ionizer temperature, 250°C; electron energy, 70 eV; electron multiplier, 1.5 kV; emission current, 0.2 μA and preamplifier, $10^{-8}$ A/V. Detection was performed in the negative-ion chemical-ionization mode with methane as reagent gas (3 $10^{-5}$ torr). Masses m/z 427 and 430 were registered in the MID mode.

RESULTS

In the present study a sensitive and specific method for the determination of estradiol in plasma is described. The recovery of antibody-mediated extraction was for all the compounds investigated so far more than 90 % (1,2,3) and seems to be a general feature of this method. The limit of detection was 5 pg per ml analyzed. Accordingly, with 20 ml, 0.25 pg/ml can be achieved.

In Fig. 2 a calibration curve is illustrated for the determination of estradiol. It was obtained by spiking water with known amounts of estradiol and the internal standard. When plasma was used, the lines were parallel with a y-intercept resulting from the endogenous amount of estradiol. In normal subjects without co-medication, the data obtained by Antibody/GC/MS were slightly lower than those found with RIA. In testolactone-treated volunteers, estradiol levels measured by Antibody/GC/MS were distinctly lower than those obtained by RIA due to a cross-reacting metabolite of testolactone which interfered in RIA but not in Antibody/ GC/MS (Table 1).

TABLE 1: Estradiol plasma levels in five healthy male volunteers before, during and after daily oral treatment with the aromatase inhibitor, testolactone 1 g

| Testolactone (1 g/d) (n = 5, males) | Estradiol (pg/ml) | |
| --- | --- | --- |
| | RIA | Antibody/GC/MS |
| pre-drug | 42 + 7 | 35 + 5 |
| 1 week treatment | 35 + 8 | 24 + 3 |
| 2 weeks treatment | 32 + 5 | 18 + 3 |
| recovery | 40 + 3 | 34 + 7 |

504

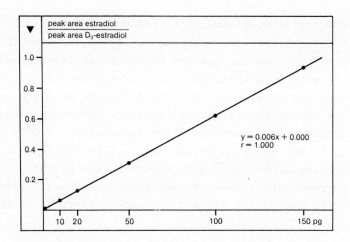

Fig. 2: Calibration curve for the determination of estradiol
obtained by spiking water with known amounts of estradiol
and $D_3$-estradiol

In summary, Antibody/GC/MS again has been demonstrated to be a
highly specific and sensitive analytical method. After iloprost
and 11-nor-$\Delta$9-THC-9-carboxylic acid this has now been shown for
the assay of estradiol in plasma.

REFERENCES
1   W. Krause, U. Jakobs, P.E. Schulze, B. Nieuweboer, and M.
    Hümpel, Prostagland. Leukotr. Med. 17 (1985), 167 - 182
2   U. Lemm, J. Tenczer, H. Baudisch, and W. Krause, J. Chroma-
    togr., in press
3   R.G. Glencross, S.A. Abeywardene, S.J. Corney, and H.S.
    Morris, J. Chromatogr. 223 (1981), 193 - 197

*Synthesis and Applications of Isotopically Labeled Compounds 1985.*
Proceedings of the Second International Symposium, Kansas City, MO, U.S.A.,
3—6 September 1985, R.R. Muccino (Ed.), 505—510

VISTAS OPENED BY FOURIER-TRANSFORM NMR IN THE AREA OF COMPOUNDS LABELED WITH
ISOTOPES OF HYDROGEN, CARBON, NITROGEN AND OXYGEN

ALEXANDRU T. BALABAN

Polytechnic Institute, Department of Organic Chemistry, Splaiul Independenţei
313, 76206 Bucharest, Roumania

ABSTRACT

Fourier-transform (FT) NMR techniques allow the detection and localization
of practically all nuclei with non-zero nuclear spin in natural abundance. In
conjunction with the synthesis of specifically labeled compounds, FT-NMR techniques provide the most convenient method for following the tracer atom(s) in
complicated molecules without any degradation.

INTRODUCTION

After the discovery of nuclear magnetic resonance (NMR), till the 1970's
NMR was actually synonymous with $^1$H-NMR but the development of FT-NMR (ref.1)
soon made it possible for average organic laboratories to acquire $^{13}$C-NMR
instruments (refs.2-5). The present-day multinuclear instruments use superconducting magnets with intense magnetic fields, various pulse sequences in the
FT mode, and multinuclear frequency generators, allowing the detection of
practically all stable or radioactive nuclides, provided that their concentration in the sample tube is high enough (refs.6-9). Another recent development is the non-invasive $^{31}$P-NMR, $^1$H-NMR and $^{13}$C-NMR imaging of living organisms for diagnosing physiological or biochemical disorders, including brain
tumors (ref.10). It is purpose of this review to highlight the interaction and
mutual stimulation between FT-NMR and isotopically labeled compounds. We shall
restrict the discussion to isotopes of H, C, N and O which are the main constituents of organic compounds. The last two elements have no medium- or long-
-lived radioisotope so that their stable isotopes have a relatively larger importance than in the case of C and H (ref.11), which have each a long $\beta$-emit-
ting radionuclide ; in addition, the short-lived $^{11}$C is rapidly becoming a
major asset in imaging by positron emission tomography.

NUCLEAR PARAMETERS

Table 1 presents the magnetic properties for nuclei of H, C, N and O which
have non-zero magnetic moments and hence give rise to NMR spectra. At the 1.1%
natural abundance of carbon-13, no C-C couplings complicate the C-NMR spectra,
and noise-decoupled C-NMR peaks extended over a range of about 650 ppm easily

distinguish each magnetically non-equivalent carbon atom of any molecule of reasonable complexity.

TABLE 1. Properties of H, C, N, O nuclides with non-zero nuclear spin.

| Nuclide | Spin | Shielding range (ppm) | Natural abundance (%) | Magnetic moment (nuclear magnetons) | NMR frequency for 2.35 T (MHz) | Relative sensitivity[a] | Electric quadrupole moment (barns)[b] |
|---------|------|------|--------|---------|--------|-------|---------|
| 1 H | 1/2 | 20 | 99.984 | +2.7928 | 100.00 | 62.89 | – |
| 2 H | 1 | 20 | 0.016 | +0.8574 | 15.35 | 0.604 | +0.002875 |
| 3 H | 1/2 | 20 | – | +2.9789 | 106.67 | 76.10 | – |
| 13 C | 1/2 | 650 | 1.11 | +0.7024 | 25.19 | 1.00 | – |
| 14 N | 1 | 1000 | 99.63 | +0.4038 | 7.22 | 0.06 | +0.0156 |
| 15 N | 1/2 | 1000 | 0.37 | –0.2832 | 10.13 | 0.06 | – |
| 17 O | 5/2 | 1500 | 0.037 | –1.8938 | 13.56 | 1.80 | –0.0258 |

[a] At constant field, assuming 100% abundance, with $^{13}$C as standard.
[b] 1 barn = $10^{-28}$ $m^2$

As a consequence of quadrupolar properties (non-spherical nuclear charge distribution) short relaxation times are obtained and broadened NMR lines result from Heisenberg's principle. Therefore the three quadrupolar nuclei of Table 1 raise more difficult problems than the other ones. In addition, deuterium has another drawback, namely its lower magnetogyric ratio than that of the proton (1/6.5=15.35 MHz/100 MHz as seen from Table 1) associated with a low chemical shift range, identical to that of protons. To achieve a spectral dispersion comparable to that of $^1$H-NMR spectra one has to use strong superconducting magnets. A further consequence is the reduction by the factor 1/6.5 of coupling constants between $^2$H and other nuclei. On the contrary, tritium has a slightly higher magnetogyric ratio than the proton, by a factor of 1.067 therefore $^3$H has highest relative sensitivity among all nuclides. Isotope effects are largest for hydrogen isotopes. Electronically, deuterium and tritium are more electron-releasing, and smaller than, protium. It was possible to dissect such isotope effects into electronic and steric components (ref.12).

NMR SPECTROSCOPY OF HYDROGEN ISOTOPES

From deuterium NMR spectra (ref.13), despite its handicaps, a lot of useful information was obtained with labeled compounds. A special usefulness of $^2$H-NMR resides in the shorter relaxation times of deuterons, due exclusively to intramolecular quadrupolar mechanisms, enabling molecular dynamics and orientations to be investigated (ref.14) by the inversion-recovery FT method using the $180°$-t-$90°$ pulse sequence. Powder spectra with quadrupole echo sequence $90°_x$-$-t-90°_y$-t are free from distorsion due to mechanical or electrical ringing in the receiver. Most reports deal with solids, liquid crystals, and synthetic or biological membranes making use of deuteration, e.g. by $D_2$ addition to triolein, or by specific labeling of fatty acid chains in various positions (ref.13). Chain mobility in polymers, molecular order in drawn linear polyethylene and other data obtained by $^2$H-NMR spectroscopy were recently reviewed (ref.15). By means of $^2$H-NMR, samples of natural origin (ethanol, essential oils, vanillin) have been analyzed for $^2$H/$^1$H isotope ratios, differentiating among $C_3$ plants such as sugar beet and $C_4$ plants such as maize (ref.16).

Despite its radioactivity, tritium has witnessed a spectacular development of NMR studies. Only a selected bibliography can be indicated here (refs.14, 17). As one example, generally tritiated phenylalanine(by heating with HTO at 130° with a platinum catalyst followed by removal of labile tritium from $NH_2$ and COOH groups) was analyzed by noise-decoupled NMR establishing that 71% labeling occurs (statistically) in the ring and only 4% in the side chain (predominantly in the β-position and very little in the α-position). This analysis with quadrature detection requires an acquisition time of about four hours, while the step-wise chemical degradation and counting lasted for one man-month (ref.14)! By working at low-level activities (0.3-30 mCi per site) and taking into account that the maximum specific activity is 29,000 Ci/gram-atom, this activity range corresponds to 0.01-0.0001% isotopic abundance per site, so that very few molecules are labeled, and then only with one tritium atom, so that no complications arise from T-T or T-$^{13}$C coupling.

It should be mentioned that FT $^1$H-NMR instruments allow by means of COSY experiments the determination of 10-100 proton-proton coupling constants, an almost impossible task even with decoupling techniques, as exemplified by latunculins (fish toxins) (ref.18).

CARBON-13 NMR SPECTROSCOPY

Although nowadays $^{13}$C-NMR spectra are routinely recorded in organic chemical laboratories, they are performed with natural abundance compounds (refs.2-5). It is possible to calculate additively $^{13}$C chemical shifts in saturated systems but more elaborate assignments are usually made by means of off-resonance proton-decoupled spectra or of partially relaxed (DEPT pulse sequence) spectra. For more complicated compounds, two-dimensional (2D) $^1$H-$^{13}$C shift correlations, and 2D-INADEQUATE spectra which indicate C-C connectivities, are extremely powerful (ref.19) ; an example for the former type of correlation is the full assignment of permethylated β-cyclodextrin (ref.20a) and for the latter a study of 2-substituted adamantanes(ref.20b).

A detailed insight into polymer structure (refs.21-29) was revealed by sequences observed in stereoregular polymers or in copolymers by means of $^{13}$C-NMR, either as solids (magic angle spinning)(refs.25,26) or in solution. The stereoregularity nowadays observable goes beyond the pentad level. Cross polarization-magic angle spinning $^{13}$C-NMR applications for carbohydrates and polymers were reviewed recently (ref.27).

Van Etten and Risley made the interesting observation that $^{15}N$, $^{17}O$ and $^{18}O$ isotope shifts in $^{13}C$-NMR spectra allowed the facile determination of nitrogen or oxygen labeling. They made use of this observation for many kinetic and structural studies (ref.28) ; one of these (ref.29) is a joint work on the isotope exchange between $H_2^{18}O$ and the pyrylium cation (ref.30). Isotope effects of $^{14}N$ in $^{13}C$-NMR spectra of solids were also reported (ref.31).

Many biosynthetic and metabolic pathways have been elucidated by means of $^{13}C$ labeling and $^{13}C$-NMR (refs.32, 33). A sensitive method for detecting $^{13}C$ and $^{2}H$ incorporation from labeled ethanol to bile acids is $^{13}C\left\{^{2}H,\ ^{1}H\right\}$ NMR difference spectroscopy (ref.34). One should recall that $^{13}C$ atoms coupled to $^{2}H$ atoms do not appear in proton noise-decoupled $^{13}C$-NMR spectra because their signals are broader and do not benefit from NOE enhancement. Many assignments benefit from the use of lanthanide shift reagents but one should be aware that in $^{13}C$-NMR spectroscopy contact shifts are more frequent than in $^{1}H$-NMR (ref.35).

NMR SPECTROSCOPY OF NITROGEN ISOTOPES

Whereas the abundant $^{14}N$ with nuclear spin 1 has a quadrupolar nucleus and gives wider NMR lines due to shorter relaxation times, the less abundant stable isotope $^{15}N$ with nuclear spin 1/2 has been used for labeling compounds which then were studied by NMR methods. The biosynthetic tracing of the origin of nitrogens in penicillin G and cephalosporin C showed that $^{15}N$-labeled L-valine and L-cysteine (containing also other labels) are incorporated intact but with stereochemical modification of the valine (ref.33).

Mateescu and coworkers used NMR for tracing the $^{13}C$ and $^{15}N$ labels of bacteriorhodopsin formed biosynthetically from $[\varepsilon-^{15}N]$-lysine (ref.36).

Further literature data on nitrogen NMR are available (ref.37).

$^{17}O$-NMR SPECTROSCOPY

As the only stable oxygen isotope with non-zero magnetic moment is a quadrupolar nucleus with low natural abundance and low receptivity, the uses of $^{17}O$-NMR (refs.38, 39) are confined to small or medium-sized molecules. Water and hydronium ion (ref.40) have been the object of intense $^{17}O$-NMR studies. The permeability of phospholipid vesicle membranes to water may be measured ; $Mn^{2+}$ ions in the external solution permit the differentiation of the two components as in spin labeling studies (ref.41). Other chemical or biochemical $^{17}O$-NMR studies were reported (refs.38, 39).

CONCLUSION

From this brief survey it results that the position of the isotopic tag in labeled compounds is most easily revealed by NMR. Though $^{13}C$-NMR is mostly performed on natural-abundance compounds, the advent of FT-NMR provides a considerable stimulus for the synthesis and applications of labeled compounds.

REFERENCES

1. T.C. Farrer and E.D. Becker, Pulse and Fourier Transform NMR, Academic Press, New York, 1971 ; D. Shaw, Fourier Transform NMR Spectroscopy, Elsevier, Amsterdam, 1976.
2. G.C.Levy (Ed.), Topics in Carbon-13 Spectroscopy, vols.1-4, Wiley, New York
3. G.C. Levy and G.C. Nelson, Carbon-13 NMR for Organic Chemists, Wiley-Interscience, New York, 1972.
4. J.B. Stothers, Carbon-13 NMR Spectroscopy, Academic Press, New York, 1972.
5. F.W. Wehrli and T. Wirthlin, Interpretation of Carbon-13 NMR Spectra, Heyden, London, 1976.
6. P. Laszlo (Ed.), NMR of Newly Accessible Nuclei, 2 vols., Academic Press, New York, 1983.
7. P. Diehl, in T. Axenrod and G.A. Webb (Eds.), Nuclear Magnetic Resonance Spectroscopy of Nuclei Other than Protons, Wiley, New York, 1974, p. 275.
8. R. Harris and B. Mann, NMR and The Periodic Table, Academic Press, New York, 1978.
9. H.C. Jarrell and I.C.P. Smith, in J.B. Lambert and F.G. Riddell (Eds.), The Multinuclear Approach to NMR Spectroscopy, NATO Sci. Series C 103, chapter 8, p. 151, Reidel, Dordrecht.
10. P. Mansfield and P.G. Morris, NMR Imaging in Biomedicine, Academic Press, New York, 1982.
11. A.T. Balaban, I. Galatzeanu, G. Georgescu and L. Simionescu, Labelled Compounds and Radiopharmaceuticals Applied in Nuclear Medicine, Wiley, Chichester, 1985.
12. A.T. Balaban, in W.P. Duncan and A.B. Susan (Eds.), Synthesis and Applications of Isotopically Labeled Compounds, Elsevier, Amsterdam, 1983, p. 237 and references therein.
13. H.H. Mantsch, H. Saito and I.C.P. Smith, Progr. NMR Spectroscopy, 11 (1977) 211 ; I.C.P. Smith in ref.6, vol.2, p. 1 ; I.C.P. Smith and H.H. Mantsch, ACS Symp. Series 191 (1982) 99.
14. J.A. Elvidge, in J.A. Elvidge and J.R. Jones (Eds.), Isotopes ; Essential Chemistry and Applications, Spec. Publ. 35, The Chemical Society, London, 1980, p. 123.
15. H.W. Spiess, in H.H. Kausch and H.G. Zachmann (Eds.), Characterization of Polymers in the Solid State. I, Adv. Polym. Sci. No. 66, Springer, Berlin, 1985, p. 23.
16. G.J. Martin et al., J. Am. Chem. Soc. 104 (1982) 2658 ; Tetrahedron, 41 (1985) 3285.
17. J.A. Elvidge, J.R. Jones, V.M.A. Chambers and E.A. Evans, in E. Buncel and C.C. Lee (Eds.), Isotopes in Organic Chemistry, vol. 4, Elsevier, Amsterdam 1978 ; idem, Tritium NMR Spectroscopy, Review 19, The Radiochemical Centre, Amsterdam, 1978 ; E.A. Evans, J.A. Elvidge, C.D. Warell and J.R. Jones, Handbook of Tritium NMR Spectroscopy and Applications, Wiley, Chichester, 1985 ; A.L. Odell, in ref.6, vol. 2, p. 27.
18. Y. Kashman et al., Tetrahedron, 41 (1985) 1905.
19. A. Bax, R. Freeman and T.A. Frenkiel, J. Am. Chem. Soc., 103 (1981) 2102 ; A. Bax, Two-Dimensional Nuclear Magnetic Resonance in Liquids, Reidel, London, 1982 ; P. Benn and H. Gunther, Angew. Chem. Int. Ed. Engl., 22 (1983) 350.
20. a) J.R. Johnson, N. Shankland and I.H. Sadler, Tetrahedron, 41 (1985) 3147 b) A.N. Abdel Sayed and L. Banner, Tetrahedron Lett., 26 (1984) 2841.
21. J.C. Randall (Ed.), NMR and Macromolecules, ACS Symposium Series No. 247, Am. Chem. Soc., Washington DC, 1984.
22. F.A. Bovey, High Resolution NMR of Macromolecules, Academic Press, New York, 1972.
23. J. Schaefer and O.E. Stejskalin ref.2, vol. 3, 1979.
24. L.W. Jelinsky, Chem. Eng. News, 62(45) (1984) 26.
25. G.E. Maciel, Science, 226 (1984) 282.
26. C.S. Yannani, Acc. Chem. Res., 15 (1982) 201.

510

27. J.J. Lindberg and B. Hartling, in ref.15, p. 1.
28. J.M. Risley, R.L. Van Etten, C. Uncuța and A.T. Balaban, J. Am. Chem. Soc. 106 (1984) 7836.
29. R.L. Van Etten and J.M. Risley, in ref.12, p. 477 and references therein.
30. A.T. Balaban et al., Pyrylium Salts. Synthesis, Reactions and Physical Properties, Adv. Heterocyclic Chem., Suppl. Vol. 2, A.R. Katritzky (Ed.), Academic Press, New York, 1982.
31. I.G. Hexem, M.H. Frey and S.J. Opella, J. Am. Chem. Soc., 103 (1981) 224.
32. R.J. Abraham and P. Loftus, Proton and Carbon-13 NMR Spectroscopy. An Integrated Approach, Heyden, London, 1978 ; T.L. James, NMR in Biochemistry, Academic Press, New York, 1975 ; R.G. Shulman (Ed.), Biological Applications of Magnetic Resonance, Academic Press, New York, 1979.
33. D.W. Young, in ref.14, p. 276.
34. D.M. Wilson, A.L. Burlingame, G. Evans, T. Cronholm and J. Sjovall, in T.A. Baillie (Ed.), Stable Isotopes. Application in Pharmacology, Toxicology and Clinical Reasearch, The Macmillan Press, London, 1978.
35. F. Inagaki and T. Miyazawa, Progr. NMR Spectroscopy, 14 (1981) 67.
36. G.D. Mateescu et al., in ref.12, p. 123.
37. M. Witanowski and G.A. Webb, Nitrogen NMR, Plenum Press, London, 1973.
38. W.G. Klemperer, Angew. Chem. Int. Ed. Engl., 17 (1978) 246.
39. J.P. Kintzinger, in ref.6, vol. 2, p. 79 ; in P. Diehl, E. Fluck and R. Kosfeld (Eds.), NMR Principles and Progress, vol. 17, Springer Verlag Berlin, 1981.
40. G.D. Mateescu, G.M. Benedikt and M.P. Kelly, in ref.12, p. 483.
41. R. Mehlhorn, L. Packer, I. Dragutzan and A.T. Balaban, in L. Packer (Ed.), Methods in Enzymology, Academic Press, Orlando (in press).

*Synthesis and Applications of Isotopically Labeled Compounds 1985.*
Proceedings of the Second International Symposium, Kansas City, MO, U.S.A.,
3—6 September 1985, R.R. Muccino (Ed.), 511—512

ADAPTATION OF BIOTECHNOLOGICAL PROCESSES FOR PREPARATION OF COMPOUNDS LABELED
WITH STABLE ISOTOPES

Zvi E. Kahana and Aviva Lapidot

Isotope Dept., Weizmann Institute of Science, POB 26, 76100, Rehovot (ISRAEL)

ABSTRACT

Modifications of the conventional biotechnological processes for preparation
of biological compounds labeled with stable isotopes are discussed. They include means of label conservation including selection of processes, modifications in their design and choice of desired strains and their metabolic regulation. Some unique preparative approaches leading to site specific label incorporation are presented to illustrate these adaptations.

INTRODUCTION

New, efficient and simple biotechnological processes for the preparation of
stable isotope labeled compounds have been introduced for several $^{15}$N and $^{13}$C
labeled amino acids. These procedures when adapted from the conventional unlabeled preparations (ref. 1,2) must be modified for two reasons: conservation
of label and site specific label introduction. These changes are discussed
and illustrated below.

RESULTS AND DISCUSSION

Means of label conservation

Selection of processes. Biotechnological processes must be assessed on the
basis of label economics. A reaction for $^{15}$N incorporation requiring the
presence of 7 N $NH_4OH$ for the preparation of phenylalanine (ref. 3) must be
ruled out, yet such reaction may be considered for $^{13}$C introduction. Fermenta-
tions, as a rule, consume much of the initial carbohydrate for biomass formation and thus are expensive approaches for $^{13}$C labeling. The isotopic yield
for L-[$^{13}$C]glutamate is below 50%, unless the process is modified to minimize
bacterial growth. On the other hand, bound biocatalysts were demonstrated to
be very effective for the preparation of $^{15}$N labeled aspartate, alanine and
tyrosine in high isotopic yields (ref. 4,5,6). Their superiority stems from
the segregation of bacterial growth from the isotopic production phase, the
ease in handling and their repeated reusability.

Changes in process design. Implementation of various means to conserve
label, such as gas flushing and entrapment for $^{15}NH_4OH$, avoidance of gel
activation with unlabeled ammonium, optimization of precursor concentrations

512

with a bias towards the isotopic precursor (ref. 6,7), change in reactant concentrations to push equilibria with unlabeled reagents; all have been practiced in several microbial preparative systems. In addition, each such scheme must contain steps, normally not necessary, for separation and recovery of residual starting materials. These are different from precursor to another and complicate the downstream processing of the labeled product.

Metabolic and genetic manipulation. Since the operating of the labeled syntheses are peculiar, further adaptation of the overproducing strains for desired products is required. Furthermore, the need to use cheap $^{13}$C precursors like [$^{13}$C]acetate, instead of [$^{13}$C]glucose for instance, may require the use of more exotic strains, and regulating them to channel most of the precursor to the desired product. An example is the metabolically repressed strain producing labeled isoleucine and leucine (in preparation).

## Site specific labeling

Because of the limited number of nitrogenous groups in biomolecules $^{15}$N label is almost inherently localized. However in the case of glutamine selective introduction of $^{15}$N into the 2-, 5-, or 2,5- positions was achieved using immobilized glutamine sythetase (in preparation), a reaction not possible with the traditional fermentative synthesis (ref. 8).

The introduction of $^{13}$C into backbone sites is difficult. The careful use of metabolically blocked bacteria and substituting of glucose, which is used for non-labeled synthesis, with [2-$^{13}$C]pyruvate allowed the preparation of L-[3-$^{13}$C]isoleucine (in preparation). Additional biotechnological processes for the preparation of other isotopically labeled compounds are being developed.

ACKNOWLEDGEMENTS

Part of this work was supported by grants from N.P.I. and from the US-Israel Binational Science Foundation.

REFERENCES

1  I. Chibata, T. Tosa and T. Sato, in H.J. Peppler and D. Perlman (Eds.), Microbial Technology, 2nd ed. Academic Press, 1979, Vol. II, pp. 433-461.
2  Y. Hirose and H. Shibai, Biotech. Bioeng. 22 (1980) Suppl. 1, 111-125.
3  S. Yamada, K. Nabe, N. Izuo, K. Nakamichi and I. Chibata, Appl. Environ. Microbiol. 42 (1981) 773-778.
4  Z.E. Kahana and A. Lapidot, Analyt. Biochem. 126 (1982) 389-393.
5  Z.E. Kahana and A. Lapidot, Analyt. Biochem., in press.
6  Z.E. Kahana and A. Lapidot, Third European Congress of Biotechnology, Verlag-Chemie, Weinheim, 1984, Vol. I, 439-443.
7  Z.E. Kahana and A. Lapidot, Analyt. Biochem. 132 (1983) 160-164.
8  K. Nabe, T. Ujimaru, N. Izuo, S. Yamada and I. Chibata, Appl. Environ. Microbiol. 40 (1980) 19-24.

*Synthesis and Applications of Isotopically Labeled Compounds 1985.*
Proceedings of the Second International Symposium, Kansas City, MO, U.S.A.,
3—6 September 1985, R.R. Muccino (Ed.), 513—514

# THE SYNTHESIS OF [13]C-ENRICHED CARBOHYDRATES AS CHIRAL SYNTHONS FOR LABELED COMPOUNDS

T. E. WALKER, C. J. UNKEFER and D. S. EHLER

Los Alamos National Lab., INC-4 MS-C345, Los Alamos, NM   87545

ABSTRACT
    Methods have been developed to synthesize labeled chiral compounds from labeled carbohydrates. During the course of these investigations, we have adapted both chemical and enzymatic methods for the large-scale interconversion of labeled aldoses and ketoses.

The Stable Isotopes Resource at Los Alamos is funded by NIH to promote the application of stable isotopes in biomedical research. It has four major components: 1) Service, 2) Collaboration, 3) Core Research, and 4) Training. The resource functions to develop new techniques for the synthesis of compounds labeled with stable isotopes of carbon, oxygen and nitrogen ([13]C, [17]O, [18]O, and [15]N). The application of stable isotopically labeled asymmetric compounds and Mass or NMR spectroscopy to the study of metabolism *in vivo* requires the synthesis of only the biologically active stereoisomer. Several approaches have been used for the preparation of labeled chiral compounds including chemical synthesis, enzyme synthesis and biosynthesis. Recently, we have used [13]C-enriched carbohydrates as chiral synthons for the preparation of other optically active compounds. During the course of these investigations, we have adapted both chemical and enzymatic methods for the efficient interconversion of labeled aldoses and ketoses.

    Barker and coworkers have developed efficient techniques for the preparation of aldoses labeled at C-1 (1) or C-2 (2). The C-1 labeled aldoses are prepared by the addition of KCN-[13]C to an aldose containing one less carbon atom and results in a mixture of C-2 epimeric sugars. This diastereomeric mixture of labeled aldoses is easily resolved by chromatography. Aldoses labeled at C-2 are prepared by the molybdate ion-catalyzed rearrangements of aldoses labeled at C-1. The combination of these techniques can be used to synthesize a variety of enantiomerically pure D- or L-aldoses which are suitable as precursors for the synthesis of labeled chiral compounds.

    Carbon-13 enriched fructose is conveniently prepared by the isomerization of D-glucose using a commercial preparation of the enzyme glucose isomerase. Thus, any [13]C-labeled D-glucose can be converted to the corresponding labeled D-fructose. The equilibrium mixture contains only 50% D-fructose; however, addition of germinate to the reaction mixture increases the

514

equilibrium fraction of D-fructose to 80% (3). Fructose can also be prepared from mannose using a modification of the Lobry de Bruyn-Alberda von Ekenstein transformation (4). In this reaction, mannose-1-$^{13}C_1$ is treated with dilute alkali (pH=12) in the presence of phenylborate (5) to produce a mixture of glucose-1-$^{13}C_1$ (17%) and fructose-1-$^{13}C_1$ (83%). The alkali treatment followed by treatment with glucose isomerase can be used for a net conversion of D-mannose-1-$^{13}C_1$ to D-glucose-1-$^{13}C_1$. The mixtures of saccharides generated by these procedures are resolved chromatographically on Dowex 50 ($Ba^{++}$) using water as the eluent (6).

The labeled fructose has been used to assign the carbon resonances in the $^{13}$C-NMR spectrum, for metabolic studies, and as a precursor for the synthesis of sucrose and dihydroxyacetone. Dihydroxyacetone-2-$^{13}C_1$ was prepared by treatment of a mixture of the methyl glycosides of fructose-2-$^{13}C_1$ with periodic acid followed by sodium borohydride. The resulting mixed acetal was converted to the diethylacetal of dihydroxyacetone-2-$^{13}C_1$. Dihydroxyacetone-2-$^{13}C_1$ will be used for the synthesis of $^{13}$C-enriched folate derivatives.

The disaccharide lactose-1-$^{13}C_1$ (4-O-β-D-galactopyranosyl-D-glucose) can be prepared by the addition of KCN-$^{13}$C to 3-O-β-D-galactopyranosyl-D-arabinose using the techniques described by Barker and coworkers(1). Lactulose (4-O-β-D-galactopyranosyl-D-fructose), the 2-ketoderivative of lactose, can be prepared either from lactose or 4-O-β-D-galactopyranosyl-D-mannose or a mixture of the two by treatment with alkali in the presence phenylborate. Lactulose is isolated chromatographically.

Aldoses and ketoses can serve as asymmetric precursors for the synthesis of chiral compounds. By combining KCN-$^{13}$C with an enantiomerically pure aldotriose (or greater), a diasteriomeric pair of C-1 labeled aldoses is created which are easily resolved. The chirality in the sugar can be transferred to the product. For example, we have synthesized L-carnitine-4-$^{13}C_1$ from 3-deoxy-D-*ribo*-hexose-1-$^{13}C_1$. The stereochemistry at C-2 of the sugar is retained in the product. This approach may have utility for the synthesis of other chiral compounds.

This research was supported by NIH grant RR02231.

1 A. S. Serianni, H. A. Nunez, and R. Barker, Carb. Res. , 72 (1979) 71.
2 M. L. Hays, N. J. Pennings, A. S. Serianni and R. Barker, J. Amer. Chem. Soc., 104 (1982) 6764.
3 S. A. Barker, B. W. Hatt, and P. J. Somers, Carb. Res., 26 (1973) 41.
4 J. C. Speck, Jr., Adv. in Carb. Chem., 13 (1958) 63.
5 S. A. Barker, P.J. Somers, and R.R. Woodbury, German Patent (1977), DT2726535.
6 J.K.N. Jones, and R.A.Wall, Can. J. Chem., 38 (1960) 2290

*Synthesis and Applications of Isotopically Labeled Compounds 1985.*          515
Proceedings of the Second International Symposium, Kansas City, MO, U.S.A.,
3—6 September 1985, R.R. Muccino (Ed.), 515—516
© 1986 Elsevier Science Publishers B.V., Amsterdam — Printed in The Netherlands

# [13]C- AND [17]O-LABELING STUDIES OF NOVEL REARRANGEMENTS WITH FIVE-MEMBERED 2,3-DIOXO-HETEROCYCLES

C.WENTRUP[1] and G.KOLLENZ[2]

[1]Department of Chemistry, University of Marburg, D-3550 Marburg (FRG)
[2]Institute of Organic Chemistry, University of Graz, A-8010 Graz (Austria)

With aid of [13]C- and [17]O-labeling unusual novel ketoketene - and furandione-furandione rearrangements were detected during pyrolysis or cycloaddition reactions of five-membered 4-acyl substituted 2,3-dioxo-heterocycles.

PART A)

Thermolysis of such compounds in general leads to the formation of reactive acyl-ketene intermediates which stabilize by dimerization or cycloaddition processes (X = O), electrocyclic ring closure (X = N) or oligomerization via valence isomerization to a thietone derivative (X = S). After gas phase pyrolysis of 2,3-[13]C labeled educts, synthesized from the corresponding 1,3-H - active compounds and 1,2-[13]C oxalic acid dichloride, the distribution of the label - no double labeled molecules were observed - makes evident an unusual 1,3 - phenyl shift (ref.1).

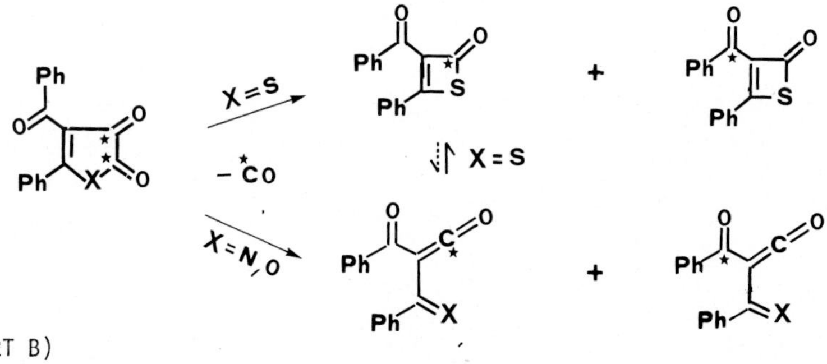

PART B)

The heterodiene-system in those heterocyclic 2,3-diones, formed by the acyl - group at C-4 and the C=C-bond of the furandione-ring, adds dienophiles e.g. isocyanides (ref.2) or heterocumulenes (ref.3,4), mostly accompanied by a surprising novel furandione-furandione rearrangement as shown in the following scheme; the two phenyl-groups formerly exchange their places.

A semi-quantitative calculation - meaning electronic and plane-calculated integration of the $^{17}O$ - signals in the educt and the products - shows the expected signal intensities indicating a nearly 50 : 50 distribution of the remaining $^{17}O$ - label in the products.

REFERENCES

1  C. Wentrup, H.W. Winter, G. Gross, K.P. Netsch, G. Kollenz, W. Ott and A.G. Biedermann, Angew. Chem. Int. Ed. Engl., 23 (1984), 800.
2  G. Kollenz, W. Ott, E.Ziegler, E.M. Peters, K. Peters, H.G. von Schnering, V. Formacek and H. Quast, Liebigs Ann. Chem. 1984, 1137.
3  G. Kollenz, G. Penn, G. Dolenz, Y. Akcamur, K. Peters, E.M. Peters and H.G. von Schnering, Chem. Ber. 117 (1984), 1299.
4  G. Kollenz, G. Penn, W. Ott, K. Peters, E.M. Peters and H.G. von Schnering, Chem. Ber. 117 (1984), 1310.

*Synthesis and Applications of Isotopically Labeled Compounds 1985.*
Proceedings of the Second International Symposium, Kansas City, MO, U.S.A.,
3—6 September 1985, R.R. Muccino (Ed.), 517—518

# SYNTHESIS OF [13]C-LABELED VITAMIN E AND INTERACTION BETWEEN VITAMIN E AND PHOSPHOLIPID IN LIPOSOME

S. URANO and M. MATSUO

Tokyo Metropolitan Institute of Gerontology, 35-2 Sakae-cho, Itabashi-ku, Tokyo 173, Japan

## ABSTRACT

Vitamin E with a [13]C-labeled isoprenoid side chain, [4'a-[13]C], [6'-[13]C], [8'a-[13]C] and [12'a and 13'-[13]C]α-tocopherols were synthesized using 6-methoxymethoxy-2,5,7,8-tetramethyl-2-[(E)-4-methyl-5-(thiazolin-2-yl)thio-3-penten-1-yl]chroman (1) as a key intermediate. These [13]C-labeled compounds were incorporated into three kinds of lecithin liposomes from dipalmitoyl phosphatidyl cholin, egg lecithin and rat liver lecithin, of which arachidonic acid contents are 0, 2.6 and 19.0%, respectively. $T_1$ values, which were measured by NMR for the labeled carbons, indicate that the segmental motion tends to increase with the increase of the distance from the chroman ring. This tendency is not affected with the arachidonic acid contents of phospholipids. This result can not be explained by Lucy's hypothesis.

## INTRODUCTION

Vitamin E, especially α-tocopherol, seems to act as an antioxidant in the matrix of biomembranes in which it is mostly located. In addition, vitamin E has been proposed to act as its structural component, which stabilizes bio-membranes containing polyunsaturated lipids. This effect is presumed to arise from a physicochemical interaction between the isoprenoid side chain of α-tocopherol and polyunsaturated fatty acid, particularly arachidonic acid, moiety of phospholipids in biomembranes. However, no evidence has been obtained to show that this interaction exists in biomembranes. One of possible techniques for the verification of the above hypothesis would be the measurement of [13]C-relaxation time ($T_1$) on vitamin E in biomembranes. For the $T_1$ measurement, we have synthesized α-tocopherol having a [13]C-labeled isoprenoid side chain and its $T_1$ in liposome was measured by the inversion recovery method.

## PREPARATION OF [13]C-LABELED α-TOCOPHEROL

As shown in Fig. 1, [4'a-[13]C], [6'-[13]C], [8'a-[13]C] and [12'a and 13'-[13]C]α-tocopherols were specifically synthesized. The overall yields based on [13]C sources were 58.7%, 19.2%, 51.2% and 33.0%, respectively.

Fig. 1

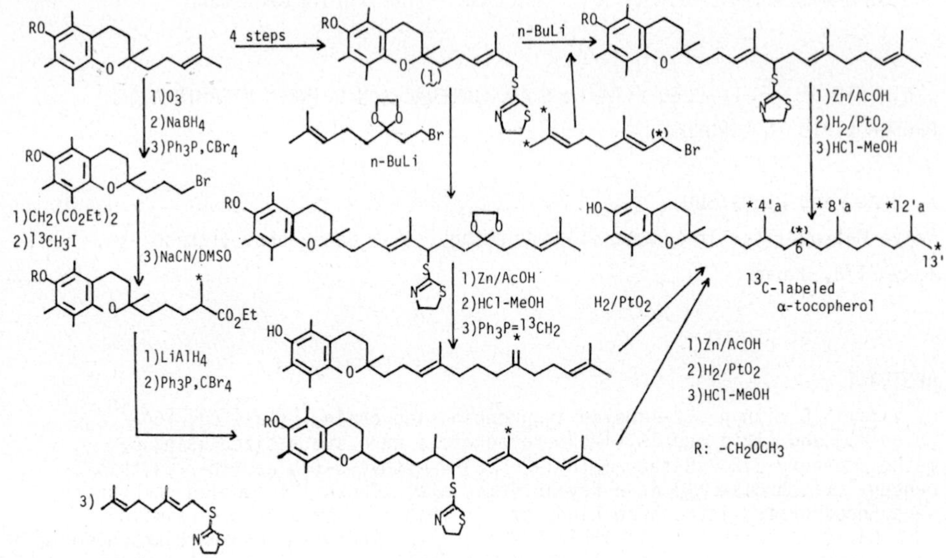

## THE MEASUREMENT OF $T_1$ OF LABELED CARBON IN LIPOSOME

As the temperture is lowered from 50°C to 20°C, $T_1$ values were decreased significantly. This decrease reflects that the bilayer packing becomes more ordered. The values of $T_1$ of the methyl carbons on the side chain increase with the distance from chroman ring. $T_1$ values of methylene carbon at 6' position in egg and rat liver lecithin bilayers were increased about 20-40% compared with that in DPPC bilayer. These increases suggest that motional freedom of methylene carbon at 6' position is increased with the unsaturated lipids. It would be considered that the motional freedom presents at the terminal carbon of iso-prenoid chain (12'a and 13') is independent of temperature due to the disruptive influence of the intercalated isoprenoid chain. When one compares $T_1$ values in egg lecithin bilayer with that of rat liver lecithin one, it is obvious that these values do not change with the content of arachindonic acid in phospholipid. These result can not be explained by Lucy's hypothesis which carbons at 4'a and 8'a position are fitted in pockets of arachidoyl chain in phospholipids.

TABLE 1. $^{13}$C-Relaxation times ($T_1$) for labeled carbons of $\alpha$-tocopherol.

| | | DPPC | egg lecithin | rat liver lecithin |
|---|---|---|---|---|
| 4'a | (20°C) | 0.498±0.012 | 0.491±0.013 | 0.463±0.019 |
| | (50°C) | 0.781±0.034 | 0.873±0.026 | 0.826±0.046 |
| 8'a | (20°C) | 0.480±0.020 | 0.625±0.028 | 0.531±0.031 |
| | (50°C) | 1.140±0.051 | 1.163±0.030 | 1.031±0.056 |
| 12'a 13' | (20°C) | 0.973±0.020 | 1.039±0.030 | 1.135±0.031 |
| | (50°C) | 2.185±0.273 | 1.606±0.092 | 1.592±0.114 |
| 6' | (20°C) | 0.127±0.012 | 0.161±0.013 | 0.177±0.017 |
| | (50°C) | 0.226±0.030 | 0.308±0.060 | 0.252±0.033* |

\* decomposed under measurement

*Synthesis and Applications of Isotopically Labeled Compounds 1985.*
Proceedings of the Second International Symposium, Kansas City, MO, U.S.A.,
3—6 September 1985, R.R. Muccino (Ed.), 519—520
© 1986 Elsevier Science Publishers B.V., Amsterdam — Printed in The Netherlands

RAPID REDUCTIVE-CARBOXYLATION OF SECONDARY AMINES, ONE POT SYNTHESIS OF N'-(4-[11]C-METHYL) IMIPRAMINE

Siya Ram, Richard E. Ehrenkaufer, Douglas M. Jewett and Keith Mulholland
Cyclotron/PET Facility, Div. of Nuclear Medicine, The University of Michigan
Medical Center, Ann Arbor, Michigan 48109 (U.S.A.)

ABSTRACT

A new rapid high yield synthesis of radiolabeled N'-(4-[11]C-methyl) imipramine has been developed using a reductive-carboxylation approach, in which [11]$CO_2$ was reacted with either N'-trimethylsilyldesimipramine or N'-lithium derivative of desimipramine, followed by lithium aluminum hydride reduction, to give <u>no carrier added</u> or <u>carrier added</u> [11]C-labeled imipramine respectively.

INTRODUCTION

Radioalkylation of secondary amines by direct fixation of [11]C-carbon dioxide under moderate reaction conditions is an attractive alternative to the most commonly used alkylating agents such as [11]C-methyl iodide ([11]$CH_3I$) and [11]C-formaldehyde (H[11]CHO), which are, in principle, themselves derived from [11]C-carbon dioxide. For example, recently, two independent syntheses of N'-(4-[11]C-methyl) imipramine based on the reductive methylation (ref. 1,2) and methylation (ref. 3) of desimipramine using H[11]CHO/$NaBH_4$ and [11]$CH_3I$ respectively had been reported in the literature. We were interested in direct fixation of [11]$CO_2$ into various organic molecules, which are potentially of biological interest such as palmitic acid, α-amino acids etc. for PETT studies. We therefore developed a new reductive-carboxylation approach, in which desimipramine derivatives (2 or 3), on carboxylation with [11]C-$CO_2$, followed by *in situ* lithium aluminum hydride reduction (ref. 4), afforded carrier-added or no carrier added imipramine (4) in very good yield.

$^{11}$C-carbon dioxide produced by $^{14}$N(p,$\alpha$)$^{11}$C nuclear reaction was quantitatively trapped in a stainless steel loop (3.2 mm OD) half immersed in liquid nitrogen. After collection, the loop was warmed up to room temperature and $^{11}$C-carbon dioxide was purged into the reaction mixture vial, which contained N'-TMS-derivative of DMI (2) in dry THF (86 $\mu$mole, 0.7 mL). The resulting reaction mixture was heated at 55-60°C for 8-10 min. The reaction mixture was then transferred with help of positive pressure of argon, to a 10 mL, two neck conical shaped reaction flask, which contained 0.1M-LiAlH$_4$ solution in dry THF (3.5 mL). The resulting reaction mixture was stirred with heating at 60-65°C for 10 min. After cooling, the mixture was decomposed with 6.25N-NaOH solution (approx. 2 mL). The product was diluted with diethyl ether (2 x 5 mL) and organic layer was decanted. The combined ether layers were dried over Na$_2$SO$_4$ and again decanted to a round bottom flask. Evaporation of ether layer on rotary evaporator, provided no carrier added $^{11}$C-labeled imipramine. The radiochemical yield and purity for purified imipramine were 77% and 99.5% respectively. In the case of carrier added synthesis of $^{11}$C-labeled imipramine, methyl chloroformate was added, after passing $^{11}$CO$_2$ and resulting reaction mixture was heated at 55°C for 10 min. The remaining procedure was the same as described above. The radiochemical yield and purity for carried added synthesis were 64% and 85% based on radio-TLC of the crude reaction mixtures, which were not optimized and are based on the single experiment. The physicochemical and spectroscopic data synthesized product checked with authentic imipramine.

High specific activity and high purity N'-(4-$^{11}$C-methyl) imipramine can be readily synthesized in excellent radiochemical yield from [$^{11}$C]-CO$_2$ using a reductive-carboxylation approach, which is easily adaptable to the synthesis of other potentially important radiopharmaceuticals such as promazine, guanifexine, nicotine, etc. The yield and purity can be optimized and time can be shorten by automation of the reaction.

## ACKNOWLEDGEMENTS

Research was supported by NCI training grant #5-T32-CA-09015 and by NINCDS grant #P01-NS-15655.

## REFERENCES

1 Comar D, Maziere M, Marazano C and Raynaud C. J. Nucl. Med. 16 521 (1975) (abst).
2 Berger G, Maziere M and Comar D. J. Labeled Compd. Radiopharm. 16 97 (1979) (abst).
3 Denutte H, Goethals P, Cattoir H, Bogaert M, Vandewalle T, Vandercasteele C, Jonckheere J and Leenher AD. J. Nucl. Med. 24 1185 (1983).
4 Holland HL and Johnson GB. Tetrahedron Letters 3595 (1979).

*Synthesis and Applications of Isotopically Labeled Compounds 1985.* 521
Proceedings of the Second International Symposium, Kansas City, MO, U.S.A.,
3—6 September 1985, R.R. Muccino (Ed.), 521—522

NEW LABELING AND SEPARATION METHODS FOR IN VIVO AND IN VITRO
DIAGNOSTICS IN HUNGARY


A. VERES, G. TÓTH, L. ZSINKA and J. MILLER
Institute of Isotopes of the Hungarian Academy of Sciences
P.O.Box 77, H-1525 Budapest (Hungary)


ABSTRACTS
    Three methods have been developed: 1. An adsorption chromatogra-
phic method for the separation of iodine-125-labeled compounds applied as tracers in the radioimmunoassay; 2. A portable sublimation generator for the separation of technetium-99m from low or medium specific activity molybdenum-99 using titanium molybdate as a
new target material; 3. A novel dry distillation method for the
production of iodine-131 from melted, pile-irradiated $TeO_2$. The
method renders possible to get rid of liquid radioactive wastes.

SEPARATION OF LOW MOLECULAR WEIGHT I-125-LABELED COMPOUNDS
    The method can be applied for the systematic separation of ra-
dioiodine-labeled compounds like iodothyronines, iodotyrosines as
well as steroids and prostaglandins to which tyrosine methyl ester
prosthetic group is coupled to enable the introduction of radioiodine via electrophilic aromatic substitution. The separation method is based upon the unique features of the Sephadex LH-20 dextran
gel that *i*. iodine substituted phenol derivatives like iodothyronines and iodotyrosines are strongly adsorbed on the gel, *ii*. organic solvents like ethanol, methanol etc. are also adsorbed, nevertheless to a lesser extent resulting in the displacement of the
iodo compounds from the surface of the gel, *iii*. water does not
displace iodo compounds from the gel at all, thus when using water/
organic solvent binary eluent the eluent strength and so the distribution coefficient can be adjusted by choosing the proper concentration of the organic solvent.
    It has been shown for several $^{125}I$-labeled compounds that the
distribution coefficient is linearly dependent on the organic solvent concentration of the eluent and the slope is increasing with
increasing number of iodine substituents per molecule. Thus complete separation of the starting material from the $^{125}I$-labeled
derivative can be achieved.

## A SUBLIMATION Tc-GENERATOR

A portable generator (SUBLITECH) has been developed for the sublimation of technetium-99m. The apparatus and the fully automatic separation method were described previously (ref.1). The newest version has even more advantageous parameters (e.g. lower weight). The application of titanium molybdate as a target opens up new vistas in the separation technique of $^{99}$Mo and $^{99m}$Tc. The special advantage of this technology is that the quality of the product is high without being necessary to use fission $^{99}$Mo. By the generator it is possible to prepare $^{99m}$Tc injections in a nuclear medical laboratory without special investments. Compared with the chromatographic and solvent extraction techniques the production of the generator is a rather simple operation.

## DRY DISTILLATION OF RADIOIODINES

In spite of its drawbacks distillation from aqueous solutions (wet method) has remained the fundamental method of routine production of $^{131}$I and $^{125}$I in many laboratories. Its main disadvantages are as follows: *i*. problems in the treatment of liquid and solid radioactive wastes, *ii*. low initial radioactive concentration, *iii*. evaporation losses when reaching the appropriate radioactive concentration, *iv*. high work and time demand. The production of radioiodines can significantly be improved utilizing the thermodesorptive or dry distillation method. This technology seems to eliminate the disadvantages listed above. The $TeO_2$ target material is melted in a furnace and heated over the melting point (733°C) as little as possible. In this way the evaporation of the target can be decreased to the minimum. The $TeO_2$ transformed into vapor remains in the sulfuric acid solution, while the radioiodines pass into the vessel collecting end products.

Research work on the generator and radioiodine dry distillation has been supported by the International Atomic Energy Agency (IAEA).

## REFERENCE

1. L. Zsinka, J. Kern in Proceedings of International Conference on Radiopharmaceuticals and Labelled Compounds Organised by the IAEA and Held in Tokyo, 22-26 October 1984, IAEA, Vienna, 1985, pp. 95-106

*Synthesis and Applications of Isotopically Labeled Compounds 1985.*
Proceedings of the Second International Symposium, Kansas City, MO, U.S.A.,
3—6 September 1985, R.R. Muccino (Ed.), 523—524
© 1986 Elsevier Science Publishers B.V., Amsterdam — Printed in The Netherlands

523

HYDROGEN PEROXIDE-ACETIC ACID AS AN IN SITU OXIDANT FOR NO-CARRIER-ADDED
AROMATIC RADIOBROMINATION AND RADIOIODINATION

S.M. MOERLEIN*, W. BEYER AND G. STÖCKLIN
Institut für Chemie 1 (Nuklearchemie) der Kernforschungsanlage Jülich GmbH.,
D-5170 Jülich (FRG).

There are several radioisotopes of bromine and iodine which can be applied to
the synthesis of radiopharmaceuticals, radioimmunoassay agents, and other
radiolabelled biomolecules. These radiohalogens are often attached to aromatic
rings for stability, and for many applications, such as receptor-binding
radioligands or pharmacologically-active compounds, the halogen must be
introduced with high specific activity (1).

$H_2O_2/CH_3CO_2H$ has been used as an oxidant for radiohalogenating alkyl (2-3) and
vinyl (4-5) positions of radiopharmaceuticals. Because peracetic acid is the
oxidizing intermediate generated (6), chlorinated side-products which are
inherent with the use of chloramine-T or N-chlorosuccinimide are avoided and
chromatographic purification is greatly simplified. We have used a series of
simple aromatic compounds with no-carrier-added (n.c.a.) $^{77}Br^-$ and $^{131}I^-$ to
evaluate $H_2O_2/CH_3CO_2H$ as an in situ oxidant for radiohalogenating biomolecules
at aromatic sites.

This method was found to be useful with $H_2O_2/CH_3CO_2H$ = 2/1 in acidic buffer or
methanol. For both $^{77}Br$ and $^{131}I$, aromatic halodeprotonation was found to be
low except in aromatic rings activated by electron-donating substituents ($NH_2$,
OH, $OCH_3$), and non-regiospecific isomeric products resulted. Radiochemical
yields were enhanced by increasing the concentration of $H_2O_2/CH_3CO_2H$.

In contrast to halodeprotonation reactions, the use of trimethylaryl Group IVb
organometals (Sn, Ge, Si) resulted in high radiochemical yields (>70%) within
30 minutes for electronically-activated rings containing Sn, Ge, or Si and for
non-activated or deactivated rings containing Sn. The radiochemical yields
obtained from n.c.a. bromodestannylation were lower than from n.c.a.
iododestannylation, results attributed to the higher oxidation potential of
bromide and competitive oxidative destruction of the aryl stannane substrate.
In contrast to the results when dichloramine-T is used as an oxidant (7),
n.c.a. radiobromination of activated arylstannane compounds gave only poor
radiochemical yields using $H_2O_2/CH_3CO_2H$.

In conclusion, n.c.a. aromatic halodeprotonation using long-lived radiohalides
and $H_2O_2/CH_3CO_2H$ as an oxidant is useful for labelling aromatic sites of molecules which are activated toward electrophiles when isomeric purity of the
products is not essential. When radioiodinating aromatic sites with short-
lived isotopes where structure-activity constraints are great, aromatic
iododestannylation gives regiospecific products with high radiochemical yields
in a matter of minutes. Similarly, when radiobrominating aromatic rings which
are deactivated toward electrophiles, aromatic bromodestannylation is recommended, but for electronically-activated systems, aryl germanes or silanes
should be used as substrates due to their greater resistance to acid
decomposition.

---

*Present address: Donner Laboratory, Univ. of California, Berkeley, CA 94720

REFERENCES

1. H.H. Coenen, S.M. Moerlein and G. Stöcklin, Radiochim. Acta, 34 (1983) 47-68.
2. S.G. Senderoff, K.D. McElvany, K.E. Carlson, D.F. Heiman, J.A. Katzenellenbogen and M.J. Welch, Int. J. Appl. Radiat. Isot., 33 (1982) 545-551.
3. J.A. Katzenellenbogen, S.G. Senderoff, K.D. McElvany, H.A. O'Brien and M.J. Welch, J. Nucl. Med., 22 (1981) 42-47.
4. R.N. Hanson and L.A. Franke, J. Nucl. Med., 25 (1984) 998-1002.
5. L.A. Franke and R.N. Hanson, J. Nucl. Med., 25 (1984) 1116-1121.
6. M.W.C. Smit, Rec. Trav. Chim., 49 (1930) 675-685.
7. S.M. Moerlein and H.H. Coenen, J. Chem. Soc., Perkin Trans. 1, in press (paper 5/177).

## N.C.A. Radiohalogenation of Anisole Derivatives

$^{77}$Br:

| | p-Sn(CH$_3$)$_3$ | p-Ge(CH$_3$)$_3$ | p-Si(CH$_3$)$_3$ | p-H |
|---|---|---|---|---|
| Relative Isomeric Distribution | OCH$_3$  5  5  0  0  90 | OCH$_3$  1  1  0  0  98 | OCH$_3$  1  1  0  0  98 | OCH$_3$  12.5  12.5  0.5  0.5  74 |
| Total Aromatic Substitution Yield:[a] | 28.7 ± 1.8 | 53.9 ± 2.4 | 43.2 ± 2.4 | 51.8 ± 0.8 |

$^{131}$I:

| | | | | |
|---|---|---|---|---|
| Relative Isomeric Distribution: | OCH$_3$  3  3  0.5  0.5  93 | OCH$_3$  1  1  0  0  98 | OCH$_3$  0.5  0.5  0  0  99 | OCH$_3$  10.5  10.5  0.5  0.5  78 |
| Total Aromatic Substitution Yield:[a] | 91.1 ± 1.1 | 80.4 ± 2.3 | 78.6 ± 0.3 | 24.1 ± 2.0 |

[a] t = 30 min for Sn, Ge, Si and 6 hr for H.

*Synthesis and Applications of Isotopically Labeled Compounds 1985.*
Proceedings of the Second International Symposium, Kansas City, MO, U.S.A.,
3—6 September 1985, R.R. Muccino (Ed.), 525—532
© 1986 Elsevier Science Publishers B.V., Amsterdam — Printed in The Netherlands

SYNTHESIS OF GIBBERELLIN ISOTOPICALLY MODIFIED IN $^{13}$C USING THE
FUNGUS FUSARIUM MONILIFORME SHELD

M.S.Dolidze, E.D.Oziashvili, M.A.Turkia

Institute of Stable Isotopes, 380086 Tbilisi, USSR

INTRODUCTION

The work described below was done in order to obtain
gibberellin isotopically modified in carbon-13. This problem
arises in connection with the study of the effects of phytohormonic preparations on the growth and development of plants. Gibberellin is known to be one of the universal components of the
phytohormonic system of plant growth regulators.

Several publications [1-5] describe the preparation of isotopically modified biologically active substances by cultivating
the autotrophic and heterotrophic organisms in isotopically modified medium.

We have studied the effect of nutrient medium on biomass accumulation and gibberellin yield. The initial experiments were
carried out under conditions similar to those in the work of
McComb [6] in which the preparation of $^{14}$C-gibberellin was
studied. The experimental results obtained showed that under
McComb's conditions the gibberellin yield was not more than 75-
80 mg/l of nutrient medium. In our further experiments using a
method that has been developed by us it was possible to increase
the yield of gibberellin isotopically modified in $^{13}$C up to 450-
500 mg/l of nutrient medium. The details are given below.

MATERIALS AND METHODS

STORAGE OF THE FUNGUS AND PREPARATION OF ACTIVE PRINCIPLE

Before use, the fungus Fusarium Moniliforme Sheld Strain $P_g$

8-10 was maintained in sterile conditions on nutrient agar slopes of the following composition (g): difco agar 15; $MgSO_4 \cdot 7 H_2O$ 0·4; $CaCl_2$ 0·2; saccharose 20; potato 200, dissolved in 1 l distilled water. To obtain the active principle, the mycelium before use was transferred to the following nutrient medium (g): saccharose 30; $NH_4NO_3$ 3·; $KH_2PO_4$ 2; $MgSO_4 \cdot 7 H_2O$ 0·2; $K_2SO_4 \cdot 7 H_2O$ 0·2, the minor element concentration volume – 1 ml in 1 l distilled water; its composition was (mg): $MgSO_4$ 590; $CuSO_4$ 75; $FeSO_4$ 590; $ZnSO_4$ 500; $(NH_4)_2NO_3$ 80, dissolved in 0·5 l distilled water. Incubation was performed in a rotary shaker at a speed of 250 r/min in a 750 ml conical flask for 5 days.

The active principle obtained in this way was used for preparation of gibberellin.

The basal nutrient medium used for the mycelium accumulation and gibberellin production was a modified Rolen-Toma medium in which a carbon source either of natural or isotopically modified composition was used depending on the investigation. We have used two variants of the medium: (1) a medium essentially the same as one recommended by McComb (g): glucose of natural isotopic abundance 100; $KH_2PO_4$ 5; $MgSO_4$ 2; $NH_4NO_3$ 2·4; to every litre of the solution 2 ml of micronutrient element concentrate were added. Mycelium cultivation was carried out for 11 days in a 3 l glass fermenter. On the 11th day the biomass was isolated from the medium by filtration on a Büchner funnel with a filter made of three layers of unbleached calico in a Bunsen flask. The mycelium was transferred to the following medium (g): sodium acetate isotopically modified in $^{13}C$ to 80 atom% 10; $KH_2PO_4$ 5; $MgSO_4$ 2; $NH_4NO_3$ 2·4; 2 ml of micronutrient element concentrate dissolved in 1 l distilled water were added; the microelement medium composition was the same as above.

The second variant of the medium composed by us had the following composition (g): Chlorella hydrolisate isotopically modified in [13]C to 75-80 atom % 100; $KH_2PO_4$ 5; $MgSO_4 \cdot 7 H_2O$ 2; $NH_4NO_3$ 2·4; 1 ml of the following micronutrient element medium: $FeSO_4 \cdot 7 H_2O$ 0·59; $CuSO_4 \cdot 5 H_2O$ 0·075; $ZnSO_4 \cdot 7 H_2O$ 0·59; $(NH_4)_2MoO_4$ 0·08 dissolved in 0·5 l distilled water. Cultivation was carried out for 11 days both on a rotary shaker with a speed of 250 r/min in the 750 ml flasks and in a 3 l glass fermenter in a thermostatic cubicle at 38°C.

## PREPARATION OF CHLORELLA HYDROLYSATE

Chlorella vulgaris thermophilic Strain 157 was cultivated on Tamiia medium (mg/l): $K_2HPO_4$ 200; $MgSO_4$ 200; $CaCl_2$ 150; $NaHCO_3$ 200; $KNO_3$ 1g/l; to every litre of the solution 1 mg of the following microelement mixture (g/l): $ZnSO_4 \cdot 7 H_2O$ 0·22; $MnSO_4$ 1·81; $CuSO_4$ 0·079; $NaBO_3 \cdot 4 H_2O$ 2·63; $FeSO_4 \cdot 7 H_2O$ 9·32; $CaCl_2$ 1·2; $Co(NO_3)_2 \cdot H_2O$ 0·02; $(NH_4)_6Mo_7O_{24} \cdot 4 H_2O$ 1; EDTA 10.

To allow Chlorella vulgaris Strain 157 to get adapted to the isotopically modified medium a method was used of differential transfer from small volume to greater one bringing the total volume to 50 l. Direct transfer of the inoculum from hard agar to vessels of 50 l capacity and illumination with 60 thousand lux produced stress which slowed down its accumulation.

Cultivation was carried out in a closed loop with 2-2·5 % [13]$CO_2$ isotopically modified in [13]C to 80-85 atom % [7] . The rest of the gas loop free volume was filled with gas nitrogen. On the 14th day after the inoculation the residue of the isotopically modified carbon dioxide was removed by passing it through throttles with barium hydroxide.

The biomass produced was removed by centrifugation at a speed 5000 r/min at +5°C. Supernatant liquid was removed after precipitation and the biomass left was dried in liquid nitrogen, ground to powder which was further dried in a vacuum exsiccator above a concentrated sulphuric acid.

The dry powder obtained in this way was put in ampules which were then filled with 6N HCl, sealed and hydrolyzed for 48 hr. After hydrolysis the excess HCl was removed on a rotary evaporator and adjusted to the neutral pH by washing in distilled water. The Chlorella hydrolysate obtained in this way contained 75-80 atom % carbon-13.

EXTRACTION AND PREPARATION OF THE SUMMARY FRACTION OF GIBBERELLIN ISOTOPICALLY MODIFIED IN $^{13}C$

After the incubation period the mycelium was separated by vacuum filtration through the unbleached calico filter. To produce the pure phase, the nutrient solution free from the bulked mycelium was centrifugated at a speed of 15000 r/min at +5°C. The liquid phase obtained in this way served as a source of gibberellin isotopically modified in carbon-13. Besides gibberellin, the fungus Fusarium Moniliforme Sheld synthesizes small quantities of toxin fusaric acid. The latter was removed by treating the liquid phase with petroleum ether in which fusaric acid dissolves well while gibberellin does not.

The method used for extracting the gibberellin produced was that described by McComb [6].

THIN-LAYER CHROMATOGRAPHY. This was done for the ethylacetate
fraction to control the presence of gibberellin isotopically
modified in carbon-13 on Silufol UV-254 plates in the solvent
system: ethylacetate-chloroform - acetic acid in the ratio
15:3:1. After chromatography the plates were dried in a cold air
stream, treated with concentrated sulphuric acid in ethyl alcohol in a thermostat for identification; then $R_f$ was measured.
From parallel untreated plates the desired substance with the
gel-carrier was scraped off, the latter was then removed by extraction in ethanol. After ethanol removing, a dry precipitate
was obtained. A spectrum of the substance was recorded on the
spectrophotometer СФ -26 at 740 nm by the G.S.Muromsev method
[8] . The melting point, 243-245°C, of the preparation was the
same as that of commercial analog. The degree of isotopic modi-
cation was determined on the mass spectrometer МИ -1321. Variations in isotopic modification for different experiments were
dependent on the initial $^{13}CO_2$ isotopic modification and amounted to 70-75 atom %.

GAS-LIQUID CHROMATOGRAPHY. Gas-liquid chromatography (GLC) [9-14]
either with radiographic analysis (GLC-RA) or with mass-
spectrometry (GLC-MS) [15-18] has been used for analysing the
gibberellins and their metabolites as well as studying their
structure. Several papers concerning the analysis of gibberellin
by high-performance gas-liquid chromatography have recently appeared [19,20]. For the analysis of the summary fraction and extraction of gibberellin in a pure form a method of adsorption
chromatography on Zorbax BP-SIL and distributive chromatography
on Silasorb Diol was used [21] . As an effective eluent, a mixture of hexane-ethanol-acetic acid of different composition was
used.Measurements were made at 210 nm on a UV detector.

The experimental results are summarized in Table 1 and Figs.1-4.

Table 1

| System N | Adsorbent | Column dimentions | Eluent con-centration | Notes |
|---|---|---|---|---|
| 1 | Zorbax BP-SIL | 85:15:0·05 | 10x0·6 | Uncomplete separation of summary fraction; $GA_3$ and $GA_1$ are recorded in one peak |
| 2 | Silasorb "Diol" | 80:20:0·05 | 10x0·06 | $GA_3$ and $GA_1$ are well separated, but an unknown component is present |
| 3 | Silasorb "Diol" | 85:15:0·05 | 10x0·06 | $GA_3$ is well separated from the unknown component, but unsatisfactorily from $GA_1$ |
| 4 | Silasorb "Diol" | 84:16:0·06 | 10x0·06 | $GA_3$ is completely separated from the unknown component and satisfactorily from $GA_1$ |

The $GA_3$ fraction isotopically modified in $^{13}C$ using system 4 was rather pure. Experiments are in progress to choose the most effective systems (mobile and non-mobile phases) that would be useful for complete separation of the components present in the summary fraction.

DISCUSSION

The objective of the method proposed by McComb[6] was the preparation of gibberellin isotopically modified in carbon-14 and their method of two-stage cultivation of the fungus on the medium of natural isotopic abundance with subsequent transfer of the biomass on a medium containing the radioactive carbon was optimal for the case.

As indicated above, in our experiments (performed in similar conditions except that acetate isotopically modified in carbon-13 and not in carbon-14, was a source of carbon) a very low yield of $^{13}$C-gibberellin was obtained.

This could be attributed either to the fact that the removal of the fungus from the nutrient medium with glucose to which it had already become adapted, subsequent filtration of the wringings and transfer to the acetate medium might have produced stress, which have resulted in reducing the growth and assimilation of $^{13}$C from the acetate. Or it is possible that the fungus accustomed to the energy-rich glucose and having accumulated 80-85 % of biomass badly assimilated acetate at the end of experiment.

The employment of $^{13}$C-biomass of Chlorella vulgaris Strain 157 which have been hydrolyzed on monomer to be easily assimilated by the fungus allowed a considerable increase of the results.

The data obtained show that a nutrient medium with isotopically modified Chlorella hydrolysate can be used for preparing biologically active compounds modified in nitrogen-15, oxygen-18 or deuterium by means of microbial synthesis.

532

REFERENCES

1 R.S.White, E.Martinelly et al. Nature, 243 (1973) 273.

2 M.Tanabe, H.Sato, Biochemistry, 9 25 (1970) 4851.

3 N.Matwiyoff, D.Ott. Science, 181 4105 (1973) 1125.

4 R.C.Pandly, R.L.Renehart. The Journal of Antibiotics, VXXIX
10 (1977) 1035.

5 R.M.Greinger. Biochemistry, 75 (1975) 513.

6 A.S.McComb, J. gen.Microbiology, 34 (1964) 401.

7 А.Н.Цоглин и др.Физиология растений,,т.26,вып.I (1964).

8 Г.С.Муромцев, В.Н.Агнистикова "Гормоны растений гибберелли-
ны, Наука, М., 1973.

9 N.Ikekawa, Y.Sumiki, N.Takahashi, Chem.and Ind.,(1963) 1928.

10 N.Ikekawa, Y.Sumiki, T.Kagawa, Proc.Japan Acad., 39(1963)507.

11 L.C.Luckwill, P.Weaver, J.MacMillan, J.Hortic Sci.,44(1968)48.

12 F.Hayashi, D.R.Barner, C.E.Peterson, H.M.Sell. Phytochemistry,
10 (1971) 57.

13 L.H.Aung, A. de Hertog,G.L.Staby, Phytochemistry,10(1971)215.

14 A.T.Perez, W.H.Hachman, Phytochemistry, 10(1971)2799.

15 R.C.Durley, R.P.Pharis, Planta, 199 (1973) 357.

16 I.D.Railton, N.Murofushi, R.C.Durley, R.P.Pharis, Phytochemistry, 13(1974)793.

17 I.D.Railton, R.C.Durley, R.C.Pharis, Plant Physiol.,
54(1974)6.

18 R.C.Durley, I.D.Railton, R.C.Pharis,Pytochemistry,12(1973)
1603.

19 Phytochemistry, 18 10 (1979) 1699-1702.

20 G.W.M.Barendse, P.H.Van de Werken, N.Takahashi,
J. Chromatography, 198 (1980) 449-455.

21 Yiann-Tsyh Lin and Erich Heftmann, J. Chromatography,
213 (1981) 507-510.

*Synthesis and Applications of Isotopically Labeled Compounds 1985.*
Proceedings of the Second International Symposium, Kansas City, MO, U.S.A.,
3—6 September 1985, R.R. Muccino (Ed.), 533—538

## MULTIPLE NUCLEUS NMR SPECTROSCOPY OF BACTERIOPHAGE T4 LYSOZYME

F.W. DAHLQUIST[1], R.H. GRIFFEY[2*], L.P. McINTOSH[1], D.C. MUCHMORE[1], T.G. OAS[1] and
A.G. REDFIELD[2]

[1]Department of Chemistry and Institute of Molecular Biology, University of
Oregon, Eugene, OR 97403 (U.S.A.)

[2]Department of Biochemistry, Brandeis University, Waltham, MA 02254 (U.S.A.)

*Present address:  Center for Non-Invasive Diagnosis, University of New Mexico
School of Medicine, 900 Camino de Salud, Albuquerque, NM 87131 (U.S.A.)

Many aspects of the structure and dynamics of biological macromolecules
are best studied through experiments which are capable of yielding information
from specific and defined sites within these molecules.  In the case of
proteins, site-specific probes may be applied in the studies of structure,
folding/unfolding, substrate or ligand interactions, and solvent exchange.
NMR is a technique particularly suited for this purpose as it allows us to
directly observe specific nuclei in selected residues of proteins in a nonper-
turbing manner.

In proteins of moderate size, the two-dimensional NMR techniques such as
COSY and NOESY have proven useful for the selective detection and assignment
of the abundant proton resonances (1). However, in the case of larger proteins, increased linewidth and greater number of resonances limit the usefulness of this approach.  In order to circumvent these problems, we have used
multiple isotope ($^{13}$C and $^{15}$N) labeling of proteins to detect and assign
resonances from a selected subset of nuclei.  Our primary focus is on the
exchangeable amide protons in bacteriophage T4 lysozyme (2).  The key advantages of this multiple labeling approach include:  (1) the potential to
resolve and detect specific resonances in an otherwise complex NMR spectrum;
(2) the ability to detect inherently low-sensitivity nuclei, such as $^{15}$N,
indirectly by observation of high sensitivity signals of protons; and (3) the
possibility to unambiguously assign resonances to specific residues in a protein of known sequence by virtue of multiple nuclei interactions.  These
methods are primarily suited for studies of proteins of known sequence and
structure.  In this communication, we will describe the NMR spectroscopy of
multiply-labeled T4 lysozyme.

## NMR SPECTROSCOPY OF ($^{13}$C, $^{15}$N) LABELED T4 LYSOZYME

Bacteriophage T4 lysozyme is a 164 amino acid protein composed of a single polypeptide chain. Wild-type and numerous temperature-sensitive mutants have been well characterized thermodynamically and structurally (3-7). The T4 lysozyme gene has been cloned into a high expression bacterial plasmid system which allows the efficient and rapid synthesis of isotopically labeled proteins (8). The $^{15}$N and $^{13}$C labeling was accomplished by growing the lysozyme-producing bacteria in a defined media, supplemented with the appropriate labeled amino acid (2). In general, an auxotrophic bacterial strain for the labeling amino acid is used. Nevertheless, the action of transaminases leads to partial loss of the $^{15}$N label.

### (a) Detection of $^{15}$N-labeled amide protons

Figure 1a displays the $^1$H-NMR spectrum of T4 lysozyme in water. Although three tryptophan indole NH resonances are resolved near 10 ppm, the region between 9.8 and 6.0 ppm is unresolved and arises from ca. 240 amide, imidazole, and aromatic protons in this protein. In order to detect amide proton resonances corresponding to a single amino acid class, we have incorporated $^{15}$N-Phe and $^{15}$N-Tyr into T4 lysozyme.

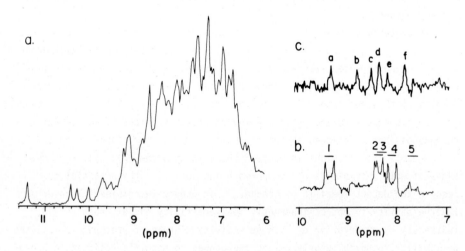

Fig. 1a. The downfield $^1$H-NMR spectrum of T4 lysozyme (30 mg/ml in sodium phosphate buffer, pH 6.5) recorded at 360 MHZ.
Fig. 1b,c. The echo difference spectrum of $^{15}$N-Phe labeled T4 lysozyme (b) and the $^{15}$N-decoupled echo difference spectrum of $^{15}$N-Tyr labeled lysozyme (c), recorded at 500 MHZ as described previously (2). The doublet resonances from the five $^{15}$N-Phe amide protons (1-5) and the singlet resonances from the six $^{15}$N-Tyr amide protons are indicated (a-f).

Figure 1b displays the resonances from the 5 amide protons directly bonded to $^{15}$N in $^{15}$N-Phe labeled T4 lysozyme, and Figure 1c shows the resonances from the 6 amide protons corresponding to $^{15}$N-Tyr residues in this protein. These spectra were measured using an "echo difference" pulse technique (2,9). It is important to note that the echo difference detection of isotopically labeled sites is not limited to $^{15}$N-H. It is equally possible to selectively detect protons directly bonded to $^{13}$C nuclei.

(b) <u>Indirect detection of low sensitivity $^{15}$N nuclei with proton NMR:</u>
<u>$^{15}$N-$^{1}$H two-dimensional spectroscopy</u>

In principle, $^{15}$N-NMR studies of the $^{15}$N-containing lysozyme could detect the $^{15}$N resonances of the labeled amides. Practically, however, $^{15}$N detection of resonances is inherently 1000-fold less sensitive than with $^{1}$H and thus direct $^{15}$N measurements, even with the INEPT pulse sequence, yield poor quality spectra. An alternative approach is to detect the $^{15}$N nuclei indirectly by $^{1}$H-NMR measurements of protons directly bonded to the $^{15}$N nuclei (10). This approach, termed a "forbidden echo experiment", relies on the simultaneous generation of $^{1}$H and $^{15}$N spin coherence. Signals are detected with the sensitivity of proton NMR but contain $^{15}$N chemical shift information. The resulting data are displayed in a two-dimensional plot of $^{15}$N and $^{1}$H chemical shifts, as shown in Figure 2a for $^{15}$N-tyrosine-labeled T4 lysozyme.

Comparison of the one-dimensional and two-dimensional spectra of $^{15}$N-Tyr labeled T4 lysozyme demonstrates a second advantage to the forbidden-echo measurements; namely, the added resolution gained by the $^{15}$N chemical shift dimension.

(c) <u>Assignment of specific $^{15}$N-$^{1}$H amide resonances by $^{13}$C co-labeling</u>

The methods described above serve to detect and resolve specific classes of resonances by $^{15}$N labeling. Assignment of these resonances to specific residues in the protein sequence can be accomplished by specific mutation of the site of interest to remove its resonance from the selectivly detected subclass. Alternatively, the protein can be $^{15}$N/$^{13}$C co-labeled with the appropriate amino acids to produce a unique doubly labeled amide (11). If a $^{13}$C carbonyl amino acid A and an $^{15}$N amine amino acid B are simultaneously incorporated in a protein, any AB dipeptide will contain a $^{13}$C-$^{15}$N labeled amide. In many cases, this will be a unique amide within the protein. By virtue of the $^{13}$C-$^{15}$N scalar coupling, it is straightforward to identify the $^{15}$N-$^{1}$H two-dimensional cross peak in the forbidden echo spectrum corresponding to the double labeled amide. Figure 2b demonstrates this for $^{13}$C-Leu and

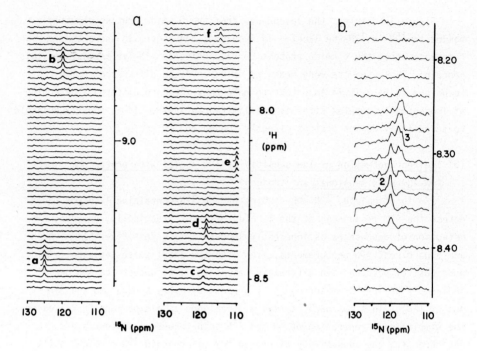

Fig. 2a. The forbidden echo spectrum of the correlated $^1H$ and $^{15}N$ chemical shifts of $^{15}N$-Tyr labeled T4 lysozyme (2). The six $^{15}N$-$^1H$ crosspeaks (a-f) correspond to the $^1H$ resonances in Fig. 1c.

Fig. 2b. A portion of the forbidden echo spectrum of $1$-$^{13}C$-Leu/$^{15}N$-Phe labeled T4 lysozyme corresponding to peaks 2 and 3 in Fig. 1b. Crosspeak 3 is a doublet due to $^{13}C$-$^{15}N$ scalar coupling and is assigned to the $^{13}C$-$^{15}N$ labeled amide of Leu66-Phe67.

$^{15}N$-Phe labeled lysozyme. The doublet resonance 3 corresponds to Leu[66]-Phe[67], a unique site in the protein. Using $^{13}C$-NMR, the $^{13}C$ carbonyl resonances from the labeled lysozyme can be directly detected. The $^{13}C$-$^{15}N$ scalar coupling also allows the assignment of the $^{13}C$ carbonyl resonance of a multiply labeled amide (not shown).

This method of assignment is clearly possible for any situation in which multiple isotopic labeling of a protein generates a unique or limited number of double labeled sites which are discernible by NMR measurements.

APPLICATIONS

The assigned resonances provide a sensitive probe of the structure and dynamics of the lysozyme molecule. The hydrogen exchange properties of the labeled amide sites can be easily measured by placing the protein in $D_2O$-based

buffer and observing the rate of replacement of the amide protons by
deuterium. We find that the amide protons of the two surface accessible
phenylalanine residues of the protein, Phe114 and Phe4, are replaced by
deuterium in about one hour at 10° at pH 5.5. The three buried $\alpha$ helical
residues at positions 67, 153 and 104 are very slow to exchange their amide
protons with half times of about one week. Thus these buried helical amides
are about 100 times slower to exchange with solvent than the residues in
accessible surface regions of the protein.

Hydrogen exchange provides information about protein dynamics in a slow
time scale of hours or days. We can also examine the dynamics of the protein
on a very rapid time scale of $10^{-8}$-$10^{-9}$ seconds using spin lattice relaxation
time, $T_1$, measurements. These reveal that four of the five phenylalanine
resonances have very similar $T_1$ values of $0.29 \pm .02$ second. The fifth
resonance, corresponding to Phe4, has a significantly longer value of 0.45
second. These data suggest more molecular motion in the polypeptide backbone
near residue 4 than at the other phenylalanine positions along the chain.

We are especially interested in how these measures of molecular dynamics
change in mutant T4 lysozymes of differing thermodynamic stabilities. We hope
such investigations will clarify the relationships between protein structure,
dynamics and stability.


## SUMMARY

By biosynthetically incorporating $^{13}$C and $^{15}$N labeled amino acids into T4
lysozyme, we can detect and assign the $^{1}$H, $^{13}$C, and $^{15}$N NMR resonances from
specific amides within this protein. Armed with these assignments, the structure and dynamics of wild-type and mutant T4 lysozymes can be studied in a
site-specific manner. Solvent exchange and relaxation measurements of the
assigned amide protons exemplify these studies.

Acknowledgements: This research was funded by National Science Foundation
Grant PCM 8304174. RHG was supported by NIH Grant GM0700. LPM is supported
by the Natural Sciences and Engineering Research Council of Canada and the
Alberta Heritage Foundation for Medical Research.

538

REFERENCES

1  G. Wagner and K. Wüthrich, J. Mol. Biol. 160 (1982) 343-361.
2  R.H. Griffey, A.G. Redfield, R.E. Loomis and F.W. Dahlquist, Biochemistry
   24 (1985) 817-822.
3  M.L. Elwell and J.A. Schellman, Biophys. Biochem. Acta 386 (1975) 309-323.
4  M.L. Elwell and J.A. Schellman, Biophys. Biochem. Acta 494 (1977) 367-383.
5  S.J. Remington, W.F. Anderson, J. Owen, L.F. Ten Eyck, C.T. Grainger and
   B.W. Matthews, J. Mol. Biol. 118 (1978) 81-98.
6  M.G. Grutter, R.B. Hawkes and B.W. Matthews, Nature 277 (1979) 667-669.
7  R.B. Hawkes, M.G. Grutter and J.S. Schellman, J. Mol. Biol. 175 (1984)
   195-212.
8  D.C. Muchmore, C.B. Russell and F.W. Dahlquist, in preparation.
9  R.H. Griffey, C.D. Poulter, A. Bax, B.L. Hawkins, Z. Yamaizumi and S.
   Nishimura, Proc. Natl. Acad. Sci. USA 80 (1983) 5895-5897.
10  A. Bax, R.H. Griffey and B.L. Hawkins, J. Magn. Reson. 55 (1983) 301-335.
11  M. Kainostro and T. Tsuji, Biochemistry 21 (1982) 6273-6279.

*Synthesis and Applications of Isotopically Labeled Compounds 1985.*
Proceedings of the Second International Symposium, Kansas City, MO, U.S.A.,
3—6 September 1985, R.R. Muccino (Ed.), 539—540
© 1986 Elsevier Science Publishers B.V., Amsterdam — Printed in The Netherlands

PREPARATION OF CARBON-13 POLYCHLORINATED BIPHENYL SURROGATES

J. H. SAUGIER*, D. H. T. CHIEN*, G. A. ROTERT*, R. W. ROTH* and J. R. HEYS**

*Eagle-Picher Industries, Inc., Chemsyn Science Laboratories, 13605 West
96th Terrace, Lenexa, Kansas 66215-1297, **Present address: Smith Kline &
French Laboratories, 1500 Spring Garden Street, P.O. Box 7929, Philadelphia,
Pennsylvania, 19101

ABSTRACT

Four carbon-13 labeled PCB congeners, $(1',2',3',4',5',6'(^{13}C_6)$4-Chlorobiphe-
nyl $(\underline{1})$, $(^{13}C_{12})$3,4,3',4'-Tetrechlorobiphenyl $(\underline{2})$, $(^{13}C_{12})$2,3,5,6,2',3',5',6'-
Octachlorobiphenyl $(\underline{3})$, and $(^{13}C_{12})$2,3,4,5,6,2', 3',4',5',6'-Decachlorobiphenyl
$(\underline{4})$ have been prepared. Gram amounts of each isomer were prepared by unequivo-
cal synthetic routes starting from $^{13}C_6$ benzene (99 atom %).

INTRODUCTION

To avoid development and validation of analytical methods for each of the
209 possible PCB's from a variety of matrices, a method has been developed
employing stable isotope labeled (carbon-13) PCB's as recovery surrogates (ref.
1). In support of this method we prepared the four carbon-13 labeled surrogates used in its development and evaluation. Isotopically labeled PCB's would
possess chemical and chromatographic properties virtually identical to their
natural abundance analogues while providing different mass spectra, allowing
for easy identification and quantification. The four congeners prepared were
synthesized from $^{13}C_6$ benzene (99 atom %), a readily available commercial
source of label. Selection of congeners prepared was based on 1) representative coverage of the complete range of PCB isomers (i.e. $Cl_1$ to $Cl_{10}$), 2) the
viability of cost-effective synthetic pathways, and 3) absence of any strong
analytical preference for specific isomers.

METHODS

Reaction schemes for the preparation of PCB congeners 1-4 are presented
below. Gomberg reaction conditions for the coupling of $\underline{5}$ with $^{13}C_6$ benzene
to give $\underline{1}$ employing a phase transfer catalysis have been developed. Literature methods (ref. 2 and 3) were used to prepare congener $\underline{2}$ labeled with
carbon-13. The general perchlorination procedure of Ballester et al. (ref.
4) was applied to $\underline{6}$ to give $\underline{7}$, which was reductively deaminated to $\underline{3}$.
Thallium-induced coupling of $^{13}C_6$ phenyl Grignard yielded $^{13}C_{12}$ biphenyl, which
gave $\underline{4}$ on perchlorination. Each carbon-13 congener prepared had a chemical
purity of greater than 98% and an isotopic purity of greater than 99 atom % by
GC/EIMS; retention times matched unlabeled reference standards obtained from
commercial sources.

$(1',2',3',4',5',6',^{13}C_6)$4-Chlorobiphenyl $(\underline{1})$

a. HCl, $NaNO_2$; b. $^{13}C_6H_6$, NaOH, 18-Crown-6.

($^{13}C_{12}$)3,4,3',4'-Tetrachlorobiphenyl (2)

a. $CF_3CO_2H$, $NaNO_3$; b. Zn, NaOH; c. HCl; d. NaOH; e. $Ac_2O$, AcOH; f. NCS, AcOH; g. HCl, EtOH; h. tBuONO, DMF, $CuCl_2$.

($^{13}C_{12}$)2,3,5,6,2',3',5',6'-Octachlorobiphenyl (3)

a. $Cl_2$, HOAc; b. $S_2Cl_2$, $AlCl_3$, $SO_2Cl_2$; c. HCl, EtOH; d. tBuONO, DMF

($^{13}C_{12}$)2,3,4,5,6,2',3',4',5',6'-Decachlorobiphenyl (4)

a. $KBrO_3$, $H_2SO_4$, $H_2O$; b. Mg, ether; c. TlBr; d. $S_2Cl_2$, $AlCl_3$, $SO_2Cl_2$

## ACKNOWLEDGEMENT

This work was supported by the U. S. Environmental Protection Agency, Contract No. 68-01-5915 to the Midwest Research Institute (Analytical Chemistry Department).

## REFERENCES

1  M. D. Erickson, J. S. Stanley, J. K. Turman, J. E. Going, D. P. Redford and D. T. Heggem, Anal. Chem., Submitted, (1985).
2  W. P. Duncan, J. C. Wiley, and W. C. Perry, J. Labelled Compd. and Radiopharm., 13 (1977) 305-309.
3  M. P. Doyle, B. Siegfried, and J. F. Dellaria Jr., J. Org. Chem., 42 (1977) 2426-2430.
4  M. Ballester, C. Molinet, and J. Castaner, J. Amer. Chem. Soc., 82 (1960) 4254-4258.

*Synthesis and Applications of Isotopically Labeled Compounds 1985.*
Proceedings of the Second International Symposium, Kansas City, MO, U.S.A.,
3—6 September 1985, R.R. Muccino (Ed.), 541—542
© 1986 Elsevier Science Publishers B.V., Amsterdam — Printed in The Netherlands

A FACILE SYNTHESIS OF TRIETHYLORTHO[14C]FORMATE AND ITS APPLICATION TO THE

PREPARATION OF A [2-14C] QUINOLINE-3-CARBOXYLIC ACID

J. H. SAUGIER, J. T. UCHIC, and M. SCHERRER DORNHOFFER

EAGLE-PICHER INDUSTRIES, CHEMSYN SCIENCE LABORATORIES,

13605 WEST 96th TERRACE, LENEXA, KANSAS 66215-1297

ABSTRACT

Triethylortho[14C]formate has been prepared from $K^{14}CN$ employing a two-step process in 55% yield. Compound I was radiolabeled with carbon-14 using this procedure. An eight-step sequence afforded compound I in 30% yield from 1 Ci of $K^{14}CN$.

INTRODUCTION

Carbon-14 has been incorporated into the quinolone moiety of compound I, 3-quinoline-[2-14C] carboxylic acid-1-cyclopropyl-7-(4-ethyl-1-piperazinyl)-6-fluoro-1,4-dihydro-4-oxo, for use in biochemical investigations. The availability of 2,4-dichloro-5-fluorobenzoyl chloride lead to the evaluation of positions 2 and 3 of compound I as possible sites for carbon-14 labeling. Position 3 has previously been labeled with carbon-13 employing diethyl-[2-13C]-malonate. Efficient labeling in position 2 required a facile preparation of triethylortho[14C]formate. The reaction scheme below depicts this preparation and its application to the labeling of compound I.

a. 85% $H_3PO_4$; b. HCl, Ethanol, Ether (ref.1); c. Ethanol, Ether, Reflux; d. Acetic anhydride, Heating; e. Cyclopropylamine, Ethanol 0° C; f. NaH, Dioxane; g. KOH, $H_2O$; h. N-Ethylpiperazine, DMSO, Heating.

## METHODS

Dry hydrogen[14C]cyanide (generated by the addition of 85% phosphoric acid to potassium [14C] cyanide, 507 mCi, 16.9 mmol), was vacuum transferred into a 25 mL flask fitted with a vacuum stopcock adapter, containing anhydrous ether (3.7mL), absolute ethanol (1.7 mL), and dry hydrogen chloride (21.1 mmol, measured manometrically). The reaction was allowed to proceed under its own vapor pressure at -13° C for 21 hours. Crystalline II (1.3 g, 70%) was isolated by removal of volatiles. A second crop (154 mg) was obtained after an additional 3 days, net 1.456 g (79%). A second run (555 mCi) was accomplished with the same results.

The imminoester hydrochloride II (395 mCi, 13.2 mmol) in anhydrous ethanol (12 mL) was treated with anhydrous ether (15 mL) . The slightly cloudy solution was heated at reflux (approx. 60° C) for 10 hours, with a heavy white precipitate developing. The reaction mixture was decanted, and the solid residue was washed twice with dry ether. A parallel run (439 mCi, 14.6 mmol) was carried out simultaneously. The volume of the combined organic solutions was reduced to 5 mL by distillation through a short Vigeaux column at atmospheric pressure under an atmosphere of nitrogen. Analysis by GLC/FID showed 72% triethylortho[14C]formate and 28% ethanol, assay 583 mCi (70%, 55% from K14CN).

Previously it had been determined that the presence of significant amounts of ethanol in the triethylorthoformate did not adversely affect the yield in step d. If neat triethylortho[14C]formate is required it may be obtained via a more exacting distillation process with moderately reduced yields allowing for considerations of scale.

Known methods were used to convert the carbon-14 labeled orthoformate to compound I. Adjustments were made allowing for scale and to optimize efficiency of utilization relative to triethylortho[14C]formate. Compound I (310 mCi, 30% from K14CN) prepared had a chemical and radiochemical purity of greater than 98% by HPLC employing UV280/radiochemical detection.

## CONCLUSIONS

The success of this synthesis was dependent on the development of an efficient preparation of triethylortho[14C]formate. Now that triethylortho[14C]-formate is readily available, it is expected to see significant use in varied applications.

## REFERENCES

1  S. Oae, W. Tagaki and A. Ohno, Tetrahedron, 20 (1964), 417-425.

POSTER SESSION A

D.S. EHLER, J.A. FEE, C.J. UNKEFER, T.E. WALKER, and J.L. HANNERS, Los Alamos National Laboratory, New Mexico-"The National Stable Isotopes Resource (S.I.R.)"

B. E. GORDON, The National Tritium Labeling Facility, Berkeley, California-"The History and Current Status of The National Tritium Labeling Facility"

YUI S. TANG, HIROMI MORIMOTO, HENRY RAPOPORT, and IWAO OJIMA*, National Tritium Labeling Facility, Berkeley, California and *Department of Chemistry, State University of New York at Stoney Brook-"Synthesis of High Specific Activity Sterospecifically Tritiated Labeled Enkephalin and Analogs via Heterogeneous, Homogenous and B-Lactam Methods"

R.J. BARANCZUK*, J.A. SPICER**, R.G. ROBINSON**, and J.A. HOLT+, *Biomedical Research Lab, Overland Park, Kansas, **University of Kansas Medical Center, Kansas City, +University of Chicago, Illinois-"Iodinated -123 Estradiol as a Radiotracer for Estrogen Receptor Positive Tumors"

R.L. HUA and C.T. PENG, University of California School of Pharmacy, San Francisco-"Relative Efficiencies of Tritium Atoms and Ionic Species in Peptide Labeling"

M.M. EBEID and M. Kralova, University of Qatar, Doha and Czechoslovakia Academy of Sciences, Prague-"Use of Mass Spectrometry in $^{15}N$ Isotope Incorporation Studies of Mesquite Seedlings Under Osmotic Stress"

L.T. SNIEGOSKI, A. COHEN, H.S. HERTZ, R. SCHAFFER, M.J. WELCH, and E. WHITE V, National Bureau of Standards, Gaithersburg, Maryland-"Determination of Organic Analytes in a Human Serum Standard Reference Material by Isotope Dilution/Mass Spectrometry"

PAUL M. HYDE, Louisiana State University Medical Center, New Orleans-"Isotopic Dilution Assay of 11-NOR 9-Carboxy$\Delta^9$ Tetrahydrocannabinol T-BDMS by GC/MS"

A. LAPIDOT and L. INBAR, The Weizmann Institute of Science, Rehovot, Israel-"The Biosynthesis of Carbon-13 Enriched L-Lysine by Brevibacterium Flavum Studied by $^{13}C$ and $^1H$ NMR and Mass Spectroscopy"

A. LAPIDOT*, M. HOD, M. DORSMAN*, and Y. OVADIA, *The Weizmann Institute of Science, Rehovot and Beilinson Medical Center, Israel-"Dynamic Parameters of Amino Acid Metabolism in Human Pregnancy, Determined by Stable Isotope-$^{15}N$ and GC-MS"

A. LAPIDOT, Z.E. KAHANA, and L. INBAR, The Weizmann Institute of Science, Rehovot, Israel-"The Biosynthesis of $^{13}C$ and $^{15}N$ Labeled Natural Compounds for In Vivo NMR Spectroscopy"

A. LAPIDOT*, M. DORSMAN*, J. AMIR, and R. STEINHERZ, *Weizmann Institute of Science and Beilinson Medical Center, Israel-"The Use of $^{15}N$-Labeled Phenylalanine and GC-MS Techniques for the In Vivo Determination of Hydroxylase Activity in Healthy Volunteers and Patients"

Z.Q. XIA*, T.C. DAI*, and Y.E. HU*, N.L. ZHANG, Y.J. LU, J. LI, Z.D. TANG, and Y.Y. QIU, *Shanghai Second Medical College, and Shanghai Institute of Test Technology/Ruijin Hospital, China-"C-13-Methacetin Breath Test: An Analysis of Some Pharmacokinetic Parameters Obtained from Normal Adults and Patients with Hepatic Malfunction"

N.Y. YI, G.P. FENG, Y.Z. LIN, Z.X. RONG, Q. YANG, S.D. ZHANG, W.M. ZHANG, and Z.Q. XIA, Shanghai Second Medical College, China-"The Effects of Some Yin Tonics and Yang Tonics on Beta-Adrenergic Receptors of Rat Kidney"

K.J. HOFFMANN*, D.B. AXWORTHY, S.D. NELSON, and T.A. BAILLIE, University of Washington, Seattle and *AB Hassle, Molndal, Sweden-"Mechanistic Studies on the Metabolic Activation of Acetaminophen"

N. NARASIMHACHARI, Medical College of Virginia, Richmond-"Preparation and Use of Deuterium Labeled 2-Hydroxyimipramine and 2-Hydroxy Desipramine in Blood-Brain Barrier Studies"

A.M. AJAMI and F.M. WALSH, Tracer Technologies, Inc., Newton, Massachusetts-"A Portable Isotope Ratio Infrared Spectrometer"

H.K. MISRA, Y.W. LEE, JOHN SAMUEL, L.I. WIEBE, and E.E. KNAUS, University of Alberta, Edmonton, Canada- "Synthesis and Biological Evaluation of Radiolabeled 1-(2'-Fluoro-2'-Deoxy-B-D-Arabinofuranosyl)-5-Halouracils"

T.R. BROWNE, J.E. EVANS, D.L. KASDON, G.K. SZABO, B.A. EVANS, and D. J. GREENBLATT, Boston University School of Medicine & Boston V.A. Medical Center, Massachusetts, Eunice Kennedy Shriver Center, Waltham, Massachusetts, Tufts University School of Medicine, New England Medical Center Hospital, and Saint Elizabeth's Hospital-"Demonstration of Staggered Stable Isotope Administration Technique for Study of Drug Distribution"

WILLIAM J. FIELDS, JR., University of Missouri-Kansas City, Missouri-"Health Physics of Four Pure B-Emitters"

A. COHEN, H.S. HERTZ, R. SCHAFFER, M.J. WELCH, and E. WHITE V, National Bureau of Standards, Gaithersburg, Maryland-"Synthesis of 2-Amino-1,5-Dihydro-1-(Methyl-$^{13}$C)-4H-Imidazol-4-One-5-$^{13}$C (Creatinine-$^{13}$C$_2$) and Measurement of Creatinine in Serum"

J. GODBILLON, A. GERARDIN, J. RICHARD, D. LEROY, E. URIEN, and D. WANTIEZ, Ciba-Geigy Biopharmaceutical Research Center, Cedex, France-"Preparation and Analysis of Deuterium-Labeled Diclofenac. Evaluation of Isotope Effects on the Plasma Kinetics"

D. VANDERVORST, P. OSINSKI, and P. DUMONT, Catholic University of Louvain, Brussels-"Identification and Quantitative Determination of Methylene Diphosphonate in Technetium-99m Medronate Kits by Proton Magnetic Resonance"

S. MLINKO, and D. BANFI, Central Research Institute for Chemistry Hungarian Academy of Sciences, Budapest-"A Possibility of the Recovery of the Carbon Content of $^{14}$C-Labeled By-Products"

D. BANFI, and S. MLINKO, Central Research Institute for Chemistry Hungarian Academy of Sciences, Budapest-"Analytical Control of High Specific Activity $Ba^{14}CO_3$ and $K^{14}CN$ Radiocarbon Basic Materials"

D. BANFI, and S. MLINKO, Central Research Institute for Chemistry Hungarian Academy of Sciences, Budapest-"A Convenient Synthesis of Isotopically Labeled Alkali Cyanides"

Y. LEUNG, and T.A. BAILLIE, University of Washington, Seattle-"Effect of Deuterium Substitution on the Metabolism and Pharmacological Properties of Ketamine"

A. W. RETTENMEIER, W.P. GORDON, and T.A. BAILLIE, University of Washington, Seattle-"Use of In Vivo Deuterium Isotope Effects to Elucidate Pathways of Drug Metabolism. Application to Studies on the Origin of Unsaturated Metabolites of Valproic Acid in the Rat"

B. D. RAY, M.D. KEMPLE, B.R. BRANCHINI, and F.G. PRENDERGAST, IUPUI, Indianapolis, Indiana, University of Wisconsin/Parkside, Kenosha, Wisconsin and Mayo Foundation, Rochester, Minnesota-"$^{13}C$ NMR Studies of[Indole-2-$^{13}C$] Tryptophan Mobility in Peptides and Proteins"

J. CHENU, M. TAKOUDJU, M. WRIGHT, F. GUERITTE, and D. GUENARD, CNRS, Laboratoire de Pharmacologie et Toxicologie Fondamentales, Toulouse, France-"Synthesis of [$^3H$] 7-Acetyl Taxol and Determination of its Binding Parameters to Mammalian Brain Microtubules and Tubulin"

M. MOCHIZUKI, S. NODA, T. MORISHITA, K. KANEKO, and G. KOIKE, Shoko Company, Ltd., Tokyo, Kagawa Nutrition College, Sakado-shi, Japan-"Determination of Heavy Water by Combined Use of Gas Chromatography and Catalyst and its Application in Clinical and Agricultural Fields"

T. V. RAMAMURTHY and K.V. VISWANATHAN, Labelled Compounds Section, Isotope Group, Bombay, India-"Applications of $^{14}CO_2$ Exchange Labelling Technique for the Micro Syntheses of Some Plant Growth Substances and p-Fluorophenyl Acetic Acid"

J. ALLEN and A. TIZOT, Laboratoires d'Etudes et de Recherches Synthelabo (L.E.R.S.), Bagneux, France-"Synthesis of $^3H$-Labeled Diltiazem"

D.B. HINES, Monsanto Company, St. Louis, Missouri-"Radioisotopes...Why not Consider Them as Your First Resort Tools?"

## POSTER SESSION B

J. RICHARD HEYS, Smith Kline & French Laboratories, Philadelphia, Pennsylvania-"Preparation and Chromatographic Resolution of Hydrogen Isotopmers of a Benzazepine Dopamine Antagonist"

J. ALLEN, A. TIZOT, and T. VASSAL, Laboratoires d'Etudes et de Recherches Synthelabo (L.E.R.S.), Bagneux, France-"Synthesis of $^3$H-Labeled Ifenprodil"

F. ETZKORN, and R. ROTH, Eagle-Picher Industries, Inc., Lenexa, Kansas-"Synthesis of [1,2(n)-$^3$H]Anthracene and [10,11(n)-$^3$H]Benz[a]Anthracene"

C.N. FILER, D.G. AHERN, R. FAZIO, and E. JOHNSON, E.I. DuPont de Nemours and Company, Boston, Massachusetts-"The TLC Isotopic Fractionation of High Specific Activity [N-Methyl-$^3$H] Ligands"

C.N. FILER and D.G. AHERN, E.I. DuPont de Nemours and Company, Boston, Massachusetts-"The Preparation and Characterization of Glycine Receptor Radioligands"

C.N. FILER and D.G. AHERN, R. FAZIO, and J.C. MORRISON, E.I. DuPont de Nemours and Company, Boston, Massachusetts-"Preparation and Characterization of (±)-[Phenoxy-$^3$H(N)] Phenoxybenzamine at High Specific Activity"

DEREK E. BRUNDISH, Ciba-Geigy AG, Basle, Switzerland-"Synthesis of [$^3$H]-Maleic Hydrazide of High Specific Activity"

S.B. HASSAM, Philip Morris Research Center, Richmond, Virginia-"Preparative Isolation of [U-$^{14}$C]Solanesol From $^{14}$CO$_2$-Chamber Grown Tobacco"

Y.M. CHOI, B. BULLOCK, N. KUCHARCZYK, and R.D. SOFIA, Wallace Laboratories, Cranbury, New Jersey-"Synthesis of [$^{14}$C]Flupirtine Maleate Labeled in the Pyridine Ring"

D. SAUNDERS, M.M. CASHYAP, D.C. OSBORNE, and M.B. MITCHELL, Smith Kline and French Research Limited, Welwyn, Hertfordshire, England-"Radiolabeled Synthesis of a Novel Histamine H$_1$-Antagonist"

P.N. RAO and K.M. DAMODARAN, Southwest Foundation for Biomedical Research, San Antonio, Texas-"Synthesis of Carbon-14 Labeled Doxylamine Succinate"

F. ETZKORN and G. ROTERT, Eagle-Picher Industries, Inc., Lenexa, Kansas-"Synthesis of o-Chloro[Phenyl-U-$^{14}$C]Benzyl Alcohol and o-Chloro[Phenyl-u-$^{13}$C] Benzyl Chloride"

C.C. HUANG, Warner-Lambert/Parke-Davis Pharmaceutical Research, Ann Arbor, Michigan-"Synthesis of Carbon-14 Labeled Dihydro-1H-Pyrrolizine-3,5(2H, 6H)-Dione (CI-911)"

A. GOPHER and A. LAPIDOT, Weizmann Institute of Science, Rehovot, Israel-"Photosynthetic Preparation of $^{13}$C Labeled Carbohydrates Using a Green Alga Dunalliela Salina"

EDWARD H. CHEW, R.W. ROTH, and N. NUNGESSER, Eagle-Picher Industries, Inc., Lenexa, Kansas-"Synthesis of [$^{14}$C-Methylene] Nalmefene Hydrochloride"

D.C. GREENSLADE and K.D. TOWNSEND, Wellcome Research Laboratories, Beckenham, Kent, United Kingdom-"Synthesis of Uniformly Ring Labeled C-14 4-Hydroxy Benzoic Acid"

SUN-SHINE YUAN and ALFRED M. AJAMI, Tracer Technologies, Inc., Newton, Massachusetts-"Synthesis of (2S,3S)-[1-$^{13}$C] Isoleucine via Amidocarbonylation"

D.F. WHITE, Imperial Chemical Industries plc, Macclesfield, Cheshire, England-"Synthesis of 2-([1,3-$^{14}$C]-Isopropyl-6-Isopropyl Phenol (Propofol)"

J.R. HARDING, Imperial Chemical Industries plc, Macclesfield, Cheshire, England-"Studies of the Biosynthesis of a Novel Ionophore Antibiotic (ICI 139,603) Using [1-$^{14}$C]Propionate"

S.G. SENDEROFF, K.T. GARNES, A.J. VILLANI, L.J. PETKA, and D.W. BLACKBURN, SmithKline Beckman, Philadelphia, Pennsylvania-"Synthesis of Carbon-14 Labeled (2,3,4,5-1H-3-) Benzazepines:  SK&F 85174-$^{14}$C"

S.G. SENDEROFF, J.R. HEYS, W. KOKKE, and D.W. BLACKBURN, SmithKline Beckman, Philadelphia, Pennsylvania-"Synthesis of an Iodine-125 Labeled Vasopressin Analog:  SK&F 101975"

ANTHONY J. VILLANI, SIDNEY LEVINSON, and DENISE LANE, SmithKline Beckman, Philadelphia, Pennsylvania-"SK&F 100168-$^{14}$C-A, Micro-Synthesis and Stability"

JACQUES CHENU and MARIE-LINE CECCATO, Sanofi-Recherche, Toulouse cedex, France-"A New, Very Efficient Synthesis of 9-Hydroxy Ellipticine [$^{14}$C-1] With High Specific Activity (58 mci/mole)"

D.F. WHITE, Imperial Chemical Industries plc, Macclesfield, Cheshire, England-"Synthesis of [$^{14}$C]-Labeled Atenolol ('Tenormin')"

P.J. MORGAN, P.W. SHEPPARD, and J.R. HARDING*, Cambridge Research Biochemicals, Ltd., Harston, Cambridge, England and *Imperial Chemical Industries plc, Macclesfield, Cheshire, England-"Synthesis of [$^{3}$H]-Labeled Zoladex (ICI 118, 630)"

GEORGE Y. KUO, MARY E. McCARTHY, RICHARD DEWEY, KENNETH M. STRAUB, ROBERT K. LYNN, CARL D. PERCHONOCK, and JOHN F. NEWTON, Smith Kline & French Laboratories , Philadelphia, Pennsylvania-"Synthesis and Metabolism of $^{14}$C-Labeled Leukotriene Receptor Antagonists: 5-Substituted 4,6-Dithianonanedioic Acid Derivatives"

EMMA JANE SHELTON and HOWARD PARNES, Syntex Research Center, Palo Alto, California-"Facile [8-$^{14}$C] Purine Synthesis from Ba$^{14}$CO$_3$ via Sodium [$^{14}$C] Formate"

STEVE de KECZER and HOWARD PARNES, Syntex Research Center, Palo Alto, California-"A Convenient Closed System Synthesis of [U-$^{14}$C]-Benzoquinone and [U-$^{14}$C]-Hydroquinone From Barium [$^{14}$C]-Carbonate"

B. MURALIDHARAN, S. MALLIKA, and K.V. VISWANATHAN, Bhabha Atomic Research Centre, Bombay, India-"Some New Approaches to the Synthesis of $^{14}$C-Labeled D-Glucosamine and its Epimers - Fructosylamine Rearrangement in Non-Aqueous Solvents"

JON D. HARTMAN, VITAUTS ALKS*, C.C. HUANG, and P. DAN COOK, Warner-Lambert/Parke-Davis Pharmaceutical Research, Buffalo, New York-"Synthesis of [2-$^{14}$C]Deazaguanine Mesylate (6-Amino-1,5-Dihydro-4H-Imidazo-[4,5-c][6-$^{14}$C]Pyridin-4-One Methanesulfonate), A New Antitumor Agent"

LISA A. SANTAY and SHERYL J. HAYS, Warner-Lambert/Parke-Davis, Ann Arbor, Michigan-"Synthesis of Carbon-14 Labeled Bevantolol, A Potential New Beta Blocking Agent"

S. LEVINSON, A. VILLANI, J. MEIER, B. SUTTON, and D. HILL, Smith Kline & French Laboratories, Philadelphia, Pennsylvania-"Synthesis of $^{195}$Au, $^{32}$P and $^{35}$S-Labeled Auranofin, A Novel Orally Effective Gold Antiarthritic Drug"

E. PONNUSAMY, U. FOTADAR, and D. FIAT, University of Illinois at Chicago, Illinois-"Synthesis of Oxygen-17 Labeled Leucine-Enkephalins"

A. WEISZ and S.P. MARKEY, National Institute of Mental Health, Bethesda, Maryland-"Synthesis and Characterization of D, L-Norepinephrine-(Phenyl-$^{13}$C$_6$)"

H. DENUTTE, G. SLEGERS, P. GOETHALS, C. VANDECASTEELE, and A. DE LEENHEER, Labo Medische Biochemie, Gent, Belgium-"The Use of Immobilized Enzymes for the Production of Carbon-11 Labeled Thymidylate and Thymidine"

G. RAJENDRAN and ROBERT L. VAN ETTEN, Purdue Unviersity, West Lafayette, Indiana-"Synthesis of $^{15}$N, $^{18}$O-Hydroxylamine Hydrochloride"

# AUTHOR INDEX

# SUBJECT INDEX